TEACHING ELEMENTARY SCIENCE:

A SOURCEBOOK FOR ELEMENTARY SCIENCE

A

SOURCEBOOK

FOR

ELEMENTARY

SCIENCE

ELIZABETH B. HONE

Associate Professor of Education,
San Fernando Valley State College;
Director, Conservation Foundation's Curriculum Center
at San Fernando Valley State College

ALEXANDER JOSEPH

Head, Department of Mathematics and Physics,
Bronx Community College of the City University of New York;
Co-director, NSF Physics Institute,
City College-Bronx Community College 1961–62;
Consultant, Physical Science Study Committee

EDWARD VICTOR

Associate Professor of Education, Northwestern University

Under the general editorship of
PAUL F. BRANDWEIN

Director, Division of Education, Conservation Foundation

HARCOURT, BRACE & WORLD, INC.
NEW YORK / BURLINGAME

COVER PHOTOGRAPH   Pat Coffey, Free Lance Photographers Guild

Printed in the United States of America

Library of Congress Catalog Card Number: 62–8337

Preface

The teaching procedures offered in this book have proved of value in many elementary science classrooms throughout the country. Certainly the book presents more techniques, demonstrations, projects, field trips, and suggestions than any teacher would need in any year. Many of the procedures are intended for use by the teacher alone; others are to be used by groups of children; still others are intended to stimulate individual investigations by groups or individuals. Some are simple in execution; some are moderately difficult; some are complex; a number may be considered too advanced for the majority of elementary school students.

Children, differing as they do in needs, aptitudes, and attitudes, are idiosyncratic in their patterns of life and interests and in what they make of them. Since methods of teaching are, and do, indeed, remain personal inventions, each teacher will select the procedures that are applicable to his or her pupils or special school situation. The procedures are meant therefore simply as the raw materials from which a lesson, or part of it, may be constructed.

The authors—out of their experience in the elementary science classroom and in the training of elementary science teachers—have included techniques and procedures useful not only for the full range of elementary science classrooms (grades 1–8) but also for the variety of individual students who make up classes. These reflect the complete scope of the scientist's way: observing, thinking, imagining, developing "models," clarifying problems, inventing hypotheses and theories, discussing, reporting—all involved in designing experiments, all giving the fabric of science its special warp and woof.

This volume is one of a series of three sourcebooks; the others are *Teaching High School Science: A Sourcebook for the Biological Sciences,* by E. Morholt, P. F. Brandwein, and A. Joseph (Harcourt, Brace & World, 1958), and *Teaching High School Science: A Sourcebook for the Physical Sciences,* by A. Joseph, P. F. Brandwein, E. Morholt, H. Pollack, and J. F. Castka (Harcourt, Brace & World, 1961). The three offer science teachers in elementary, junior high, and senior high schools a full review of demonstrations, field methods, and laboratory procedures in science.

The purpose of the authors is clear: to be of service to their colleagues, teachers of children.

PAUL F. BRANDWEIN

Contents

Chapter 19   Clothing / 314

Chapter 20   Housing / 326

Chapter 21   Magnets and magnetism / 337

Chapter 22   Electricity / 357

Chapter 23   Communications / 389

Introduction

This book gathers for you in one place most of the tested activities and experiments connected with the elementary-grade study of science. The experiments are so ordered in the text that you may use them in the sequential development of a concept or select from the collection in order to answer a specific problem. You will find closely related experiments which you may use to approach a problem from different angles in order to achieve maximum understanding. Since we have been teachers of both children and adults, we have tried to anticipate your needs in the various phases of science study.

This book assumes that you know children even if you protest a modest background of science. It aims to provide you with the ammunition to let science come from and through the children, as it will if given half a chance. Our suggestions are intended to be simple and clear so that you and the children will have a thoroughly enjoyable as well as interesting time in science.

Another intent of our writing has been to share with you what we have found to be the easiest and most practical methods for conducting a study of science. The shadow of an overloaded curriculum and bulging school day has always been over our shoulders. We have tried wherever possible to point out possibilities for integrating science with other curriculum areas and for relating it to everyday living and everyone's environment.

Finally, we have tried to make bridges for you between the fields of science—for example, the analogy between orbital motions of the electron and those of the sun's wheel of attendant planets.

We shall have succeeded in our purpose if this book gives you the courage to find out that science is fun and that you can teach it.

TEACHING ELEMENTARY SCIENCE:

A SOURCEBOOK FOR ELEMENTARY SCIENCE

1

The classroom:

a place for daily discovery

SETTING THE STAGE

One of the most interesting things you can do is to ask children to name one thing in their surroundings which scientists have not improved.

In our experience, children react vigorously to the challenge. They name articles of clothing—shirts, stockings, shoes. But soon they realize that even though the plant grew the cotton, scientists have improved the cotton plant, even improved the soil, bleached the cotton, dyed it, and so on. Some of the children may name your handbag, their pencils, their lunchboxes—all of which they will eventually agree are improved by science.

Ask your children to think of something outside schoolrooms which science has not changed. They will probably mention automobiles or perhaps ice cream. Suppose someone points out a tree as not to be "improved upon." Don't we prune and spray and fertilize plants better today because of science?

Your classroom, as part of the modern world, surrounds the children with science experiences. But you will select those which feed into your current social studies or science unit or into the children's immediate interests or community problems. It is our immediate purpose here to indicate the general use of different parts of the classroom. Techniques mentioned will be described more fully later. As a classroom teacher, one of the first things you can do is to utilize the science teaching potential of your classroom by putting all available space to work for science.

WINDOW SILLS AT WORK

Window sills are probably the most valuable aids for teaching science in the classroom. As display space, they have the best light and are at a good height for youngsters to observe and handle objects.

Many teachers fill window sills with growing plants to create a more attractive room. Why not put these same plants to work to illustrate basic principles of life and growth (Chapter 6)? North or east window sills are good locations for aquariums and terrariums. Suggestions for construction, maintenance, and utilization for teaching will be found in Chapters 2, 3, and 6.

Nor is the window sill necessarily limited to investigations in biological science. You may wish to try experiments on the effect of light on samples of colored cloth, paper, and plastics (Chapter 20).

Outdoor window sills at work

If it is possible to erect a simple plank shelf just outside the window, classroom science may be enriched with a whole range of activities not possible indoors. You may find details for construction and utilization of such a classroom extension in Chapter 6.

THE SCIENCE CORNER

As you read further, we hope you will see how it is possible for many parts of the classroom to be used for daily discovery in science. However, for purposes of organizing materials and focusing interest in science, you and the children may wish to designate one area of the room as the "Science Corner." All that is needed to open many avenues to science learning is some of the following components: display space including a bulletin board and a bookcase for children's collections, library reference and file space, a work table, and storage facilities. Methods we have used in displaying children's contributions, in filing articles and pictures, and in storing equipment, all in a limited space, are explained in the appendix. How to make the usual bulletin board come alive by a 3-D technique is also suggested there.

FIRE AND WATER

Many interesting and worthwhile science experiments require water and/or heat. Most of us teach in classrooms where the nearest running water is down the hall in the custodian's mop closet. The nearest current electricity is an overhead chandelier. Some ways to get around such obstacles are described (see appendix).

HOUSEKEEPING

Good housekeeping in elementary science is a must, especially for reasons of example and hygiene. Science equipment must therefore be designed and organized in such a way as to demand a minimum of care for a maximum of usefulness and cleanliness. Suggestions are offered throughout the book and especially on p. 5.

Just as science has increasing impact on life and living, your classroom will indeed reflect that impact.

But science is not only a study of things and what happens to things. It is also a *way* of studying these things and what happens to them. The way scientists seek knowledge includes *many* approaches to facts and how facts can be put together. You may wish to embody some of the suggestions to be found in *Teaching High School Science: A Book of Methods* by P. F. Brandwein, F. G. Watson, and P. E. Blackwood, 1958 (Harcourt, Brace & World, New York).

2

Animals in the classroom zoo

Whether you teach in a rural or urban school, you will have an opportunity to care for a variety of animals in the classroom. During a study of "The Farm," a child may bring his pet duck for the day. A study of nutrition becomes much more meaningful if you secure white rats from a hospital or test laboratory. If schools laws permit, an injured wild animal may be brought in for treatment and temporary observation. Some communities have a junior museum with an organized animal loan service for schools. A few school systems have their own service. In any case you will be eager to provide the animal visitor with the best possible care and an appropriate home.

HOME AWAY FROM HOME

Whether wild or domestic, an animal in the classroom can best be housed in a cage that is big enough for a rabbit or cat, yet can be folded up when not in use. The cage should be all metal to facilitate thorough scrubbing and rinsing in laundry bleach solution. A debris-catching metal tray that can be easily cleaned and a water fountain that provides fresh water on demand and seldom needs refilling must also be built for the "cage" home.

Materials and tools

Before beginning construction of a cage, decide whether a 2′ or 3′ square cage will better meet most of your needs. For dogs and rabbits, the 3′ size is preferable; the 2′ cage is adequate for guinea pigs, hamsters, white rats, etc. Cage wire of ½–¾″ mesh often comes in rolls 36–48″ wide. For the 2′ cage you will need about 7′ of 48″ width in order to provide four sides, a top and bottom, and an exercise wheel (Fig.2-1; see also Fig. 2-8). Hold the wire together with clips (generally available from pet stores) or with bell wire. Construct the metal debris tray from a piece of lightweight galvanized iron big enough to allow for a

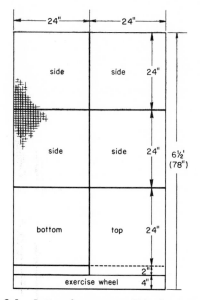

Fig. 2-1 Pattern for pet cage. This plan provides for four sides, bottom, top with overlap, and exercise wheel (Fig. 2-8).

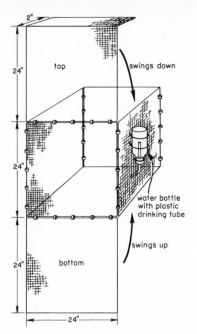

Fig. 2-2 Pet cage assembly. The figure shows points of permanent attachment. To set up, use clip fasteners along three open edges of top and bottom. For compact storage, remove clips and fold in sides, top, and bottom.

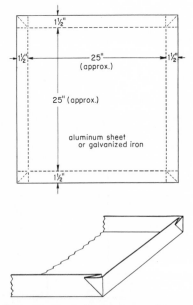

Fig. 2-3 Tray base for pet cage, with construction detail for size and for side and corner folding of metal base.

1–2″ overlap to bend up around the bottom of the cage. For a 2′ cage you will need a piece about 28″ square. Obtain sheet iron that is galvanized to prevent rusting. Or you may decide to use sheet aluminum, since it is a very lightweight metal, is highly resistant to corrosion, and is easily cut and shaped.

You will need the following tools for construction: a pair of tin-snips, a pair of side-cutting pliers, and, if possible, a pair of special pliers for closing the cage clips (clips are more effective than wire for fastening the sides to each other). The clips and pliers are usually available from a pet store or specialty hardware shop. The clips can be closed with the inner jaws of an auto mechanic's pliers. A ball-peen hammer is best for forming the sides of the tray. An ordinary claw hammer will do.

Making the pet cage

With materials and tools assembled, your first step in construction is to spread the wire mesh on the floor and carefully cut down the middle, making two strips each 24″ wide. Trim any protruding ends of wire with side-cutting pliers, and cut 5 squares each 24″ × 24″. Trim closely as before and fasten 4 squares together to form the sides, using clips or wire at intervals. The fifth square forms the bottom and is fastened only along one edge to permit opening (Fig. 2-2). As shown in Fig. 2-2, cut a piece for the top with enough overlap to make it secure when bent down over the side. Fasten the top parallel to the bottom piece to permit folding. Fasten a water bottle to the outside of the cage with the tip of the tube inside the cage (Fig. 2-2).

You are now ready to make the tray in which the cage is set. Cut the sheet metal at corners (Fig. 2-3). Bend and hammer flat, using a block of wood as a form on which to flatten the metal. Lap the corners (Fig. 2-3). Hammer down to flatten any sharp edges. When you are ready to set up the cage inside the tray, fasten together at intervals with metal "alligator" clips available from dime or hardware stores. (Wood pins absorb odor or may be chewed to splinters, and therefore should not be used.) When the cage is occupied, place sufficient weight on top to prevent the animal from pushing his way out or tipping over the cage.

Water supply

Here again we desire equipment which requires a minimum of care. A "perpetual fountain" may be assembled from a medium-sized pill bottle (e.g., for vitamins), a bent feeding tube (see Fig. 2-2), and a one-hole stopper. A plastic tube, available for 15–20¢ from the drugstore, is safest. The stopper can be made by drilling a cork with the blunt end of a rattail file. The "business" end of the file will help smooth the hole. The "fountain" should be checked daily to see if it is feeding properly. However, it will probably not need to be cleaned and refilled more than once a week. The principle of air pressure involved may lead the children into a new area of questions and experiments (see Chapter 9).

Rather than a water bottle, amphibious pets such as frogs, toads, and water turtles need a shallow dish in which to "muddle" and soak their skins. Use a glass or enamel dish; do not use one made of tin-coated steel since it tends eventually to rust. An open dish must be cleaned and refilled daily, and animals should be able to enter and leave it unaided.

Feeding animals

Feeding habits of different animals are remarkably varied. You may wish to request for your reference library several publications listed in the bibliography. Two general principles, however, apply in most cases. Offer the widest imaginable variety of foods, but in *small* amounts. The animal may then select the foods that best meet its dietary needs. *Do not overfeed.* Heavy glass ash trays are excellent containers for most foods; cardboard boxes serve well for dry foods. Always remove uneaten food and continually practice the strictest possible good housekeeping in your pet's culinary department. Nothing promotes sickness in animals as quickly as putrefying food, dirty water, and foul quarters.

Housekeeping for pets

Some teachers hesitate to keep animals in the classroom lest they lend undue "atmosphere." Any odor from classroom pets may indicate poor housekeeping. Daily removal of uneaten foods and of soiled bedding is a minimum essential. Place in the debris tray softwood shavings or sawdust to absorb odors, and wash the cage weekly in laundry bleach solution. These housekeeping habits virtually guarantee sweet-smelling pet "homes."

Nest boxes

Most animals should have a nest box for shelter from drafts, especially if the cage is on the floor. Children can understand this if you perform a single demonstration for them. Secure a pair of inexpensive thermometers and take simultaneous readings on the floor and close to the ceiling. Children will note the difference in temperature. If it is permitted to burn a candle in the classroom, the children will observe the movements or flickering of the flame in different parts of the room. A special word of caution about pets and their exposure to cold weather during weekends: Some schools turn the heat off completely. It may be necessary to take the pets home or to cover the cage with a cloth or blanket. During a harsh cold wave electric heaters have been used in some schools.

Animals also need a dark retreat for rest

as well as for shelter. Cardboard is less sturdy than wood for a nest box but can be more readily replaced. For smaller animals, the entrance hole should be near the top of the box, thus permitting a dark cavity below. The children may be able to recall having seen bird boxes with doorways drilled at the bottom by kind but ill-informed people who then wondered why the houses stood vacant.

COMMON CLASSROOM CREATURES

Children who own pets or whose parents own pet stores in the community will have helpful suggestions for the care of animals in your classroom zoo. Following are some suggestions for the care of commoner classroom creatures.

Earthworms

The children can dig up earthworms from the school garden or collect them from the ground surface after a heavy rain. Earthworms are interesting and valuable to keep in the classroom. Quite literally they go quietly about making the earth a better place. If need be, they also serve as winter food for frogs, toads, snakes, and turtles in the classroom. To illustrate the way in which these "Little Ploughmen," as Darwin called them, improve the soil, obtain two wide-mouth pickle or mayonnaise jars. Moisten some dark soil (loam or leaf mold) and some light-colored soil (sand). Make three layers of soil in each jar—light, dark, or vice versa. Put the earthworms on top of the soil of one jar. Wrap the jar with a sheet of dark or black paper, which should act to lure the worms to tunnel at the periphery of the jar where they can be seen, rather than to bury themselves in the center. In a few days you should begin to see dark tunnels through the sand layer until eventually the soil in the jar is quite thoroughly mixed.

Compare the mixing with that of the jar without worms. Thus in nature earthworms, by bringing up subsoil and taking down topsoil, contribute inestimably to soil fertility and hence to human welfare. Watch the soil pass through earthworms as they tunnel through it. They have no teeth but a remarkable gizzard which grinds and pulverizes the soil they take into their systems. Observe how they pull bits of leaves into their mouth with the upper lip. Where tunnels against the glass permit watching the earthworm in its hole, note how they hold onto the top of the hole with the tip of the tail and move in a circle searching for food. When not observing the earthworms, be sure to replace the black covering around the jar.

Soon you will notice worm castings of digested pulverized soil on top of the soil in your jar. A second grade class planted beans in pots of such "wormy" soil and more beans in pots of ordinary school garden soil. The seeds in the worm-casting soil grew and flourished abundantly as compared to those in the control pots.

At commercial worm farms, worms are fed such succulent soft diet as olive pits and walnut shells! Anglers who keep a supply of worms on hand feed them a mixture of coffee grounds and cornmeal, in small doses. If the children wonder why one finds worms above ground after a downpour, they can answer their own questions by a simple experiment. Pour in the worm jar more water than its soil can hold and watch how the worms will come to the top of their tunnels for air. Be ready to rescue them from drowning and to move them to new quarters.

When children ask where worms come from or if they should become curious about the egg collar they see on some worms, a teacher who is able to give simple factual answers helps children attain a healthy attitude about the process of reproduction.

Meal worms

The immediate value of meal worms is to provide a ready and acceptable live food supply, especially during winter, for pet reptiles or amphibians that hibernate but briefly in a warm classroom. Their partial metamorphosis from larval to adult (beetle) form will contribute to the child's understanding of the life cycle of various creatures. Meal worms are usually available at pet or feed stores. Secure a small quantity and put them in a quart or half-gallon glass jar partly filled with wheat bran, bran flakes, and/or cornmeal. For variety you might occasionally add a bread crust or small chunk of apple or carrot. Punch air holes in the jar's tin cover or cover with cloth or netting. Keep in a *warm, dark* place. For faster multiplication divide the supply into two containers, one to be left undisturbed for breeding, one to be used for pet food.

Silkworms

If there is a mulberry tree anywhere near the school, do not miss the experience of keeping silkworms in the spring. There is more than one variety of mulberry commonly planted in the United States and any medium-sized tree with *some* mitten-shaped leaves (Fig. 2-4) bears inspection. It may be a mulberry. Silkworm eggs from the previous spring will hatch if kept at room temperature. You will want to order these eggs in early spring from a scientific supply house (see appendix). Keep the eggs in a refrigerator until the mulberry leaves are well out. Then bring into room temperature and keep a few fresh leaves on hand for the moment the tiny larvae begin to emerge. Silkworms will never leave their food supply. Both eggs and leaves, as well as the silkworms when they emerge, may be kept in an open box top on a table or window sill (not in hot sun). Since silkworms eat only the margins of leaves, your supply will go further if cut in

Fig. 2-4 Mulberries have rounded leaves, often glossy green. The red mulberry has these characteristic notched leaves. Many schools plant one of the nonfruiting varieties for shade and silkworms. (Hugh Spencer.)

pieces. Leaves should not be fed wet but blotted dry with paper toweling. Osage orange or lettuce leaves may serve as a temporary, but only temporary, substitute for mulberry leaves. You may wish to cover the silkworm container with a piece of windowpane or cellophane, not to restrain the larvae but to reduce evaporation in the leaves. Silkworms will grow in proportion as they are supplied with fresh food. This should be fed daily, including weekends. Most children vie for the privilege of playing host to the silkworms. However, it may be wise first to ascertain parental feeling on the matter!

Old dried leaves and debris should be removed before each feeding. You can save time in doing this by laying coarse wire mesh or netting over the silkworms and the old leaves. They will crawl up through it to the fresh leaves you place on top and save your having to find and pick off each larva to be transferred to the new food.

When the silkworms have grown large, they will stop feeding and begin swinging their heads from side to side. They are looking for a place to spin. Now place them in an open shoebox containing twigs to which they can anchor their cocoons. Some teachers use plastic tubes (toothbrush containers) or transparent plastic refrigerator food containers (pint or half-pint) containers. But these must contain some rough object or surface to which the cocoon may be attached. In about ten days from the making of the cocoon, moths will begin to emerge and mate. Before this happens you may wish to boil up a few cocoons in order to try finding and with needle or tweezers gently unraveling the end of the silk thread with which the cocoon was made. Meanwhile the children should be allowed to watch the mating process freely and without comment on your part. Questions should be answered directly and briefly. Children in an urban environment particularly need such simple and natural object lessons in reproduction.

TROPICAL AND FRESH-WATER FISH

Often among your children there is a young expert on tropical fish. If not, do not be deterred from setting up an aquarium for lack of equipment or experience. You may wish to use a widemouthed gallon pickle jar for a container. Globes are easily tipped over and tend to distort one's view of the inhabitants. In rural areas you may be able to locate a glass battery jar which was once part of a home power plant. Wash carefully with baking soda to neutralize any residual acid and rinse several times with water. The children helping you may ask why, and lead you to try some simple experiments (Chapter 12). Old-fashioned glass candy and cookie jars also make good tanks. An open-topped

modern glass brick provides an attractive small aquarium.

Guppies

If you are a beginner in aquariums, the best fish to learn on are guppies. They are cheap, hardy, and breed almost too easily. Unlike most fish, guppies are born alive, the eggs hatching inside the female's body. The male may eat them unless he is put in another tank. Males are smaller than females, with a spot on the tail.

Guppies require a little more than a moderate even temperature (60–70° F), whereas for most other tropical fish a heater and thermostat are needed to keep the water at constant temperature. Since most schools have a master switch which shuts off all electric current after school, the heater alone will not obviate dead fish in the morning. Heating equipment for aquariums is available from pet shops or from larger mail order houses. If you plan to keep tropical fish, it is wise to confer with your local pet shop.

When you buy guppies, get a small amount of food at the same time. You may also wish to invest in a snail to keep down algae and remove dead material. One snail per gallon is recommended. Your pet store dealer will also help you decide if you want to buy washed sand for the bottom, or wash your own and bake it in the oven to kill mold. He will also advise you to invest in a few sprigs of such common aquarium plants as sagittaria, elodea, vallisneria, cabomba, or myriophyllum. The first three are particularly valuable as sources of oxygen for your fish. Above all, the dealer will help you decide how many plants you will need to balance the number of fish in your tank. The fish, of course, give off the carbon dioxide which plants use in making food.

If you have access to a stream or pond, you may wish to use small native fish which the children collect, such as dace, perch, stickleback. You may add some tadpoles but not a crayfish. Unless the crustacean is much smaller than the fish, the latter are apt to disappear!

Pond, stream, or rain water is best for filling a tank because it may contain microorganisms which multiply and become fish food. If tap water must be used, let it stand for at least 3 days to allow the chlorine, which is poisonous to plant and animal life, to escape and any lime to settle. Aquariums stay cleaner and require less frequent addition of water if kept covered. Do not add tap water except that which has been allowed to stand as suggested.

Before planting your aquarium, be sure it is thoroughly cleaned. Cover the bottom with sand, in not too level a layer, group your water plants, and imbed an inch into the sand, anchoring with pebbles. Let the stems trail. They will rise as water is added. Remove broken or discolored leaves. If plants do not thrive, replant them in a sand layer spread on top of rich soil which, in turn, rests on a bottom layer of sand. Lay a piece of paper between the plants and gently siphon water onto the paper. The paper keeps the plants from being washed out of place and cuts down roiling of the water. The use of the siphon here is a fine way to illustrate air pressure at work (Chapter 9). Before adding inhabitants, remove paper and let aquarium stand until water clears.

Early morning sunlight from an eastern exposure is desirable for an aquarium. If the aquarium is placed on the window sill, the resultant growth of algae may be reduced by fastening dark paper to the side next to the window. Do not place too near radiators.

Fresh-water insect aquarium

If you or your children have access to a fresh-water stream or pond, you may enjoy watching aquatic insects change from the larval to the adult form. This change occurs most frequently in late spring. Secure and clean thoroughly a widemouthed jar or container. Place clean sand in the bottom, fill partly full of pond or stream water. (Do not use beach sand; it is very hard to remove the salt which is fatal to fresh-water life). Plant a few specimens of water plants which you collect when you find the insects. Add a branch or slanting stick which is partly out of water and a floating block of wood on which the insects emerge. Try to collect nymphs of dragon and damsel flies, caddis worm cases, some water boatmen and water striders, and even a scoop or two of mosquito larvae. For more detail on what to look for and how to collect it, see Chapter 4.

Classroom tidepool

For children living near the sea coast, a small marine aquarium may be the capstone to a long anticipated and carefully planned trip to the beach or tide flats. In these days of rapidly vanishing native animal life, you and your class can make your contribution to the cause of conservation by collecting no more than one or two of a kind among the common species only.

The salt-water tank must obviously be ready for use on your return from your shore trip. The container must be cleaned and tested for leaks. Water may be brought from the ocean or be synthetic brine.[1] Sea salts in cloth bags (secured from scientific supply houses) should be dissolved ahead of time according to directions. You will also need some sea sand and a few barnacled rocks for the bottom.

Tidepool animals will not survive overnight without an aerator. Common aerators for fresh-water tanks will suffice if you use more than one per tank (usually two

[1] For more on salt water see E. Morholt, P. Brandwein, and A. Joseph, *A Sourcebook for the Biological Sciences,* Harcourt, Brace & World, 1958, p. 355.

(a)

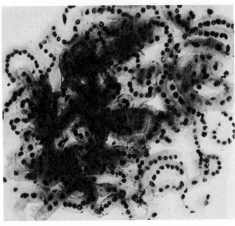

(b)

Fig. 2-5 (a) Gelatinous mass of frog eggs. If possible collect some pond water with the eggs. Note water temperature. (Hugh Spencer.) (b) Gelatinous strings of toad eggs. (W. J. Jahoda from National Audubon Society.)

are enough). Specimens such as clams, hermit crabs, sea anemones, starfish, and a few small fish will survive for a considerable period in such a tank.

AMPHIBIAN PETS

Frogs and toads

The development of a dark spot in a mass of frog eggs into a tadpole and then into the adult frog is one of the perennial wonders of spring. Early in the spring, bor-row or buy "Voices of the Night," a Cornell University recording of amphibian voices. Without comment, play it for the children and elicit their explanation. The ensuing discussion should bring out some interesting questions. This might be the day to bring in some amphibian eggs. Children may have been requested the day before to bring in enough pond water and green scum in which to float the eggs and later feed the newborn. Toad and salamander eggs are laid in strings of jelly while frog eggs come in masses of jelly (Fig. 2-5). The jelly serves as the tadpole's first food when it emerges from the egg. Later it feeds on green scum or algae.

Cover the glass container in which you are keeping the eggs. This will reduce evaporation and keep out foreign matter such as chalk dust which may be toxic to them. It is by far best to use distilled water available in most communities from a local bottling firm. If necessary to add tap water, be sure to let it stand several days. This is to permit chlorine to dissipate. Keep in a relatively cool place with some sunlight, but not enough to overheat the water. Normal room temperature without much variation should keep the water about the right hatching temperature.

From egg to frog usually takes about 3 months though this varies from species to species. Some species, as, for example, bull frogs, require 2 years to mature. Watching the legs appear is always interesting. Do both emerge at the same time? A high school or juvenile biology text (see bibliography) may provide a review which will enable you to help your children acquire a knowledge of the pre-natal changes in all animal babies.

Among other references which give additional detail on raising amphibians in school, Greenlee[2] gives a delightful description of how a first grade met the problem

[2] Greenlee, Julian, *Better Teaching Through Elementary Science*, Wm. C. Brown, 1954, pp. 1 ff.

of hatching salamander eggs and at the same time taught the science consultant a great deal about young children!

The adult amphibian will feel comfortable in a moist woodland terrarium (Chapter 6). If a child finds a spring peeper or treetoad, he will enjoy watching how it can scale the vertical walls of a glass container or terrarium. Perhaps when the room is quiet, it will even feel comfortable enough to "peep." Thin rocks built into a miniature "grotto" or formed into a rough wall in one end of a terrarium or aquarium furnish a bit of "coolth" which is most desirable to frogs and toads.

Perhaps you can train your frog or toad to eat an insect or bit of hamburger or earthworm dangled and moving in front of it. Children will be astonished to see the speed with which the tongue, fastened in front not the rear of the mouth, flicks out and gathers in the offering.

REPTILE PETS

Turtles

Larger turtles (except, of course, snappers) are one kind of animal that can be allowed to roam the classroom when children are present. Most turtles are omnivorous. Ant eggs, most insects, bits of hard-boiled egg, earthworms, meal worms, lettuce, and fruit provide a good diet. Some turtles like a small amount of chopped meat or canned fish. Be especially careful, however, to remove promptly all uneaten portions. Desert tortoises, of course, are vegetarians but need a wide variety of food to keep healthy in captivity. Even in a warm climate and indoors, almost all turtles attempt to hibernate for part of the winter. The length of time depends upon the latitude. For instance, around latitude 40° turtles hibernate about 5–6 months. Provide a dark cool place for them to retire. When they emerge, they may look somewhat emaciated, especially around the neck. If they do not eat, you may have to force feed them. This usually takes two people, one to hold the unwilling reptile, and one to pry open his beak with a blunt-ended tool and stuff in the food. Do not overfeed. In all cases, in the interest of good conservation, attempt to return the turtle to its native habitat after a brief sojourn at school. Toy turtles and some larger species will need shallow enamelware or glass dishes where they can sit and soak. Help children understand why it is cruel to paint a turtle's back; its back is composed of partly living tissue. Help the children estimate the age of a living turtle by the major growth rings in each scale. Perhaps with the loan of a strong magnifying glass or a high school microscope or toy microscope, they can also see growth rings in fish scales.

As a general rule for feeding, land turtles are usually vegetarians, and water turtles are meat and fish eaters. Mud turtles feed underwater as do many water turtles.

Snakes

The small snakes appropriate to keep in school—garter, green, DeKay's snakes—would crawl through the mesh of the multipurpose cage described earlier. A more adequate snake box can be constructed from a wooden apple box in which one side is replaced by a glass pane that slides in and out of a close-fitting wooden groove or slot nailed to the box (Fig. 2-6). (Wood already grooved is available at lumber yards.) The slits in the box's side can be covered with tape. Snakes need a shallow enamel or glass water dish, as, for example, an ash tray. They also need a branch on which to climb and a rock or bark under which to hide. During shedding time these rough surfaces enable them to work loose from the old skin. Snakes, like other animals in the classroom, need a place where they can get into

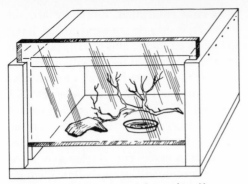

Fig. 2-6 Observation box for snakes. You may wish to insert a cake-tin base in which to spread sand. Place water dish in one corner and some rock or bark for a hiding place in another.

the shade at will. They also need *some* sunshine as their body metabolism depends upon the air temperature. However, do not allow the snake to broil in the sun. In the western Sierra we have seen a rattlesnake literally cooked to death in a matter of minutes when kept in the hot open sunlight.

Large snakes, if brought to school at all, should remain but a few days. During this period it is not necessary to feed them. Smaller kinds and young of large species should be offered worms, grubs, insects. Most snakes feed irregularly. Dangle bits of chopped meat and/or earthworms in front of them, as they accept only live or moving food.

Never attempt to keep poisonous snakes in an elementary classroom, particularly in a glass jar. In case of questionable identification, it is wiser not to pick it up until you are sure. A copperhead covered with roadside dust may not at first show its typical markings. However, you should remember there are very few kinds of poisonous snakes in the United States.

Lizards

Lizards may be kept in a cage similar to that described for snakes. Like snakes, they become sluggish unless they are kept relatively warm. The best temperature is 80° F; it should not be below 65° F. Children often bring to school the little green or brown lizards sold at circuses and carnivals as "chameleons." These require living food such as flies, moths, meal worms—not sweetened water as is often prescribed. Chameleons, also called the Carolina anolis, will sometimes eat very ripe bananas. It is possible for pet lizards to catch their own "bait" if they are housed in a cage in which the mesh is large enough to admit flies. Put in some fruit, syrup, or meat to attract flies, and set the cage on the window sill (but not in continuous sunlight). Horned toads prefer ants and can catch their own if you place their cage near an ant colony with a trail of sugar or grease leading to the cage.

A potted growing plant in the cage gives the lizard something to climb. Like snakes, lizards also like bark, branches, and rocks, and need a shallow water dish (enamel or glass). One way of insuring that their skins absorb moisture is to spray the plant and the lizard at the same time with lukewarm water, say once a week. Another way to get water into a pet lizard is to hold it, head *out,* in a dish of water. You can almost see the skin soaking up moisture like a blotter.

BIRD PETS

The usual caged birds, such as canaries, can thrive in the classroom if they are properly fed and cleaned. The principal problem is exercising the bird. It is not recommended that parakeets or other members of the parrot family be brought to school. They are susceptible to a virus disease, psittacosis, which is communicable to humans. If there is a place outside the school where the birds will be safe from cats and other predators, it is possible to keep members of the parrot family as pets, but only in areas such as southern California since the parrot family is tropical in origin. One may have to force feed the occasional wild baby birds which are brought to school. Open the beak gently and, with forceps or tweezers, put the food in the back of the throat. The food must touch the swallowing center on the back of the tongue. Keep the little thing in shredded paper in a cup or berry basket in a warm place.

Children enjoy letting ducks, chickens, and other pets "make tracks" on newsprint or painting paper spread on the floor. Dip the pet's feet in any water color tempera. Let the animal walk across the paper and then thoroughly rinse the feet.

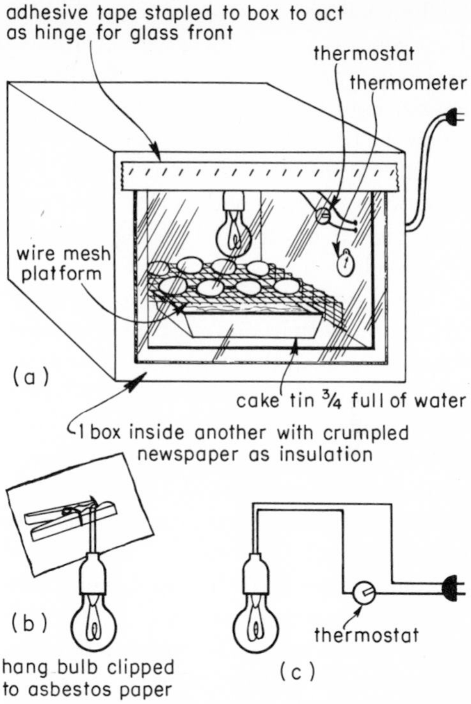

Chicken incubator

Watching chickens hatch in the incubator of a commercial hatchery was a profound experience for one first grade. It is possible to secure one-egg electric incubators or larger commercial incubators. However, you may prefer to give children the experience of making their own (Fig. 2-7A, B, C). The materials are simple and inexpensive.

Two cardboard cartons are required; one should be about $10'' \times 10'' \times 14''$, and the other, about $12'' \times 12'' \times 16''$, or enough larger to allow paper to be stuffed between the two boxes for insulation. You will also need a short lamp cord, socket and bulb, a wall thermometer, and a thermostatic switch (such as the Farmaster Automatic Temperature Control, Model 594.405, approximate cost $3.00). Obtain one large cake pan, about $8'' \times 10''$, and a piece of ¼'' or ½'' wire mesh, about $12'' \times 14''$, or big enough to fit the floor of the box with enough overlap to fold under and make a platform to hold the eggs suspended above the water in the cake pan. Cut one end from the small box. Then cut a large

Fig. 2-7 Classroom incubator. Consult with high school science teacher or local poultryman for specifics and supplies.

square window in a side of the large box which will fit against the open end of the inner box (Fig. 2-7A).

Cut a hole in the top of the smaller box and suspend a light bulb with a clothespin. Above the light anchor a piece of asbestos paper (Fig. 2-7B). Be sure one wire to the light bulb goes through the thermostat (Fig. 2-7C).

Fit a large pane of glass over the window aperture. Tape all the edges for safety. Use a double thickness of 1½–2'' adhesive to make a flap along the top edge (Fig. 2-7A). Staple to box to form a hinge so you can open the window at will. Paint the inner surface of the cake (water) tin to inhibit rusting. Bend the wire to fit above it and fit into bottom of smaller box.

Fasten thermometer and thermostat to inner wall of inside box. Line box with kitchen foil to reflect heat toward eggs. Pack space between boxes with crumpled newspaper or other insulation. Try different size light bulbs until you have one that keeps the box close to 103° F all the time. It will help to make three or four ¾"–1" holes to be plugged with corks. These can be removed or inserted to regulate the heat level.

The children will have an opportunity to gain more than one concept of science through such an experience, e.g., heat reflection and radiation, differential heating (thermostatic principle), insulation, and electric circuits. Thus the experience provides many overlearnings in addition to what they learn about reproduction and the life cycle of chickens.

Once an even 103° F temperature can be maintained you are ready to secure a dozen fertile eggs. The chicken farmer may show the children how he "candles" these to determine fertility, or the children may wish to recheck with some very simple, safe equipment, e.g., a light bulb shielded inside a small tin can with a small hole aperture cut in it.

At the end of 3 days remove one egg and crack it just enough to slip contents into shallow dish. The heart beat should be discernible in a 3-day embryo. You may want to make a pencil mark on the egg as a record. Repeat every 3 days to let children observe the development. The eggs should be turned daily and water kept in the pan underneath the wire platform to maintain viable humidity.

Hen's eggs take 21 days to hatch. Once the chicks have hatched, wait a day and then reduce the incubator temperature a few degrees a day to room temperature. The incubator can serve as their home until they are about 3 weeks old. To allow them to go in and out of their home at will, cut out one wall of their box 2" above the floor. Cover this opening with cloth

thumbtacked to the carton. Outside make a 12"-high fence of wire mesh or screening. A sheet of lightweight metal under the incubator and runway may be quickly removed and hosed off. Baby chick mash can be purchased at a feed store that also sells food and water dishes.

MAMMAL PETS

Almost any small pet that can be safely kept at home can be kept at school. Never keep any animal long confined. About 2 weeks is the maximum except when training white rats for pets and for keeping animals for nutritional experiments. If the fur of a mammal pet is in poor condition, try adding a small amount of Vitamin A and/or milk of magnesia to the diet. Provide plenty of food for wild pets, for there is nothing more pitiable than a half-starved caged animal. Wild animals do not usually overeat. Feed baby animals with a doll nursing bottle. Use the smallest opening to avoid strangling the little creature by too rapid feeding. Milk bubbling from the nostrils is a sure sign of this.

One way of permitting pets not otherwise possible at school is to plan a "Pet Day."[3] Each child who brings one may plan to tell about feeding, cleaning and training his pet.

Rabbits

A tame rabbit is another creature that may be permitted the freedom of the classroom. This is good for both rabbit and children! Rabbits need exercise and children need to get used to animals. However, do not keep wild rabbits as pets. They sometimes carry the disease tularemia. In a mild climate or in spring and fall, Bunny can live in a cage on the out-

[3] Greve, Anna M., "Let's Have a Pet Show," *Natl. Humane Review,* Vol. XXXI, No. 5, May, 1943, pp. 18–20.

door window sill safe from dogs and cats. In the classroom, he needs a cardboard box shelter (which can be disposed of and replaced when sanitation demands) where he may retreat and rest. Cut one end from the box for an entrance way. For overnight and weekend quarters, the 2' or 3' square mesh cage is adequate though it is cramped for a full-grown rabbit over more extended periods. It is of utmost importance with rabbits, or, indeed, with any animals in the classroom, to have equipment which is easily and quickly cleaned by the children with a minimum of help from the teacher. Rabbits will need heavy, nontippable containers for food and water. One can build a rack or manger for green food from wire screening. This should be attached low and to one side of the cage. All animals choose one spot in a cage or room for excretion. Once this choice has been made, spread newspaper and change it frequently. A dirty pen, damp food, and poor ventilation may soon produce a sick rabbit. In such a case, take the animal immediately to a veterinary.

Never lift rabbits by their long sensitive ears. Pick them up by the loose shoulder skin, at the same time supporting the hind quarters with a gloved or cloth-protected hand as a guard against their long hind claws.

White rats

For the elementary classroom white rats are preferable to white mice. They smell less "mousey," and their larger size makes it easier for children to pick them up. They move less quickly than guinea pigs, and, in our experience, are less inclined to bite than hamsters. White rats are usually available from hospital or medical research laboratories. These sources are often glad to have the school return parents and progeny at the year's end.

Keep rats in the multipurpose wire cage

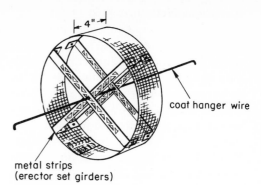

Fig. 2-8 Animal exercise wheel, made from wire scraps left over from pet cage construction (Figs. 2-1, 2-2). The coat hanger wire axle is long enough to hook through the sides or across one corner of the cage.

(Fig. 2-2). For them and for other animals such as squirrels, mice, chipmunks (almost all rodents), you may wish to add an exercise wheel. The "ferris wheel" type can be made from a leftover strip of wire screening for the tread, coat-hanger wire for the axle, and metal strips or Tinkertoy sticks for cross-arms or braces (Fig. 2-8). The wheel must run easily with one "rat power."

Rats require about 3 weeks for gestation. During late pregnancy the male should be removed to another cage. His presence at this time sometimes makes the female so nervous she may kill the newborn young. Give the mother some partially shredded newspaper or paper toweling with which to make a nest.

The young grow hair and open eyes in 16–18 days. They should stay with the mother about 21–24 days. Prolonged nursing is hard on the mother. Begin weaning by feeding the babies milk, bread soaked in milk, and lettuce. A few drops of cod liver oil on bread should be given twice a week. When the young are a month old, they may be given the same diet as the adults, i.e., bread, bread and milk, lettuce, carrots, sunflower seeds, etc. Offer pets small samples and they select or reject as the various foods meet their needs.

The babies may be picked up as soon as their eyes are open and it seems not to worry the mother. Condition her to accept your handling by slow gentle movements, talking to her and feeding her a bit of carrot or chocolate as you return her to her young. Frequent brief and judicious handling of white rats gentles them quickly. Show children how to pick up the rats without squeezing and yet with gentle firmness so the animal does not fear falling. All animals fear nothing so much as close physical restraint. Therefore one must give even semidomesticated white rats a chance to get used to handling. Always move deliberately, never hurriedly or nervously, with animals. Gentle them by frequent quiet fondling, a little at first, more as they cease to show fear. Talk softly meanwhile, and scratch them behind the ears and eventually under the chin. Above all, keep your white rats clean, comfortable, and amply but not over-supplied with a varied diet which can include a bit of anything that humans eat. Now and then bring in some green sticks so they may gnaw the bark. You may even wish to launder your pets or at least their tails. A more natural method of cleaning is to give them a small sand box in which they can rub off any grease on their fur.

White rats are often used in school nutrition experiments. For further details see Chapter 13.

CAPSULE LESSONS

2-1 After a rain, encourage children to bring in earthworms. When you have enough, let each child spread one out on a damp paper towel. Ask "What Do You See?" Help them decide how the earthworm moves. Let them describe its body. What are its habits? Are earthworms to be valued? (See Comstock, Hogner in bibliography.)

2-2 Compare native American silkworms and their cocoons and moths to the stages of metamorphosis in the silkworm used to produce silk thread.

2-3 Encourage the children to discuss associations with the terms hibernation and estivation. Let them look up definitions and examples. They may wish to induce temporary hibernation by subjecting animals to short periods of artificial low temperature. Zoologists sometimes use this method with reptiles in order to secure photographs in slow motion. Lead the children toward the major concept of animal adaptation and implications for space travel.

2-4 Let children make flannel board drawings to illustrate phases of insect or amphibian metamorphosis they have observed. Why should these be arranged in cyclical order? Again lead toward major concept of like producing like.

2-5 If children can secure snake skin, let them observe how the eye cover came off with the skin. Let the children discuss the relationship of this fact to the notion of snake blindness and irritability during shedding. Let them read about the elliptical pupils of poisonous snakes. We do not usually encourage elementary age children to *collect* snakes. We know of one youngster who came on the school bus bearing a huge copperhead inside a *glass* jar. Suppose the jar had been broken!

2-6 Superstitions about snakes, bats, and the like provide a wonderful opportunity for the teacher to help the children by research and observation distinguish between fact and fancy. *Teaching Science in the Elementary School* reports an excellent example of objective dissipation of superstitions about a grass snake, pp. 74–77, and about astrological superstitions, pp. 49–50.

2-7 Let the children bring in samples of different types of hair (fur). Examine under magnification. Let them discover that hair is not the same all over an animal's body. Let them learn to recognize outer guard hairs vs. soft underfur, and have them learn the function of each. Let them look at their pets and see that the fur is thinner underneath, next to the body, and in places where it would be bulky if it were equally thick. Compare human and guard hair.

2-8 One teacher helped the children make a feather collection. Their charts and pictures showed examples of the following:

Bird name		
wing	*breast*	*back*
(to fly)	(to keep warm)	(to shed water)

BIBLIOGRAPHY

Aistrop, Jack B., *Enjoying Pets,* Vanguard, 1955. For the intermediate grades.

ASPCA, Education Dept., *Suggestions for Holding a Pet Show.* Valuable information. 12 pp. mimeo.

American Humane Assn., Leaflet No. 262, *The Classroom Turtle;* No. 512, *Children and Their Pets in the Home.* Simple and practical.

Backyard Zoo Kit, contains handbook (10 pp.), cages, signs for cages, hand magnifier. Handbook tells where to find and how to handle animals, how to fix cages, and what to feed creatures. $5.95 complete, Models of Industry, 2100 Fifth St., Berkeley 2, Calif.

Blough, G., and M. Campbell, *Making and Using Classroom Science Materials,* Holt, Rinehart and Winston, 1954. "Animal Feeding," pp. 62–67. A list of suggestions for 32 kinds of creatures commonly brought to school.

Brown, Vinson, *How to Make a Home Nature Museum,* Little, Brown, 1954. Specifics by an expert.

———, *How to Make a Miniature Zoo*, Little, Brown, 1956.

Buck, Margaret W., *Small Pets from Woods and Fields,* Abingdon, 1960. Concise text and fine illustrations.

Burnett, R. W., *Teaching Science in the Elementary School,* Holt, Rinehart and Winston, 1953. Excellent teacher reference.

Chrystie, Frances N., *Pets,* Little, Brown, 1953. Emphasizes relationships of pets to children rather than details of cage construction, breeding, feeding, and diseases. Intermediate and upper grades.

Comstock, Anna, *Handbook of Nature Study,* Cornell U. Press (Comstock), 1947. Designed for teachers with little or no background in science. The most valuable single reference on content and thought questions, especially in the area of biological science.

Cooper, Elizabeth K., *Science in Your Own Back Yard,* Harcourt, Brace & World, 1958. Interesting and well written.

Darby, Gene, *What Is a Turtle?,* Benefic, 1959. Primary level. One of an interesting and well-illustrated series.

Foster, Polly, and Larry Foster, *About Your Kitten,* Melmont, 1955. Clear, simple drawings and directions; can be read by second grade.

Greenberg, Sylvia, *Home-Made Zoo,* McKay, 1952. Specific directions for collecting, keeping, and observing usual and unusual pets.

Greenlee, Julian B., *Better Teaching Through Elementary Science,* Brown, 1954. Easy to read and challenging teacher reference. The science supervisor learns with the children.

Hatt, Robert T., "Stocking a Home Zoo," reprint *Natural History* magazine, Vol. 32, No. 6, Nov.-Dec., 1932. Excellent photos of small native mammals and illustrations of live traps.

Hogner, Dorothy, *Earthworms,* Crowell, 1953. Intermediate grade children will find it fascinating to follow directions for classroom or school yard earthworm farm.

———, *Odd Pets,* Crowell, 1951. Directions for care of many outdoor animals. Photos useful in identification.

Hoke, John, *First Book of Snakes,* Watts, 1952. Intermediate. Directions for making cages. Presents myths vs. facts about common snakes.

National Audubon Society. Free list of publications on all aspects of outdoor science and conservation.

Pels, Gertrude, *Care of Water Pets,* Crowell, 1955. Intermediate. Excellent sourcebook on care of fish, turtles, frogs, snails, and the like.

Podendorf, Illa, *True Book of Pets,* Childrens Press, 1954. How to care for common pets. Two valuable pages of suggestions for keeping pets comfortable and healthy.

Russell, David W., *Suggestions for Care of Pets in the Classroom,* Scott, Foresman, 1942. Useful but difficult to obtain.

Turtox Service, *White Rats,* Leaflet No. 40, General Biological Supply House, Chicago, Ill. Over 60 leaflets on various aspects of high school biology. Excellent teaching reference materials. The set available to school or district if not to the individual.

Vessel, M. F., and E. J. Harrington, *Common Native Animals,* Chandler, 1961. Brief descriptions and life data on forms most readily found in or near urban areas and on those on loan from "junior" museums. Suggestions for care and feeding and for teaching activities. Useful appendix and bibliography.

Walker, Ernest P., *Care of Captive Animals,* from Smithsonian report for 1941, pp. 305–66, publication No. 3664, Smithsonian Institution. Very useful and inexpensive, with 12 plates.

———, *First Aid and Care of Small Animals,* Animal Welfare Institute, New York, N.Y., 1955. The most valuable publication for its size and price.

Wormser, Sophie, *About Silkworms and Silk,* Melmont, 1961. Delightful for primary grades. Much information.

Insects and related animals

Why study insects? Is it worth the trouble? In answer to the first question, we believe children learn about themselves by studying other living things. Children watching insects learn to observe. They are practicing a part of the methods of science when they use patience and care in their observations. They forget about being annoyed by insect life if they are encouraged to watch it. They begin, even without being told, to see interrelationships with plant and other animal life, with climate and seasons. They begin to have a basis for understanding more general concepts such as adaptation, variety, and balance.

CARE OF INSECTS

If you are squeamish about handling insects, some of your children will be proud to handle and care for insect guests. Better still, they will find and collect insects for you in almost limitless quantity and variety. In the warm days of early fall (September is the best month in temperate zones) bring in one or more insects in a plastic container. A "brace" of crickets who feel enough at home to chirp during a quiet interlude will loose a flood of discussion, and a subsequent flood of insects will likely be brought to school!

Cricket cage

Making your crickets, or indeed any insect visitors, comfortable in the classroom requires close observation (bolstered by research or reading) to see how insects live. Learning how to care for insects should ideally precede capturing an insect, but generally it does not. In order that you can be somewhat forewarned and forearmed, this is how you may set up a cricket cage. Plant a plug of fresh grass or clover in a small flower pot (Fig. 3-1). Set over this and imbed firmly in the soil a glass lamp chimney or a roll of heavy cellophane or fine wire mesh. Lamp chimneys are usually available from hardware stores; heavy cellophane is safer but more easily tipped over; wire mesh affords less visibility. Cover the top with cheesecloth. If you entertain tree crickets, place inside the chimney a twig on which they can climb.

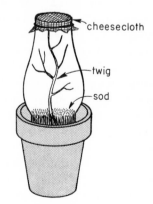

Fig. 3-1 Cricket cage. Set the flower pot in a saucer of water from which it can absorb moisture.

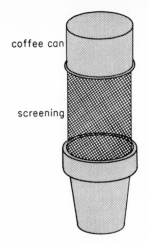

coffee can

screening

Fig. 3-2 Cage for large insects. The wire mesh affords less visibility than the lamp chimney but may be safer for young children.

Cage for large insects

Use a strawberry basket cage (plastic mesh) for larger insects, or use a big flowerpot with a roll of wire mesh or stiff cellophane capped by a coffee can (Fig. 3-2). Plant with a plug of grass or clover. A shallower can provides greater visibility. For example, use an inverted pie tin on top instead of the coffee can and weight it down with a brick or book. (See p. 49 for instructions to set up a fresh-water aquarium for dragonflies.)

A temporary cage can be made from an ice cream or cereal carton. Window screening may be cut with garden scissors and stapled in place over an observation window cut in the carton. A wire kitchen strainer may serve as the cover. Since such a container obviously does not provide the natural humidity evaporating from the soil and plants that is provided in the cricket cage, it is only for temporary quarters.

Grasshoppers, walking sticks, praying mantises, and the like will be comfortable in a cage made from a pint jar inverted over a bunch of grass and twigs set in a container of water (Fig. 3-3).

Make a hole in the bottom of a carton and invert over the foliage, covering the hole with the jar as shown.

Terrarium garden

To make a terrarium garden for insects, use a terrarium or aquarium or gallon jar with cover. Cover the bottom with an inch layer of fine gravel. Scatter a few small pieces of charcoal (available at a pet shop) on top of the gravel. By absorbing waste gases, the carbon will prevent the soil from becoming sour. A piece of limestone neutralizes soil acidity. Add a layer of soil, a layer of sand, and another layer of garden soil. Now plant grass seed, mixed whole bird or chick feed, corn, oats, or any of the grains. Put crickets, katydids, or grasshoppers into the container. Sprinkle enough water on the soil to keep it moist but not soggy. If you put in caterpillars, bring in some of the plant leaves on which you find them. Stick the stems into the soil or into a pill bottle sunk into the soil so the mouth of the bottle is flush with the surface. Perhaps you will let the children discover for themselves that praying mantises, spiders, and other insect-eaters should be placed in solitary confinement. Or you may wish to help children plan for such problems ahead of time.

Spider observation cage

A good observation cage (Fig. 3-4) for smaller spiders may be made from six 2″ × 2″ square pieces of glass of the sort used to cover 35 mm color film slides. These are available in quantity from a camera store. They can be put together with Scotch tape to form a cube. There is sufficient air in the cage for small spiders, enough for a week's time. You should never keep insects or any other creatures in the classroom for more than a week or two at most. Since the children tend to disregard them after this time, the creatures ought to be turned loose once more.

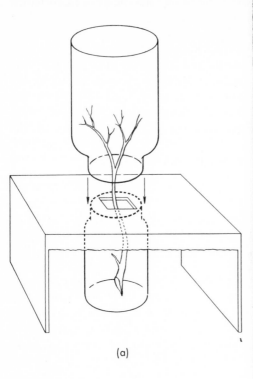

(a)

(b)

Fig. 3-3 (a) Another cage for large insects. This container gives the insect more room than that in Fig. 3-2 and keeps it from drowning. (b) Walking stick beetle. Note how it blends in with the twigs and bark in your "vivarium." (Leonard Lee Rue III.)

Insect incubator

With silkworm eggs or any other egg masses that the children may bring in, you will need a container that provides both visibility to you and shelter to the emerging insects. Place the egg mass inside the box. Make a hole in the side of a cardboard box just big enough to insert the neck of a vial, bottle, or tube. When the insects emerge from the eggs you have placed in the box, they will move out into the glass bottle or tube where you can see them. (See also p. 7.)

Insect collecting

Children can often find many different

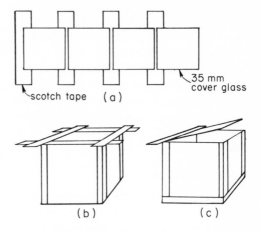

Fig. 3-4 Individual insect cubicles for 1-day close observations.

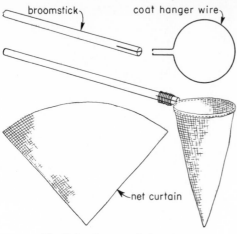

broomstick

coat hanger wire

net curtain

Fig. 3-5 Homemade insect net.

kinds of insects in a weed patch. For collecting, use an old net curtain or netting stretched between the children, in the manner of fishermen seining in shallow water. At the edge of the weeds, the children on the end move in and those helping move together to fold the curtain in a small ball. This must be done quickly before the insects fly off. The curtain is then unrolled very slowly and whatever remains sticking to it is popped quickly into containers. Small plastic boxes and containers are much safer for collecting than the traditional glass jars. Caution children to free stinging insects (e.g., bees, wasps, hornets). Encourage them to look for a fly which resembles a bee.

For individual collecting of fast-moving insects, children can make nets from a wire coat hanger, an old net curtain, and a broomstick (Fig. 3-5). The net should taper to a point and be long enough to fold over to entrap the catch.

Insect anesthetics

For close examination, insects can be temporarily anesthetized with carbon dioxide. Generate carbon dioxide (CO_2) gas (see Chapter 12) from vinegar on baking soda or from a lump of dry ice in a bottle.

The carbon dioxide leaves the bottle through a one-hole stopper fitted with a tube. Place insects in a bottle from which carbon dioxide gas has displaced water. When the insects become quiet, the children can look closely at a bee's stinger, a hornet's jaws, the antennae of a moth, the wings of a butterfly, spider spinnerets. The insect usually recovers within a few minutes from the effects of carbon dioxide.

Killing jar and relaxing jar

Screw-top pint jars or any widemouthed jars will do. Place a wad of cotton in the bottom. Cover the cotton with a circle of blotting paper, a cardboard full of holes, or separate strips of paper laid on each other to form a mesh. Soak the cotton with Carbona (carbon tetrachloride) or some insecticide containing DDT. *Do not use potassium cyanide in the elementary classroom!* However, caution children against direct inhalation of fumes from either Carbona or dust from DDT. Re-cover the jar and put in the insects, screw the cover on tightly, and leave until the insects are undoubtedly dead. A bottle or jar with an ounce or so of rubbing alcohol in it will kill most insects except moths and butterflies.

A dead insect is usually very dry and stiff and must be relaxed before it can be mounted. For this, prepare another jar in the same way as for the killing jar, but instead of cotton, use a small sponge dampened with water. Leave until the insect's body is flexible and its legs can be moved without breaking.

Stretching board

Once the dead insect's body is made flexible by the relaxing jar, the insect must be spread out to dry in the position required for mounting. Commercial stretching boards are not expensive (see appendix for list of supply houses). However, children may enjoy making their own. The main requirement is a material into which pins will go easily. Use soft wallboard such as Cellotex obtainable from lumberyards. The second requirement is to space two strips of wallboard 2″ wide and 12″ long with space between for bodies of different sized bugs (Fig. 3-6). Most commercial stretching boards are mounted on a slight angle, but this is not essential. However, it is important that the slot be tapered, varying gradually in width from ¼″ to ¾″.

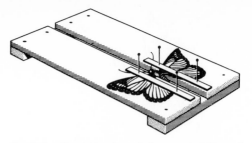

Fig. 3-6 Stretching board. A commercial board could serve as a model. (From G. Blough and M. Campbell, *Making and Using Classroom Science Materials in the Elementary School,* Holt, Rinehart and Winston, 1954.)

Mounting insects

If you can secure long thin insect pins from a biological supply house, they will readily go into the bottom of a cigar box. Use corrugated paper to make a false bottom for the box. The label bearing the insect's name, the date and locality of collection, and other data go on the pin just below the insect (Fig. 3-7). Regular common pins sometimes split the bodies of small insects and are too short to reach the bottom of a cigar box, but they will do. Cigar boxes and pins are suitable for beetles, grasshoppers, etc. Be sure to include a moth ball or lump of paradichlorobenzene.

Wide-winged insects such as moths and butterflies mount better in a different way. Adapt the traditional glass-covered Riker mount by using a shallow box such as a hosiery box. Cut out all but a narrow margin near the rim of the cover and replace with cellophane. Fill box nearly to the top with absorbent cotton. Arrange the butterflies or other insects on top of the cotton, add labels beside them, and close the cover. Again include a few moth flakes to deter creatures which might wish to eat the soft bodies of insects in the collection.

A "Berlese" funnel

If you have a good hand glass or low-power microscope and set up the equipment as shown in Fig. 3-8, you will be astonished to see the variety of animal life existing in most soil. Scoop up a cup or two of well-rotted woods soil or garden soil under shrubs. Place in a paper funnel under a 100-watt bulb overnight. Window screening across the bottom of the funnel

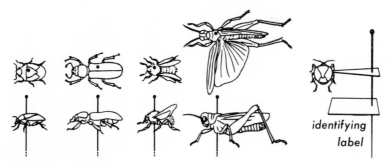

identifying label

Fig. 3-7 Insect mounting. Inasmuch as the small printing required on labels may be difficult for children, numbered tags corresponding to a numbered list may be substituted. (From G. Blough and M. Campbell, *Making and Using Classroom Science Materials in the Elementary School,* Holt, Rinehart and Winston, 1954.)

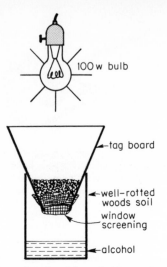

100 w bulb

tag board

well-rotted
woods soil

window
screening

alcohol

Fig. 3-8 A "Berlese" funnel. A larger funnel will collect more light to drive out the soil insects.

keeps dirt from falling through. Underneath place a jar of alcohol to preserve insects which drop through. Since soil insects detest light and heat, they will burrow down through the soil and through the screening.

Now that you know ways of collecting and caring for insects in the classroom, what insects should you study? Generally, those which you and your children can find. The preceding suggestions for care may have to be amplified for some species. We will not attempt to make recommendations for the nearly 750,000 *identified* species of insects. In the following discussion some of the more common forms are described.

SOLITARY AND SOCIAL INSECTS

Ants

Ants are valuable for study because they can be found almost at any time and any place, even in a city. Children will find ants of various sizes, from minute to large. Medium-sized ones are best to watch in the classroom. Ants are found in various colors: black, "red," brown, and combina-

tions of colors. Sometimes children will find ants of different colors in the same nest. For example, one kind has a rust-red head and thorax with brown legs and abdomen. In the same colony we may find black or ash-colored ants. These last are the slaves of the brown species. They have been stolen as larvae or pupae from another nest by the "slavers," brought home, and reared as part of the family.

Children know or will observe that ants are always found living together. Ants, like bees, are social insects. Wasps, bumblebees, and many other forms are solitary insects.

Children looking for ants to bring to school will find them in a variety of homes. The largest kinds often build a hill or mound made up of a bushel or two of small pieces of plant debris. Some ants make tunnels in rotten logs. The carpenter ants make tunnels in living wood. Their homes are indicated by small telltale piles of sawdust at the foot of a tree. The sawdust is finer and in smaller amount than would result from woodpecker work. Most ants make labyrinthine tunnels underground. Those which have tunnels under a flat stone have a cozy nursery for their young, for the stone will hold the sun's midday heat through the night. If it gets too warm in the daytime, the nurse ants carry the young deeper in the ground. And in winter the whole colony lives deep in the ground.

Ant observation house. Children who are looking for a colony to bring to school should be urged to replace the stone carefully. Otherwise the inhabitants may be frightened away before a classroom home is ready for them to move into. The simplest kind of ant nest for school observation is a screw-top quart or gallon glass jar. Find a block of wood or a tall thin empty can to make a hollow core in the center of the jar. Fill in around it partway with sandy garden soil. Leave room for some soil from the ant hill and the ants; then permit enough room for a small water dish or sponge to go just under the cap (Fig. 3-9). If the jar is set on a block of wood in a pan of water, the ant guests will be dissuaded from leaving. Put black or dark paper around the jar, except when watching the ants. Otherwise the ants will make their tunnels toward the center where they cannot be seen. Keep the jar in a relatively warm place but not in direct sunshine. The soil should be relatively moist.

Another kind of nest may be constructed from two window panes of the same size and modeling clay (Fig. 3-10A). Lay one pane on a block of wood which rests in a shallow pan of water. Make clay labyrinths about 1" wide and 1" high. Press down the second window pane as the cover to be lifted when you wish to feed or water the colony. The glass should be covered with dark paper when the ants are not being observed.

A third kind is made from a pair of window panes set vertically in wooden blocks. This is done by routing out two channels in the wood just wider than the thickness of the glass (Fig. 3-10B). The glass is separated by four ¾-1" wood strips. The whole is taped together at the edges except the top strip which can be lifted out. Drill

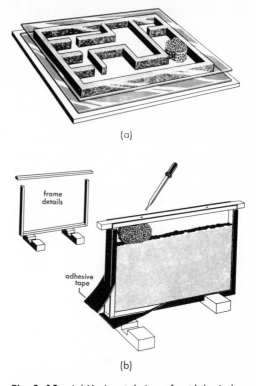

(a)

(b)

Fig. 3-10 (a) Horizontal view of ant labyrinths; (b) cross-sectional ant nest. This observation frame, if large enough, might also be adapted for use as an observation beehive. (See Fig. 3-13.) (From G. Blough and M. Campbell, *Making and Using Classroom Science Materials in the Elementary School*, Holt, Rinehart and Winston, 1954.)

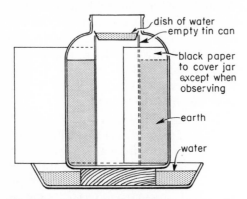

Fig. 3-9 Pickle-jar ant nest. The moated enclosure restrains "little wanderers." The hollow core makes ant tunneling more easily observable.

three small (½") holes in the top strip. These holes should be corked except during addition of food or water. Use a medicine dropper to avoid giving too much water. Tape the sides and bottom with colored masking tape no less than 1½" wide. Cut the tape so that it lies over itself to make secure corners. Commercial nests complete with inhabitants are available through large department stores or scientific supply houses. The nest is very similar to the third kind of nest suggested.

Ant food. As with many other animals temporarily detained in the classroom, ants should receive a varied diet in very small amounts. Uneaten food should always be removed before any more is added. Try bread or pastry crumbs, sugar water, honey, fruits, bits of bacon, other insects, vegetables, and seeds. Ants can swallow only food which they chew up and reduce to liquid form. The proportionately large abdomen of the ant is for storage of this liquid nourishment. Usually the food gathered is carried back to the nest to feed the growing larvae or grubs. Occasionally the children will see examples of "refueling" of other ants. One of these may halt the food carrier, touch it with the feelers, and presently be rewarded with a drop of liquid food from the mouth of the worker.

Ant collecting. With a classroom home prepared and plans for feeding made, the children will soon help you bring in a colony. Go equipped with a garden trowel, a large piece of old bedsheet or other white cloth or paper, and two narrow-necked plastic bottles with stoppers. Lift off the stone cover of the nest and lay one of the bottles flat on the ground. Steer the ants into the bottle until you have about one hundred. Stopper securely. In order to have a colony that will last more than 2 or 3 weeks, you must now find a queen. Dig rather deeply and spread out the soil on the white cloth or paper. Find one ant which is much larger than the rest. This is the queen. She is merely an egg-laying machine, not the ruler of the colony. Guide her into the second bottle, along with some of the earth in which you find her. The colony tends to thrive longer if the children also collect in a shoe box as many of the immature ants as possible. Ant eggs are so tiny they are almost impossible to find except with a hand lens. The grubs or larvae look like translucent rice grains, pointed at one end. One author compares them to miniature crook-neck squashes. The cocoons which contain the pupae are the third stage in ant metamorphosis. These are yellowish and about

the size of wheat seed. They are commonly sold as food for miniature turtles. One of the authors met a young business man in third grade. He had found or started an ant colony in an old bathtub abandoned on a vacant lot. He did a thriving business selling the ant "eggs" (really cocoons) to his friends who owned turtles and goldfish. The soil from the old nest and the immatures should be put into the new home first; then include the workers and lastly, with care, the queen. Once the nest is settled and the queen begins laying, the nest may be unplugged or removed from the pan of water. If the nest is placed near some opening to the outdoors, the workers will come and go freely for the entire year.

Ant castes. As the children will soon learn, life in the ant world appears almost as highly organized as human society. There may be as many as eight castes in an ant hill. Except for the queen and the drones who provide the continuation of the species, the most important caste consists of the workers. The first eggs the queen lays in a new nest will hatch into workers. You have already read about the nurse ants who are kept constantly occupied moving the young from upper to lower nurseries, depending on the temperature. We have seen food gatherers "bringing home the groceries" and stopping en route to pass a mouthful of liquid nourishment to a fellow worker. The myriad tunnels in an ant nest are the work of the builders. As in any communal living, cleanliness is essential. Some workers seem to have the special task of carrying refuse to a heap in one corner far from the brood.

There are the soldiers who guard the entrance of the nest. Let the children introduce some ants from another nest and watch what happens. Whichever ant is the guard will rear on its hind legs, throw its formic acid toward the intruder, and close in, trying to cut him in two with its jaws. Or remove an ant from the nest and put it

Fig. 3-11 Aphids, aphis, or plant lice. These tiny, innocuous looking insects are a scourge to plants. Some species are mealy white; others are juicy green. (Hugh Spencer.)

back after a few days. Notice how the soldier ant on guard will carefully go all over the intruder with his feelers. It is said that ants depend on their sense of smell to know other members of their nest.

One very interesting group of workers is that group which herds ant "cows." By ant cows we mean aphids or plant lice (Fig. 3-11). (See also pp. 30–31, on aphids.) Both the common green and the woolly aphids are slow creatures which settle on the stem or leaf of a plant and live by sucking sap through the bill or sucking tube. Through the alimentary canal they give off a sweet juice sometimes called "honeydew." Ants like this honeydew. By stroking the aphids with their feelers or antennae, they can "milk" their "cows" of the sweet juice. Usually where one finds aphids on outdoor plants, one finds ants climbing or descending the stem. Some kinds of ants carry aphids underground in winter to suck on the roots of plants. Thus the ants have a year-round supply of "milk." One interesting species of ants carries pieces of green leaves underground to rot and form leaf mold. In this leaf mold these ants grow mushrooms upon which they feed.

One morning at a desert campsite, one of the authors watched the most astonish-ing parade of ants. Each ant was holding over its head a moon-shaped section of leaf. Since it was late spring and the desert sun became hot early in the day, we thought the ants were sensible to provide themselves with parasols! Probably these ants were mushroom growers, carrying their bits of vegetation quickly underground to preserve its precious moisture and promote molding. In the Southwest deserts, one can see a solitary velvet ant bustling along—a brilliant speck of scarlet chenille which turns out to be an insect.

Winged ants and termites

Now and then an area may become clouded with what appear to be winged ants. The queen and the male ants of the nest have grown wings and taken off on a nuptial flight. One of the males mates with the queen, who then returns to the nest. She sheds her wings and starts the egg-producing process all over again. All species of ants do this. Sometimes the winged forms are the queen and males from a termite colony.

Not all winged ants are termites. But all winged ants are either male or female. The workers are sexless. Since termites are found almost everywhere, the children may be able to bring in examples of termite work. If they bring in living termites, handle them carefully lest some escape in the school building. A builder or contractor will save samples of termite damage for you. Some builders or contractors or insect exterminators will take time to visit the school to answer the children's questions about termites. (Check your telephone directory for local pest control experts.)

Your children may wish to observe termites at work. In a pan of damp soil imbed a block of soft wood about 2″ thick. Drill 1 or 2 holes in the wood to accommodate the termites. Drop them in and plug

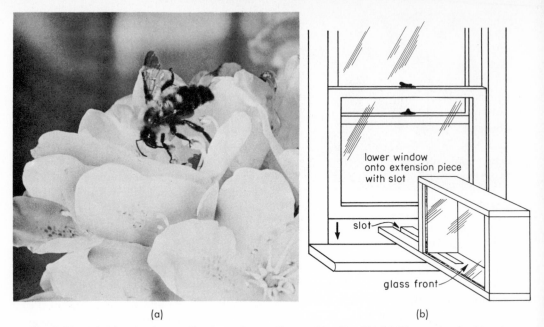

lower window
onto extension piece
with slot

slot

glass front

(a)   (b)

Fig. 3-12 (a) A bumble bee, pollinating a flower. (Leonard Lee Rue III.) (b) Observation beehive, to be installed in a classroom window.

with soil. Cover the sides of the block with glass panes. Seal the top of the block with tape or a strip of glass.

Much remains to be discovered about the habits of ants. For instance, scientists believe ants recognize each other by a sense of smell. They apparently communicate with their feelers. Yet no one has proved this idea. We suspect, but do not really know, that the sense of smell enables ants to find their way back to the home nest. A study of ants or other social insects may lead children to draw some interesting comparisons between the organization of human and insect societies. A primary grade study of community helpers should help children see that humans (in democratic society) have some choice of jobs.

Bees

Much of the detail in the preceding section on ants also applies to bees. Bees are also highly organized, social insects. They are so successful in their adaptation that some other insects try to imitate them. Children often mistake harmless flies that closely imitate the bee for the real thing.

Not all bees are social insects. The carpenter and bumble bees (Fig. 3-12A) and most wasps are solitary insects. Perhaps the children will enjoy Charles Darwin's famous speculation about bumble bees. He once said that the English soldier would have to go without his bully beef if it were not for the old maids of England. For the old maids kept cats which caught mice. And vacant mouse holes made ideal homes for bumble bees. The bees were responsible for pollinating the clover on which English beef was fattened. The story goes that the first Australian clover crops were a failure until somebody thought to import hives of bees.

Observation hive. An observation hive with an opening to the outside is a year-long source of interest and information to the children (Fig. 3-12B). Secure a standard frame from the nearest beekeeper and build the "beehive" around it as shown in Fig. 3-12B. The "hive" is set up at the classroom window with egress to outdoors through the slot down in Fig. 3-12B. Check your local town ordinances to be sure there is no prohibition of beekeeping. Perhaps a local beekeeper can help you set up the observation hive. Watching a beekeeper hive a swarm is an unforgettable experience.

Help children understand the chemical reaction in neutralizing the acid of a bee sting or other insect bites. Diluted household ammonia or milk of magnesia is very soothing, but ordinary mud is usually a more available neutralizer.

Wasps and hornets

As with bees, some species of wasps and hornets are solitary, and some are social insects. Again, as in all our insect study, close observation begets interest, skill, and respect—and dissipates fear and superstitions. (See Fig. 3-13A, B for a comparison of the wasp and hornet.)

The curious nests of the mud-dauber wasp lead us to a study of a solitary wasp. We find these tube-shaped cells under window ledges, under the eaves of a building, or under the overhanging planks of a bridge. If we break open the cells, we find tubes—some empty, some with a fat white grub and a half-eaten spider, some with a silken cocoon, or some nearly full of spiders and the wasp's egg at the top of the tube. If the life cycle (metamorphosis) has been completed, we might find all the tubes empty.

Look especially for mud wasp nests near water. In the early summer watch for wasps at the edges of pools or puddles. Here the wasp leaves many little holes from which she draws mud to mix with her saliva to make cement for her nest.

There are about 70 species of mud wasps in our United States. Some, such as the potter wasp or jug-builder, provision their nests with caterpillars instead of spiders. The jug-builder uses animal hairs to reinforce her nest.

Yellow jackets and white-faced hornets are wasps that live as social insects. They may be regarded as the original papermakers for both make nests of chewed wood pulp. These nests are a marvel of design and construction. However, the yellow jackets make somewhat finer-textured paper. They make the wood pulp from bits of wood pulled off old fences or boards which is then laid on in thin layers. Depending on the wood source, the layers may have different colors. The method is exactly the same in principle as that used by commercial papermakers today.

Sometimes a windstorm brings down one of these wasp apartment houses. It deserves careful and close examination. Check first to be sure the former adult inhabitants have departed. Yellow jacket bites can be toxic to some individuals.

WINGED AND WINGLESS INSECTS

Ant lions

In dry fine pulverized soil along a roadside or stream, one may notice a series of miniature craters or pits (Fig. 3-14). These are made by the larval form of an insect that looks like a small dragonfly. These "doodlebugs," as some children call them, lie in wait at the bottom of the pit for whatever unwary creature may tumble in. To find out which pits are manned and which are empty, use a grass stem or fine twig to start a few grains of sand tumbling down from the rim of the pit. If this causes a spasmodic twitch at the bottom, Mr. Doodlebug is at home. It takes a quick and mighty scoop of the soil around the crater to catch the trapper. Even then, you may miss him if you do not look sharply, for his soft oblong body is coated

(b)

(b) A mud-dauber wasp and its nests. The mud dauber may be distinguished by its slender, shiny black body with its threadlike waist. Its wings, which glisten green, blue, and purple, fold beside each other over its back. It is a solitary insect. (Alfred Renfro from National Audubon Society.) The mud dauber mixes mud with saliva to form cement which it plasters to the underside of a roof or other sheltered spot in a tube about 1″ long, with a smooth inside and rough outside. It then proceeds to sting spiders so as to paralyze, but not kill, them. After filling the nest with the spiders and depositing an egg, the wasp seals the end of the tube with more cement. The egg hatches into a grub, which feeds on the fresh spider meat provided by its mother. (L. G. Kesteloo from National Audubon Society.)

(a)

Fig. 3-13 (a) A European hornet and a hornet's nest. This hornet, like the yellow jacket, has a rather heavy waist and folds its wings like a fan so that they do not obscure its body. It is a social insect. (Stephen Collins from National Audubon Society.) The nest in which the hornet lives with other members of its species is constructed of papery chewed wood pulp. It is fastened at the top to a tree branch or some similar support and has its entrance near the bottom. (George Porter from National Audubon Society.)

and camouflaged with sand and dust. If you catch a few, they may dig pits for you in the school room if you put them in a jar or empty aquarium with fine, dusty sand of the consistency they like.

Aphids

Aphids suck sap from plants. Some ants draw honeydew from their aphid cows or carry aphid eggs underground for the winter. In the spring the ants carry the

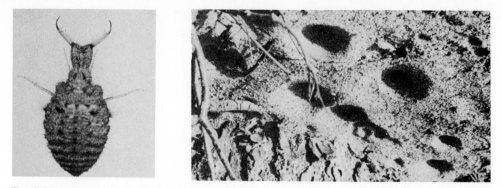

Fig. 3-14 An ant lion (Myrmeleonidae) and its ant traps. These are common in fine dry sand even in city parking lots. (Hugh Spencer.)

eggs to a plant stem or leaf where the eggs will hatch. Sometimes children will notice ladybugs among the aphids on a plant. Ladybugs and the larvae from which they hatch both eat aphids. In fact, commercial growers buy ladybugs to combat aphids in their orchards and truck gardens. Anyone who likes roses, cherry, apple, and other rose relatives, and citrus trees should be especially hospitable to ladybugs.

Sometimes people spray plants infested by aphids and next day the aphids are thick as ever. Perform two experiments to understand why. Find three branches of about the same size with about the same size infestation of aphids. To a quart jar of *warm* soapy water add a teaspoon of oil (mineral oil or kerosene). Shake thoroughly and spray one branch with the mixture. Tie a plastic vegetable bag around the branch. Clean the spraygun thoroughly and spray the second branch with any kind of insect spray designed for insects that injure by chewing plant parts (e.g., rosebugs, Japanese beetles, potato bugs). Also cover this branch with a plastic bag. Do nothing to the third branch except tie it up in a bag. In a day or two, unless the sun is so hot it has caused steam to form inside the bags, you should find very few aphids on the branch sprayed with the oil-water emulsion. Aphids belong to that group of insects that sucks rather than chews. For this reason, the oil emulsion clogs the spiracles or breathing holes along the sides of the aphids, and they literally suffocate. Conversely, the poison spread *on* the leaves and stem will not affect the aphids. This experiment will remind you of the occasional soap and water bath recommended for plants in the classroom (p. 78). The third branch should illustrate how aphids hurt plants and how fast they multiply. Try again with an infested indoor plant. Make a rough estimate of the aphid population when you bag the branch and again in a few days. Let the children suppose what would happen to our plant population if aphids multiplied unchecked. Estimate the eggs in insect egg cases, e.g., praying mantis. Suppose 50 per cent of insects did not live on other insects. The insect population would be that much more abundant than it is already.

There are over 8000 forms of aphids. You are most apt to find these "drops of sap on legs" represented by the green aphid, almost the color of the plant, and the woolly aphid, the body covered with tiny cottony fringes. Urge children to bring in empty insecticide containers. By studying the labels, they will see that the

(a) (b) (c)

Fig. 3-15 Three stages in the life cycle of a cecropia moth. (a) The caterpillar feeds on leaves, generally of orchard and shade trees, for about 5 weeks. It grows in length from about ¼″ to as much as 3″, becoming quite thick, and sheds its skin four times, changing color from all black, to yellow with black tubercles, to yellow with blue and orange tubercles, to green with blue, yellow, and orange tubercles. (b) The cocoon, often called the "cradle cocoon," is shaped like a hammock and suspended from a branch. It has a thick, paperlike outer wall and a thin, firm inner wall, with insulation of loose silk between. After the cocoon is complete, the caterpillar sheds its skin for the last time and passes the winter as a pupa. (c) The adult moth emerges in the spring. Its wings are brown with clay-colored margins and are crossed by a red-bordered white band. Note the characteristic quarter-moon markings, also white with red borders, and the short, feathery antennae. The adult, which never eats, may have a 6½″ wing-spread. It is the largest of the American silkworms. (Hugh Spencer.)

liquids are to be used against chewing insects, the powders against the sucking types of pests. A study of insecticides could also provide opportunity for safety lessons on care in storage and handling of household chemicals.

Butterflies

Your children will probably try to catch some of the larger brightly colored species. Help them to see that butterflies are such delicate creatures that they are generally damaged too seriously for mounting unless captured in a net and carefully handled. In any case you can help the children find out that a butterfly's life span is short. If any moths are brought in, help the children see the difference in the antennae of moths and butterflies. Butterflies have two single long antennae, usually ending in a knob. Sometimes the antennae are coiled up like a spring. Moth antennae are shorter and feathery in appearance. If some cocoons and chrysalids are found during the fall and winter and cared for (see p. 34), the children will find out for themselves that butterflies issue from a naked chrysalis whereas a moth issues from a cocoon which encloses a chrysalis (Figs. 3-15, 3-16). If you have a toy microscope, look at the scales which make up the color in a butterfly's wings. The butterfly that one notices sailing along high in the air at various seasons is the Monarch. A native of tropic America, it has learned to follow its food plant, milkweed, northward in the spring. Toward fall large flocks of Monarchs drift southward, spots of color high in the sky.

Cabbage butterfly (tomato worm). Through the summer and early fall, children may bring in a huge, soft green cat-

(a)   (b)   (c)

(d)   (e)   (f)

Fig. 3-16 Three stages in the life cycle of a Monarch butterfly. (a) The caterpillar feeds only on milkweed, eating day and night with intervals of rest. It attains a length of about 2″, maturing in about 11 days, and is green with yellow and black stripes. Note the long whiplike organs. These organs, two in front and two in back, lash the air and frighten away parasites. (b, c) After spinning a thin silk chrysalis, the caterpillar sheds its skin for the last time and pupates for about 12 days. The chrysalis, which hangs from a fence, rock, or leaf, is a beautiful green with gold and black flecks. (d, e, f) The adult Monarch emerges and rests on a thistle. Its wings are copper-colored on their upper surfaces and yellow underneath, with black veins and white-spotted black borders. Note the two rows of white dots on the wings, the white-spotted black body, and the long antennae, with knobs on the ends. The Monarch has a long coiled tongue, for feeding on nectar, and very small front legs. Since it is distasteful to birds, it flies leisurely, not with the dodging, zigzag movements characteristic of most butterflies. (a, b, c, d, e, Louis Quitt from National Audubon Society; f, Lynwood M. Chace from National Audubon Society.)

erpillar. It has a ferocious-looking face armed with a rhino-like horn and smaller horns along its sides. If it is kept and given plenty of fresh tomato leaves, it may spin its chrysalis. Children may be surprised to see what a small greenish white butterfly hatches out. Keep the green leaves fresh inside moist plastic vegetable bags or a screw-top gallon jar. For another caterpillar and chrysalis see Fig. 3-16A, B.

Clothes moth. Through research and observation help the children understand that it is not the tiny flying moth which makes holes in wool and fur. It is the larva. The children may bring in samples of different kinds of moth repellent used as home. Reading the labels to discover the chemicals used is a valuable reading as well as science lesson. A parent may be invited to help the children make a list of different ways to fight insect pests. This list might be duplicated and distributed to parents of the group.

Care of chrysalids and cocoons. Whether bought from a dealer or found outdoors, chrysalids and cocoons must be properly cared for in the classroom. The problem is to keep them from getting so dry from indoor heat that the moths or butterflies die or emerge imperfect or misshapen. Try putting them into a terrarium or into a quart jar with sod on the bottom. Cover with wire screen or netting. The sod must be kept moist. In both cases, as in nature, the cocoon or chrysalis should not lie directly on the moist earth. It will mold. It is best to suspend it in mid-air from a thread or twig.

As soon as the inhabitant shows signs of emerging, remove it to a quart container large enough for it to spread its wings to dry. A twig to rest upon will help. When the insect is all out, add a dab of cotton soaked in sugar water. Watch to see if the insect unrolls its long tongue to feed.

Cockroaches (Croton bugs)

Cockroaches deserve our attention for their history if not for their habits. Cockroaches with 4″ wing spread have been found fossilized in rock layers 200 million years old. Fossil roaches identical to our modern pests have been found. And their survival in abundance today is evidence of a durable and adaptable organism. City children living in older buildings can usually catch some for observation. Or a pest exterminator may be able to oblige. Keep the roaches in a large glass jar with secure screw top. Keep out of direct sunlight. The bottom should be damp at all times. The name, Croton bug, derives from the insects' association with water pipes bringing water to New York City from Croton Reservoir. As with ants, keep the jar covered when the insects are not being watched. Put in some strips of newspaper, toweling, twigs, or bits of bark for the insects to hide under. Feed with small amounts of table scraps. The female carries eggs in a small brown capsule at the end of the body until she finds a place to lay them. If the children find a capsule, let them imbed it in damp sand or cotton in a smaller jar with tight cover. Watch the young emerge and the changes as they mature.

Silverfish (Lepisma)

This curious creature, often seen scuttling about the bathroom floor or in the tub, is a living fossil. It has no eyes. It is the only member of its species. It is harmless. It may attack the starch in the paste used in the binding of books.

Crickets

Let the children find out by trial and error what crickets like to eat. If the children can catch a pair or more of crickets, place them in a flower-pot-lamp chimney cage. Keep, if possible, on a sunny window sill and keep the sod moist but not soggy. If the food, shelter, and temperature are to their liking, the patent-leather fiddlers may delight the children by chirping during a lull. Make rough blackboard sketches of the detail of a male cricket's file and scraper (Fig. 3-17A). Female crickets are identified by the long ovipositor (Fig. 3-17B). There is not room here to give many other interesting details about these little singers.

Keeping crickets in the classroom may lead the children to look for and bring in examples of other famous insect "noise makers"—the katydid, the cicada, and the tiny but loud-voiced tree cricket.

Dragonflies

Dragonflies hatch from eggs laid in the water. (See pp. 49, 52, 57.) We hope that some of your children will use the name "darning needle" in speaking of a dragonfly. We hope that others will ask "Do they really sew up children's lips?" This will be only one of your opportunities in elementary science to combat superstition—to help children see for themselves, to decide on the basis of evidence, not hearsay, and to use rational rather than emotional thinking.

Fireflies

Children who live in the country in the East usually have seen fireflies. Children from the West have not. The same beetle lives in both areas. Yet the eastern form can be seen at night; the western one cannot because it does not glow. Like many of the beetle family, the firefly has two pairs of wings. The outside wings form a hard protective cover for the animal. The inside wings are soft and thin and fold up except when flying. Larvae live in the ground and are often known as wire worms.

Fruit flies

With all man's skill in developing pesticides, the insects are still with us, and in huge numbers. To illustrate the sheer force of insect multiplication, grow a hatch of fruit flies. Usually all this takes is a pair of pint jars with covers and some very "mellow" (ripe) bananas and/or grapes. Cover the jars and set in a warm room (not sunlight) until fruit flies begin

(a)

(b)

Fig. 3-17 (a) Male cricket, showing file and scraper. (b) Female cricket, showing ovipositor. (Hugh Spencer.)

to develop from the ripe fruit. Some use corn meal boiled 5 minutes in addition to the fruit. Keep a record of the number of flies in each bottle every day for a week. You will probably note an increase. Depending on their facility with numbers, the children may be able to estimate the rate of increase and project it for a month or a year. The figures tell the story. If insects multiplied unchecked, this would soon be a world of insects.

Another method of raising fruit flies illustrates the complete life cycle. Cut off the top of a cone-shaped paper cup to make a funnel for a jar. Put some over-ripe bananas or other fruit in the jar. As soon as half a dozen fruit flies have hatched from the fruit or entered from outside and been trapped, cover the jar

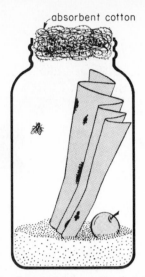

absorbent cotton

Fig. 3-18 Fruit fly hatchery. The fruit fly is used in advanced experiments in genetics because of its very short life cycle.

or plug with cotton (Fig. 3-18). Among this half dozen there should be some fruit flies of both sexes. The females are larger and have a slightly broader abdomen with small lines across the end. Males can be distinguished by a black-tipped abdomen. You may need a hand glass to make sex differentiation.

The eggs may already be in the fruit or laid by the visitors. In a day or two the larvae should emerge and feed about a week before pupation. They can be seen better if a bit of crumpled paper or rag is dropped into the jar (Fig. 3-18). They will crawl out on this to pupate. In about five days the pupae change to adults and mate soon after they emerge. You now have two generations of fruit flies—the ones you caught and those you raised. Grandchildren can be raised as quickly by preparing another habitat jar. For closer observation place fruit flies in stoppered test tubes wrapped in foil. The flies will move into the part that is open to the light.

Insect plant galls

Insect galls on plants are so common

that children are bound to bring them in and ask "What is it?" Furthermore, galls illustrate a high degree of specialized adaptation of certain insects to certain plants. For example, the insect which causes the oak apple is not the same as the one which causes the willow cone gall nor the goldenrod stem gall. In each case, however, the insect deposits an egg in the plant tissues. The larva hatches and begins to eat its way out. Apparently it secretes a substance into the surrounding plant tissues. Irritated by this foreign secretion, the plant tissues begin to enlarge almost like a tumor, thus forming a constantly expanding house around the creature responsible for it all. Let the children cut green galls in half and look for the inhabitant. Dry brown galls will generally be found vacant. Close looking will usually disclose a tiny hole by which the tenant escaped to the world of free flight.

Grasshoppers

Arrangements for keeping crickets, katydids, and the praying mantis will work for their relatives—the grasshoppers (see pp. 19–20 for details on making insect cages). One word of caution: Do not put grasshoppers into a terrarium planted with choice small plants. They are heavy eaters and will chew the foliage unmercifully.

Most children already know a good deal about grasshoppers. For example, they have great respect for a grasshopper's ability to jump and escape. Ask the children to estimate and then measure the height of a grasshopper's jump in relation to his size. Many children know it is easier to catch grasshoppers in the early morning. (Grasshoppers do not jump as well when it is cold.) A few may know this is related to the temperature. Grasshoppers, in common with snakes and frogs, do not have a constant body temperature like ours. The body temperature of these cold-blooded animals is usually a few degrees higher than the air temperature.

Ask the children how grasshoppers survive the winter. If they have noticed the long ovipositor of the female, they may figure out that grasshoppers live through till spring in the egg stage. A few nymphs emerge none the worse for wear.

Ask how many kinds of grasshoppers the children have seen. Eventually they should bring in or tell you of greater differences in size than of appearance. The smaller forms without fully developed wing covers are the nymphs or immature grasshoppers. There is no resting stage or pupal stage in grasshoppers.

Chill (refrigerate) or anesthetize (with CO_2, see above) some grasshoppers, enough to permit the children to look carefully at the body parts—the leg mechanism and its terrific leverage for jumping, the feet with the toe pads of sticky *tenent hairs* which permit climbing the side of a glass container. The grasshopper's facial expression is a cartoon of solemnity. The great compound eyes give the grasshopper 180° vision, useful in saving him from becoming breakfast for a bird or small mammal. Some insects have as many as 30,000 simple eyes compounded in one eyepiece. Show the children where to look for the grasshopper's ear and the breathing pores (Fig. 3-19). These pores or openings, called spiracles, are located just above a lengthwise suture or crease which opens and closes like an accordion as the insect breathes.

In addition to all its defense mechanisms, the grasshopper can defend itself, as most children have experienced, with a good nip and secretion of "tobacco," a bitter and evil-smelling brown liquid.

Houseflies

Houseflies are our most dangerous insect because they are our most common carriers of disease. If possible, secure 2–4

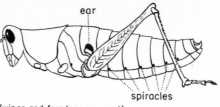
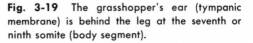

(wings and fore legs removed)

Fig. 3-19 The grasshopper's ear (tympanic membrane) is behind the leg at the seventh or ninth somite (body segment).

sterile Petri dishes of nutrient agar from a high school biology teacher or hospital laboratory. Capture a housefly and put it inside one of the Petri dishes. While it is walking around on the layer of agar, let a child cough several times into another dish, re-cover quickly, wipe a pencil over the surface of the third and re-cover, and keep the fourth covered as a control. Remove the fly from the first and label all four with wax crayon or adhesive. Seal all the dishes with tape and put in a warm dark place for a week. At the end of the time, compare the resulting bacteria colonies.

Mosquitoes

Next to the housefly, the mosquito is probably most harmful to man. However this is true only in subtropical and tropical latitudes where malaria and yellow fever are common. It has been said that 250 million of the world's inhabitants suffer from malaria. One of the largest cities in the United States is in subtropical latitudes. Here the city park department every year introduces into its park ponds very small fish similar to guppies. These Gambusia keep down the mosquito wigglers in the ponds. The role of the mosquito in obstructing the digging of the Panama Canal is an exciting chapter in American history and geography. Mosquito wigglers develop in stagnant water. If you can get some from a pond or puddle, keep a jar of

Fig. 3-20 Praying mantis, so named for its reverent position. This is a pose, for the insect is poised to "prey" upon other insects. The mantis is a fine yard bug catcher, however odd-looking! (Dade Thornton from National Audubon Society.)

able to suggest a less expensive and more efficient way of controlling mosquitoes which maintains the myriad and valuable forms of life in a marsh.

Praying mantis

This relative of the grasshoppers and especially its cousin, the walking stick beetle, illustrate the effective use of camouflage by insects. If you see a stick move, it may well be the praying mantis. Although the praying mantis is related to grasshoppers, they are his favorite food. He catches them by lying in wait, his stout front legs poised to pounce. He is often a green color like a katydid or tree cricket, and therefore hard to find unless you see him move. He moves slowly and with dignity, as befits an insect 3–5″ long when full grown. If the children find one and bring it to school, they must catch live insects to feed it.

Like the grasshopper, the mantis has an incomplete metamorphosis; that is, there are only three stages in its life history. If the children know how one looks (Fig. 3-20), they may find its large egg mass in a weed patch. Bring an egg mass into the schoolroom and put it into the terrarium or gallon jar with sod on the bottom. Be sure to cover the jar with fine screening or netting. Otherwise the room will be crawling with tiny mantises as the warmth hastens hatching. Put in twigs on which the young can climb. Since several hundred hatch from one egg mass, the children will realize that, as with other insects, there is overproduction to allow for high mortality. Keep a few to watch. Feed them on fruit flies and other small insects. Let the rest go free. The carnivorous and sometimes cannibalistic mantis is one of the reasons we are not overrun with insects; e.g., don't put two in one jar with no other food.

them in your room until you can see the larvae (see Fig. 14-1). Put some in each of two other jars. Use the same pond water. Sprinkle a drop or two of any kind of light oil on the water in one jar. Put a goldfish or tadpole in the third jar as the wigglers begin to change into adults. Thus the children have practiced on a small scale two methods of controlling mosquitoes. In some parts of the country the U.S. Bureau of Reclamation and/or the Army Engineers have spent vast sums in draining marshes to control mosquitoes. At the same time another government service appointed to take care of our fish and wild life spends much money in flooding areas to provide waterfowl for hunters and muskrat for fur farmers. The children, from their two experiments, should be

The mantis was introduced to the United States as a control measure. It is

(a)

(b)

Fig. 3-21 (a) Damsel fly larva; note visible gills (tail appendages). (Hugh Spencer.) (b) Damsel fly adult; this insect has a slenderer, more brilliantly colored body than the dragonfly, and it folds its wings together over its back when resting, whereas the dragonfly rests with its wings outspread as if in flight. (Jennie Lea Knight from National Audubon Society.) (See Figs. 3-23 and 4-11.)

generally found along the coast and not inland. Its cosmopolitan tastes may be illustrated by the fact that one of the authors once saw one on the wall of the United Nations building in the largest city of our country.

Silkworm

See Chapter 2 for a discussion of the silkworm.

Woolly bear (Isabella tiger moth)

Often during autumn, your children may bring in a furry brown and black caterpillar. They usually call it the "woolly bear." Some people thought that the width of the bands was an indicator of the severity of the winter. However, this idea has been studied and proved to be untrue. This caterpillar is unusual in that it winters as a caterpillar and normally spins its cocoon in April or May. The moth which emerges is somewhat nondescript. Because of its late cocoon spinning, a woolly bear should be kept outdoors in a box to protect it from storms. Keeping it indoors in a warm room may kill it.

WATER INSECTS

Just as you have enjoyed studying insects which inhabit the world of air, you will enjoy getting to know those which live in a world of water. Try looking along brooks where the water runs slowly, in ponds, or in swampy places. There are more apt to be insects where there are plants growing in the water. A kitchen strainer lashed to an old broom handle makes a fine dip net. People who do a lot of such collecting use white enamel pans in which to spread their catch. The forms they want to keep go into small bottles of water. Encourage your children to collect small plastic containers which may be carried together in a canvas knapsack. Remember to take along a clean gallon can to bring back enough pond water. Your new pets will feel more at home in it and find food in it which you cannot see except with magnification.

Your "haul" may include larvae of damsel flies (Fig. 3-21) or May flies (Fig. 3-22). If these pupate into adult form, your aquarium needs a top of netting or cloth. Most of these larvae use the air dissolved

(a)

(b)

Fig. 3-22 (a) May fly larva, showing feathery lateral gills. (Hugh Spencer.) (b) May fly adult, showing characteristic curved body, not horizontal as in damsel and dragonflies. (John H. Gerard from Monkmeyer.)

in water through their gills. Instead of being in front as in fish, the gills in these creatures are usually in the rear. Some, like the young whirligig beetle, have these feathery gills along the sides of the body. Young diving beetles do not have gills. They have a breathing tube at the rear of the body. This means they must "come up for air." Water beetles also come up for air, but, like the water spiders, they take some down with them. By pushing the tail ends of their wing covers above the surface, they take in more fresh air under their wing covers. Two very interesting and active insects look much alike. These are the water boatman and the back swimmer. The back swimmer does just that and the water boatman uses a pair of legs like oars. Like the aphids, these water insects suck food through their beaks. Boatmen suck on plants, and back swimmers suck other small creatures in the water.

You will have noticed that water insects are built for speed and indeed move quickly. You should see water striders skimming about on the surface. They can "walk on the water" because of the same surface tension which sometimes enables you to overfill a glass without spilling. Water striders are a beautiful example of protective coloration. Their bodies are dark above and pearly white below. If the underparts were not lighter than the back, the ground shadow would make the belly darker and cause the animal to be conspicuous instead of blending with the background.

You may be sharp enough to see down on the bottom how a young dragonfly moves when it is frightened. The gills with which it breathes are inside the rear opening. Breathing in draws water into this opening; breathing out squirts it out. The sudden expulsion of water makes the young dragonfly shoot ahead like a jet plane.

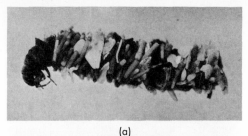

(a)

(b)

(c)

Fig. 3-23 Assorted caddis worm cases. These interesting stream dwellers build "houses" around themselves of such native materials as shells, pebbles, sticks, and leaves. (a, b, American Museum of Natural History; c, Hugh Spencer.)

Making a fresh-water aquarium

The fresh-water aquarium need be nothing more elaborate than one of our familiar gallon jugs. Set it up as follows.

(1) Wash the jar and put in enough sand to make an inch layer on the bottom of the jar;

(2) In this layer imbed (plant) roots of any native water plants, (e.g., utricularia, spirogyra, nitella) you may find on your collecting field trip. Hold these down with some pebbles or gravel.

(3) Bring from the trip a gallon jug of pond or brook water. Tilt the aquarium

jar so you can pour in this water without roiling the bottom. Fill to within a couple of inches of the top. If you are also using jam jars to make individual insect habitats, fill these to within an inch of the top.

(4) Set the large or small aquariums in a north or perhaps an east window and let them settle until the water is clear. Add a stick and a rock for perching and hiding.

When you return from your field trip, you will bring back many forms for the aquarium. In addition to water insects, collect tiny-fresh-water snails and sponges clinging to rocks. Under rocks in the stream you may find the amazing tiny houses of stone or sticks which the caddis fly larvae build themselves (Fig. 3-23). On your first trip, you may be lucky and find dragonfly larvae (Fig. 3-24). Certainly you will find the cast skin of these nymphs, split open along the back and still clinging to the rock on which the dragonfly emerged to dry and spread his iridescent wings in the sun. That anything so fairy-like as a dragonfly could hatch from such a grotesque goblin as the larva is one of the surprises we think you will enjoy.

OTHER INSECTS

Leaf miner and leaf roller

Sooner or later your children will bring in examples of the work of these insects and ask "What is it?"

The familiar "serpentine mine" (Fig. 3-25) is caused by the tiny grub of a ¼″ moth which lays its egg on the leaf. The grub spends its entire life until it pupates between the top and bottom of a leaf. This, if nothing else, will prove that leaves however thin and papery are composed of layers of cells or tiny rooms.

Insects which cause leaf-rolling are very choosy about their leaves. Certain species of insects pick only certain kinds of leaves. When the egg first hatches, the tiny grub

(a)

Fig. 3-24 (a) Dragonfly larva, or nymph. (Harold V. Green.) (b) Dragonfly adult, here shown eating a bee. (Treat Davidson from National Audubon Society.) The dried skin of the nymph splits open along the back for the adult to emerge. (See also Fig. 4-11.)

(b)

first feeds underneath out of sight. Then when it is still almost too small to be seen, it manages to fold itself over one edge of the leaf, and fold or roll the leaf down. As yet no one really knows how this tiny creature achieves such a Herculean task.

SPIDERS

For the sake of convenience, we have included in this chapter some discussion on spiders. However, children should be helped to see that spiders are not true insects but arthropods (8-legged), relatives of crabs. Spiders have a head, abdomen, and 8 legs. True insects have a head, *thorax,* abdomen, and 6 legs. For children acquainted with fractions, you can draw a crude spider on the blackboard and point out the 2/8 (2 body parts and 8 legs) relationship of parts. Point out that this number can be reduced to ¼. Then sketch an ant on the board and note the 3/6 (3 body parts and 6 legs) relationship. Show that this fraction is reducible to ½ (Fig. 3-26). Point out the greater bulk or weight of a true insect compared to that of a spider of

about the same size. A spider is "all legs"; fraction 2/8 is smaller than 3/6, although the spider "denominator" is larger.

Of all the structures made by lower animals, the great radial web of the orb weaver is the most outstanding in design and workmanship. Point out the analogy between the cables of the largest suspension bridges and the outer cables securing the spider's web. Encourage the children to discover why the spider can walk on its own web without getting caught. Those

Fig. 3-25 Leaf-miner "tracks" in white oak leaves. There are many varieties of this insect, each specialized to a specific plant. (Hugh Spencer.)

who watch closely will see that the creature uses only the radial threads. The encircling threads are sticky.

Grass spiders build another kind of web for catching dinner. A funnel-shaped structure is spread out among the grass stems. At the mouth of the funnel, out of sight, sits the weaver waiting for some hapless insect to cross the web. Children and adults alike cannot resist lightly touching the edge of the funnel to see if the spider will rush out, as indeed it does if the intruders have kept out of sight and not been too heavy handed.

Then there is the beautiful little crab spider which hides among the petals of the flowers. We used to find them among the lemon lilies where they were such a perfect color match that they could scarcely be seen until they were dispossessed.

Other spiders catch their prey by running or jumping. The wolf spider has such long legs and is so timid that it usually runs out of sight before you can get a good look at it. The little jumping spiders are so delightfully ugly that one cannot bear to harm them. Usually we carry them outdoors to continue helping us keep down the pressure of insect multiplication.

In just one section of the United States is found a most unusual spider, the trap-door spider. It is known to most observant boys and girls who explore the canyons and arroyos of Southern California. When spading gardens in that area, one often breaks into one of the spider's tunnels and uncovers it. One should quickly cover the spider with earth and hope it will soon make another home in one's yard because of its ability to control the insect population. These spiders are insignificant looking, medium-sized, and naked of the tiny hairs which make most spiders appear so formidable. But their burrows are works of art. The trap door of the burrow has an inner lining of silk to which the spider

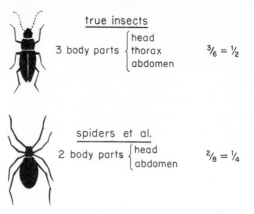

Fig. 3-26 Fractional relationships of body parts in insects and in spiders.

clings to keep his door locked. From above, the entrance looks just like part of the surrounding earth. It takes sharp looking to find one, although they are common in certain sections of adobe overlay.

Spider bites, like those of many other insects, tend to cause irritation unless they are neutralized with an alkali such as household ammonia (diluted). A really infected spider bite is usually due not to the spider but to infectious organisms already present in dirt on the skin when the spider punctures the surface.

The only really poisonous spiders in the United States are the black widow and the tarantula. The danger tends to be much overrated. The black widow is a medium-sized spider, glossy black, but the poisonous female is always distinguishable by the red hourglass on the underside of her abdomen. Always wear gloves when working in the yard, clearing rubbish from under shrubs, moving old lumber, etc. Whenever one encounters a shiny black spider, it should be overturned to check for the telltale hourglass. Children should be cautioned to treat spiders with respect and never keep them for study except in an unbreakable container. In common with all spiders, this one is not aggressive and seeks only to get out of the way. The hairs which make spiders look so uncouth serve as antennae to receive noises and vibrations. Spiders are among the most timid and retiring of creatures.

Tarantulas are very hairy, large, and timid spiders also found in the subtropical sections of our country. They are kept as pets and handled and fed without any difficulty.

Spiders are solitary insects, even to the point where females will devour their mates (males) and their own young. Hence spiders kept for observation in the classroom should be kept alone. Any small jar or plastic container will do. However, it should be big enough for some soil on the bottom to absorb moisture and provide the humidity the creature needs. For any of the orb-weaver spiders, put in a branch upon which they can weave a web. Let the children try improvising a web with thin grocery string.

Children overturn stones and sometimes find on the undersides silvery patches we call "fairies' pocketbooks." If you slit one of the little envelopes with a knifeblade, you find many tiny eggs inside. It is a spider egg case.

CAPSULE LESSONS

3-1 How to tell temperature by crickets: If you have a watch with a second hand, count the number of chirps (black cricket) in 14 seconds and add 40. The higher the air temperature, the faster the chirps, and vice versa.

3-2 Children living in an agricultural area might be able to contact personnel from a government experiment station attempting to find ways of controlling one species of insect with another, as, for example, control of scale insect on citrus by introduction of exotic species of beetles.

3-3 Children living in urban areas may find it interesting to contact pest control firms to discuss methods of insect control.

3-4 Encourage a child to read and report on the story of how the gulls saved crops in Salt Lake City from annihilation by grasshoppers. Perhaps a child can locate a picture of the statue erected by the residents to honor the gulls.

3-5 How do you tell an ant from a termite?

Children living in termite country might make diagrams showing that termites have thick bodies, ants are "wasp" waisted, and other differences. A pest control firm may have useful reference specimens to loan.

3-6 Compare the whitish cave crickets sometimes found in a cellar with common black field crickets.

3-7 Make an exhibit of insects grouped by size, color, or such other criteria as the children may suggest.

3-8 Compare handmade paper with paper fibers in a paper hornet's nest. Soak fibers from the nest and spread out to dry on blotter or felt cloth.

3-9 Collect samples of insecticides. Use labels for practice in reading. Compare carefully proportions of various chemical ingredients. Encourage research on controversial question of DDT.

BIBLIOGRAPHY

Bartlett, Ruth, *Insect Engineers,* Morrow, 1957. Upper. Collection and indoor observation.

Conklin, Gladys, *I Like Caterpillars,* Holiday, 1958. Primary. Good for young children.

Dodge, Natt N., *Poisonous Dwellers of the Desert.* Southwest Monuments Assn., Pop. Ser. No. 3, Santa Fe, New Mexico. 44 pp. Photographs and brief descriptions of common arid region insects and other desert creatures.

Earle, Olive L., *Crickets,* Morrow, 1956. Middle. Life cycles of different common forms. Directions for keeping as pets.

Hogner, Dorothy C., *Spiders,* Crowell, 1955. Middle. Valuable first reference.

Huntington, Harriet E., *Praying Mantis,* Doubleday, 1957. Middle. Life cycle and suggestions for classroom care and observation.

Hussey, Lois J., and Catherine Pessino, *Collecting Cocoons,* Crowell, 1953. Middle. Collection, identification, and indoor care of cocoons and larvae.

Hutchins, Ross E., *Insects: Hunters and Trappers,* Rand McNally, 1957. Entertaining for young naturalists. Lively text and excellent photographs.

Lavine, Sigmund A., *Wonders of the Hive,* Dodd, Mead, 1958. Middle. Sourcebook for use with observation hive.

McClung, Robert M., *Green Darner: The Story of a Dragonfly,* Morrow, 1956. Upper. Ecology and habitat of common large dragonfly. Excellent treatment of nymphal stage.

———, *Tiger: The Story of a Swallowtail Butterfly,* Morrow, 1953. Primary. Well-illustrated annual cycle of common butterfly.

Pistorius, Anna, *What Butterfly Is It?,* Follett, 1950. Middle. Identification and characteristics of over 50 species.

Politi, Leo, *The Butterflies Come,* Scribner's, 1957. Middle. Annual migration of monarch butterflies at Monterey peninsula, California.

Sears, Paul M., *Firefly,* Holiday, 1956. Middle. Life cycle of the firefly and related insects in the soil.

Sherman, Jane, *Real Book About Bugs, Insects and Such,* Garden City, 1952. Middle. Brief but lively text.

Shuttlesworth, Dorothy, *Story of Spiders,* Garden City, 1959. Middle. Good on webs and web construction.

Sterling, Dorothy, *Insects and the Homes They Build,* Doubleday. 1954. Middle. One of the best books on the subject. Excellent text and illustrations.

Swain, Su Zan Noguchi, *Insects in Their World,* Garden City, 1955. Upper. Insect collection, identification, and observation. Well described and beautifully illustrated.

Tibbetts, Albert B., *First Book of Bees,* Watts, 1952. Middle. Mine of information on types of bees and their work; how to remove a sting.

U.S. Dept. of Agriculture. Publications on various aspects of entomology.

Life in the water

AN AQUARIUM COMMUNITY

It is usually not practical to build a homemade aquarium that will remain watertight. If the school cannot purchase an aquarium, set up several in wide-mouthed gallon pickle jars. One pair of fish needs at least a gallon of water. If possible, a 4–5 gallon tank is recommended. In the long run, good tanks usually cost less than cheap ones. The first step is to wash the tank with soap and warm water. Do not use hot water because it may loosen the aquarium cement. Rinse several times in cold water, fill two thirds full, and let stand for several days. Secure coarse sand (not beach sand) or gravel and wash in boiling water. You will also need some stones to hold down the sand and plants. Wash the stones in boiling water. As an additional precaution you may want to bake the sand and rocks to insure sterility. Get a half dozen pieces of water plants from the variety store or pet shop. The salesman or store owner usually is most helpful with regard to selecting appropriate plant and animal life and giving suggestions for planting and care.

While some children work on problems of securing and setting up an aquarium, others can participate in solving problems of aquarium housekeeping. The best way to fill or empty a tank without unduly disturbing the plants is to use a siphon. Let children *play* at siphoning long before they need to put it to use in the aquarium. Begin with drinking straws. Let children use some as dip tubes by closing the top end with a finger. The differential in air pressure, of course, allows the children to pick up a few drops of water just as a scientist uses a glass pipette in the laboratory. If possible, secure some 18″ lengths of plastic or rubber tubing of ½–¾″ diameter. These will be useful for daily removal of debris from the tank. Let the children practice using a tube to remove loose dirt from the bottom of a jar. Now let the children use rubber tubing to remove debris. Let them try different ways. Some may know the principle of siphoning liquids. They can fill the tube in the way shown (Fig. 4-1) or by immersion. Once a tube is filled, the ends are pinched while it is transferred into position to work as a siphon.

Adding water to replace that evaporated from the tank can be accomplished by pouring over a plate without scaring the fish or dislodging plants. Encourage the children to think of ways they can measure the amount of water which has evaporated. They will also think of ways to cut down the evaporation (i.e., by using glass or cellophane cover). How can fish have enough air even if tank is covered? The answer is that the plants produce oxygen (Fig. 4-2). (See p. 48.)

A fish tank can illustrate one of the major conceptual schemes for the elemen-

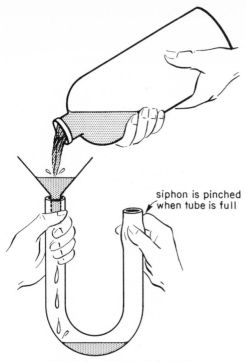

siphon is pinched
when tube is full

Fig. 4-1 Filling a siphon tube.

call this plant manufacturing process *photosynthesis*. Let the children discuss this word and its associations, *photography*, *synthetic*, etc., according to their level of understanding. Some may enjoy following the schematic symbols (chemical formula) for the process. (The power source is light energy.)

raw materials

$6 CO_2$ (carbon dioxide *from* the fish)

$+ 6 H_2O$ (water)

finished product

$C_6 H_{12} O_6$ (glucose —— sugar)

$+ 6 O_2$ (oxygen to be used *by* the fish, snails, etc.)

Setting up an aquarium involves filling the tank 24–48 hours ahead of planting in order to bring it to room temperature. Let the children note and record water temperature as it comes from the tap. Compare with room temperature. Upper-grade children may record and graph the rate at which the tank water warms up.

Tank water is also drawn several days ahead of time in order to allow chlorine to escape from it. Store some in gallon jugs for future use. Using household bleach, the children may wish to experiment with the effect of varying

tary school—namely, that under ordinary conditions matter may be changed but not destroyed. The carbon dioxide which all living creatures produce is put to use by the aquarium plants to make their food (sugar) in the presence of sunlight. We

Fig. 4-2 A balanced aquarium. Plants use carbon dioxide given off by aquarium animals, while producing oxygen necessary to support the animal life in the water. (General Biological Supply House, Inc., Chicago.)

amounts of chlorine on different organisms. They will find upon investigation that their municipal water department usually uses minute amounts of chlorine for water purification. Let the children experiment with a medicine dropper and several jars or tumblers of the same size to find the effect of different strength solutions on living things. Use similar sized samples of algae or other abundant small water plants.

Most children know that one should handle fish as little as possible, and when handling is necessary, one should moisten hands before touching. A small cloth dip net purchased at the dime store will facilitate any handling. Usually the fish can be "poured" into the tank from a container. (For observation of blood circulation in a goldfish tail under the microscope, see Chapter 5.)

What can you learn from watching a goldfish? How a fish swims, of course, but more—how an organism adapts to its environment. Let the children tell you from observation about the way their goldfish moves, the number and location of fins. Which fin does what? Does your goldfish rest on the bottom or near the surface? Can it stay still without moving a fin? Does it tend to float? If so, why? Illustrate the action of a fish's air bladder with a small capped bottle or corked vial in which there is some trapped air. Vary the amount of trapped air to show how a fish can balance its buoyancy.

One of the observations your children should make is of gill movement. The fish appears to be continually opening and closing its mouth. If you can secure at the market a whole fish so children can examine the gills, they will see that the bright red color is due to the thin skin which permits the blood to come close to the surface. Oxygen in the water continually passing over the gills is taken up by the blood and carried to all parts of the fish's body. At the same time carbon dioxide is returned to the water. Here is an opportunity for discussion to help the children learn about their own respiratory system by contrast and counterpoint. (See Chapter 14.)

To be sure that children know there is air in water, draw some tap water and let stand in glass containers. In a relatively short time, depending on the difference between room and water temperature, they should begin to see air bubbles on the sides of the glasses.

Further, heat some water until most of the air is driven out. Then let it stand until cool. Draw a similar sized container of fresh water. All the containers and the aquarium should be within 2–3° of each other in temperature. Place a goldfish in each jar; watch carefully. Soon the fish in the water which was heated (and then cooled) will come to the top. Here at the top the water will have taken up more oxygen from the air and the fish will be better able to "breathe." (Watch that the fish in the airless water does not suffocate.) You may be able to help the children make the analogy to problems of air and space travel caused by the very narrow range of environments in which man can secure the oxygen he must have to live. (See Chapter 26.)

The next step may be to place some sprigs of a water plant such as elodea or anacharis in a container of water on a sunny window sill. Soon the children should see bubbles forming at the top of each leaf. Green plants give off oxygen when the sun's energy starts their food factories. An aquarium needs plants not only for their esthetic but also for their functional value. They supply oxygen to the animal life in the tank. This oxygen may be supplemented by that absorbed at the surface. This is why a widemouthed container or rectangular tank is desirable.

Using the aquarium as an example, you may wish to lead the children toward an understanding of the fact that plants and animals need each other—interdependence—and that there must be a proper amount of each in a successful community —balance.

COMMUNITIES WITHIN A COMMUNITY

Observations, discussions, and research experiments with regard to your classroom aquarium provide fine preparation for field trips. Scarcely any community exists that does not provide some remnants of water-life communities. Usually the children will know the nearest pond, stream, slough, or marsh. With the least encouragement they will bring in a host of live specimens from the locality. Let them set up simple fresh-water aquaria (Fig. 4-3). These may be no more than large glass jars with netting covers, sticks on which dragonfly or damsel fly larvae can crawl out and pupate, rocks, and some mud in the bottom. The organisms will get along better in some of the water in which they normally live. Make a point of having the children carry metal or plastic containers for safety. A kitchen strainer lashed to a stick makes a fine dip net. The children may bring in various insects from among the visible forms in pond, stream, or marsh water. There may be larval forms of dragon- or damsel flies. Among the most charming and interesting insects are the various species of beetles such as back swimmers and water boatmen. Water striders are most interesting for the way they can walk on the water. In reality they are able to do this because of the surface tension characteristic of liquids. For example, to illustrate surface tension, let the children observe as you fill a tumbler full just to the point of brimming over. Watching at eye level, the children should know how water forms a slightly curved meniscus. Let them lower a dry needle slowly to the surface of water in a cup or bowl. If

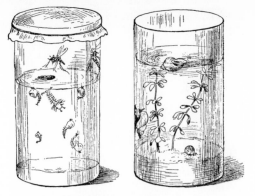

Fig. 4-3 Simple fresh-water aquaria. (From Ann H. Morgan, *Field Book of Ponds and Streams*, G. P. Putnam's Sons, 1930, Sixteenth Printing, London.)

this is done without breaking the film, the needle will float, due to the surface tension that forms a tight "skin" on top of water. A razor blade flat side down will also float this way.

Perhaps it will be possible to make a class or small-group field trip to the locale from which the children brought their specimens. Such a trip may help the children see the boundaries between the various plant zones or communities in and around water. Most of your collecting will occur in the shallow water close inshore. Here sun and light reach to the bottom. The water, warm all the way through, favors a wealth of life both visible and invisible. This shallow zone is characterized by emergent plants such as cattails which grow with their "feet" in the water and their heads in the air (Fig. 4-4A). Under water the stems of such plants are covered with simple microscope plants (algae) that provide food for swarms of minute crustaceans, plant-eating worms, and smaller water beetles (Fig. 4-4B). Here is a complete community of interdependent plants and animals to be found neither on dry land nor in deeper water, but only in this shore line zone.

Farther out where the water is knee-deep, we find the zone of floating-leaved

Fig. 4-4 (a) Plant zones around a pond. Note low-growing plant area nearest the water, higher shrubs in the background (*left*). Cattails signal such a littoral zone of plant succession. (U.S. Department of Agriculture.)

(b) Diving beetles. Note smooth streamlined body, boat-shaped "hull," and hind legs like oar blades. (Hugh Spencer.)

plants, such as water lilies, duckweed, spatterdock (Fig. 4-4C), pondweed, and eelgrass. Usually the bottom is soft mud, which "boils" up around one's feet. This makes poor walking, but it provides a rich pantry for the myriad forms of animal life usually present in this zone. The under-

(c) Duckweed. These small floating plants with dangling rootlets make a green blanket on still water. (Hugh Spencer.)

sides of the lily pads are floating hatcheries for eggs of water insects and snails. A dip net should bring up a host of carnivorous insect forms. The plant stems provide anchorage for countless algae, fresh water sponges, bryozoans, and the snails or worms that feed upon the green slime.

These smaller forms, in turn, are food supply for larger pond animals such as fish, amphibians, frogs (Fig. 4-4D), toads (Fig. 4-4E), salamanders, and reptiles (turtles, snakes). You do not often see a snake near water unless you live in the range of the Southern cottonmouth moccasin snake. To see a swimming snake is an infrequent and interesting sight. However, black water snakes (*Natrix sipedon*) are common in many areas of the Northeast.

The film *The Window* (Audubon Assoc., 16 mm sound) is an excellent illustration of a water collecting trip and other outdoor science instruction for children.

FOOD CHAINS

Big fleas have little fleas
Upon their backs to bite 'em.
Little fleas have lesser fleas
And so ad infinitum - - -.

From observation and from reading the children learn that all larger forms of ani-

(d) Pickerel frog hiding in the grass. Once it senses discovery, it speeds away with leaps and bounds. (Leonard Lee Rue III.)

(e) "Toad tenor." The male trill is amplified by the resonator throat sack visible here. (Leonard Lee Rue III.)

mal life live on smaller forms which, in turn, ultimately live on plant life. Let the children observe and study until they can draw or describe the food chains of which each form they collect is a link. (See Fig. 4-5.) Lead them to the conclusion that all animal life ultimately depends on plant life because animals cannot manufacture their own food. The children may be easily motivated at this point to wonder how plants make their own food—photosynthesis. To illustrate, place some green pond scum on a sunny window sill. After a few hours, put the scum into a Pyrex pint jar or saucepan and cover with rubbing alcohol. Set this glass container into a saucepan of water on an electric hot plate. (*Caution: Do not use open flame heat.*) Heat until green color is dissolved out by alcohol. Cool, rinse thoroughly, and cover with dilute iodine. The filaments turn a blackish color, indicating the presence of starch (see Chapter 12). Repeat with algae that have been kept in complete darkness under a black cover for several hours. Which sample showed the most starch present?

PLANT ZONES

Characteristic plants are indicators of life zones or belts. Children who live near the mountains will notice changes in vegetation and associated animal life as the altitude *changes*. Children who live near the coast will know that characteristic animals of the marine littoral zone (i.e., tide pools) do not exist in deeper water. A visit to the aquarium, discussions with skin divers, or reading about marine collecting will acquaint them with the fact that life zone levels exist in the ocean just as in fresh water or on the side of a mountain or around a desert oasis or marshy pond.

Let the children attempt to sketch or map the plant zones around the nearest body of water. They may wish to illustrate this by a mural. A cross section would show how plants continually invade or infiltrate a water body (see Fig. 4-4A). Children may wish to build cardboard dioramas or illustrate with flannel board cutouts. Eventually, living plants and plant debris will choke up a small pond. Thus runoff water must eventually seek another depression to fill. The process of plant succession as related to water plants illustrates one aspect of the universal and continuous leveling and smoothing of inequalities on the earth's surface.

The time allotment for a unit of study

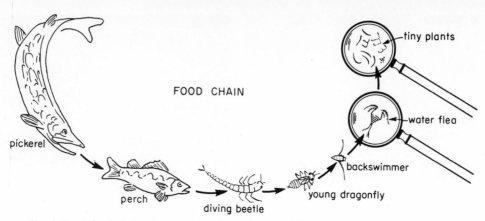

Fig. 4-5 A food chain, demonstrating that all animal life ultimately depends on plant life.

on pond life is usually insufficient for children to observe plant succession. However, they can usually find an old resident in the area who remembers bodies of water where now little or no water remains. Man, too, must be taken into account as a geological force. The building of reservoirs, the lowering of continental water tables, the occupation of large areas by buildings and streets are only a few of the ways that he changes ecological and geographical interrelationships.

LIFE OUT OF THE DEEP

Geological evidence appears to substantiate the Biblical description of the face of the earth as once covered with mists. As the mists began to condense and fall as rain, water collected in the depressions on the earth's surface. Some primitive cells began to form in the warm shallow waters of these ancient seas. Since the moon's and sun's gravitational pull created tides then as now, these primitive cells (probably not too different from single-celled water plants and animals today) were alternately left stranded and then inundated. Those which could withstand the alternate drowning and dessication survived. Probably the odds were greatest in favor

of the forms on the very edge of the tide zone. These reproduced in kind. Possible mutants which could withstand greater extremes moved further away from the water. Knowing this, the children may be led to see water plant succession in ponds as recapitulation in nature of the long span of evolutionary time. An excellent way for the child to comprehend these small life forms is to let him sketch diatoms, protozoans, and other pond or aquaria creatures (Fig. 4-6; see also Figs. 5-10 and 5-11) as he sees them under magnification.

A warm shallow pond provides an ideal "climate" for plant life. Plenty of water, sunshine, and warm temperatures facilitate rapid plant growth, food manufacture, and reproduction. Witness a marsh crowded with cattails, a sluggish stream or pool with duckweed, a myriad of green algae forms underwater. Animal life dependent on such forms, particularly on microscopic plants, can therefore grow profusely. Larger animal life which lives on protozoans (microscopic animals) can flourish and multiply.

Lead the children to the discovery of the pond as a fascinating community. Further study shows certain plant indicators and key animal forms related to shallow or deeper water or to the shore

Fig. 4-6 Model of life in ½″ of pond water, magnified 100 times, showing a variety of one-celled plants and animals as well as more complex forms. The plants range from the higher utricularia (stem proceeding from *left center* to *right top,* with many bladder-like traps) and elodea (*right center* to *top right,* with tapering leaves) to the green algae spirogyra (slender stalks at *left*) and closterium (a desmid, crescent-shaped, appearing over the utricularia stem in the *center*). The animals include the tiny bell-like protozoans vorticella (*left center*), rotifers, fairy shrimp (bubble shape at *bottom center*), hydra (large tentacled form bending from *bottom center* to *bottom right*), and a watermite egg (*center left,* with nucleus). (American Museum of Natural History.)

line. From this lead the children to see a pond or stream as comprised of communities within a larger community (Fig. 4-7A). Help them to draw analogies to human communities they know. Some children with opportunity and encouragement may go on to study other subdivisions of water communities: e.g., dry versus permanent pond life, life in lakes, slow streams or marshes, rapids and waterfalls (Fig. 4-7B). A typical distribution of life in a waterfall is related to the current: e.g., water pennies (really young beetles) on the underside of rocks in the swiftest current, case-bearing caddis worms, midge and beetle larvae clinging to water mosses growing just under a miniature waterfall, a phoebe sitting on a branch above waiting for winged adult forms to emerge, trout fingerlings in the fast water, water striders in the back eddies, a frog hiding beside a rock.

WATER PLANTS

A close look at ponds, streams, and even classroom aquaria can give children a fine introduction not only to some interesting adaptations of living organisms but also to the great plant groups. For example, if they are using a microscope in this study, they will have found out that the green scum in an unbalanced aquarium or from a pond is composed of (green) cells which may occur singly or in chains. Common types of algae include desmids and spirogyra (Fig. 4-8A, B). The single cells, called diatoms, are generally rather colorless. They occur in a wide variety of forms. Masses of them make brook beds and water weeds golden brown.

Although fresh-water algae occur in a variety of forms, the filamentous green algae such as spirogyra are perhaps best known. Children need be more concerned with observing and perhaps drawing the forms they see under magnification than the exact design. Marine algae tend to be reddish brown rather than green. If children live near the seashore, they may enjoy preserving seaweed, especially the filamentous or branched forms, by mounting them on paper. Float the seaweed in a shallow pan. Float white drawing paper under the seaweed, separate the strands, center on paper, and drain off water. The gelatin in the seaweed makes it adhere to the paper as it dries.

LIVERWORTS AND MOSSES

Close to the edge of streams are mats or clusters of small, green shade-loving plants called liverworts (Fig. 4-9A). Having no water storage cells, they lose water very quickly and cannot stand drying out any better than the skin of the frog. We have tried innumerable times to keep liverworts in a terrarium but never succeeded until a friend showed us some thriving in a New York apartment. The secret was that the rock on which the liverwort was spread was half submerged in water. A brick will do nicely (Fig. 4-9B).

Mosses can grow further away from water. The sphagnums and bog mosses, however, grow best when water soaked.

Water plants must live near enough to the surface to receive ample light (Fig. 4-9C). They need light to make food. Let

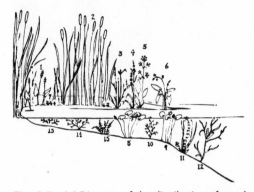

Fig. 4-7 (a) Diagram of the distribution of pond plants. In the background are the emergent water plants: 1, pickerel weed; 2, cattails; 3, bulrush; 4, burreed; 5, water plantain; 6, arrowhead. In the foreground are the floating-leaved plants: 7, Polygonum; 8, lily pads; 9, spatterdocks; 10, hornwort; 11, eelgrass; 12, pondweed. Also in the foreground are the submerged plants: 13, Riccia; 14, bladderwort; 15, water milfoil.

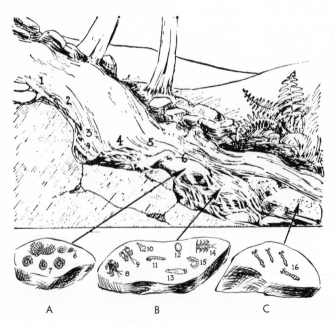

(b) Diagram of the distribution of animals in a waterfall. The stones A, B, and C are shown enlarged, with their inhabitants; A and C are right side up; B is wrong side up. 1, egg masses of midges; 2, water moss, *Fontinalis*; 3, midge larvae; 4, alga, *Cladophora*; 5, May fly, *Chirotenetes*; 6, nets of caddis worm, *Hydropsyche*; 7, pupa cases of caddis worm, *Helicopsyche*; 8, 9, May flies, *Heptagenia* and *Epeorus*; 10, planarian; 11, caddis worm; 12, water penny; 13, leech; 14, stonefly nymph; 15, caddis worm; 16, black fly, *Simulium*. (From Ann H. Morgan, *Field Book of Ponds and Streams*, G. P. Putnam's Sons, 1930, Sixteenth Printing, London.)

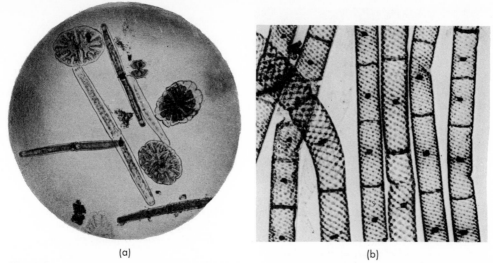

(a)   (b)

Fig. 4-8 (a) Desmids. These single-celled species of green algae occur in a wonderful variety of shapes and designs. Under magnification they appear pale greenish yellow. (General Biological Supply House, Inc., Chicago.) (b) Spirogyra. These filamentous green algae are composed of cells linked in chains. Note chloroplasts, green bodies that seem to fill the cell. The dark central spot in each cell is the nucleus. (General Biological Supply House, Inc., Chicago.)

the children think of experiments to prove that light doesn't pass as well through water as air. Focus a beam of sunlight or projector lamp through a shallow and then a deeper glass jar of water. Repeat the experiment with the jar empty to determine relative distortion that occurs when light passes through glass (see Chapter 16). Think of some experiments to show that plants such as eelgrass and pondweeds live completely in water and send leaves near the surface for light. Plants such as cattails have their feet in the water and their leaves in the air. Duckweed and giant kelp are free floating on the surface. Water lilies and arrowroot have submerged stems and leaves at the surface. If a microscope is available to show stomata with their surrounding guard cells, let the children look for stomata on the surfaces of water plant leaves. Let them decide why stomata are not found on the undersurface of lily pads.

The insect-eating habits of bog plants such as sundew and pitcher plant can be observed at first hand if one sets up a bog terrarium of sphagnum, wild cranberry, and other native bog plants. These may be secured from a scientific supply house or from Armstrong Assoc., 13 Ash Street, Basking Ridge, N. J.

CARBON DIOXIDE-OXYGEN CYCLE

Select sections of water plants, either native or pet-store kinds or both. Set each in a tumbler of water on a sunny window sill. Watch for bubbles to appear on the plant.

Do they occur at the same rate for each kind of plant and in the same parts of the plant? These bubbles, of course, are oxygen given off by the plant in the course of its food manufacturing process (photosynthesis). Some children may wish to collect some bubbles from a large water plant sample and apply the laboratory test for oxygen (see Chapter 12)(Fig. 4-10). Place the plant in plain soda or club soda to provide carbon dioxide. Allow the soda to stand open ½ hour before using. Invert the glass funnel over an aquarium plant in

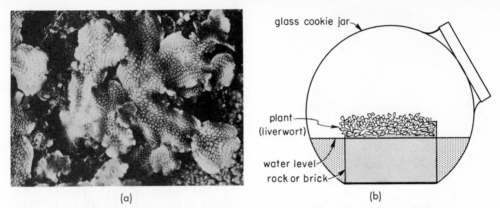

glass cookie jar

plant (liverwort)

water level
rock or brick

(a)

(b)

Fig. 4-9 (a) Liverwort (Marchantia). This primitive plant has a shiny green, leaf-like body and is common in damp shady places. (Hugh Spencer.) (b) Liverwort "in captivity" affords a primitive and interesting example of one stage in plant evolution. Keep cover closed. Paint to inhibit rust. Porous rock such as a fragment of a clay pot should be used.

sunlight. Fill the funnel tube with water. Fill the test tube with water and invert over the funnel tube. As the plant leaves begin to make oxygen in sunlight, water in the test tube is replaced with bubbles of oxygen. Light an end of a wooden applicator. Blow out the flame quickly, remove the test tube, and insert the glowing tip of the applicator. Oxygen generated should re-light the flame.

Fish breathe to live just as do higher animals, though fish breathe through gills instead of lungs. Like other living things, they give off carbon dioxide. Place goldfish for a short time in clear limewater (see p. 69). The liquid will turn milky from carbon dioxide given off by fish. Let children review the test for carbon dioxide by exhaling into clear limewater (see Chapter 12). Fish need the oxygen given off by water plants. Plants use the carbon dioxide given off by animal life in the aquarium to carry on photosynthesis (see above). Lead the children by discussion

(c) Note how lily pads are spread out to receive maximum light. This mosaic leaf arrangement is also observable in many dry land plants. (Roche.)

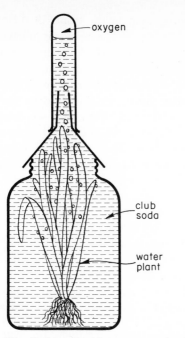

oxygen

club soda

water plant

Fig. 4-10 Carbon dioxide-oxygen cycle. One interesting variation might be to place another plant in a container of plain water. Another, to set the plants away from sunlight.

and diagrams or pictures to gain partial concepts of the more general concept of interdependence of life.

LIFE CYCLES IN WATER LIFE

Water life both in an aquarium and in a stream offers endless illustrations of the persistence, continuity, and adaptability of living forms. For example, the snail eggs within the aquarium hatch into tiny snails, which grow and lay more eggs to hatch into more snails. The "rites of spring" often furnish the classroom with a supply of amphibian eggs for nurture and observation. A fall field trip to a brook usually brings back the empty body castings of dragonfly (Fig. 4-11) and May fly nymphal forms. A winter field trip usually uncovers under stream boulders or logs at least some examples of caddis worm cases (see Fig. 3-23). If you see a tiny bunch of sticks moving across the bottom, you are not imagining things. You are seeing a caddis worm case made of tiny sticks glued together with the insect's own saliva. Some caddis worms make their "houses" of tiny pebbles. One form builds cup-shaped nets to snare food floating downstream.

Guppies differ from most fish in that they omit the egg-laying stage. Their young are born alive from eggs. Since guppies are usually devoured by goldfish and since they require warmer water, it is best to keep guppies in a separate container, e.g., gallon jar. Be sure to include plenty of floating plants. They are needed to provide cover for the babies against the cannibal appetites of big guppies. As soon as you see baby guppies in your tank or jar, remove the parents to another container (see Chapter 2).

Fig. 4-11 Two stages in the life of a dragonfly: the body casting of the nymph; and the adult (see also Fig. 3-24). Note the plane surface of the wings as contrasted to those of the adult damsel fly (see Fig. 3-21). (W. T. Davidson from National Audubon Society.)

OCEAN WATER

Let the children study globes of the earth and guess what fraction of the globe is covered by ocean water—actually about three quarters. A group of children in a coastal state were studying the Age of Discovery and Colonization of the New World. When they were asked to tell where our early settlers would go for salt, not one thought to mention the ocean barely 20 miles away. It was suggested that they boil down seawater or a brine solution and report results.

Let the children add a tablespoon of salt to a quart of hot water in an open saucepan. Let two children taste the solution. Boil 10–20 minutes. Blow to cool and taste again. It is saltier. Let children speculate why, and if necessary guide their discussion back to evaporation experience and observation (e.g., evaporation from aquarium). Boil 10–20 minutes more and taste again. This time it will be saltier because even more water will have evaporated. Let children taste drops of water condensed inside a saucepan lid; replace the lid with a cold glass plate to hasten condensation. If possible, repeat the distillation experiment (Chapter 11).

SEA SHELLS AND CORAL REEFS

Ask children if they know why a sea shell is like a chicken bone. Secure strong vinegar or, better, dilute hydrochloric acid from a drugstore or a high school chemistry teacher. Immerse chicken bones and sea shells in vinegar or acid and let stand several days. Both should become soft and rubbery because the lime has been dissolved out by the acids. The outside of the shell may not feel as limp as the inside. Recheck this by using another shell and observing its reaction to acid. Use a medicine dropper or pipette to apply a few drops first to the outer brown covering, then to the inside of the shell. What happens? The outside is much more resistant to acid. Why? The inside should be etched by application of acid.

If it is possible to secure small samples of rough coral, let the children test the coral with acid. They will see that the bony skeleton of the coral animal is largely lime. These tiny animals, like many other marine forms, tend to live in groups for protection. The coral reef islands which dot the South Pacific are really coral cemeteries built up year after year one on top of another.

Marine creatures such as mollusks therefore have in the seawater all about them the dissolved lime from which their shells and outer covering are made. A very convenient way to build a limestone house, just by sitting in the middle of it!

LIFE IN THE SEA

The ocean floor has higher mountains and deeper canyons than anything we can see on dry land. In adaptation to these variations in depth, pressure, and light, life in the ocean has developed in myriad forms, shapes, and sizes. For example, some of the largest creatures, the whales, live on the smallest creatures, the plankton (microscopic plants and animals). Kipling's "How the Whale Got His Throat"[1] is a delightful fantasy to read aloud and to precipitate discussion and research. Encourage children to construct a cardboard box diorama illustrating life in the sea.

Even a superficial consideration of sea life will suggest comparisons with life in a pond, i.e., communities within a community. Life in a tide pool is very different from the plant and animal life on a sandy beach or life along a muddy shore or tidal

[1] Rudyard Kipling's *Just So Stories,* a recent edition published for libraries in 1954 by the Macmillan Company.

estuary. The offshore shallows again represent a different community. Lead the children to see that the transitions between salt-water communities are sharper than between fresh-water life zones. Lead them to deduce the reason, e.g., the more rigorous conditions of life. Lead them also to note the greater proportion of animal as against plant forms in marine life zones. Such observation could lead to some interesting discussion and research with regard to the world's population explosion and food problems.

Most children know that meat and other proteins are the most expensive items in the family grocery bill. They know that fish is usually a less expensive kind of meat. Social studies of life on other continents has shown that most of the rest of the world is underfed as to proteins. To produce beef protein takes many acres of range pasture, corn, and expensive labor for processing. To produce fish protein is less costly because of the endless pastures of the sea and the apparently endless beds of algae and animal plankton needing no cultivation and no irrigation. Perhaps the children will have read of government experiments in growing algae for food. Gelatin produced from seaweed (Irish dulse) is often available from the drugstore. The problem is to educate ourselves to its taste. The protein is there. Let the children review and apply protein test (see Chapter 13).

Learning how to travel underwater has interesting counterparts with space travel problems. Let children trace the development of the submarine, and let them demonstrate a model (see Chapter 9). Help them review and reinforce the partial concepts they have already derived about air pressure. Draw analogies between changes in pressure as one descends the ocean depths or goes into outer space. The medium is water instead of air, but a bathysphere carries oxygen tanks and has thick steel walls to withstand pressure.

Today's enthusiasm for skin diving should provide accounts of the effect of water pressure at different depths. There are many other opportunities for interesting discoveries and conclusions about life in the sea. Let children report on research about salmon and eel migration, and compare with bird migrations. Government representatives for fish and game regulations are most cooperative about giving children insight into modern "fish farming," e.g., controlling the Great Lakes lamprey, building farm ponds, finding schools of fish by radar.

Let the children study to find out which forms of sea life move in schools and why. Let them read and report on similarities and differences between communal forms such as corals and the social insects. Marine mammals such as whales, dolphins, porpoises, seals, sea lions, cows, and sea otters have particularly interesting habits and interrelationships with other animals including man.

Among the most interesting developments of our times as related to the sea is the idea that we can "mine" seawater and the sea's bottom for all the elements which have been carried down in solution. For example, magnesium, used to make airplanes because it is both strong and light, has been discovered in quantity on the ocean bottom. Bromine to make ethyl gas is also being mined from the sea. The biggest operation is the removal of bromine from seawater (see any high school chemistry book). Dow Chemical has a bromine extraction plant on the Carolina seacoast.

Salt is a valuable mineral. By boiling seawater in an old pan, you should have a residue of tiny crystals which are mainly table salt (sodium chloride). Chemical tests would find traces of many other minerals.

CAPSULE LESSONS

4-1 Set up gallon pickle-jar aquariums with different combinations of plants and animal inhabitants. A jar which contains carnivorous water insects usually shows population reduction. Who eats whom?

4-2 What conditions of light are best for water life populations? Place pickle-jar aquariums on a sunny window, in a dark closet, in a cool dark place, in a warm bright location, and watch for changes.

4-3 How does a pond or stream community illustrate "balance of life"? Let the children watch for and describe or draw evidence of "food chains."

4-4 Observe and illustrate complete and incomplete metamorphosis in animal forms and evidence of life cycles.

4-5 Encourage children to discover by observation and research evidences of interesting adaptations to living in the water, e.g., plant and animal "skin divers."

4-6 What about locomotion in water animals? How do water striders walk on the water? Compare movements of water boatmen, back swimmers, and whirligig beetles. Which are the fastest?

4-7 Look for and compare egg stages of water life such as frogs, snails, and insects. Egg masses are often attached to underwater plant stems or leaves, sticks, or rocks.

BIBLIOGRAPHY

Adrian, Mary, *Fiddler Crab,* Holiday, 1953. Middle. Life cycle of common species at tide line along the beach.

Andrews, Roy Chapman, *All About Whales,* Random House, 1954. Upper. Story form information about whales.

Axelrod, Herbert, *Tropical Fish as a Hobby,* McGraw-Hill, 1952. Middle. Children's guide for raising tropicals.

Broekel, Ray, *True Book of Tropical Fishes,* Childrens Press, 1956. Middle. Interesting facts and suggestions for setting up and maintaining home aquaria.

Buck, Margaret W., *In Ponds and Streams,* Abingdon, 1955. Middle. Intriguing account of fresh-water life.

————, *Pets from the Pond,* Abingdon, 1958. Upper. Detailed suggestions for setting up fresh-water aquaria for local forms of life.

Carson, Rachel, *Sea Around Us,* ed. by Anne T. White, Simon and Schuster, 1958. Upper. Modern classic adapted for children.

Carter, Katherine, *True Book of Oceans,* Childrens Press, 1958. Middle. Ocean tides, currents, and zones of animal life.

Cousteau, Jacques, and Frédéric Dumas, *Silent World,* Harper, 1953. Upper. Pioneers of the aqualung write the amazing story of underwater exploration.

Darby, Gene, *What Is a Fish?,* Benefic, 1958. Primary. Typical structure and function. Simple concepts of adaptation and survival.

Darling, Louis, *Penguins,* Morrow, 1956. Middle. Interesting facts about these strange birds.

Downer, Marion, *David and the Sea Gulls,* Lothrop, 1956. Middle. Well laid out and illustrated.

Dudley, Ruth H., *Sea Shells,* Crowell, 1953. Middle. Sure to motivate the hobby of shell collection and study.

Earle, Olive L., *The Octopus,* Morrow, 1955. Middle. Simple, basic information on this marine animal and related forms.

Epstein, Samuel, and Beryl Epstein, *Real Book About the Sea,* Garden City, 1954. Middle. Fascinating account of possible origin and spread of the sea—its topography and strange denizens.

Erickson, Phoebe, *The True Book of Animals of Small Pond,* Childrens Press, 1953.

Gallup, Lucy, *Spinning Wings,* Morrow, 1956. Exciting life story of black tern.

Gaul, Albro, *The Pond Book,* Coward-McCann, 1955. Middle. The pond world through the seasons. Vividly and carefully written.

————, *Wonderful World of the Seashore,* Appleton, 1955. Middle. Interdependence of marine plant and animal life.

George, John L., and Jean George, *Dipper of Copper Creek,* Dutton, 1956. Outstanding life story of western water ouzel or dipper.

Goff, Lloyd L., *Run Sandpiper Run,* Lothrop, 1957. Middle. Nesting and annual migration of sandpipers from Labrador to South America.

Hahn, Jan, *A Reader's Guide to Oceanography,* Woods Hole Oceanography Institute (Woods Hole, Mass.). 8 pp. Recently compiled by staff.

Harris, Louise, D., *Little Red Newt,* Little, Brown, 1958. Primary to middle. Life history of red eft salamander and pond ecology.

Hausman, Leon, *Beginner's Guide to Fresh Water Life,* Putnam, 1950. Middle. Simple pocket guide.

Hinton, Sam, *Exploring Under the Sea,* Garden City, 1957. Middle to upper. Ocean ecology, tides, and currents.

Hogner, Dorothy C., *Snails,* Crowell, 1958. Middle to upper. Structure and habits of common mollusks. Suggestions on fresh- and salt-water aquaria.

Holling, Holling C., *Pagoo,* Houghton Mifflin, 1956. Upper. Life cycle of hermit crab by author of other interesting children's books.

Huntington, Harriet E., *Let's Go to the Brook,* Doubleday, 1952. Primary. Plant and animal life along a brook.

———, *Let's Go to the Seashore,* Doubleday, 1941. Upper. Picture-story book.

Hylander, Clarence, *Sea and Shore,* Macmillan, 1950. Upper. Interesting information about marine life on both east and west coasts. Many photographs and detailed sketches helpful in identification.

Lavine, Sigmund A., *Wonders of the Aquarium,* Dodd, Mead, 1956. Middle. Information on setting up and keeping an aquarium and on common, inexpensive tropicals.

Maryland State Dept. of Education, *Our Underwater Farm,* Conservation Series Book No. 3, 1953. 45 pp. Upper. Graphic and readable reference for children and teachers on the fishing industry and marine life off the coast of Maryland.

Morgan, Alfred, *Aquarium Book for Boys and Girls,* Scribner's, rev. ed., 1957. Middle to upper. Setting up an aquarium, using native and local materials.

Neurath, Marie, *The Deep Sea,* Sterling, 1958. Primary. Some interesting creatures from the depths.

———, *Wonder World of the Sea Shore,* Lothrop, 1954. Primary. About jelly fish and other shallow-water plants and animals.

Parker, Bertha M., *Pebbles and Sea Shells,* Row, Peterson, 1959. 36 pp. Middle. Another of the excellent Basic Education Series, with simple text and a wealth of attractive colored pictures. Introduction to basic concepts in geology as well as in marine biology.

Pels, Gertrude, *Care of Water Pets,* Crowell, 1955. Middle. Excellent sourcebook on setting up and maintaining water life.

Shannon, Terry, *At Water's Edge,* Sterling, 1955. Primary. Colorful presentation of life forms along the littoral zone of water bodies. ·

Selsam, Millicent E., *See Through the Lake,* Harper, 1958. Middle. Cross section of life cycles in a lake.

Spectorsky, A. C. *Book of the Sea,* Grosset and Dunlap, 1958. Upper. Treasury of illustrations and pictures of underwater life from whales to microscopic algae.

Knowlton, William, *Let's Explore Beneath the Sea,* Knopf, 1957. Upper. Excellent introduction to skin diving, spear fishing, and other methods of underwater investigation.

Invisible worlds

Another dimension may be added to your classroom science by using magnifying glasses and a microscope. Small plastic magnifying glasses can be purchased from a newsstand or variety store for 10–20¢ apiece. If a sympathetic optometrist will give you discarded convex lenses, the children can have the fun and experience of making their own magnifying glasses. Use a pair of eyeglass lenses made for a farsighted person. Fill one to the brim with water. Cover with second lens and tape together with Scotch tape (Fig. 5-1), leaving only a small hole. With a medicine dropper complete filling the space, and then seal. Cover a small square of newspaper with Saran Wrap. Through a drop of water on the surface of the Saran Wrap the newsprint appears magnified. If a pig's eye or eye of another animal is available through the local butcher, cut out the transparent lens center from the surrounding opaque tissue and place on newsprint. The children will be surprised to see how much bigger the print appears "through a pig's eye"! A large hand magnifying glass is always desirable in the classroom. In our experience, the common tripod magnifier and hand lens often used by botanists in field work are difficult for young children to focus. (See Fig. 5-2.)

GLASS-BEAD MICROSCOPE

A simple microscope can be made by pupils or the teacher (Fig. 5-3). This is a working model of the original microscope invented by Leeuwenhoek. You need a sheet of thin plywood or other thin wood no more than ¼" thick; the over-all dimensions are 2" × 3". For lenses, obtain

(a)

(b)

Fig. 5-2 (a) Tripod magnifier. (W. M. Welch Mfg. Co.) (b) Hand lens. (Selsi Company, Inc.).

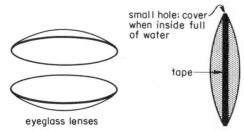

small hole: cover when inside full of water

tape

eyeglass lenses

Fig. 5-1 Water-drop lens. When filled with water, close-fitting spherical eyeglass lenses or other convex glasses bend light rays to produce magnification.

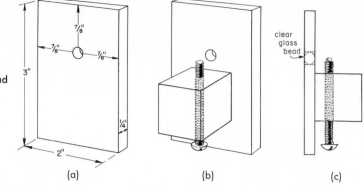

Fig. 5-3 Simple glass-bead microscope.

(a) (b) (c)

solid glass beads (available from a scientific or chemical supply house, the local high school chemistry department, or a local chemical laboratory). The purchase of one pound for a few dollars will supply hundreds of these tiny beads that serve as simple lenses of great magnifying power.

First drill a ¼" diameter hole in the wood at the point indicated in Fig. 5-3A. Into this hole force one of the glass beads with the flatter faces of the beads parallel to the front and back of the little board. For the next step cut a block of soft wood in the shape of a 1" cube. Drill a hole ⅛" in diameter in the center of the block. (If necessary ask a carpenter or workshop teacher to drill the hole for you.) From a hardware or radio shop get a 2" or 2½" long 6/32 machine screw. Thread this into the ⅛" hole. This will give you a snug turning arrangement. Dip the point of the screw in pond or aquarium water. Place the lens to the eye and adjust the screw until you see algae or microscopic protozoans in the water. With an ordinary screw you can hold a drop of water on the flat tip for examination. You can also use a screw that has been filed to a point to hold nontransparent objects for examination.

With any of the above equipment, your children may enjoy deciding which things look the same and which look different when magnified. Let the children try to imagine how things would look if they were Lilliputians in a grassroot jungle. In the summer and fall, look at the breathing holes or spiracles along the sides of a grasshopper (Fig. 5-4). The children will soon discover that not all insects have spiracles. They will then begin to understand why we have to use eating poisons for such insects and breathing poisons to control those with spiracles. Look for the uninvited guests—invisible pests on indoor plants and animals. The bud scales and leaf scars on twigs in winter are wonderfully interesting and symmetrical when studied through magnification. Springtime brings pussy willows and other microscopic flowers whose parts need to be magnified to be truly seen.

CHOICE AND CARE OF MICROSCOPES

Borrowing a good low-power (100× magnification) microscope from the nearest high school even temporarily is usually

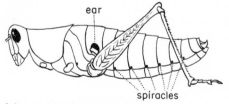

(wings and fore legs removed)

Fig. 5-4 Grasshopper spiracles (breathing holes). Sucking insects such as house plant aphids inmune to poison on their food can be controlled by suffocation with soap dip or oil emulsion spray.

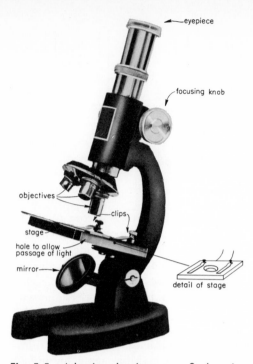

Fig. 5-5 A beginner's microscope. Such an instrument, with magnification 30–200 ✕, may be purchased for under $10. (Science Materials Center.)

Labels in Fig. 5-5: eyepiece, focusing knob, objectives, clips, stage, hole to allow passage of light, mirror, detail of stage

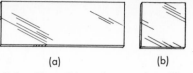

(a)   (b)

Fig. 5-6 Glass slide and cover glass. The cover glass may be round.

place a glass slide (Fig. 5-6A) or any small piece of glass on the stage, making sure the material to be examined is *directly* under the lens. Very slowly and carefully lower the lens with the focusing knob (see Fig. 5-5) until the objective *almost touches* the slide. Now focus by turning the knob to *raise* the lens slowly until you see a sharp image. Never attempt to focus by lowering the lens. Always start by bringing the lens close to the material on the slide. Then bring into focus by raising the objective. To clean slides use your breath or alcohol.

better than investing money in the so-called toy microscopes. However, some junior microscopes are good. Ask a biology teacher to help you select one. Your microscope can be used to show materials to the whole class by projecting the image on the ceiling or on a side screen. How to do this is described below. Many children *can* be taught the use and care of a microscope for individual viewing (Fig. 5-5).

For individual use, place the microscope on the window sill where the mirror under the stage can pick up strong daylight (not direct sunlight, however). It may be safer for the microscope to use it on a table in the room with a desk lamp as light source. Adjust the substage mirror until it picks up the lamp light. Looking through the eyepiece, you should be able to see a bright circle of light from the lamp. Now

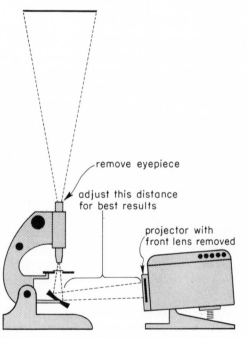

Fig. 5-7 Inexpensive micro-projection. The projector should be 2–3 feet from the light source.

Labels in Fig. 5-7: remove eyepiece, adjust this distance for best results, projector with front lens removed

MICRO-PROJECTION FOR THE GROUP

A room which can be well darkened and a strong light source such as a lantern slide projector lamp are needed to make a micro-projector out of an ordinary microscope. Remove the front lens of the projector. Unscrew the eyepiece of the microscope. Aim the projector lamp light into the microscope mirror (Fig. 5-7). If you raise some chalk dust with blackboard erasers, the outline of the beam becomes visible. You can then adjust the projector so that the beam hits full on the microscope mirror. With the room darkened, focus the microscope as before. On the ceiling you should see an enlarged image of the onion skin cells or whatever material is on the slide. Or, with an ordinary pocket mirror, reflect the light from the top of the microscope tube to a screen on the side wall (Fig. 5-7).

INSIDE AN ONION SKIN

Beginners are often disappointed by what they can see with a microscope because they try to look at material which is too thick or too large. Try, for instance, looking at plant cells in a tiny thin piece of onion skin. Make a razor cut anywhere on the onion. Starting from the cut, peel off the thinnest possible layer. Place on a slide and with medicine dropper, add 1 drop of water. Drop a cover slip (see Fig. 5-6) on the water. If you do not have cover slips, do not use water, but replace the specimen every 10–15 minutes with a fresh piece of onion skin. If you have a sufficiently thin piece in focus, you should be able to see rectangular or brick-like cells. Try staining the pieces of onion skin with a drop of iodine diluted in water. In about 5 minutes you should be able to make out the nucleus of each cell, a small round body. See Fig. 5-8.

INSIDE A LEAF

Kalanchoe or peperomia plants, carried by most florists, have interesting leaf structure under a microscope. Kalanchoe is preferable, although either will do. Tear a leaf in half. Some of the lower layer will adhere to the underside or skin of the leaf. Remove this with tweezers and place on a slide. With careful focusing, you should be able to see the stomata (Greek, meaning "little mouths") through which air enters and leaves a leaf. (For the complete story of the oxygen-carbon dioxide cycle in plants, see Chapter 6.) You should be able to see the two halves of the stoma, each shaped like a lip. These two lip-like parts are called guard cells. In dry weather they are slightly open so that the plant does not lose too much water (for explanation of transpiration in plants, see Chapter 6).

To illustrate that plants like animals need to breathe, try smearing Vaseline lightly on both sides of a leaf. Do not detach the leaf from the plant on which it is growing. At the end of a day or two the leaf will wilt because the stomata are plugged. Some kinds of leaves will wilt if only one side is coated with Vaseline. Herein lie some interesting possibilities for experimenting. Children will now be-

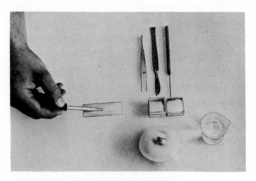

Fig. 5-8 Equipment for preparing onion slice for microscopic examination. A drop of water is being put on slide, and the onion slice is to be placed in the drop of water. (Stanley Rice.)

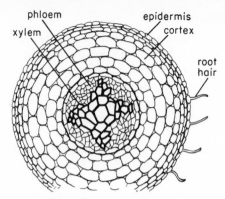

phloem   epidermis
xylem   cortex

root
hair

Fig. 5-9 The edible part of a carrot is an enlarged cylinder with a core of conducting tissue. Water moves up through the xylem tissue. The dissolved food manufactured in the carrot leaves moves down through the phloem cells for storage. In most plants this conducting tissue is just under the cortical layer.

gin to understand why indoor plants need to have their foliage washed or dusted to keep the stomata open and functioning.

If you allow one of a pair of similar plants to go without water for a week, the microscope will show a difference in the stomata from the two plants. Those from the watered plant are open, while those from the dry plant have closed to conserve water.

The microscope shows skin cells but no stomata on the top surface of kalanchoe leaves. Water lilies have stomata only on the upper surface. Grasses have them on both sides of the blade. In general, most plants have stomata on the underside of the leaf.

INSIDE A ROOT

Using a razor blade, make an exceedingly thin cross section of a carrot. Under a microscope you can see the tubes or conducting tissue which carry water and minerals up and food down (Fig. 5-9). Tubes similar to these function in the "patriotic"

celery set in the sun to draw up red and blue solutions (see Chapter 6).

LIFE IN A LEAF CELL

Motion from life processes is visible inside the leaves of aquarium plants such as elodea and vallisneria. Warm a slide in lukewarm water and place a leaflet in the center. Add a drop of lukewarm water and a cover slip. You should be able to see the chloroplasts (green chlorophyll bodies) streaming slowly around inside the cell. This is protoplasm in motion inside the living cells.

WORLD IN A FISH TANK

A balanced aquarium may be a gold mine for microscopic plant life. Any green

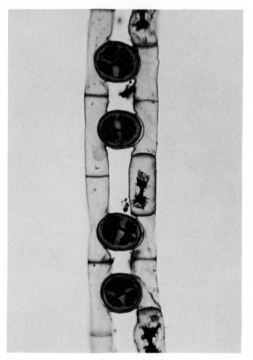

Fig. 5-10 Algae cells showing chloroplasts. Chloroplasts contain chlorophyll, the substance enabling green plants to create their own food supply. (General Biological Supply House.)

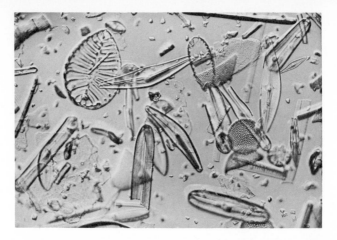

Fig. 5-11 Mixed diatoms. Some 12,000 species have been described. These one-celled plants have cell walls made of glassy material. These shells accumulate in layers many hundred feet thick. Beds of diatomaceous earth are mined for their many commercial uses. (General Biological Supply House.)

scum on the sides of the tank or in the water is caused by the growth of primitive green plants called algae. On a slide these appear as sections of a miniature jigsaw puzzle. These sections are cells. The tiny green bodies filling the cells are chloroplasts (Fig. 5-10).

In the course of collecting frog eggs or other water life, you may pick up some green scum. Under the microscope this may show as thread-like plants composed of chains of box-like cells. You should be able to see the chlorophyll in each cell. Most pond scum contains more than one kind of green alga and some interesting single-celled cells called diatoms (Fig. 5-11). (See also Chapter 4.)

THE WORLD OF NONGREEN PLANTS

There is a whole array of plants which do not have the all-important green matter, chlorophyll. Therefore, like animals, they are dependent upon other plants for food. Although they might be thought lazy, they do many things which make a big difference in our daily lives. Take, for instance, the yeast plant, without which bread would not rise.

A hand magnifying glass will suffice to begin our study of this lowly but interesting group of plants. For example, we might begin by magnifying the spore print of a common mushroom. If it is not the season for wild mushrooms, use one from the grocery store. Break off the stem and place the cap, gills down, on a piece of white paper. If you use an amanita or other white-spored variety, black or brown paper will give you more contrast. Invert a glass or other bowl over the mushroom cap. Leave undisturbed for 24–48 hours; then remove glass and cap carefully. You should find that the spores have fallen out to make a radial design (Fig. 5-12). The tiny round dots of which this design is made are the primitive equivalents of plant seeds.

Ferns are another type of plant which bear spores instead of seeds. The spore cases are interesting brownish structures to be found on the underside of fern fronds in summer and fall. These spore cases look very different under magnification from the way they appear to the naked eye. The individual spores are so small that they are hard to observe under low magnification. Plants related structurally to ferns, such as ground pine, horsetail, or scouring rush, shake out a yellow powder when the spore cases are mature, and are worth a closer look. Spores from the strange-looking horsetail have an interesting projectile device wrapped around

mushroom cap

Fig. 5-12 Method for obtaining mushroom spore prints. Try the same technique with other spore-bearing plants, e.g., ferns, horsetail, and other fern allies.

the spore. When weather and humidity are right for the spores to germinate, this structure uncoils and propels the spore as far as possible from the parent plant.

Primitive plants such as mosses, liverworts, and lichens also bear spores instead of seeds. The fruiting bodies of the different species are interesting and different under magnification. The haircap moss, for example, carries its spores in a bell-shaped cap which has an opening that looks and works like the top of a pepper shaker when it is time for the spores to scatter. Liverworts are found often along streams. The odd-shaped fruiting bodies called gemmae cups grow in the center of the leaf-shaped thallus or plant structure. (see Fig. 4-9A). Lichens which are a curious combination of a green plant, alga, and a fungus-like nongreen plant are worth magnification.

Molds in our homes may be something we strive to avoid. Yet if it were not for molds and bacteria, there would be no formation of organic material to rebuild the soil. Leaves would fall and never disintegrate into leaf mold, or humus. To prove that more is floating about "than meets the eye," i.e., spores of molds and other plants, try growing mold gardens on a piece of bread. Close-covered plastic sandwich boxes which retain a bit of moisture work well. Exposing to air as little as possible, place one slice in a covered container in a dark place. Also, exposing to air as little as possible, place another slice in a covered box or dish where it will get light or sunlight, as on the window sill. The third slice of bread should be exposed to air in the classroom for a half day, then put away in a warm dark place. A fourth slice should be placed in an *open* saucer or box top where it is allowed to dry out. Since dampness, warmth, and the absence of light promote the growth of mold, you should eventually have a flourishing mold garden on your third slice. Examine with a hand lens or microscope. Be prepared to re-run the experiment as a double check and because it is difficult to place the first and second slices in containers without momentary exposure to mold spores and other bodies in the air.

To illustrate the principle of infection, secure a moldy piece of citrus. With a needle first sterilized in flame or alcohol, pierce the moldy spot on the infected fruit, then pierce the skin of unblemished fruit. Put the fruit away in a warm, dark, damp place and check daily to see if mold forms where your needle pricked the good fruit.

INVISIBLE PLANTS IN A LOAF OF BREAD

In answer to the perennial question, "What makes bread rise?" challenge the children to discover by experiment, using the main ingredients listed in bread recipes. Which one makes bread rise? Let the children suggest various combinations, for example,

flour and water
sugar and water
yeast and water
flour, sugar, and water
flour, yeast, and water
sugar, yeast, and water

and others.

Secure similar containers for the experiment, viz., pint-sized plastic food containers such as those used to package ice cream. Use the same amount of water and dry ingredients in each container. Try nine parts of water to one of sugar by weight. If you can use warm water, the children should soon see bubbles in the mixtures containing yeast. The yeast-sugar mixture should show most change. In about 2 hours a drop of this mixture should show the cells have changed shape or budded (Fig. 5-13) to form new cells. Use one yeast cake for each mixture for fast action. The mixtures without yeast will show no change.

Many children know that "soda pop" contains carbon dioxide. In order for them to see for themselves that the same gas is used to make bread rise, you may wish to initiate the following activities. From the druggist get some limewater solution or make your own by dissolving limewater tablets in water. Perhaps an older student with a chemistry set can supply calcium oxide (CaO), a white powder which is mixed with water to form limewater. Allow excess powder to settle out of solution. Use only the clear portion of solution. Make a delivery tube (Fig. 5-14) with a one-hole stopper, a plastic or glass drinking tube, and about 2 feet of rubber tubing, also available from the drugstore. The rubber tubing terminates in your container of limewater. Open a bottle of "pop." Cork quickly with a one-hole stopper and delivery tube apparatus. The gas released from the "pop" should begin to turn the clear limewater milky. Repeat, with a clear batch of limewater, this time using a solution of sugar being "worked" by yeast. Since soda-acid fire extinguishers (see Chapter 17) put out fire by producing carbon dioxide (a heavier-than-air gas), you may wish also to simulate and check this reaction. Again, using a clear batch of limewater, attach the delivery tube apparatus to a bottle containing vinegar just poured on bicarbonate of soda. Any or all of these reactions may be accelerated by shaking the pop bottle, the sugar and yeast solution, or the soda-vinegar solutions.

THE WORLD OF BACTERIA

Bacteria, like molds, are ever-present in the air. There are many kinds, some of which cause disease and others which are most useful and necessary to mankind. Though very similar to one-celled primitive animals or protozoans, bacteria are nevertheless members of the plant family, albeit the nongreen plants. Using Pyrex Petri dishes and nutrient agar solutions, teachers may grow bacteria gardens for classroom study. This method requires sterilization, which can be achieved by heating agar in the Petri dish in a pressure cooker. However, interesting observations and conclusions may be drawn with the help of two or more potatoes. Sterilize by boiling a pair of Mason or screw-top jars big enough to accommo-

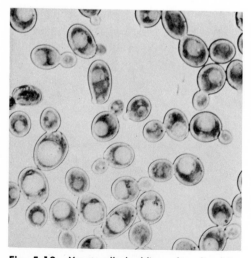

Fig. 5-13 Yeast cells budding after dissolving and standing in warm sugar water. The cells are usually colorless. (Dr. Dan O. McClary, Southern Illinois University.)

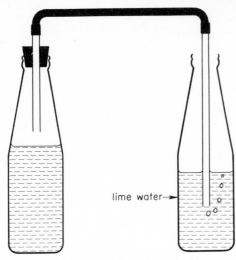

Fig. 5-14 Test for carbon dioxide.

lime water→

lumps or nodules on the roots of any leguminous plants such as clover, alfalfa, peas.

Recall the discovery of the wonder-plant *penicillium* and the related molds in the cure of disease. Some of the large insurance companies have developed much interesting and helpful material for school use.

INSIDE OF YOU

The study of bacteria may lead the children to want to know more about themselves. A safe, readily available source of body cells is the cheek lining of the mouth. Rub inside the cheek with the tip of a sterile tongue depressor available from the school nurse. Wipe the tip of the tongue depressor against the center of the glass slide. Use a medicine dropper to stain the slide with iodine dissolved in water. Under the microscope you should be able to see irregularly pentagonal-shaped cells (Fig. 5-15).

Through the school doctor or nurse you may be able to secure a blood smear slide. Stained with Wright's stain, it should show the small circular red cells and the larger white cells or disease fighters (Fig. 5-16). These latter stain purple. Unstained smears show only red cells. If it is possible to have slides made of the chil-

date the potatoes. Select or have the children elect two children, one with very clean hands and fingernails, and the other with dirty hands and fingernails. The student with clean hands must not touch even the door knob until the potatoes have been peeled and placed inside the jars with covers sealed. Place both jars in a warm dark place and observe daily. A third grade teacher who was having great difficulty motivating hand-washing before lunch, found this experiment most helpful. The potato peeled by the more casual contestant grew such a mass of mold and bacteria colonies, that a near-stampede to the lavatory for hand-washing ensued. Try also laying a hair on a slice of potato or letting a fly walk over the potato.

Your school doctor or nurse may be able to secure and project for the children some slides of common disease bacteria.[1]

Lest children be left with the notion that all bacteria are harmful, you will want them to look through the microscope at the amazing nitrogen-fixing bacteria which you can find in the small

[1] E. Morholt, P. Brandwein, A. Joseph, *A Sourcebook for the Biological Sciences,* Harcourt, Brace & World, 1958, pp. 380–81.

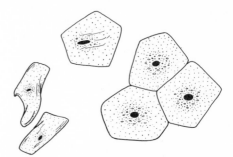

Fig. 5-15 Epithelial cells from the cheek lining of the mouth. This layer of inner and outer body covering tissue is called the *epithelium*. (From E. Morholt et al., *A Sourcebook for the Biological Sciences,* Harcourt, Brace & World, 1958.)

dren's own blood, it is important to have parents' consent before the school doctor or nurse can collect the necessary drop of blood. It is illegal and unsafe for children to prick their own fingers for the required blood sample.

A sample of dried skin such as that which peels after sunburn shows under magnification the cubical-shaped cells (Fig. 5-17) of the human skin.

GOLDFISH "X-RAY"

It is a thrilling experience for children to observe circulating blood and living cells in the tail of a goldfish. This can be done without injuring the fish in any way. Wrap your pet in wet cotton and place him in shallow water in a glass or plastic saucer (Fig. 5-18). Focus the microscope on the tail, which is outside the cotton wrappings. You should be able to see the many criss-crossed tiny tubes or blood capillaries. Some of the red corpuscles coursing through the blood vessels will move in one direction, some in another. Because the microscope lens reverses everything (see Chapter 16), the blood that seems to move away from the tail is really moving toward it. This is arterial

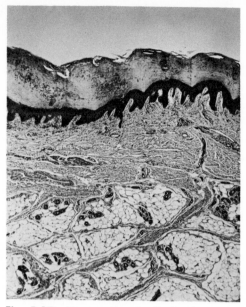

Fig. 5-17 Human skin: detail of cubical cells from outermost layer.

blood coming from the heart. Blood moving in the opposite direction is traveling through veins back to the heart.

INVISIBLE AQUARIUM ANIMALS

Most balanced aquariums contain microscopic one-celled animals, called protozoans, and often more complex forms, such as the hydra (Fig. 5-19A). The ani-

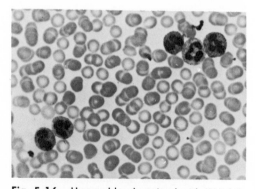

Fig. 5-16 Human blood, stained with Wright's stain. The many small circular bodies are red cells; the five large dark bodies with complex nuclei are white cells; the three small dark bodies are clusters of blood platelets. (General Biological Supply House, Chicago.)

wet cotton to keep goldfish alive

Fig. 5-18 Observation of blood circulation in the capillaries of a goldfish tail.

COMMON PROTOZOANS

(a)

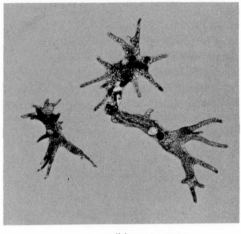

(b)

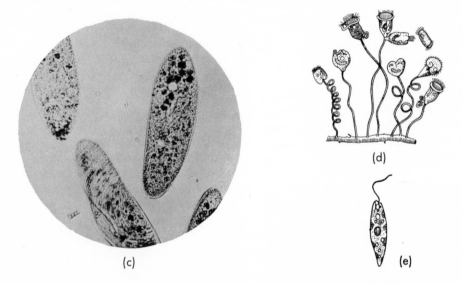

(c)

(d)

(e)

Fig. 5-19 (a) The hydra, a fresh-water relative of the jellyfish. (Bausch & Lomb Optical Co.) (b) Amoebae. Under the microscope an amoeba looks like a dab of jelly. Watch the margins bulge and the cytoplasm flow in that direction until the whole animal moves into the bulge. Amoebae "flow" around their food. They reproduce by dividing. (Carolina Biological Supply Co.) (c) Paramecia. The specimen of this common slipper-shaped protozoan in full view shows the two contracting vacuoles, one at either end of the body. Its whole body is covered with *cilia* which it uses for propulsion. (Bausch & Lomb Optical Co.) (d) The vorticella, first described nearly 300 years ago by the lens-maker Leeuwenhoek. You may find some in pond water or in a hay-infusion culture. (From G. Simpson et al., *Life*, Harcourt, Brace & World, 1957.) (e) The euglena, an organic puzzle claimed by both zoologists and botanists. It moves actively by lashing the whip-like *flagellum* appendage. (From G. Simpson et al., *Life*, Harcourt, Brace & World, 1957.)

mals are usually near the food which sinks to the bottom of the tank. Use a medicine dropper to bring up small samples of water from the bottom. A drop of this on a slide may show such protozoans as amoeba, paramecium, and vorticella (Fig. 5-19B, C, D), and such algae as spirogyra. The euglena (Fig. 5-19E), being a borderline case between plant and animal, is classified as both alga and protozoan.

RAISING YOUR OWN CIRCUS

A "hay infusion" culture usually provides an interesting crop of protozoans. If you use pond or spring water, the culture may also include some microscopic plants such as filamentous algae and diatoms.

Boil about a quart of water. As it comes to a boil, add a handful of Timothy hay and boil for 10 more minutes. Allow it to cool and add 5 grams of uncooked rice or wheat grains. Let stand undisturbed in semidarkness. At the end of a week you should see a dark area around the grains. With a medicine dropper suck up a drop of this to spread on a slide under the microscope. You may see such protozoans as

amoeba, euglena, volvox, and common algae such as spirogyra, cladophora, ulothrix, vaucheria.

To start other colonies, put rice grains in another jar of cool boiled water and add a dropper of solution from the bottom of the first jar. If pond water is available, compare the kinds of microscopic inhabitants with those from your hay infusion. Protozoan cultures are also available from biological supply houses (see appendix).

As in the study of bacteria and molds, part of your protozoan study may include but should not overemphasize the role of protozoans in disease.

MICROSCOPIC CRYSTALS

Whenever possible, draw parallels between the worlds of physical and biological science. For example, use the microscope to observe crystals from Epsom salts, table salt, or granulated sugar. Gradually add the salts to one half a glass of hot water until no more will dissolve. Dip a paint brush in the solution and "paint" a slide. Watch crystals form as the solution evaporates under the microscope.

CAPSULE LESSONS

5-1 Encourage children to look at many familiar objects under magnification. Newspaper, for example, looks very different as do various fabrics, pieces of wood, sugar, soda, etc.

5-2 Secure a mailing tube or construct a tube of thick paper which fits snugly around a hand lens. If you have a second hand glass the same size, cut a slot for the handle so you can slide it up and down until you can focus with magnification through the stationary glass. If the second glass is smaller, secure another tube to fit inside the first and move the tubes instead of the second glass.

5-3 If none of the children think of it, let them try using different lenses on a ruler. For

example, with a lens power of 8 a line ⅛" long will appear to be 1" long.

5-4 Let the children make fingerprints using thick washable paint. Another medium for fingerprinting is an ink pad, either the commercial kind or homemade from ink poured over layers of cotton. Let the children study these to decide in truth if everyone's print is different. Then study the pattern of skin on the fingers.

5-5 Study pictures in the newspaper under magnification. The children may be surprised to find they are composed of many dots. Encourage them to study newspaper and magazine photos in the same way. Some may make the analogy between printed photos made by spacing of dots and the same principle as it applies to television.

5-6 Secure a watch with a radiant dial. Let children carry it into a dark closet and examine under magnification. As soon as their eyes become accustomed to the dark, they should observe tiny flashes caused by the breakdown of the atoms of the radiant paint used to coat the watch dial. Each flash is an exploding atom. There is of course no danger to the children. Allow 10–20 minutes for eyes to become accustomed to the dark.

BIBLIOGRAPHY

Beeler, N. F., *Experiments in Optical Illusion,* Crowell, 1951. Middle. Fun and information on the way the eye works.

———, and F. M. Branley, *Experiments with Light,* Crowell, 1958. Upper. Experiments to explain characteristics of light and principles of optics in lenses, microscopes, and other optical instruments.

———, *Experiments with a Microscope,* Crowell, 1957. Upper. How to grow and study microorganisms. Structure and use of microscopes.

Cosgrove, Margaret, *Wonders Under a Microscope,* Dodd, Mead, 1959, Middle. How to use a microscope. What to look for and how to make and stain slides.

Hutchinson, William M., and Kathleen Henderson, *Book About Life Under the Microscope,* Maxton, 1959. Upper. Microorganisms in pond water. Methods of collection.

Lewis, Lucia Z., *First Book of Microbes,* Watts, 1955. Middle. Accurate, simple, interesting factual material.

Neurath, Marie, *Too Small to See,* Sterling, 1957. Primary. Everyday objects through a hand glass.

Perry, John, *Our Wonderful Eyes,* McGraw-Hill, 1955. Middle. Interesting information about light and seeing, together with eye structure and function.

Rogers, Frances, *Lens Magic,* Lippincott, 1957. Middle. Story of glass. History of scientists who experimented with microscopes and telescopes.

Schatz, Albert, and Sarah Riedman, *Story of Microbes,* Harper, 1952. Upper. Two microbiologists tell comprehensive story of role of microbes in everyday life. Several simple experiments.

Schwartz, Julius, *Through the Magnifying Glass,* McGraw-Hill, 1954. Middle and upper. Things to look at under magnification. Intriguing suggestions for further investigation.

Selsam, Millicent E., *Microbes at Work,* Morrow, 1953. Upper. The role of microorganisms in soil, food, and the body. Variety of experiments using household equipment.

Tannenbaum, Harold E., and Nathan Stillman, *We Read About Very Tiny Living Things (Microbes),* Webster, 1960. Well-illustrated pamphlet.

Yates, Raymond F., *Fun with Your Microscope,* Appleton, 1953. Upper. Excellent handbook for the "science-prone."

Plants in the classroom garden

Many teachers make a classroom more attractive by adding a few house plants. Even one plant might lead to a discussion as to why we think plants are beautiful. What if foliage were red instead of green? Why are plants green rather than some other color? Such questions lead directly into photosynthesis (pp. 47, 48, 55, 89) and into the study of light, color, and wave length (Chapter 16).

Plants also make a room more healthy and comfortable. For instance, in order to maintain a constant 50% humidity, 1 gallon of water should be evaporated into the average steam-heated classroom every day. The moisture and oxygen that plants give off in the classroom are worth the time and trouble involved in keeping plants.

THE TEACHER WITH THE GREEN THUMB

The knack of successful plant growing in school is not necessarily the hereditary possession of a favored few. Those who appear to have this knack will probably be observed to have an insatiable curiosity about plants and how they grow. And these green-thumbed folk appear to have also developed an acute awareness of the conditions that make plants "feel" like flourishing. For instance, they are quick to note that a plant "looks" dry before this lack becomes critical. Since plants are relatively slow to show the effect of neglect, one may fail to relate cause and effect.

Sunlight and temperature

One of the secrets of success with house plants at school is to select the kind of plants that fits your room climate and exposure. For example, geraniums, spring bulbs, and other flowering plants need a sunny window. African violets need a north or east exposure. Philodendrons and most of the shade lovers, which do well in a terrarium, also need a north or east window. For example, a first grade struggled for weeks with the problem of surplus algae in its aquarium. It finally became evident, by the process of scientific elimination, that the tank was placed where it got too much sun.

If a foot-candle meter is available through school health authorities, or a photo light meter through parents, the children who are planning with you for schoolroom plants will be astonished at the variation in light reading found in different parts of the room. Also note the variations at different times of the day. There is, of course, a correlation here with the study of seasons and latitudes (see Chapter 10).

Temperature is another variant in room climate which affects the choice of plants. Take temperature readings at various hours and in various parts of the room. As an extreme illustration, take simultaneous

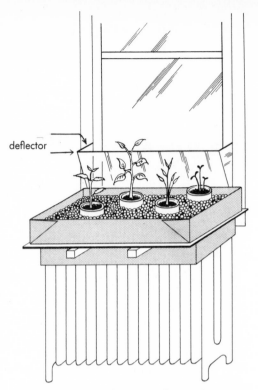

deflector

Fig. 6-1, 6-2 Radiators too frequently monopolize the only sunlit space for house plants. Here is one method for solving this problem.

can prove that more effective room ventilation is secured by opening windows at both top and bottom (see Chapter 14). When the windows are left open at the bottom, plants may be protected from cold air by plate glass or Plexiglas air deflectors (Fig. 6-1). In very cold weather, plants on the window sill may freeze at night unless insulated by newspapers placed between the plants and the window.

The drying effect of radiator air on plants may be counteracted, and room humidity thereby improved, by keeping the potted plants in a pebble tray. This may be made in the same manner as the tray for the pet cage (Chapter 2) from thin rust-resistant galvanized iron or from medium-weight sheet aluminum. Measure the window sill or other space where you plan to put the pebble tray and add 8–9″ to each dimension in order to have a tray about 4″ deep (Fig. 6-2). Bend up the edges with pliers or use a vise. Bend into a "pig's ear" (see Fig. 2-3) folded back to seal the corners. Hammer the folded edges flat with a wooden mallet or an ordinary hammer. If you wish, you may plan to place the pebble tray directly on top of a radiator if the latter has a flat metal cover or top. In this case, you can insulate from the heat by several layers of thin asbestos paper. For further insulation place a few sticks of wood, say about ¾″ square, to separate the metal bottom from the asbestos. Sprinkle a thin layer of pebbles on the bottom plus some charcoal that will absorb some of the acids produced by decaying organic matter in soil. Then set potted plants in place with the arrangement desired; fill in around them up to the level of the tray's top with small pebbles. Modern Vermiculite, a wall-insulating material available at building supply yards and florists, is lighter in weight and color than pebbles and can be used in their place. Sprinkle water on pebbles or other "filler"

readings from a pair of identical thermometers, one reading on the floor and one near the ceiling. Once you have information on your room's exposure, its average temperature, and average light intensity, the neighborhood florist or nurseryman should be able to help you make a wise selection of plants for your room. He will, in addition, be impressed with the scientific way you taught your children to go about solving this problem.

Window sills provide necessary sunlight for plants. However, they do impose rigorous climatic extremes on plants. In cold weather the plant is exposed both to blasts of cold air from an open window and to waves of hot dry air from radiators that are so often situated next to the window. A study of air in motion (see Chapter 9) until, by probing with finger tips, you can feel water up to about ½″ from the bottom. By capillary action (Chapter 11) the water rises around the pebbles so that the pots are always moist but not soggy. Do not water pots directly but carefully watch the level of the "water table" and the appearance and feel of soil in the pots. Keeping track of the amount of water needed and the variation in this amount depending on weather or season may be very useful in developing concepts necessary in a study of evaporation and humidity in relation to weather (Chapter 7). At the end of each school year, clean out your pebble tray and repaint it with metal paint so that it is ready for next season. Aluminum trays, of course, will not need painting.

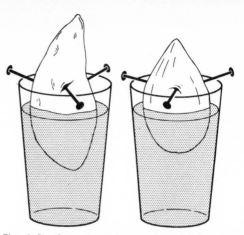

Fig. 6-3 Sprouting tubers and seeds. Ask children to consider reasons for partial, not total immersion.

Watering

In addition to correct exposure for the type of plant selected, our chief concern will be correct watering.

In general, in our superheated indoor winter temperatures, plants tend to dry out quickly. As in our gardens, plants should be watered thoroughly and then permitted to dry out before being watered again. By "drying out" is meant that the soil turns light brown and dry but not bone dry to the touch. The "feel" of soil is a better indicator than color. It should contain enough moisture to feel cool. If the plant is let go too long without water, the cells lose their normal turgidity or fullness and the plant looks ever so slightly limp. If allowed really to become limp, the plant, even if it does not succumb, will require days or even weeks to go through the process of sloughing off the damaged tissue and putting out new growth.

The usual method of watering plants from above is less adequate than "bottom watering." By this is meant setting the pots in a dishpan, pail, or other container deep enough to permit pots to be *nearly* (not totally) immersed in water. The soil surface and the rim of the pot should not be underwater. Within an hour or two, the plants soak up the water they need, and the soil looks and feels moist. The pots should then be removed and set in saucers.

If it is not possible to set pots in water, water from the top until water ceases to soak in. Of course, bottom watering is of no value except for plants in porous clay pots. Decorative china or glass pots should be used only as outside containers for porous pots. Silver and gold florists' foil should be removed from pots in order to let air get to the roots. Painting clay pots also destroys their porosity.

Bulbs and sweet potato or avocado may be forced in nonporous containers. However, the bulbs are imbedded in gravel, providing drainage. The sweet potato and avocado are suspended midway in water, either by the diameter of the container (Fig. 6-3) or by toothpicks or nails driven into the sides. Suspend the avocado seed broad end down. Rudimentary buds, nodes, or eyes indicate the end of the sweet potato that should be up. Set in the

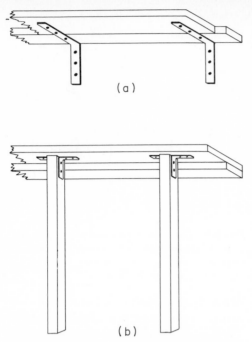

(a)

(b)

Fig. 6-4 Outdoor extension of window sill, construction detail. Drill drainage holes in the horizontal surface.

Perhaps the common black ants for whom green aphids serve as "cows" can be observed "milking" the aphids (Chapter 3).

Encourage the children to examine the undersides of leaves with a magnifying glass. Some plant pests are so minute that they multiply in force before they become noticeable. Your local florist or nurseryman will help you decide which pests are on your plants and what to do about them.

Remove dust from the leaves at least once a month. Dust and dirt clog the pores, or stomata, on the leaf surfaces. Chalk dust is particularly harmful. Use Kleenex or a soft small rag. Remove all dead foliage. It tends to harbor pests.

GARDEN ON THE WINDOW SILL

Once you have experienced some success keeping potted plants in the classroom, growing your own plants for instructional purposes will not be difficult. Let us suppose your current social studies unit might be enriched if the children could experience, on a small scale, some of the problems and practices of those who raise the food we eat.

Depending on the season and the daily temperature range, you may be able to utilize your outside window sills. If they are too narrow for seed beds, extend them by a simple plank shelf laid across strap iron braces attached to the building (Fig. 6-4A), or to a shelf driven flush against the wall, that nests on wooden legs (Fig. 6-4B).

Seed beds or flats such as those used by gardeners can be made from apple boxes. Cut down the boxes to a depth of 3″ to 4″, and tighten the corners with a few additional flat-headed nails. Drill a number of small holes in the bottom of the box. Good drainage may keep the box from rotting out the first season. Use a soil made up of equal parts of sand, loam, and leaf mold.

dark to stimulate root growth first. Keep water at original level.

Even with adequate "bottom watering" classroom plants do better with an occasional foliage bath. Once a month at least, take all the pots to the nearest sink where the foliage can be thoroughly rinsed off. A small shampoo shower head is excellent for this purpose. Plants in the pebble tray can be rinsed off on the spot, without moving them. A sweet potato vine grows much more luxuriantly if given a daily or bi-weekly shower. Such washing removes dust and tends to keep down infestations of red spider and the like. An infestation of aphids may be discouraged by a light soap spray. The soap bubbles literally suffocate the aphids. If it is ladybug season, preserve a few aphids alive so the children may have the chance to watch how quickly ladybugs can eradicate aphids in our gardens and backyards.

Planning for spring planting is a natural lead into weather study. Your children may first investigate what part of the school grounds is the warmest, which the coldest. They will begin to note newspaper records of daily temperatures and precipitation. If it is too early for flats outdoors and there is no place in the classroom or school building for flats, plant your seeds in cigar boxes, clay flower pots, or any waxed container such as those used for dairy products. The cigar box and waxed containers should have drainage holes punched in the bottom with an ice pick or other sharp tool. Do not use glass containers. Seeds planted in tin cans usually do not thrive: the soil is either dry or soggy unless one has punched drainage holes with a small nail. Try planting the same kind of seeds in two pots in soil which is kept dry, another pair in soil which is kept moist, and a third pair in soil which is kept soggy. Soggy soil keeps air from the seedlings while dry soil brings them no moisture. It may be necessary to let the seeds get started with normal good treatment before showing the effects of cutting off air or water supply.

What kind of soil?

The selection of the best soil should be based on tests of several kinds and mixtures of soil. Make test plantings of lima beans, radishes, oats, or other quick germinators, in soil samples from local sources. For example, test sand from the kindergarten sandbox, a nearby construction site, a fresh-water beach, or the school playground, or nearby topsoil from the school garden or a neighbor's garden or window box, or humus from beneath school scrubs or from the nearest woods. Test soil from the center of a lot as well as from its borders or hedgerows. If possible, secure from a nearby road-cut or excavation topsoil from the thin dark layer on top as well as from the sub-

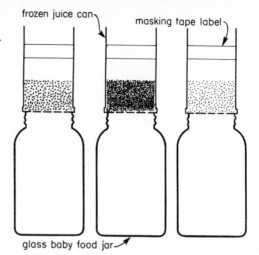

frozen juice can

masking tape label

glass baby food jar

Fig. 6-5 Method of testing soil samples for water-holding and runoff variations.

soil layer just below. Plant at least two containers of each soil sample. Label with wooden tongue depressors or ice cream sticks. Treat all samples strictly alike as to planting procedures, watering, etc. In the accompanying illustration we attempt to show general techniques for planting in clay pots. These are applicable to any other containers. The children may notice that water runs very quickly through sand whereas clay tends to hold moisture almost too well. The children may then set up experiments (Fig. 6-5) to discover the water-retaining capacity of various soil samples. Another way to compare soil properties is to roll small amounts of different soil in squares of paper. Let dry and examine for consistency, hardness, and friability (see Cornell Rural School Leaflet *Underfoot*, Vol. 49, No. 4, Spring, 1956).

The standard greenhouse potting mixture consists of equal parts of sand, loam, and leaf mold or peat. Your soil experiments are apt to approach a rough approximation of this. If there is a real difference, encourage your children to follow the evidence of their experiments. In the first place, you are more concerned

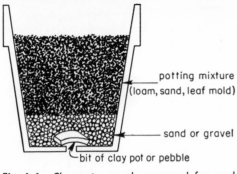

potting mixture
(loam, sand, leaf mold)

sand or gravel

bit of clay pot or pebble

Fig 6-6 Clay pot properly prepared for seed planting.

to teach children the value of acting on evidence than to have them memorize standard potting mixtures. Secondly, there may be some elements in your local soils that would account for the discrepancies.

Seed planting

A successful seed planting experiment may depend upon several individually minor factors. For one thing, clay pots should always be soaked in water just before use. Otherwise they draw moisture out of the soil and away from the seeds. Enough water should be kneaded or worked into the soil for planting to form a soft (not muddy) ball which holds its shape in the palm after you open your hand. The pot or container should be nearly filled with soil and then tapped on the bottom until the soil particles settle to within about 1″ of the top (Fig. 6-6). Spread seeds on top of the soil. Too many induce rot. Too few do not allow for "duds" or casualties. Cover with ½–¾″ soil and firm with bottom of milk bottle, orange juice can, or the like. Small fingers are apt to compact the soil too firmly about the seeds. On the other hand, soil which is too loose and full of air spaces allows sprouting seeds to dry too quickly.

Placing a pane of glass or bit of Saran Wrap on top of the seed containers produces a miniature hotbed which keeps seeds warm and moist until they have pushed up through the ground. Some cover seeds with a light cloth or board which is removed as soon as the plants are up.

Small seeds and baby plants may be washed out of the ground by overzealous watering. It is advisable to employ "bottom-watering" techniques or to sprinkle lightly with a toy watering can or a rubber squeeze sprinkler.

In many states seeds are available to schools free or in penny packages. The directions on the packages often constitute quite a reading lesson in themselves. Many include maps of the United States showing when to plant in various sections. Most quality seeds guarantee a high percentage of germination. This, too, is stated on the seed packet and may furnish an incidental lesson in percentage. Follow planting directions carefully. Use quick germinators such as beans, corn, and radishes. Very small seeds are hard for children to handle. Wheat and oats will grow well on your window sill "farm" especially if a little clay (even art clay) is added and well mixed in. A little clay helps soil hold water. As an indoor control, try sprouting seeds on a plastic sponge set in a saucer of water. Try any of the above-mentioned seeds, mixed bird seed, or some chick feed (whole, not ground). Of course, once the seeds have sprouted, they will have to be transplanted into earth if you want to keep the seedlings alive. A pleasant outdoor activity can be the transplanting of sunflowers to borders of playgrounds or home yards to feed birds in the fall and winter.

Seeds sown in flats can be handled much the same way as those in pots. However, they will be firmed into the soil with a ruler or flat stick. Rows should be marked and labeled. Watering will have to be from above. It is better to water thoroughly every 2 or 3 days than a little every day. Frequent light sprinkling tends to draw moisture out of the ground by capillary attraction (see Chapter 11). This fact is one of the reasons the farmer cultivates lightly and not deeply in warm weather. Compacted soil loses its moisture much faster than soil whose top layer is loose or mulched. Illustrate this in miniature with sugar lumps, powdered sugar, and food coloring. The liquid immediately moves up through the lump by capillary attraction from one particle to another. Scatter a little powdered sugar on top of the lump. The liquid will not pass through it.

Cultivate your window sill farm in order to keep down weeds and retain subsoil moisture. Use toy hoes or rakes but dig lightly and well away from roots of seedlings. You have probably planted with a plan of periodic thinning which would allow the children to observe the development of the root system in their crop. Note how in some plants (e.g., alfalfa) the root system may be much longer than the plant is tall. Thin one plant for every two children so they can observe closely with magnifying glasses. If you secure some discarded lenses used to correct farsightedness, you can have the fun of making your own magnifying lenses (see Chapter 5). Help the children see the tiny root hairs which really do the work of absorbing water and minerals from the soil into the plant. The root proper functions as a passageway or pipeline and as an anchor for the plant.

Children may see the progressive development of a plant by planting bean or corn seeds every 2 or 3 days for 2 weeks. After this time they uproot the plants and lay them out in order of development. This method, of course, does not lend itself to an activity involving all the children looking at something at the same time.

Annual flowers may be grown from seed in your farm on the window sill. But for rapid blooming, it is probably worth the expense to get seedlings and transplant them.

Once a season you may wish to add a small amount of lime. Sprinkle lightly and water in. The soil will bubble if too much lime is present. You may desire at this time to show children how to test for lime with vinegar or dilute acetic acid. Most chalk dust will bubble vigorously with the application of vinegar. Perhaps you can secure a clean chicken bone and set aside well covered with vinegar. As the vinegar dissolves the lime, the bone should become rubbery (several days). This experiment helps children realize the importance of lime in our diet for bone building and teeth.

A PIECE OF THE FOREST FLOOR

A moist woodland terrarium provides a comfortable habitat for small snakes, frogs, toads, toy turtles, and salamanders or newts. Large specimens will disarrange and tramp down the miniature landscape in your terrarium. If your children ask, "What is a terrarium?," you can show them that it is a container for land-dwelling plant and animal life, just as an aquarium is for water life. A terrarium may be set up in a gallon pickle jar (wide-mouthed), a leaky aquarium, or a glass box especially constructed for the purpose. A glass globe tends to distort the interior view, and holds very little as well.

Desert or marsh terrarium

The children may also wish to construct a desert terrarium and a marsh terrarium. The techniques are much the same, except that for your desert you will select miniature cactuses and other thick-leaved plants which are planted in sand or sandy loam and seldom watered to prevent their

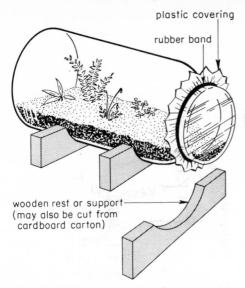

plastic covering

rubber band

wooden rest or support
(may also be cut from
cardboard carton)

Fig. 6-7 Pickle-jar terrarium. One enterprising teacher taped a lens from an old hand glass to the mouth of the jar in place of a plastic cover.

Leave some to spread and eventually hide your "robbery." In your backyard there may be tiny ferns, baby tears, wandering Jew, or other shade lovers. Of course, the local florist or dime store will have an assortment of small plants in pots. Miniature ivy and the philodendrons are the safest investment. Buy only the smallest pots.

Having collected plants for your terrarium, you will need a small amount of woodland soil or leaf mold, some sand for drainage, and a few pieces of charcoal to go in the bottom. Beginners tend to use too much soil, making the terrarium too heavy and leaving too little room for plants. Use only enough to imbed your plants and cover their roots. The soil should be moistened before being spread in your container. In larger containers, contour the soil into a miniature hill. To save weight, use an aluminum foil pie plate to form a hollow core for the hill.

If you have bought potted plants, remove from pots by inverting with two fingers around stem of plant. Tap rim of pot to loosen soil and plant should slide out. If necessary push from bottom through drainage hole. Handle carefully to keep soil as intact as possible around roots. Set plants around on top of the soil to secure the best arrangement. If you use moss, plant some with the green side out. Meanwhile imbed a container for water, level with the soil base. A glass custard cup is about the right size lake for your miniature landscape. Now you are ready to set in the plants, covering roots completely and firming in place. Remove any bruised or broken leaves, trimming off with scissors to make a clean cut. Wipe the inside of the glass clean with paper toweling. Wet down with a sprinkler and close jar mouth with Saran Wrap or other transparent pliofilm. Discard the metal cover. It will rust and is not transparent.

growing too large for the container. In this case, do not cover the mouth of the jar except with screening to keep in desert visitors such as a horned toad or lizard. Botanical gardens sell miniature desert plants that can survive even on a radiator.

The marsh terrarium should contain such typical wet-foot plants as sphagnum, sedges, pitcher plants, and the like. You will need a watertight container if you build on an incline with a space for water at the end (see Fig. 6-9) for your amphibian guests.

Making a pickle-jar terrarium

The pickle jar, though soon too small for many plants, makes a sturdy terrarium. It will need a simple wooden or cardboard box cradle (Fig. 6-7) or plaster of Paris base to keep it from rolling. If you have access to a woodland, look for small, compact, shade-loving plants such as moss, ferns, wintergreen, and liverworts. Dig them up with an old knife or trowel in order to get some soil with them. Take no more than one from each group of plants.

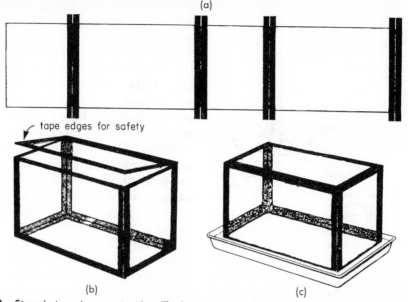

(a)

tape edges for safety

(b)   (c)

Fig. 6-8 Steps in terrarium construction. The bottom is taped on after the sides are taped and set up. The top is taped all around and rests on the sides. (From G. Blough and M. Campbell, *Making and Using Classroom Science Materials in the Elementary School*, Holt, Rinehart and Winston, 1954.)

After its initial "baptism" a terrarium should never have to be watered. Moisture evaporating from the plants and the water dish will condense on the glass inside and precipitate, a perfect example of the water cycle which takes place in nature. The first day or two, the terrarium will be so foggy or dewy one can scarcely see inside. Remove the cover and wipe the inside of the glass with paper toweling. Repeat when necessary, especially the "window washing." In proportion as you remove moisture, you may need to refill the water dish at long intervals. Be sure to remove moldy plants and to keep the glass clean. Succulents such as the sedums, ice plant, and the like will mold in a moist woodland terrarium. Use them in a desert terrarium for contrasting environments.

Glass-box terrarium

One can construct a larger though inexpensive terrarium from window glass for the sides, top, and bottom, from a cake or cookie baking sheet as a base, and from adhesive tape to bind the glass edges together (Fig. 6-8).

Measuring carefully and allowing for the thickness of the glass at the corners, one may find that standard window glass (four rectangular sheets for top, bottom, and two sides and two square sheets for the ends) will not fit a standard cake or cookie tin. One may then make a tray from a sheet of medium gauge aluminum. This should be at least 2½" larger all around than the bottom glass to allow for the sides of the tray which will be made by bending the edges up.

Or one can have a hardware store cut the glass to order, to fit the cake tin. Again, remember to allow for the thickness of the glass in over-all measurements. The cake tin must be painted to prevent rusting. Smooth the edges of the glass with emery paper. Sandpaper does nearly as well. Have on hand two rolls of 1½" colored adhesive tape such as the Mystik brand. This tape should last several years.

Spread the glass sides and ends on a

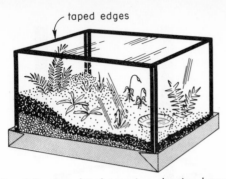

taped edges

Fig. 6-9 Completed terrarium showing home-made metal base, contouring, planting, and water dish.

work table. Cut a piece of tape which will extend about 1½″ beyond each side of the glass. Then apply tape to a little less than half its width, about ⅝″, and with 1½″ extending beyond glass at each end of the tape. Lay the adjoining piece of glass on the other half of the tape, but allow about ⅛″ space between two sheets of glass. This permits sheets to be set up at right angles to each other. Split the overhanging ends of tape and press to glass in order to provide a free-moving corner joint. Only half the width of tape attached to the first piece of glass is fastened down. The outside half is left free for the outer edge of the last sheet. When ready to attach these two, set up the four pieces so they make a hollow square.

To attach the bottom, cut four tapes, each extending well beyond the width or length of the glass, as was done for the sides. Again, use half the width of the tape pressed to the bottom glass. Use the other half to bind the bottom to the side. Lap at the corners. Repeat this for each edge and corner of the bottom. The terrarium is now complete except for the cover or top. This should be bound on all four edges with tape. Bind top edge of sides and ends also. Such binding makes it safer to work around the terrarium and makes the cover just enough bigger to fit better and to prevent it from falling in.

No, don't worry about enough air in the terrarium. Remember, plants give off oxygen, plenty for the few creatures you may wish to keep in the terrarium. Set the completed glass box into a close-fitting aluminum tray or tin cookie sheet (Fig. 6-9).

Plant as you did the pickle-jar terrarium. The water dish should be larger. A lightweight aluminum foil pie plate can be bent to fit into the corner. You may wish to add a bit of lichen-covered bark or rotting wood to please your salamander guests. Frogs and toads like to sit on a cool smooth stone. Snakes like to run against bark or climb on twigs.

A moist woodland terrarium provides a most comfortable environment for members of the amphibian group. However, they will starve if they have no live food. Sweep an insect net through the grass or weeds outdoors or set a fly trap indoors. Do not put snails in a terrarium. They will chew your plants to pieces. It is better to keep them separate in a quart jar "snailery." For more about food for animals see Chapter 2.

Many children can make a pickle-jar terrarium, either individually or in teams. For the larger glass terrarium just described, the teacher can divide the children into committees for Materials, Construction, Planting, Care, and the like.

PLANTS AS LIVING THINGS

If we have encouraged you to grow plants in your classroom, we would now like to urge you to consider further experiments to help children understand and appreciate plants. Many children and even adults do not think of plants as living things that must face the problems faced by all living things. It is important for children to learn that ultimately all animal life depends upon plants; that even man, no matter how clever he is, cannot yet achieve what the lowliest dandelion does every sunny day— make its own food.

What is a plant?

Take your children to the nearest vacant lot or weed patch and ask them to show you a plant. They will point to several, in the commonly accepted sense of the word. Shake your head and say nothing, even if they pick some and hold them up for you to see. Wait until some enterprising youngster pulls up an entire plant —root, stem, and some soil still clinging to the roots. A plant, of course, is a complete organism when it is part of its environment, which includes soil. When removed from this environment, it is no longer a total organism and usually does not survive.

With this introduction you are now ready to consider the various parts of a plant and the functions of each.

From the ground up

Most children and many adults do not realize that plants never become confused as to which way is up or which is down. Roots always respond positively to the pull of gravity by growing down.

In order to watch this process, line the sides of six tumblers or plastic containers with blotting paper. You may wish to fill

Fig. 6-11 Even seeds react to the force of gravity, roots always sprouting downward, and leaves and stems upward.

the centers with peat, cotton, sawdust, or the like. However, this is not essential. Push some bean, radish, or corn seeds between the glass and the blotter about an inch apart. Keep a small amount of water in the bottom of each tumbler. As soon as the seeds begin to sprout and roots and stems show, set two tumblers on their sides; invert two more which you have taped or done up with rags or screening to keep the contents from falling out. Compare the roots in a few days; then return one of each experimental pair to the control or normal position. In a few days, again note direction of root growth. Try the same experiment with three medium-sized potted geranium plants (Fig. 6-10). Here you will see stems responding negatively to gravity, i.e., growing away from its pull.

A third experiment that illustrates this principle of geotropism in plants requires two squares or panes of glass the same size, some damp cotton or blotters, and fast-germinating seeds. Lay glass on work table, cover with blotters or cotton, and then place seeds about an inch apart on the blotter. Cover with the second glass square and tape together. Set on edge in ½–1″ of water in a glass casserole or other container (Fig. 6-11). As soon as the roots show, give your glass "sandwich" a quarter turn and watch the roots respond. Return to the original position in 3 or 4

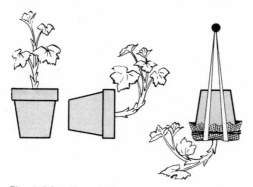

Fig. 6-10 Plants insist on growing upward! The experiment illustrated uses geraniums.

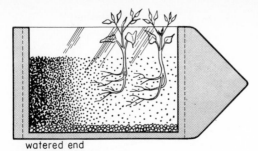

watered end

Fig. 6-12 An illustration of how plants reach for water.

days and watch the roots reverse themselves.

Plants look for water

Cut two adjacent sides from a half-gallon milk carton. Lay the carton on one of its remaining sides. Slip in glass windowpane to replace one side (Fig. 6-12). Punch a few small drainage holes in the bottom with an ice pick, and spread a thin layer of sand and/or gravel in the bottom. Fill three quarters full of potting soil. Plant seeds in one end where the roots will grow close to the glass. As soon as seeds have sprouted, water only in end of the box opposite seeds. Covering the glass with dark paper will stimulate root growth. Watch how roots grow toward water.

Construct another milk carton seed box with a glass front. This time imbed a small empty flower pot in the soil in the center of the container (Fig. 6-13). The pot should be unpainted, and the bottom drainage hole should be corked. Keep the pot partly full of water. Plant seeds at both ends of the container close to the glass. The roots will grow toward the water source in the middle.

How thirsty are plants? Here is one way to measure the amount of water used by a plant such as philodendron, which will grow in water. Use a glass container to show water level. Insert the plant's stem. Mark the water level each day with wax crayon on the outside of the container. Prevent evaporation from the water surface by sealing the top of the container with foil and a rubber band. Press the foil tightly about the plant's stem. Some children may wish to set up a more scientific apparatus for measuring water loss in plants. Help them to secure a small funnel, some rubber tubing, a plastic or glass drinking tube, and some aluminum foil, paraffin, or chewing gum. Connect the funnel and one end of the drinking tube by means of rubber tubing. Seal the geranium cutting into the other end of the tube with chewing gum or soft wax (Fig. 6-14). Add water daily by means of the funnel. Measure and record the amount necessary to maintain the water level in the tube.

The root

Remove some seedlings from your glass "sandwich" or tumbler garden. Look closely at the roots. Even without a magnifying glass or low-power microscope, you can see the tiny root hairs on the roots. These, rather than the roots, do the work of bringing water and minerals out of the soil into the plant. Replant your seedlings, stripping the root hairs from some and handling others as carefully as possible. In most transplanting, root hairs are destroyed and later replaced by new ones. However, we try to destroy as few as possible to minimize the shock to the plant.

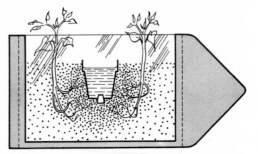

Fig. 6-13 Another example of water-seeking in plants.

To illustrate the effects of careless transplanting, select six seedlings from among those planted in soil. Pull up two rather carelessly and replant in soil. Using a trowel, spoon, or putty knife, dig up two more, trying to disturb soil around roots as little as possible. Transplant carefully. Leave two plants undisturbed. Compare growth of the three sets.

There are two schools of thought on watering transplants. You may wish to try both methods and decide for yourself. In the first method you transplant seedlings into holes prepared for them, fill with soil, and then fill with water. In the second method you fill holes with water, then put in plants, and then fill around roots with soil. Either way requires firming seedlings in place with your hands.

Roots, like icebergs, are often more extensive below than what we see above the surface. Alfalfa roots have been known to go down 300′ in dry soil. Try digging up some weeds and examining the root system as compared to the part above ground. The roots of any leguminous plants (alfalfa, clover, lespedeza, etc.) will show very small knobs or nodules. These contain nitrogen-fixing bacteria which can take nitrogen out of the air and make it available to the plant. Without heat or noise, these tiny organisms can accomplish what it takes many hundred kilowatts of electricity to accomplish at huge power plants. Try planting seeds in soil in which you have mixed some of these nodules. Compare with seed growth in control pots of soil to which you have not added these nitrifying agents.

Roots, of course, provide a passageway for water and minerals to move up into the plants. Encourage children to look for the bundle of stringy conducting tissue in the center of mature root vegetables such as parsnips and beets (Fig. 5-9).

Roots also have an important function in anchoring the plant in place. Help chil-

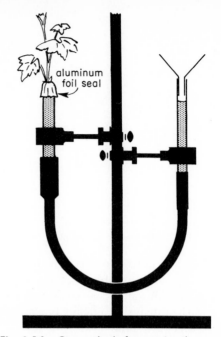

Fig. 6-14   One method of measuring the amount of water used by plants. This experiment uses a geranium cutting.

dren to see how firmly some weeds are held in place by their root system, and why other kinds are easy to uproot. Help them to notice how trees with shallow root systems, such as the black acacia, are among the first to go over in a wind.

If any children return from a trip to the mountain with specimens of lichen-covered rock, show that plants are not as weak as they look. Except for winter frost, which cracks and splits big rocks into smaller ones, there would be little soil formation on the mountains, if it were not for lichens. These, the first plants to gain a foothold on rock, combine carbon dioxide from air and moisture from the plant to form weak carbonic acid that very slowly disintegrates the rocky host. At this point, you may demonstrate how acid can disintegrate rock. Pour vinegar on soft limestone or chalk. The resulting bubbles are formed by carbon dioxide released from the limestone or chalk by vinegar. The

Fig. 6-15   Sweet potato plant.

children also need to observe the force of water expanding as it freezes. Fill a screw-top bottle with water, close cover securely, and refrigerate inside a heavy bag or box (to restrict glass splinters).

Gardens from roots.   Although Irish potatoes are really underground stems, the sweet potato is a root. Many teachers grow a luxuriant, attractive room plant from a sweet potato. Select one which will be only partly submerged in water. If the container is too wide, keep the potato partly out of water with toothpick skewers (Fig. 6–15). Place the pointed end in water and keep in the dark until roots are well developed. Keeping the potato in a warm place (e.g., the top of a hot-

water boiler) at home and daily sprinkling of the part out of water will hasten plant development.

Try cutting down an inch or two from the tops of such root vegetables as beets, carrots, turnips, onions, and parsnips. Trim back any foliage, being careful not to injure new central growth. Imbed these tops in gravel or Vermiculite in a shallow dish. Water should come up only part way. Attractive green sprouts will soon emerge (Fig. 6-16).

Make a carrot basket by hollowing out the center of a large fleshy carrot from the top down. Tie up with strings (Fig. 6-17) and fill with water. If roots sprout from your "basket," you may eventually wish to transplant it into soil.

Why stems?

Most children soon realize that roots and leaves are necessary to a plant. The purpose of plant stems is less obvious. Ask the children to suggest what functions some might have, and write these on the

note water level

Fig. 6-16   Winter greenery. Let children try a variety of vegetables, even some you know will not sprout. We eat, as vegetables, plants which store food in roots, leaf bases, and underground stems.

Fig. 6-17   Food stored in the fleshy lower stem of a carrot may even in mid-air produce root sprouts.

blackboard or chart for reference. Ask for ways of verifying the suggestions. If children suggest that stems provide pipelines for food and water, test this view by the following experiment.

Patriotic celery.   Secure stalks with leaves turning yellow. Place one in clear water, one in red ink or food color solution, and one in blue; leave in bright sunshine for a few hours. You should note some change in the leaves. Also use lettuce leaves. A cut across a piece of celery left in solution should reveal that celery "strings" are really the "pipes" or conducting tissue. Repeat your first experiment but use one stalk of celery split three ways and straddling all three solutions (Fig. 6-18). Try the same methods with white carnations. Using celery or carnations and one color solution, cut one stalk at right angles and one obliquely. Observe which transports liquids most quickly. Freshly cut stems provide better conduction than dry and partially sealed cuts. An oblique cut provides more absorptive surface. Apply conclusions to care of cut flowers at home.

If you have access to jewelweed (*Impatiens*), the fresh-water, stream-side plant, hold it up against the light and note the fibrovascular bundles or plant pipelines in the stem.

Trees and stems.   Watching trees sway in the wind, children may need your help to realize that trees are big plants and that the trunk must carry water and minerals to the top as well as bear the great weight of the branches. Little children enjoy the dramatic play of simulating with upraised arms the shapes of trees and their motions in the wind.

Trees have bark to protect themselves since they cannot run away or fight, as do animals. Like trees, plants with tough stems are often perennials, rather than annuals which live but a season. Perhaps the consideration of plant stems may lead

Fig. 6-18   Celery stalk split to stand in three colored solutions. The colored solutions travel up through the xylem cells (see Fig. 5-9). This experiment should be done first with a single stalk of celery and a single color, then three as shown.

to thinking about tree rings. The trunk of a discarded Christmas tree may be cross-sectioned very quickly with a hand saw, and thereby provides arithmetic counters as well as examples of tree rings. If it is possible to examine fish scales under low-power magnification, the children may see the analogy between trees and other living organisms. A pet turtle shows growth rings in each individual scale, particularly along the margins of its back.

Stems support leaves.   The second major function of plant stems is to hold the leaves up to the light in order for the process of photosynthesis or food-making to take place in the leaf. On class trips to a nearby weed patch, compare the display possibilities of weeds with tall stems and those without stems. Notice how low-growing plants often have developed a rosette arrangement of the leaves to permit maximum exposure to light. Look carefully at a shrub or small tree and see how few leaves are shaded by the others. Look at the way leaves grow on a stem, either in opposite or alternate whorls, not haphazardly, but in an arrangement that provides the greatest amount of light for each leaf.

THE BUSINESS OF PLANTS

Any discussion of where our food comes from soon leads children to realize that the whole of our daily diet (except salt and water) comes directly or indirectly from plants. A social studies unit on the grocery store can be enriched by a bulletin board plant. In a study of nutrition, we pinned up a stylized plant cut out of construction paper—the roots blue, the stem red, the two or three leaves green, and the conventional five-petaled flower yellow. The children enjoyed adding colored cutouts of foods derived from roots, from vegetable stems, and so on. The same method might be applied to uses of plants in construction, as for example, in a social studies unit on lumbering. A 3-D bulletin board might effectively illustrate the "Garden in the Grocery Store," the "Garden in the Dry Goods Store," and other activities.

PLANTS IN THE FALL

In most sections of the country there are some activities in relation to plant study that are more easily motivated in fall than at other seasons. In some areas early September days at school may be quite warm. School may seem all the more confining to children who have had three months of freedom. Outdoor tree study may therefore provide some release

for youngsters in addition to educating them.

Tree study

Even if you do not know the names of trees around the school, your custodian or principal may be able to help you name a few. Bring in one leaf each from five to ten selected trees, and ask teams of two to three children to find the tree from which each leaf was picked. When everyone has located and matched his leaves, the class makes the rounds together to give each team a chance to prove their "match" and tell anything more about their tree. Such a tree-matching game would, of course, be limited to the school grounds or some small area where children could be supervised and safe from traffic hazards.

Another day you might reinforce the tree-matching activity by introducing children to the joys of making blueprints (see Chapter 12) of a tree leaf which they can identify. Spatter-printing is also an enjoyable way of becoming familiar with tree leaves.

As your children learn to know the trees around school, they may wish to make a plant map of the school grounds. This might lead to suggestions for further planting, especially for a mulberry tree to provide food for silkworms in spring. In the East, fall is a very good time for transplanting trees and shrubs. The Audubon Society, 1130 Fifth Ave., New York City, has lists of shrubs and trees containing fruits attractive to wild birds.

Another way of learning about trees is to make sketches of them. The district art supervisor will suggest simple techniques for drawing trees—from the bottom up or the top down. Some preliminary classroom practice will enable children to draw recognizable trees. On the first day of Indian summer weather they will be prepared to go outdoors to sketch trees. Date the sketches and keep them for comparison with sketches to be made in winter or spring.

Autumn colors

In those parts of the country where autumn is announced with a defiant splash of colored leaves, children and adults alike become very conscious of tree leaves. With the least encouragement you will have enough for a fine display. Some of the leaves may be preserved for a time by coating with wax. Iron the leaves between two layers of wax paper covered with newspaper to absorb excess wax. Or dip the leaves in melted paraffin (not hot). One method that permits immediate mounting on tagboard is to dip the leaf in glue.

At the end of each leaf stock (petiole) notice the corky layer that has formed to seal off the leaf from the parent tree. You should be able to see the knobby scars of the food and water "pipes" or bundle scars. These too have been sealed off to help the leaves fall in autumn.

After the leaves are off, it is easier to find abandoned bird nests, hornet nests, and other insect homes. The children may enjoy taking a bird nest apart and listing the "contents." A third grade listed nearly 300 separate items, including a dollar bill in one phoebe's nest. Do not take a hornet nest apart indoors. The warmth may cause some of the larvae to hatch!

Discuss what would happen if leaves did not fall. Share experiences about the weight of snow. What would snow do to leaves? Could deciduous trees bear the weight of snow if they kept their leaves? Notice how rigid and often upturned are the branches of most deciduous trees. Observe how Christmas tree branches are more often horizontal and can bend without breaking.

The inaccessibility of water—one fun-damental reason for leaf fall—can be illustrated by simple demonstrations that also show how plants maintain humidity in the air. Secure two geranium plants about the same size, and envelop the foliage of each in a cellophane vegetable bag. Place one plant on a sunny window sill, but keep the second away from the sunshine. If the children think that the moisture which collects in the first bag comes from soil, repeat, covering the soil with a circle of cardboard or plastic. Repeat the next day and add a pot of soil in which you have stuck a dead branch. Cover this with a cellophane bag and place in the sunshine. Because the branch is not living, no transpiration of water will take place. Freeze some soil in the refrigerator to show the children how winter locks water away from plants.

SEEDS IN SEASON

As seed planting comes with spring, so seed gathering comes with fall. One might plan with the children a display of seeds from the grocery store or seeds from the pet store. Fall is the season for collecting wild seeds such as burdock or sticktight seeds. Encourage children to collect as many kinds as possible. Dragging a cloth through a weed patch collects quite a few seeds. Store in cellophane bags with available data on location, general description of plant, and possible identification. Although you have already considered the problem of organization and arrangement, you will wisely not vouchsafe any suggestions until the children themselves see the need of sorting seeds, for example, according to ways seeds travel—by air, water, wind, animals, gravity, etc. The peripatetic habits of western tumbleweed, for example, make it of greater interest and value to cattlemen than to songwriters. Draw analogies between fliers' parachutes and the mechanics of such airborne cargo as dandelion seeds. Notice how maple seeds whirl earthward like the blade of a helicopter. The air propulsion material that causes the "itching powder" in sycamore balls should be examined and discussed. The number of seeds in a ball might be estimated and then counted. There are many seed pods which, like sycamore, illustrate the principle of plant "insurance."

Call the children's attention to the economy of arrangement and beauty of design of seeds in a milkweed or jacaranda (subtropical tree) pod. Note the elastic attachment of seeds in the magnolia "cone" which lengthens as the seed ripens and permits it to swing and scatter further from the parent tree.

Evergreens

The season's green evergreen cones may be brought in to dry and allow the seeds to drop out. Observe the wing on each seed and the "nest" or special place for each seed on the bract scales. Point out the naked seeds typical of cone-bearing trees. Help children draw a comparison with the covered seeds of other plants. Children who have visited the Rockies may have seen the heaps of pine cone bracts or scales discarded by Douglas squirrels harvesting cones. The chickaree (squirrel) buries its green cones in these damp "silos" which keep the seeds from falling out until it is ready to eat them.

Most evergreen cones take on a polished appearance if one places the dry, open cones in a very slow oven. Place on newspaper to catch excess pitch. The consequent polished look is due to the resin being brought to the surface by heat.

Christmas season is timely for securing samples of different kinds of evergreens. Help children realize that needles are really leaves and how evergreens are able to keep their leaves. The Garden Club of America, 598 Madison Ave., New York

City, will send information on Christmas greens such as ground pine and groundsel which are becoming scarce and should be spared in favor of more common species.

Deciduous trees

Deciduous trees in winter reveal their true shape. When weather permits, the children may enjoy making sketches of the same schoolyard trees they drew in early fall. The comparison with earlier sketches should be interesting. Look again at buds, bud scales, leaf scars, and bundle scars which you saw in the fall. Bring in twigs or branches of various trees and shrubs for indoor forcing. Forsythia, flowering quince, and some fruit trees may be forced into bloom indoors. Other species may not sprout flowers but will sprout new leaves. Daily sprinkling accelerates growth.

Cabbage chemistry

When red cabbage is in season, children can find out that the juice turns different colors when mixed with acids or alkalies. Try mixing with such weak acids as vinegar or lemon juice; then compare color when cabbage juice is mixed with such alkalies as ammonia or dissolved soda. Using crayons, make color cards showing gradation of color produced by mixture with various substances.

WINTER DISH GARDENS

The tops of fleshy vegetables as a source of green in winter have been described above (Gardens from roots). Try the same method, using a pineapple top cut 1–2" below the base of the leaves. Make horizontal and vertical sections of onions to observe "the plant inside." Cut under water to prevent the eyes from watering.

Scatter birdseed, chickfeed (whole, not ground), or grass seed on sponges in a shallow dish of water. The resultant seedlings will eventually have to be transplanted to soil in order to survive.

Start narcissus bulbs in the dark to promote strong root growth before the tops get started. Imbed in enough pebbles to keep the plant from tipping over when it blossoms. Keep the water level just above the roots, no more, or less. To discover which part of the plant grows fastest, mark the tip of one with India ink at close intervals and watch whether the intervals remain the same. Better-quality bulbs, like more expensive seeds, often justify the additional expense in the percentage of bloom.

Make leaf cuttings of *Rex Begonia*. Cut at junctions of the large veins underneath and peg down with toothpicks in damp sand or special soil for cuttings. The leaf should be placed surface or top down. An inverted glass casserole will keep the plant moist. Roots sprout at slits. Strawberry plants can be propagated by pegging down the stolons or runners with hairpins. When new growth has taken root, snip the connecting stolon.

Pint jars make miniature greenhouses for cuttings of roses or geraniums. Place the cutting in sand and invert a pint jar over it.

SPRING AGAIN

For Easter prepare an eggshell garden. Paint shells bright colors, fill with soil and small flower seeds or seedlings, and suspend from a branch of driftwood or another display rack.

Pussy willow and other branches brought in for forcing often sprout roots which permit later transplanting in soil. Be sure to trim the cut ends under water and immerse, in the event that the branches have been exposed to air for any length of time. Examine pussy willow catkins with a magnifying glass. The children will soon notice that there are two kinds

of flowers, the male and female. In other tree flowers, help the children see whether there are two kinds of flowers or two kinds of parts to each flower. Look for male and female flowers on evergreens. Place fragrant tree flowers such as Norway maple on the window sill and watch for bees attracted by the scent.

In general we are more apt to look at flowers than to collect them. But if children have been helped to know which kinds are scarce[1] and should be left to grow, they will collect and press a few common flowers or weeds. Spread out one of a kind on a 3 × 5 card and cover completely with Scotch tape or with cellophane and Scotch tape in order to retain color and form. Entrancing art work may emanate from a study of common weeds. Mount them on art paper, using the weed as the basis of a stick figure. For example, foxtail grass heads make a beard for Grandpa Foxtail or chaps for the dashing cowboy, Johnny Foxtail.

Take a short quick field trip around the school grounds to find out where plants are growing. In what kind of soil do you find the most plants, the fewest plants? The chances are that the children will see that few or no plants grow in thoroughfares where the soil is packed down; most plants grow along fences, where there is little wear and tear and more moisture. Along these same fences, the children may wish to plant sunflower seed or other plants to provide bird seed for next fall or winter.

To show that plants need sun, lay a board over some grass for a week or two, remove, and compare the color of the covered grass with that of the grass around it. See how long it takes for the grass which was under the board to turn green again.

[1] Wild Flower Preservation Society, 3740 Oliver St., Washington 15, D.C.

WHAT'S INSIDE A SEED?

Many children have no realization that there is a tiny plant within a seed, and a food supply to take care of its first needs. Draw the analogy here with the jelly surrounding frog eggs, egg white, and the like.

Let children examine the hard outer coat on corn, peas, and bean or pumpkin seeds. Soak overnight and try removing what was the hard outer coat. Remove the food part of the plant and try replanting. Think about the energy needed to split such a hard coat and to push up through the ground.

Make a temporary seed box from a 'half-gallon milk carton. First remove one side and enough of a second to permit slipping in a glass windowpane. See Fig. 6-12 and Fig. 6-13. Next plant seeds at different depths against the glass. Cover the glass with dark paper when not observing. Cover the box with cellophane to retain moisture until seeds have sprouted. On a calendar keep track of the time required for seeds at different depths to send shoots up to ground level. Plant other seeds at normal depth in the rear of the seed box. Each day dig up one or two seedlings to observe development.

Try to secure an avocado seed which has already begun to sprout. Suspend it in a jar broad end down so that it will be only half covered with water. Keep in the dark for a few weeks until the seed splits and sprouts. Don't forget to water. When the plant has a good start, transplant to soil.

Rag-doll seed tester

Some germination experiments not only help children learn about plants but may serve as a valid reason for using methods of figuring percentages. Mark off a strip of old sheeting in 6″ × 6″ squares. Place peas, beans, buckwheat, petunia, or other seeds in sample lots of 10 or more in the center of each square, about 1″ apart. In each square write name of seed, date, and name of child who planted or brought the seed. Seeds tend to stay in place better if cloth is damp. Cover with another strip of sheeting. Roll carefully and fasten with rubber bands. Set in a shallow dish of water for a few days. Unroll every few days and observe results.

CAPSULE LESSONS

6-1 Suggest to the children that they notice which plants the florists keep out of the window, and why. They are probably the shade lovers such as fern and philodendron.

6-2 Plan in the fall with children for spring-flowering bulbs. Before Thanksgiving you should see the bulbs advertised for indoor winter forcing. Reading up on planting directions and writing for bulbs and materials can be more interesting than some language lessons from the book. Children can usually bring appropriate bulb containers from home. Easy-to-grow paperwhite narcissus bulbs are best set in gravel, hyacinths and tulips in soil in clay pots. Consult your local nurseryman for details, again a useful community life experience.

6-3 Younger children are fascinated with the shape, size, and texture of various seeds. Provide four or five kinds (e.g., corn, peas, sunflower seeds, radishes) for them to examine under a hand glass. They will no doubt bring additional kinds to add to the seed collection.

6-4 Many children do not really think of plants as living things. Whenever possible, try to help children become conscious of problems and adaptations that are parallel in plants and animals.

6-5 Let children experiment with vegetable dyes and plants such as celery to watch the rising color. Let them cut the plants in cross section to decide which part of the stem carried the dye.

6-6 In the late fall take a shovel and cardboard box to a vacant lot and look for perennial weeds which grow through the winter in green rosettes close to the ground. Yarrow brought indoors and potted may become as attractive as a fern. In England, our common mullein is called American velvet plant. The feathery leaves of Queen Anne's lace are exquisite. Field daisies and dandelions subjected to indoor "forcing" bloom within a few weeks. Look also for oxalis, which resembles a shamrock, and St.-John's-wort with its "pinhole" leaves. Pennyroyal brought indoors may give you a delightful "hint of mint" on a cold winter day.

6-7 If you can, secure the Cornell Nature Study Leaflet, Vol. 50, No. 1, Fall, 1956. Therein you will find reprinted, with slight revisions, the short description and numerous sketches by L. H. Bailey, the great horticulturalist, to explain *How a Squash Plant Gets Out of the Seed*. Written in 1896, it is as interesting and charming as when it was written. You may wish to encourage upper grade children to read and check it against growth in their own seed experiments.

6-8 You may want your pupils to do some soil testing. Soils from swamps and moist woodland usually show an acid reaction to litmus testing. Normal soils tend to be slightly alkaline. In solution they turn red litmus blue—just the opposite of the acid test reaction. Let children test soils from different sources for alkalinity or acidity. They may use litmus or inexpensive soil-testing kits available from a nursery or science supply houses.

6-9 Ask children where plants grow, i.e., which part grows most quickly. Let them think of ways of finding out. If not suggested, let them mark tips of fast-growing corn or grass seedlings with India ink. Mark at close intervals, e.g., ⅛″. In a few days the children should note that greatest growth is concentrated at the tip. For this reason, we prune the "leader," the fastest growing central branch, when we wish to keep a fruit tree from growing too tall.

6-10 Your children will find it easy to make an attractive door triangle of Christmas greens. Wreaths are hard for children to make. Secure squares of ¼″ or ½″ mesh wire. Cut in triangles. Poke butt ends of greens through mesh and hook in place.

BIBLIOGRAPHY

American Forest Products Industries, 1816 N St., N.W., Wash. 6, D.C. Various pamphlets.

Atkin, M., and R. W. Burnett, *Working with Plants,* Elementary Science Series, Holt, Rinehart and Winston, 1959, 58 pp.

———, *Wait for the Sunshine,* McGraw-Hill, 1954. Primary. The important concept of photosynthesis told and illustrated for young children.

Blough, G., *Tree on the Road to Turntown,* McGraw-Hill, 1953. Intermediate. Interrelations in nature as illustrated by life cycle of an oak tree.

Brown, Ann T., *How Does a Garden Grow?,* Dutton, 1958. Primary. Children plan a garden, select seeds, plant flats, and transplant and care for a garden through the season.

Cooke, Emogene, *Fun-Time Window Garden,* Childrens Press, 1957. Intermediate. Growing house plants from slips and seeds.

Darby, Gene, *What Is a Tree?,* Benefic, 1957. Primary. Tree physiology and development for young children.

Dickinson, Alice, *First Book of Plants,* Watts, 1953. Intermediate. Good section on physiology. Some experiments.

Downer, Mary L., *The Flower,* Scott, 1955. Primary. The story of seeds well told and illustrated. Cross section shows step by step changes in the seed.

Gould, Dorothea, *Very First Garden,* Oxford, 1943. Primary. As title implies, introduction to gardening.

Horwich, F. R., and R. Werrenrath, Jr., *Growing Things,* Rand McNally. Primary. How a sweet potato grows in water.

Kirkus, Virginia, *First Book of Gardening,* Watts, 1956. Intermediate. Detailed information.

Muenscher, Walter, *Weeds,* Macmillan, 1955. Intermediate. Excellent for identification.

Schneider, H., and N. Schneider, *Plants in the City,* Day, 1951. Intermediate. Clear and well illustrated directions for indoor gardens from bread mold to terraria.

Selsam, Millicent, *Play with Leaves and Flowers,* Morrow, 1952. Intermediate.

————, *Play with Plants,* Morrow, 1949. Primary.

————, *Play with Seeds,* Morrow, 1957. Intermediate.

————, *Play with Trees,* Morrow, 1951. Intermediate.

————, *Play with Vines,* Morrow, 1950. Intermediate.

Stefferud, Alfred, *The Wonders of Seeds,* Harcourt, Brace & World, 1956. Intermediate. Formation, structure, and germination of seeds. The work of plant breeds. Activities suggested.

Sterling, Dorothy, *The Story of Mosses, Ferns, and Mushrooms,* Doubleday, 1955. Intermediate. Remarkable microphotos and clear, strong text about less familiar plants.

Wall, Gertrude W., *Gifts from the Grove,* Scribner's, 1955. Intermediate. The story of citrus growing, processing, and transportation.

Webber, Irma E., *Bits That Grow Big,* Scott, 1949. Primary. Growth of plants from seeds and cuttings. Experiments illustrating growth factors.

————, *Travelers All,* Scott, 1944. Primary. Illustrations of plant dispersal.

————, *Up Above and Down Below,* Scott, 1943. Primary. Plant dispersal and root development.

Zim, Herbert, *What's Inside of Plants?,* Morrow, 1952. Intermediate. Elementary botany.

7

Weather

Every day thousands walk to work through a small park near the center of the biggest city in the world. Sometimes even before the sun is high the pavements along one side of the park are damp while those across the park are dry underfoot. Here we have two climates in miniature. The damp climate is caused by the longer period of shade as cast by the buildings on that side of the park. The dry climate side, being relatively unshielded, gets more afternoon sun, absorbs more heat, and thus dries out more thoroughly. Whether our school grounds are small or large, whether in an urban or rural area, they surely afford us some interesting opportunities to learn about the world around us, both near and distant. We can learn a great deal about the climates of our country and of the world by studying the "Elfin Forests" of our school shrubbery, the grassy prairies of the school lawn, the deserts of the hard-packed playground soil.

Climate is the result of the interaction of temperature, pressure, and humidity as affected by the rotating earth. Begin the study of climate and each of its causes in your locality. You will find it convenient to map the school grounds, to inventory the terrain, and to pinpoint locations for a more careful look at the ocean of air in which we live. Use large paper, divided into squares, each square to represent 1', 10', or whichever unit is appropriate to the size of the school grounds. Groups of two or three children working in teams can measure and draw a small section that will be transposed to a large master map. The map need not be too detailed. It should show the outlines of the buildings, the boundaries, the general locations of such areas as shrubbery, trees, bare playground, lawn, etc. (Fig. 7-1). Each child can then make on graph paper his own copy of the master map.

TEMPERATURE AND CLIMATE

What does the thermometer read?

Primary grade children like to learn to read the room thermometer especially if it enables them to help the teacher by acting as "window monitors" in charge of room ventilation. To help children learn to read thermometers easily and without embarrassment, make or secure giant-size thermometers. We have also used successfully a thermometer made of tagboard and a long zipper (Fig. 7-2). Calibrations are drawn directly on the chart, or a strip of graph paper is pasted down the center. The zipper is sewn or glued to the chart, and the metal strip and handle are painted red with nail polish. The children

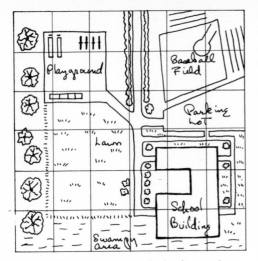

Fig. 7-1   Master map of school grounds.

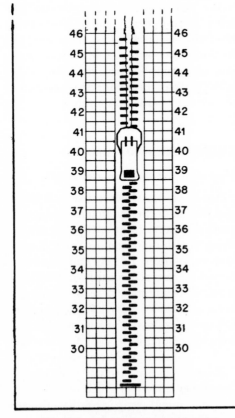

Fig. 7-2   Model zipper thermometer.

love to raise and lower the zipper handle and "read the thermometer." As interest grows, it may be possible to install an outside thermometer for reading, recording, and comparing indoor and outdoor temperatures over a period of time.

It is possible to make a simple thermometer from a milk carton. Make a hole in the center to hold a straw made of non-inflammable plastic. Seal the straw in place with candle wax or gum (Fig. 7-3). Fill the container with colored water. Seal the container opening and add about an inch of colored water to the tube. As the temperature rises, the colored *water* in the tube will rise as the water in the sealed container becomes warmer and expands. You can keep a record by measuring the column of liquid with a ruler and compare this with measurements made at other times or under other temperature conditions.

Use the same device *without liquid* to make another kind of thermometer. Invert on a wooden stand (Fig. 7-4). The plastic tube sits in a tumbler of colored water. When the temperature increases, the liquid in the tube will go down. When the temperature decreases, the liquid rises. An increase in temperature expands the air in the container and forces the liquid down in the tube. When the temperature drops, the air in the container contracts, and the air pressure on the surface of the liquid forces water up the plastic tube.

Warmth and plant life

Government naturalists collecting specimens of plant and animal life in our Western mountains began to wonder why certain species were found at some altitudes but not at others or were found on the south face of a peak but not on the north side of the same peak. They began to believe that the mean average temperature for the year was the underlying cause. Their idea has been called the "life

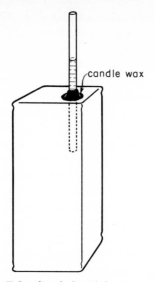

candle wax

Fig. 7-3 Simple liquid thermometer.

around the bulb, and read as soon as the liquid stops moving.

Snow often serves to insulate and protect plants and animals against very low temperatures. Use a yardstick or, if the snow is too deep, a broom handle or piece of doweling marked off in inches. Fasten the thermometer to the bottom of your measuring stick. Observe and record the temperatures at difficult depths in the snow. Read aloud what Justice Wm. O. Douglas wrote about camping out in snow in his book *Of Men and Mountains*.

Daylight and dark

Your temperature records will soon lead the children to note the relationship between temperature and light. The city park is a good locale for observation. In the same locations as used for other observations, place stones or stakes to mark the borders of shadows cast by a tree, a building, etc. To illustrate you might drive a shingle into the ground and mark its varying shadow areas (Fig. 7-5). Do this at mid-morning, noon, and afternoon. Where

zone" theory. If we take accurate temperature readings through the year in selected spots on our school grounds, perhaps we shall begin to see for ourselves why some shrubs, for example, can flourish on the south side but not on the north side of our buildings. To make this study we need several dime store thermometers showing the same readings at the time of purchase. Places for making temperature readings include the lawn, the school garden, the bare playground, under shrubs and trees, above the sidewalk, one foot inside or outside the eaves of the building, all four sides, etc. Use one of the small maps showing these locations to record air temperatures taken daily at the same time. Air temperatures are considered to be more accurate if you keep swinging the thermometers at the end of a string. Be sure to shade the bulb when making readings in sunlight.

Compare air temperature readings with ground temperatures read by placing thermometers bulb down on the ground. Get underground readings by making a 3″ slot in the soil. Slip the thermometer into the opening, press the soil close

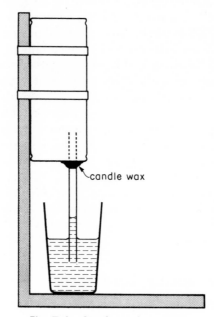

candle wax

Fig. 7-4 Simple air thermometer.

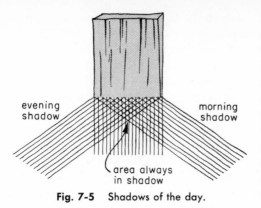

evening
shadow

morning
shadow

area always
in shadow

Fig. 7-5 Shadows of the day.

the shadows intersect is a permanently shaded area. Is there any difference in the plant or animal life in permanently shaded areas, partial shade, or permanent light? Watch the change of shadow patterns over a period of, say, a month. Compare with sunrise and sunset time as given in the daily paper.

With the widespread popularity of photography, there should be a good chance of locating a light meter among the parents or friends of your class. Because these are sensitive instruments, easily broken by careless handling or a sudden fall, it is advisable for the owner or the teacher to use the meter. The children can take the responsibility of recording the light readings at different stations on the school grounds. Place a sheet of white paper on the selected spot, and aim the meter at it, about 1′ from the paper. The paper reflects the light actually reaching the surface of the spot. Take several readings, holding the meter at different angles, until you find a position which gives a median reading. Use this same position for other readings in other places. You also might compare readings of the same place for different times of the day.

AIR PRESSURE AND CLIMATE

Next to the thermometer, the most obvious instrument for a classroom weather station is a barometer. A barometer shows *changes* in pressure. Cut out the top of a milk carton (Fig. 7-6). Warm the box by placing it in hot water, and stretch a section of toy balloon over the top of the container securing it with rubber bands or tape. Glue a small cork to the top *center* of the stretched rubber. Glue a broomstraw to the top of the cork. As air pressure increases, the rubber is pushed down causing the cork and broomstraw indicator to move. When air pressure decreases, the rubber sheet pushes the cork and straw upward. Make a scale on cardboard by extending lines from a protractor. Mount cardboard behind broomstraw tip. Check changes in daily position on the scale and barometer reports over radio or TV. Mark these in pencil on the scale. A glass milk bottle makes a more permanent container than the carton (Fig. 7-7). Each, however, is temporary since the rubber diaphragm is porous. The barometer should be kept in a location which varies as little as possible in temperature.

Evaporated milk can barometer

An empty evaporated milk can used as the aneroid unit provides a more permanent barometer. You will also need a wooden base about 3″ × 10″, a 12″ balsa strip about ⅛″ × ⅛″ (available at a model airplane shop), a small cork, and some Tinkertoy sticks. Wash the can, stand in hot water, and seal the holes at the top

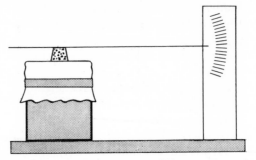

Fig. 7-6 Simple "aneroid" barometer.

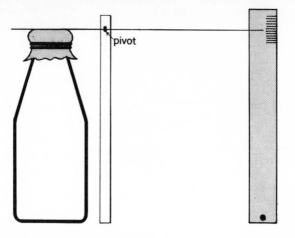

Fig. 7-7 Milk bottle barometer.

with hot sealing wax or chewing gum. It is preferable to solder the holes shut (in the school shop or elsewhere). Place the can on the wooden base (Fig. 7-8). Cement a cork to the center of the can. To the right, mount a Tinkertoy stick in a ¼″ hole drilled in the wood base. Or use a Tinkertoy hub glued to the base with a stick inserted in the hub. Attach the balsa wood strip to the Tinkertoy stick by means of a common pin or extremely fine nail. The balsa wood strip should be free to move on the pin or nail. The strip then rests on top of the cork on the can. As air pressure increases, the can top and cork are depressed and the end of the balsa strip goes down. When the air pressure decreases, the can top rises, lifting the strip. Behind the end of the strip place a cardboard scale. The children then calibrate the position of the needle by marking the barometer readings daily as received by radio or TV weather broadcasts.

Barograph

A barograph which records the changes in the barometer for a 12-hour period can be built from the evaporated milk can barometer. You will need an old alarm clock in working condition and a cardboard disk. The minute hand of the clock is carefully removed. Cement a manila disk to the hour hand shaft with the clock facing the pointer (Fig. 7-9). The disk is sooted by means of a candle. Care must be taken not to set the manila disk aflame. Set the pointer of the barograph to make a trace on the disk.

HUMIDITY AND CLIMATE

How dry—how wet

Most children are aware only of extremes in the amount of moisture in our ocean of air. On warm damp days a glass of ice water is soon coated with moisture

Fig. 7-8 Milk can aneroid barometer.

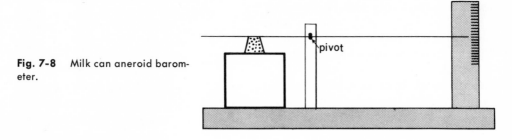

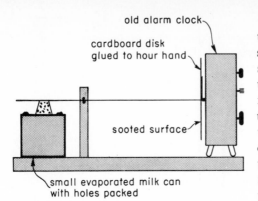

old alarm clock

cardboard disk
glued to hour hand

sooted surface

small evaporated milk can
with holes packed

Fig. 7-9 Simple barograph (recording barometer).

condensed from the atmosphere (not through the glass!). On cool damp days children may come to school through fog. On cool dry days they enjoy stimulating contacts with static electricity! In general they are quite unaware that relative humidity plays any part in weather or in our daily ways of living. Note also "snow" on refrigerator coils and "frost" on a glass container of dry ice. Illustrating the importance of humidity, Forest Service lookouts in our national forests keep close tabs on the relative amount of moisture. At lookout stations every day they carefully weigh a standard-sized cube of kiln-dried wood after it has been exposed to air. On damp days it weighs more. When the air is dry, the wood dries out (loses moisture to the air) and weighs less. The danger of forest fire increases during dry weather.

Anyone who has ever tried to develop film knows how unmanageable film can be on dry days. This characteristic is a useful indicator of relative humidity. Thumbtack a strip of 35 mm, or other film inclined to curl when dry, to an old ruler or stake marked off in inches (Fig. 7-10). Place several such film sticks in selected areas. In an hour or more, note how far the film has curled or uncurled in each location chosen.

With blue cobalt chloride paper obtained from the druggist, we can make simple tests of relative humidity on the school grounds. With clothespins, hang the paper in selected areas. Time the number of seconds or minutes required for the paper to change from blue to gray-white or pink. Try this at different times of day and on different days. Try some under a rock or piece of bark or in the mouth of a culvert. (When not in use, the paper should be stored in a well-closed bottle in company with a drying agent such as calcium chloride or silica gel.)

Hair hygrometer. There are several devices which children can make to measure the amount of moisture in the air around them. The simplest is a human hair hygrometer. A long human hair is attached to a simple stand made from a Tinkertoy or erector set (Fig. 7-11). Attach a steel nut or nail to the bottom of the strand as a weight. Place a cardboard behind the hair as a scale. Each day note the relative position of the weight and mark it on the scale. Try brunette, blond, or red hair (brunette is best). Freshly shampooed hair is preferred because it has been freed

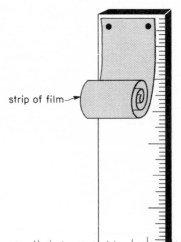

strip of film

Fig. 7-10 Photographic film used as a moisture indicator.

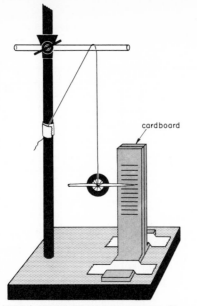

Fig. 7-11 Human hair hygrometer. (From A. Joseph et al., *A Sourcebook for the Physical Sciences,* Harcourt, Brace & World, 1961.)

of oil particles which make it unable to absorb moisture.

String hygrometer. Another simple hygrometer is made from a ukelele gut string. This is set in a Tinkertoy or other simple wooden stand with the gut tied securely to the top bar (Fig. 7-12). Attach the bottom of the string to the base by means of a rubber band. Insert a tooth-pick through the gut as an indicator. As moisture in the air varies, the gut will twist or untwist. A circular scale on a 3 × 5 card is glued or tacked to the base. Each day the children can note the position of the narrow end of the indicator (the toothpick) and mark it on the scale. They may also mark the per cent of humidity as indicated by TV or radio broadcasts. After a month they will have a fairly good in-strument. During the winter in steam-heated classrooms the results show about 25% relative humidity. Readings should be made outdoors, as, for instance, on an outside window sill. However, do not leave the instrument in the rain or snow.

Wet- and dry-bulb hygrometer. Older pupils may make several other more ac-curate types of humidity indicators. For a wet- and dry-bulb hygrometer, pupils need two identical inexpensive wall thermome-ters, a small board, a vial, and a small piece of gauze. The thermometers are mounted on a board. The bottom of one thermometer board is cut away and the bulb wrapped with gauze. The gauze dips into a vial or little bottle of water attached below the thermometer by tape and thumbtacks. The other thermometer is simply fastened with tacks on the other side of the board. In the center, place a copy of the humidity table (Table 7-1). After fanning the wet bulb until it reaches its lowest reading, read each thermometer temperature and note the difference be-tween the wet-bulb (with gauze) and the dry-bulb (open to the air) readings. To use the table, match up the wet- and dry-bulb temperatures. The figure in the

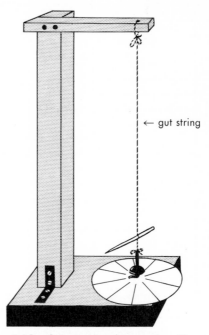

Fig. 7-12 Catgut string hygrometer. (From A. Joseph et al., *A Sourcebook for the Physical Sciences,* Harcourt, Brace & World, 1961.)

Table 7-1
Relative humidity

temperature of dry bulb

	61	62	63	64	65	66	67	68	69	70	71	72	73	74	75	76	77	78	79	80	
41	7	4	2																		41
42	10	8	6	4	2																42
43	14	12	10	7	5	3	2														43
44	18	16	13	11	9	7	5	3	1												44
45	22	20	17	15	12	10	8	6	5	3	1										45
46	27	24	21	18	16	14	12	10	8	6	4	3	1								46
47	31	28	25	22	20	17	15	13	11	9	7	6	4	3	1						47
48	35	32	29	26	24	21	19	16	14	12	10	9	7	5	4	3	1				48
49	40	36	33	30	27	25	22	20	18	15	13	12	10	8	7	5	4	3	1		49
50	44	41	37	34	31	29	26	23	21	19	17	15	13	11	9	8	6	5	4	3	50
51	49	45	42	38	35	32	30	25	24	22	20	18	16	14	12	11	9	8	6	5	51
52	54	50	46	43	39	36	33	31	28	25	23	21	19	17	15	13	12	10	9	7	52
53	58	54	50	47	44	40	37	34	32	29	27	24	22	20	18	16	14	13	11	10	53
54	63	59	55	51	48	44	41	38	35	33	30	28	25	23	21	19	17	16	14	12	54
55	68	64	60	56	52	48	45	42	39	36	33	31	29	26	24	22	20	18	17	15	55
56	73	69	64	60	56	53	49	46	43	40	37	34	32	29	27	25	23	21	19	18	56
57	78	74	69	65	61	57	53	50	47	44	41	38	35	33	30	28	26	24	22	20	57
58	84	79	74	70	66	61	58	54	51	48	45	42	39	36	34	31	29	27	25	23	58
59	89	84	79	74	70	66	62	58	55	51	48	45	42	39	37	34	32	30	28	26	59
60	94	89	84	79	75	71	66	62	59	55	52	49	46	43	40	38	35	33	31	29	60
61	100	94	89	84	80	75	71	67	63	59	56	53	50	47	44	41	39	36	34	32	61
62		100	95	90	85	80	75	71	67	64	60	57	53	50	47	44	42	39	37	35	62
63			100	95	90	85	80	76	72	68	64	61	57	54	51	48	45	43	40	38	63
64				100	95	90	85	80	76	72	68	65	61	58	54	51	48	46	43	41	64
65					100	95	90	85	81	77	72	69	65	61	58	55	52	49	46	44	65
66						100	95	90	85	81	77	73	69	65	62	59	56	53	50	47	66
67							100	95	90	86	81	77	73	69	66	62	59	56	53	50	67
68								100	95	90	86	82	78	74	70	66	63	60	57	54	68
69									100	95	90	86	82	78	74	70	67	63	60	57	69
70										100	95	91	86	82	78	74	71	67	64	61	70
71											100	95	91	86	82	78	74	71	68	64	71
72												100	95	91	86	82	79	75	71	68	72
73													100	95	91	87	83	79	75	72	73
74														100	96	91	87	83	79	75	74
75															100	96	91	87	83	79	75
76																100	96	91	87	83	76
77																	100	96	91	87	77
78																		100	96	91	78
79																			100	96	79
80																				100	80
	61	62	63	64	65	66	67	68	69	70	71	72	73	74	75	76	77	78	79	80	

temperature of wet bulb

square where these intersect is the relative humidity. For example, suppose the dry-bulb thermometer reads 72° F, and the wet-bulb thermometer reads 63° F. Then the relative humidity would be 61% (circled in the table).

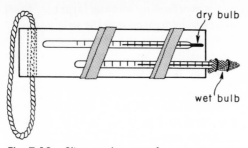

dry bulb

wet bulb

Fig. 7-13 Sling psychrometer for accurate measurement of relative humidity.

A portable version of this hygrometer is made by mounting both thermometers inside a cardboard box. Hang the box as you would a picture frame; at the bottom make a hole in the cardboard under one thermometer, just big enough to squeeze in the neck of a tiny perfume or pill bottle. Fill the bottle with water. Dip in one end of the gauze or rag tied around the thermometer bulb. Water travels up the cloth as up a wick by capillary attraction. It generally lowers the reading on the wet-bulb thermometer.

Sling psychrometer. A slightly more accurate device is simply a wet and dry bulb on a sling. Place two ordinary thermometers on a narrow board, and attach a wet gauze to one bulb. Attach the thermometers securely by means of wood screws or several layers of strong tape. Bore a hole to carry strong cord near the top of the thermometers (Fig. 7-13). Pass a strong cord tied in a loop through the hole. Have a pupil whirl the device overhead for 2 minutes (Fig. 7-14). Note the difference between wet- and dry-bulb readings. Use Table 7-1 to find the relative humidity or per cent of moisture in the air compared to the maximum amount of moisture that air can hold at that temperature. The higher the temperature, the greater the amount of moisture the air can hold. This is a concept usually fairly difficult to develop except with upper-grade children.

Cloud in a milk bottle

Children enjoy producing a cloud in a quart milk bottle. Get a cork or two-hole stopper to fit the bottle. If you use a cork, bore two ¼″ holes. Fit the cork or stopper with two short lengths of stiff plastic tubing or drinking straws. Attach a short length of flexible rubber or plastic tubing to one tube. From the druggist buy an atomizer replacement bulb and its short rubber tubing connection. Attach it to the second tube. Add a shallow layer of water to the bottle. Now you are ready to make the cloud. Since clouds start as tiny droplets of water that condense on dust particles, you need some fine dust. To secure this, hold a smoldering match in the open bottle and then cap the bottle. Next darken the room and shine a light beam from a flashlight or projector through the bottle. Close the short tube with a spring type clothespin. Squeeze the atomizer bulb several times to pump air into the bottle. Then suddenly remove the pinch clamp while squeezing the atomizer bulb. A cloud will form. If dry

Fig. 7-14 Demonstration of use of a sling psychrometer. (From A. Joseph et al., *A Sourcebook for the Physical Sciences*, Harcourt, Brace & World, 1961.)

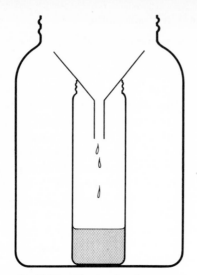

Fig. 7-15 Homemade rain gauge.

ice is placed against the outside walls of the bottle, you will find rain or see a few tiny snow flakes inside.

Precipitation patterns

You are beginning to realize that moisture in the air depends upon several variables. These variables determine the amount of rainfall. U.S. Weather Bureau statistics show rainfall figures for most locations, and the daily newspaper usually includes some data on local precipitation. However, the children need to have the chance to gain a concrete concept of local rainfall patterns by keeping their own records of it. They need to see for themselves the seasonal pattern of rainfall which exists in certain sections and its relation to what people do and how they live.

Rain gauge.   An effective rain gauge can be constructed with a 2″ diameter olive bottle and a 4″ funnel (top diameter), the whole set being placed inside a gallon glass jar (Fig. 7-15). With equipment of these proportions, 4″ of water collected in the bottle means 1″ of rain per square inch of surface. One inch in the olive bottle therefore means ¼″ of rainfall. Any

water overflowing into the larger jar must of course be poured into the smaller bottle and included in the measurements. Set the apparatus on the open grassy lawn and wire it to a short stake. If the roof of the school building is accessible to students, the rain gauge is less likely to be disturbed and more likely to be accurate in this location.

Keep records over a period of months, both spring and fall. Note whether rain fell gently or in a downpour.

WHO HAS SEEN THE WIND?

As teachers know, children are often affected more by windy days than they are by hot or cold weather. No classroom weather station could be complete without a wind vane. To make one you will need an empty milk carton, a stick, a small board, and a nail. With a saw make slits in the ends of the stick. Fit pieces of milk carton into the slits. One piece is cut to form a 3″ triangle as the pointer; another is formed into a rectangular piece to be the tail of the vane (Fig. 7-16). Secure by driving fine tacks through the stick and waxed carton. Drill a hole in the measured center of the stick. With a small nail anchor the stick to the center of the wooden base. On a breezy day take the vane outdoors and watch the pointer turn into the wind. With the aid of some compasses (directional), help children see that we name a wind by the direction of its source. Some may wish to substitute

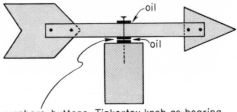

washers, buttons, Tinkertoy knob as bearing

Fig. 7-16 Wind direction vane.

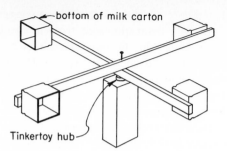

bottom of milk carton

Tinkertoy hub

Fig. 7-17 Simple anemometer (wind speed indicator).

pieces of aluminum pie plates for pointer and tail pieces.

Wind speed or strength

Cup anemometer. To measure the speed of wind, a cup anemometer can be made from the bottoms of milk cartons. Mount with tacks on a pair of crossed sticks (Fig. 7-17). The sticks are secured with strong plastic tape. A finishing nail through the center acts as pivot and, if oiled, should permit free movement. The nail passes through a Tinkertoy hub used as a bearing into the top of a short length of wood. The faster the wind, the higher the speed of rotation of the cups in a circle.

Ball-bearing wind vane. A more sophisticated weather vane can be made by

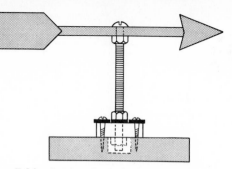

Fig. 7-18 Improved wind direction indicator. (From A. Joseph et al., *A Sourcebook for the Physical Sciences,* Harcourt, Brace & World, 1961.)

using a roller skate wheel as a ball bearing. The wind vane stick is bolted to the center of the wheel and kept clear of the wheel by several washers (Fig. 7-18). The wheel sits on a small board and is secured by four bent nails or by four long screws and washers set against the rim. A hole in the center of the board allows clearance for the bolt on the wheel. Aluminum is used for the pointer and tail. For good results, make the tail about twice the size of the pointer. Mount on a pole on the school grounds at a distance from the classroom windows. Metal letters may be used to indicate north, south, east, and west.

Soup-dipper anemometer on roller skate wheel. A close approximation of a com-

Fig. 7-19 Soup ladle anemometer. (From A. Joseph et al., *A Sourcebook for the Physical Sciences,* Harcourt, Brace & World, 1961.)

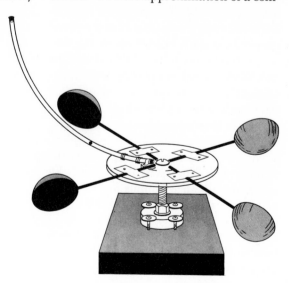

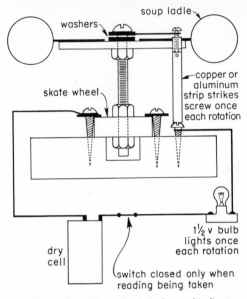

Fig. 7-20   Remote-reading wind speed indicator.

the edge of the disk. A small bare copper wire runs from the strip to the large center bolt. On the baseboard attach a copper wire to one screw that holds the skate wheel in place. Now insert a small brass screw into the base so that the rotating strip on the disk strikes the screw as the anemometer rotates. Connect another wire to the brass screw. Now connect the wire from the skate wheel to one terminal of a dry cell battery. Then connect the other terminal to a miniature socket and 1½-volt flashlight bulb. Connect the other side of the socket to the wire on the small brass screw. The stronger the wind, the faster the light flickers. The anemometer can be mounted at a short distance from the classroom by extending the two wires from the anemometer. The lamp and battery remain in the room. On a windless day the device can be calibrated by holding it out the window of a moving vehicle. Count the number of flashes per minute at car speeds

mercial model may be made of three cheap aluminum soup ladles. Mount 120° apart on a small wood disk (Fig. 7-19). Fasten by means of thin wire passed through small holes or by means of strong staples. Also attach to the disk a curved glass tube containing a small metal ball and sealed at both ends with corks or tape. The height of the ball in the tube indicates the wind speed. In the center of the disk drill a ¼″ hole to carry a ¼″ bolt. Raise the disk an inch or so from the wheel proper by a stack of washers on the bolt (or use Tinkertoy hubs). Then attach the bolt to the center of the skate wheel. Attach the wheel, in turn, to a larger wood base with screws and washers. Notice that there must be a hole in the wood base so that the bolt on the skate wheel clears. If you wish, varnish, shellac, or wax the wooden parts. The device is now ready for use. Some advanced pupils may want to make it flash its speed electrically (Fig. 7-20). For this activity attach a strip of copper or aluminum to the disk. Use a small nut and bolt to hold the strip in place through a small hole drilled near

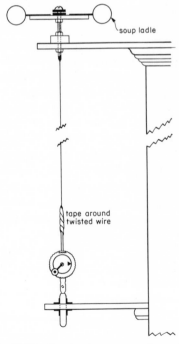

Fig. 7-21   Egg-beater anemometer project.

of 5, 10, 15 ,20, 25, and 30 mph. Thus you will have a means of reading the wind speed by counting the number of flashes per minute. A small reference card can be tacked up next to the bulb, together with a clock with a sweep second hand. Turn off the device by loosening or removing the bulb.

Egg-beater anemometer. Another method for reading wind speed involves the use of an ordinary egg beater. Make a cup anemometer on two crossed sticks as explained earlier in this chapter. This type is best mounted at the side of the school building, if permission is obtained. Perhaps the school custodian can help you put it up. A stick is securely fastened to the building so that it extends over the edge of the roof. Make a ⅛″ hole in the stick near the overhanging end. A long #14 gauge stiff iron wire passes through the hole and is fastened to the anemometer center (Fig. 7-21). Notice that several oiled metal washers hold the anemometer above the stick. The wire extends straight down to your window sill. Here another overhanging stick is fastened. To the stick attach an egg beater in an inverted position. Remove the beaters and retain only the gears and center shafts as in Fig. 7-21. The eggbeater handle is securely fastened to the stick with clamps or electricians' metal straps. Attach the wire from the roof to one of the center parts of the beater attached to the small gear. The best way is to twist the wire and the part together and cover with strong plastic tape. Next cover the large gear wheel with white cardboard attached by cord or thin wire to the gear wheel. Mark

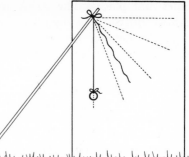

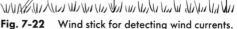

Fig. 7-22 Wind stick for detecting wind currents.

a black pointer at one spot as in the figure. When the wind blows, the anemometer will turn. This spins one small egg-beater gear, which in turn spins the large egg-beater wheel. The large wheel will turn more slowly than the small gear because it has many more teeth. Thus if the small gear has ten teeth and the larger gear has fifty teeth, the larger gear will turn at one fifth the speed of the smaller gear. This reduction in speed makes it easier to observe high wind speed.

Wind is really moving air

Most children have experienced the cooling effect of evaporation, i.e., air-drying of wet skin after a swim. Some may have seen the pruning effect of wind on trees at timberline or at the seashore. To study wind currents in the school yard, make a wind stick (Fig. 7-22) by tying two lengths of white grocery cord to the end of a slim stake. Weight one cord with a metal ring. The angle formed between the two strings as the wind blows across them provides a rough basis of comparing the force of moving air at various

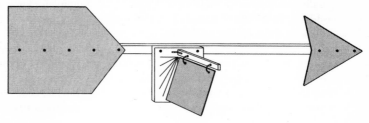

Fig. 7-23 Combination wind speed and wind direction indicator. (From A. Joseph et al., *A Sourcebook for the Physical Sciences*, Harcourt, Brace & World, 1961.)

times and places. The string must be lightweight. Such an angle may be better shown by holding a calibrated card behind the strings. Use a compass to record wind direction as well as force when making readings with a wind stick.

Or you can make a simple wind gauge by hanging a heavy cardboard sheet on loose-leaf rings (Fig. 7-23). Calibrate by holding out the window of a moving automobile on a windless day. Work out the position of the card for 5, 10, 15, 20, 25, 30, and 40 mph.

Evaporation experiments

To demonstrate that continual winds dry out the land, fill two flowerpots with soil immediately after a rain. Fill so that both weigh the same. Place one in a protected spot, say in the teacher's closet, the other directly in front of a small electric fan. Reweigh both at the end of the day.

To give children some inkling of the extent of evaporation going on all the time around them one can make good use of wet paper towels. Wet several towels thoroughly, and squeeze them out so they will not drip. Hang in selected areas outside and note order in which towels dry out. In order to make valid comparisons, all towels should be hung out at the same time. Or place saucers or paint dishes filled with equal amounts of water in selected spots inside the classroom. With wax crayola mark the water level in each container every day at the same time.

CAPSULE LESSONS

7-1 Encourage children with ability in numbers to report with audiovisual aids on the arithmetic involved in weather, as, for example, with regard to a rain gauge, the relative area of funnel compared to collecting can.

7-2 Some children may wish to make a special exhibit or collection of weather in the news. In addition to daily records, they might include information about weather radar, weather satellites, Coast Guard weather ships, Navy hurricane patrol, weather reports for commercial flying, samples of U.S. Weather Bureau teletype reports, and facsimile weather map transmittal.

7-3 Children who have made a simple air thermometer may be challenged to use it to calibrate another made after the manner of the soda straw barometer.

7-4 Study and report on wind belts of the earth as compared to upper air (stratosphere).

7-5 Illustrate relative humidity by this activity. Soak a large sponge in water until it is completely or 100 per cent saturated. Squeeze out the water and divide into two equal parts. Pour one part over the sponge, which now will be 50 per cent saturated. Repeat for different humidity values.

BIBLIOGRAPHY

Adler, Irving, *Weather in Your Life,* Day, 1959. Upper. Theory of ice ages; cloud seeding.

Barlow, John, *Building Your Own Weather Station,* California Education Press, 1954. Upper.

Bechdott, Jack, *Oliver Becomes a Weatherman,* Messner, 1953. Upper.

Bell, Thelma, *Snow,* Viking, 1954. Middle.

Gallant, Roy, *The Nature of Weather,* Science Service, 1959. Upper. Well illustrated.

Hurd, Edith T., *It's Snowing,* Sterling, 1957. Primary. Large drawings.

Krick, Irving, and Roscoe Fleming, *Sun, Sea and Sky,* Lippincott, 1954. Upper.

McGrath, Thomas, *Clouds,* Melmont, 1959. Primary.

Sandman, Howard E., *Who's Afraid of Thunder?,* Sterling, 1953. Middle. Will also interest beginners.

Schneider, Herman, *Everyday Weather and How It Works,* Whittlesey, 1951. Middle. Many ideas for simple instruments and experiments.

Williams, Lou, *Weather Handbook,* Girl Scouts of America, 1942.

The earth's surface

One morning during social studies class a fourth grade teacher was asking the children to name the major geographic features of their state. One child mentioned the ocean, another the desert, but none mentioned the mountains. All the while a nearby mountain range lay shimmering in the sun in plain view of the classroom windows. Not many schools have a view of mountains, but there are few schools that are not near one or more of the other major land forms—hills, valleys, or plains. Some are near wind-built sand dunes; others are near river-built bars, deltas, or flood plains. A great many schools are near water, whether salt or fresh, and hence near some of the water carved land forms, such as canyons, arroyos, draws, washes, caves, and cliffs.

All too often the study of geography and how it affects people is only an abstraction. Home geography, and the way it has determined the location of the town or of business or homes, is sometimes ignored for a study of distant lands. For example, our school might have been located on a hill, for the sake of drainage. Or local topography may have determined the size and shape of the school grounds. Next time we make a tour of the neighborhood, or talk about the location of our homes, we might notice upon what sort of land surface they are built. Has local geography affected the layout of streets in our city or town? Is there a near-

by road cut where we may see exposed the tilted layers of bedrock which have given us our hills? These layers must at one time have been horizontal, since they were deposited as sediments by the water which covered our area. To see how far above horizontal the rocks have been warped, hold a jump rope or clothesline level against the rock (Fig. 8-1). To make sure the line is level, use a "pop" bottle half full of water, as some farmers do in laying out level contour lines. Other examples of local rock structure may help us see our modern landscape as the result of many stages in the endless cycle of erosion, dep-

Fig. 8-1 Tilting or bending of rock layers in contrast to a horizontal line. Use a level made from a bottle, as shown, to determine the horizontal line.

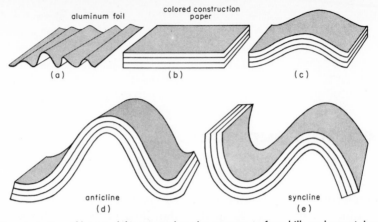

Fig. 8-2 Demonstration of how rock layers are bent by pressure to form hills and mountains: (a) folds or wrinkles created when aluminum foil is bent from each end simulate hills and mountains; (b) using a stack of colored construction paper, push against each end until the pile arches or humps up (c) to simulate hills; applying greater pressure, you can simulate such hill or mountain features as (d) anticline and (e) syncline.

osition, and uplifting of the earth's crust. For the "everlasting hills" are that in name only. The only constant is change, in mountains as in other things.

MOUNTAINS

Model mountain formation

There are several ways to illustrate how horizontal layers of rock have been bent or folded into hills or mountains. Spread a sheet of kitchen foil on a desk or table. Push with fingertips from each end of the sheet (Fig. 8-2A). Resultant folds or wrinkles will simulate hills and mountains.

Use a stack of colored construction paper with several different colors to give a banded effect to the pile. Push from each end (Fig. 8-2B and C) and the layers will arch or hump up like hills and mountains. Try the same procedure with thin layers of colored sponge rubber.

Use layers of colored modeling clay which is not too soft. If you press the layers between two boards, the clay will buckle and form "mountains." The different colored layers illustrate different rock strata. Continue to press until lay-

ers "crack" under pressure. In actuality, the bending of rock layers takes hundreds or thousands of centuries. Any of the methods described above may help children understand how rocks are often bent so much that they form an *anticline* (shaped like "A") or a *syncline* (shaped like "S"). (See Fig. 8-2D and E.) Such rock forms are frequently revealed in road cuts.

Mountain blocks and ocean blocks

Children are often unaware of the great weight of even a small quantity of dirt. Fill a widemouthed glass pickle jar with garden loam, another with sand, and a third with leaf mold. Ask the children to guess the weight of each; then verify by weighing on household scales or scales in the nurse's office. Estimate and weigh other amounts.

The immense weight of accumulated sediments carried to the sea may cause shifting and faulting of the nearby coast and inland areas. If it is possible to secure a platform balance, place a book and/or a pile of paper on each side of the scale. These are to illustrate layers of sediment. On one side place a pan of water to symbolize oceans. On the other side place a pan of rock and soil to stand for mountains. Balance carefully. Review with the children some of the means by which the land was eroded and resulting sediments were carried to the sea. Transfer a teaspoon of earth to the "ocean." Note how the balance is easily disturbed between continental land masses or blocks and ocean bottom blocks. This may cause faulting and sometimes earthquakes. Seismographs are used to detect and record the motions of an earthquake. For the design of a model seismograph, see A. Joseph et al., *A Sourcebook for the Physical Sciences,* Harcourt, Brace & World, 1961.

A batch of dough provides another way to show uplifting of mountains by the sheer weight of land masses. When the dough is well kneaded, spread into a thick even layer on the bottom of a large dishpan. With a handbreadth space between the palms, press down. The dough will rise between your hands. The pressure simulates the effect of an unbalanced weight on the land mass, which causes the rising of other parts of the earth. Help the children realize that such action requires thousands or hundreds of thousands of years.

Faulting

Figuratively speaking, earthquakes are a sign that the earth is stretching and shifting the great weight it carries. In an earthquake the rocks slip along cracks formed by bending the layers of rock until they crack and slip, just as did the layers of plasticene under heavy pressure above. These cracks or breaks in rock layers are called "faults." Sometimes the heat generated by the friction is so great that the areas of contact are partly melted. The resulting patches of smooth or slick-looking rock surface are called "slickensides."

The sidewalk may again serve to illustrate faulting. If erosion has undermined part of the foundation, the walk may have dropped or tilted to one side. Where this has occurred, a slab is apt to have cracked. One side of the crack may have risen while the other dropped. Similarly, when rocks become pushed up into mountain ranges, the stresses are so great that one side of the fault may become much higher than the other side. A fault-block range such as Sierra Nevada was uplifted to form a mass of peaks culminating in Mt. Whitney. East of the fault is Death Valley, the lowest point on our continent.

Whenever you pass exposures of parallel rock layers, watch for a break or fault in the continuity of the structure or formations (Fig. 8-3A). Watch also for syncline formations (Fig. 8-3B) and for anticlines (Fig. 8-3C). Often the State Division of Mines or a member of the community with some training in geology can verify your "fault break" and introduce you to other interesting local geology.

A nonchemical volcano

A simple, safe, and effective method of illustrating volcanic action is with powdered asbestos, a funnel, and a bicycle pump (Fig. 8-4). The asbestos is used as insulation and should be available at the hardware or building supply store. Moistened, it can be modeled around a large funnel to simulate a volcanic cone. When the asbestos paste is dry and hard, insert the bicycle pump tube into the base of the inverted funnel. Heap powdered asbestos around the cone. As you pump, the stream of air coming up through the funnel nozzle will scatter the asbestos just as erupting volcanic gases spew powdered pumice and ash over surrounding terrain.

ROCKS AND MINERALS

Any rocks your children may bring to school can be put into one of three categories: *igneous* (heat-made), *sedimentary*

(a)

(b)

(c)

Fig. 8-3 Typical formations due to folding and faulting of rock strata: (a) fault shown below a road cut, part of the San Andreas fault, Los Angeles County, Calif.; the lighter-textured rocks (on right), part of an alluvium deposit, have faulted down against the granite rock (on left); (b) the Devil's Kitchen syncline, in San Emigdio Canyon, Kern County, Calif.; (c) an anticline, showing the Bloomsburg Arch, part of the Hancock Quadrangle, Md. (U.S. Geological Survey.)

(water deposited or sometimes wind deposited), and *metamorphic*, that is, changed by heat and pressure. Some common examples of igneous rock are granite, basalt, diorite, pegmatite (coarse granite). Sandstone, limestone, shale, and conglomerate are the best-known types of sedimentaries. The metamorphics are widely illustrated by gneiss (pronounced "nice") (metamorphosed granite), quartzite (metamorphosed sandstone), marble (metamorphosed limestone), slate or mica schist (metamorphosed shale).

Igneous rock

Scientists believe that the oldest rocks are igneous. The rocks in the bottom of the Grand Canyon were once molten. They were probably formed when the earth cooled billions of years ago. Some common igneous rocks are granite, basalt, pumice, lava, and obsidian. The last three are usually associated with volcanic action and become molten fairly near the surface inside volcanoes. Sometimes they are erupted and flow over the surface. Or a molten mass may squeeze up through weak places in the bedrock and spread out between the layers as a dike. The basalt Palisades along the Hudson River were once a molten volcanic mass which was squeezed up and between layers of red Jersey sandstone to form the straight cliffs we see today.

A partly used tube of tooth paste may be squeezed from one end of the tube to the other to illustrate how molten magma moves. Roll the tube up as tightly as possible; then puncture near the top with a pin. The contents squirting out act much as molten rock would erupt through a volcano. Igneous rock, particularly that of volcanic origin, is usually characterized by great weight or density and compact crystalline structure. Pumice and lava are the exceptions, having been extruded with much attendant hot gas and then cooled

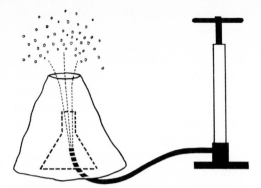

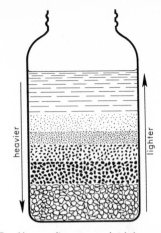

Fig. 8-4 A "child-proof" volcano, which can be used over and over while the children are developing partial concepts about air pressure and resistance. Remove the funnel from the molded cone before the asbestos paste hardens completely.

Fig. 8-5 How sediments are laid down. If the jar is covered and not too heavy, it may be used repeatedly to illustrate the principle of sedimentation.

relatively quickly. Obsidian, the handsome black volcanic glass, was valuable tender for trading among the Indians, who used it to make arrowheads because of its glass-like conchoidal fracture planes. Obsidian has the same basic chemical composition as commercial glass, silicon dioxide (sand).

Encourage children to see what kind of rock is most commonly used in buildings and in road construction. The chances are it will be granite, which is composed of three minerals: *quartz,* the glass-like translucent crystals which can scratch glass; *mica,* the black or white shiny flaky crystals; and *feldspar,* pinkish crystals which have flat, rectangular faces like the facades of modern skyscrapers.

Sedimentary rock

To show how sediments are laid down, secure a cupful each of such materials as gravel, sand, garden loam, and local subsoil. Partly fill a jar with water. Dump in all or part of each sample. Shake the jar thoroughly; allow the soil to settle. By next day you should see that the heaviest material has settled to the bottom, the sand next, and the finer particles in successive layers (Fig. 8-5). Construction en-

gineers treat soil samples in much the same way in order to determine the composition of the soil across which they must build roads, bridges, and buildings.

To make samples of sedimentary rock, collect discarded milk cartons and small amounts of cement, lime plaster, and sand (Fig. 8-6). Cement and water produce a kind of shale. Lime plaster and water make a limestone which can be tested with vinegar to see if it bubbles. A synthetic sandstone results from a sand, cement, and water mixture. The cartons can be peeled off when each mixture hardens. In nature, however, the hardening of sediments into rock takes hundreds of centuries.

Try also adding colored chalk. Pulverize the chalk and fragments of flower pots by hammering inside a square of rag

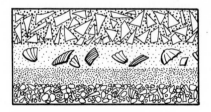

Fig.8-6 Synthetic sedimentary rock layers.

Fig. 8-7 Crystal formation. Most crystals in rocks are only partially visible. Not free to form in solution as on the nail shown here, the crystals are half hidden within the rock matrix.

pulled together to make a sack. Make a fossil-bearing layer by adding bits of shell from the fish market or the beach. Raccoons will often pile up mussel shells for you along fresh-water creeks. Make different kinds of layers, e.g., pebbles or shells and cement to form a conglomerate. A large milk carton on its side with one side cut off makes an excellent form in which to harden a series of different layers of earth materials.

Sidewalks may be regarded as a kind of artificial conglomerate or pudding stone. Look for slabs which include water-worn or rounded pebbles. Those which include angular fragments simulate a kind of conglomerate called *breccia* (Italian, meaning "broken"). In older cities one may find slate sidewalks. Slate is metamorphosed shale. Fossils are nearly always found in what was originally sedimentary rock. However, the fossils to be seen in the black Tennessee marble of a famous skyscraper are of greater interest to some passers-by than other better-known aspects of the building.

There are some easy tests for sedimentary rocks. For example, shale has an earthy or oily smell. Sandstone has tiny grains of quartz which are hard enough to make glass. Limestone will bubble under vinegar. (The bubbling will proceed faster

if one concentrates household vinegar by heating it or allowing the water in it to evaporate for several days.) Try dissolving sea shells in concentrated vinegar or dilute hydrochloric acid. (HCl is usually available at the drugstore; it should never be handled by children. It should be corked with a rubber stopper, since it will eat away wood corks.)

If sedimentary rocks are pulverized with a hammer, the crystals can be seen under magnification. (For safety you can put the rocks in a sack before striking them.) It will be noted that each kind of rock has a distinct crystalline form. Review crystal making (Chapter 12) by suspending a string and nail in a saturated solution of sugar, salt, alum, borax, or Epsom salts (Fig. 8-7).

Metamorphic rock

Some of our very common rocks were so changed by intense heat, pressure, and chemical action deep within the earth that they are quite different from their original sedimentary or igneous character. For example, granite may have been subjected to such pressure that all the dark mica crystals in it become aligned and the resultant banded gneiss looks almost sedimentary. On closer inspection gneiss will be seen to have a much harder, crystalline structure than the typical sedimentary rock.

Another common rock, especially through parts of New England, is mica schist metamorphosed from a soft shale which contained many flakes of white (sometimes black) mica. Marble, a hard rock used in architecture, is metamorphosed limestone, originally a soft sedimentary rock.

Rock collecting

Most children like to collect rocks but need guidance, or they tend to make a meaningless, indistinguishable (at least to anyone else) collection of stones and pebbles. Stiff papier-maché egg boxes or plastic egg containers are excellent for smaller rocks as for small shells. The name or at least the place of collection can be written inside the cover.

Children need to be encouraged to collect larger and more distinguishable rock specimens. For these, use an empty cigar box with cardboard separators as for eggs. A fourth grade teacher motivated an intense interest in the geography of the state by connecting a state road map with colored ribbon to a few rocks and minerals she had collected as a hobby. The children and their parents eventually added to the collection in the classroom.

Rocks vs. minerals

Many people are confused as to the difference between rocks and minerals. We have seen that granite rock, for example, is made up of three components: quartz, feldspar, and mica, each of which is a mineral. In the same way, the rock mica schist is made up of mica crystals, occasional tiny garnets, etc. Minerals are combined in many different combinations and proportions to produce different rocks. By analogy a cook uses salt, sugar, flour, and shortening to produce a delectable variety of breads and pastries to please us.

Minerals and mining. A study of the history and geography of our country often leads children to wonder about mining days and ways. Since minerals often occurred as crystals, it may be helpful to review what the children observed about the growth of crystals in saturated solutions (p. 116).

Hydraulic mining depends on gravity and the relative greater weight and density of most valuable minerals as compared to the ore. Illustrate this by mixing a small quantity of sand, clay, old bricks, bits of metal such as tacks, nails, bits of wire, solder, lead sinkers in a jar partly full of water. As you shake the jar, the heavier materials separate out to the bottom of the jar.

"White gold." A simple experiment may illustrate why oil is not found everywhere. With a hammer and a cloth sack, pulverize different rock materials to provide two small piles each of gravel, sand, pebbles, clay, shale, shells, and so forth. Apply a drop of oil to each pile. Which one soaks up and holds the oil? Which kind of rock layer would be most apt to bear oil?

SPRINGS, WELLS, AND ROCK LAYERS

In country where water comes from wells, there is a whole body of interesting science as well as folklore related to the problem of locating and bringing up water. A simple illustration of one aspect requires a large container, gravel, and a tin can with top and bottom removed. Cover the bottom of the container with 3 –4″ of gravel; countersink the tin can in the gravel until it touches the bottom of the container. Remove the gravel from inside the can. Add water to the gravel outside the can. As the water rises through this gravel, it will rise to the same height inside the can or "well."

A kitchen geyser

If you remove the glass top from a percolator, water will boil up through the central tube much as it does in the geysers of Yellowstone and other hot springs. As a safety measure, keep the heat low while observing the spurts of boiling water coming up from below.

Artesian wells

Where artesian wells are used, children often do not understand why they flow without pumping. A working model can be set up inside an aquarium tank (Fig. 8-8). Construct a hill out of modeling clay

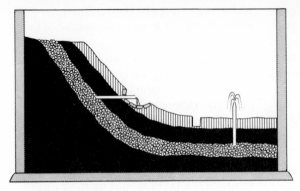

Fig. 8-8 Why do we find springs and wells in some places and not in others? The answer relates to the aquifers or permeable rock and/or soil layers through which water moves underground. The tubing inserted horizontally explains the location of a hillside spring. Let children experiment also, creating and draining a swamp in the lower end of the container. Try also a kettle-hole lake, illustrating its glacial origin. (From A. Joseph et al., *A Sourcebook for the Physical Sciences*, Harcourt, Brace & World, 1961.)

or papier-maché. Add pebbles in a porous layer to represent porous rock. Add a third layer of colored modeling clay. Note that the top layer is open near the top of the "hill." The hill represents a mountainside with three layers of rock. The top layer must make a watertight seal against the glass walls of the tank on all sides except at the peak of the hill. Test by pouring water on it. None should leak below the clay layer. Then pour or siphon out the water. Paraffin may be used in lieu of modeling clay.

Drill the well at the base of the "hill" by pushing a ½" rod or dowel through the top layer of clay. Into this hole, set an inverted medicine dropper tube; seal the clay around the tube at the point where it leaves the top of the clay.

Test the well by pouring water into the porous layer at the top. In mountains where layers of rock are upturned and open on the surface or under the soil, the rainwater and melting snow find their way into layers of permeable, or porous, rocks located between nonporous (impermeable) rocks (the clay layers in the model). When the porous layer fills with water, the water will spurt out of the medicine dropper if enough water is added. Some artesian wells must be pumped because the water pressure is too low for the water to be forced up out of the pipe.

Kettle-hole lakes

In country once glaciated one often finds and enjoys small, round deep lakes which formed where a huge chunk of ice broke off the glacier and was imbedded in soil and gravel carried by the glacier. When the ice chunk melted, the resulting depression became a lake. Imbed a chunk of ice in sand or sawdust. Note the depression it leaves when it has melted.

LAND, WATER, AND EROSION

Young children, left to themselves outdoors, will often explore and find more of interest in a limited area than will the average adult. For instance, a child may find a hole where an earthworm came up for air. He may spy a snail or other lowly creature and learn more about it by watching and poking than can be found in the average elementary school library. During or after a rain, our hero, blissfully unconscious of soggy shoes, becomes a hydraulic engineer as he wades the running gutters on his way home from school. Studying the water he decides to build a dam of debris and mud. And when the dam breaks, he views the resulting flood plain with interest and wonder. Such a child has an intuitive knowledge of what water can do to soil. We need only to give this knowledge and observation breadth and depth to make it truly functional for the rest of his life.

The child is often a better scientist than adults realize. He has intense, wide-ranging curiosity in the world around him. He practices the experimental method of finding out answers to questions. Above all, he observes long and closely. Here, perhaps, he has an advantage in being closer in stature than adults to the world underfoot.

Whether our school grounds include 1 acre or 18, whether we teach in a rural or urban school, there are a surprising number of learning experiences available to children along the school sidewalk and around the grounds. If we walk down the sidewalk, we may see a tiny mound of soil at the joint or crack between two sections of the walk. No doubt this has been brought up grain by grain from the subsoil underneath the walk by persistent worker ants. Is it the same color and texture as the soil at the surface? Does it contain any grains of quartz, mica, or feldspar eroded from the bedrock core in nearby hills or mountains?

After a rain we may find earthworm burrows in the grass next to the walk. Often there is a lumpy ring of earthworm castings around the holes. These are the residue of soil and other substances fed on by the earthworm who pulverized the soil which passed through its remarkable gizzard. If you find some piles of castings after a rain, break a clump in your fingers. You will find that the soil is not at all sticky. Quite the contrary, it is soft and easily crumbled. If you moisten some and it feels gritty, the chances are the soil is predominantly sandy. If it feels smooth, the soil is largely silt. Clay particles feel harsh when dry, sticky when wet. Earthworm castings can tell you a good deal about your soil.

Sheet erosion

If the ground along the sidewalk is not completely level with the walk, look for signs of sheet erosion or even miniature gullying. Sheet erosion is more insidious because it removes topsoil so gradually that the loss is not usually observed and checked before gullying begins. Many farm pastures begin to look bare and rocky where overgrazing has exposed the soil to sheet erosion. The fine topsoil is carried to the foot of the slope, the pasture produces less and less feed, and gullying ultimately starts in the steepest spots. Moving a fence in most areas is such hard work that some farmers are understandably guilty of fostering erosion.

Along the school sidewalk or curbing or short cut worn across a corner, look for fine soil washed out into the grass. Are the particles the same size throughout? Or is the sifting action of the water apparent as the slowing current dropped heavier particles but carried the finer ones further along?

Any water running over bare sloping soil is apt to carry off finer soil, leaving coarser, less fertile ground. In such places look for larger stones or pebbles atop little pillars of finer soil held in place by the stones. In these structures we have tiny replicas of the great sandstone buttes one sees in parts of the West.

Simulate pedestal erosion by using containers such as the pie tins with perforated

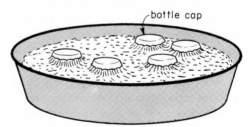

bottle cap

Fig. 8-9 Pedestal erosion. Using different soil mixtures, the children will see that some soil types are more erosion-prone than others. This conclusion could lead to further experiments to determine soil structure and composition.

bottoms used in splash erosion studies (p. 122). Fill level with firmly packed soil. Imbed bottle caps or pebbles in the surface. Sprinkle with water and note soil pedestals left under the caps and pebbles (Fig. 8-9).

Look for signs of sheet erosion around the roots of trees. Can you see any indication that the present soil level is lower than when the tree roots started growing?

Gullying

In one instance tons of sand were washed down into what was an attractive foothill stream valley. The huge gully started from a cow path down a sidehill pasture. The chances are the pasture had been overgrazed. There are usually many signs of gullying in the raw land around new school buildings and grounds until planting and seeding take hold. Find the largest gully, locate its head, and drive a stake parallel to the exact starting point. You will want to go back after a rainstorm to see if the gully has eaten further. Along the main channel of the gully do you find rocks and pebbles? From where do you think they came? Does the channel run a straight or crooked course? Are there any smaller gullies branching from the one you are studying? Look for miniature cliffs and caves in the side walls. Perhaps where water swirled around a rock or other obstruction you will find an islet held in place by tough grass. There may still be a pool of water in a low place along the channel. Look for debris along the bank. Where has it lodged and why? Side effects? Kind of debris? Follow the gully to its mouth where you may find a miniature delta or flood plain. Mark the widest part of the gully with stakes on each side. After a rain, check these and the stake at the head of the gully to see if the gully has lengthened or widened. What became of the soil which originally filled the gully?

Try to estimate the amount of soil removed.

Take back to the classroom some soil from the gully channel and from the sides and top. Which kind produces the best bean plants from seeds?

Gutters near the school should also be watched for evidences of erosion. During or right after a rain, collect water running in the gutters and set aside to settle in glass or plastic containers. Try to get samples from different gutters. Compare for possible differences in amount and kind of sediment in solution. If there is soil in the gutter after a rain, are the particles uniform or sorted by water? Do you think any larger flotsam is being further fragmented as it is washed along? Is there any relation between the amount of sediment and debris and the amount or intensity of rainfall? If the children have set up a rain gauge (Chapter 7), they may begin to see relationships.

A child who enjoys taking pictures might be interested in photographing local stream bank erosion or other evidence of gullying. The children might have a rich experience developing a picture story about their stream.

To illustrate the relationship between slope and erosion, cut one end from each of several shoeboxes (Fig. 8-10). Line with aluminum foil so as to form a spout at the open end. Add some soil. Raise the closed end of the box an inch. Sprinkle with a measured amount of water. Measure runoff and sediment. Raise the end of another box 3" and repeat. A 20" square seed flat raised an inch on one side provides a 5% slope (1" divided by 20" $\times$ 100% = 5%). Raising the side to other heights provides good problems in percentage (Fig. 8-11).

To find the per cent of slope around the school, obtain a yardstick, a straight 50" stick, and a small carpenter's level. Hold yardstick vertical, 50" stick horizontal until the bubble shows the level is even (Fig.

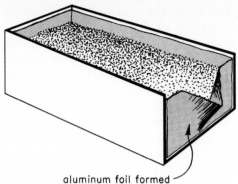

Fig. 8-10 Box for illustrating relationship between slope and erosion. Introduce such variables as a sod cover for one box, and sticks, bark, and pebble surface debris; for another, harder, heavier "rainfall" and such soil components as sand, clay, and leaf mold.

8-11). The number of inches on the yardstick (the "rise") divided by the horizontal distance (50") × 100 gives the per cent of slope. Older children will see that the "rise" × 2 gives the same total.

Build a pile of soil near a hose bib outside the school. Or pile sand into a large shallow carton just outdoors. The sand should be several inches deep. The children may wish to make a model of the stream or gully they have been studying. Their exhibit might include, for example, a bank cut by water, exposed tree roots, a sand bar, silt deposits, waterworn pebbles. The children will think of others.

To show how swift running water forms a canyon, allow water to pour rapidly onto the pile of soil. A deep river bed will form. As the water flows the length of the table, it will slow down and deposit a delta of the silt it has cut away. If the water flows in slowly onto a gentle slope, it will act as an old river and form meanders or sinuous curves. If more water is added, the shallow river bed will flood. Old rivers usually have flood plains. The water will tend to cut new channels if the speed of flow is increased.

Try making a "mountain" of sand. Notice the flood plain formed at the base as the fine sprinkling of "rain" wears it away. The wet soil can be dumped out to dry and later raked into the ground.

To construct land forms such as a hill, spread plaster of Paris over a mound of crumpled newspaper. When dry, cover with a thin layer of soil. Sprinkle and watch the water seek lower levels, carrying soil along. Again watch for the sorting action of water. Water running fast enough to roll a 1-pound rock will, if running twice as fast, move a 64-pound boulder.

Soil cover and erosion

Plants may become agents of erosion (pp. 122–23). Primarily they are our most important ally in making the "running water walk." Secure hosiery or stationery boxes. Remove covers, and nest bottoms inside for greater strength. Fill with soil. Set outdoors (or in large wash basin), one end propped up so the soil surface is at a slant. Into the soil of one box stick leaves and twigs. Leave the other bare. Sprinkle with the same quantity of water and compare runoff for quantity and clearness.

Or line two shoeboxes with aluminum foil. Cut out one end of each box and

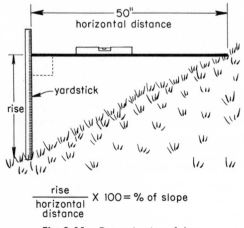

Fig. 8-11 Determination of slope.

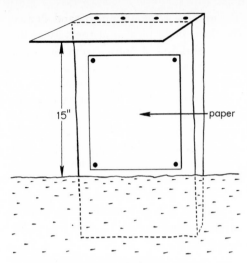

Fig. 8-12 Splashing, which may cause erosion, can be observed on wheels and mudguards of bicycles and automobiles. You can feel it where you can't see it.

form a spout with the help of a protruding piece of foil lining (Fig. 8-11). Add soil with leaves and twigs to one box, bare soil to the other. Using a sprinkler-head watering can or a clothes sprinkler, apply equal amounts of "rain." Compare runoff. For a touch of realism, plant an "elfin forest" of trees and shrub seedlings in one box. In the other simulate a burned forest with charred sticks and ash. Compare results after "rain."

The reason for contouring sloping crop lands can be shown with a washboard. Note the time required for a measured amount of water to run from top to bottom when the corrugations are horizontal. Does the water run much faster when the corrugations are vertical, that is, with the washboard on its side? Try to hold the washboard at the same slant for both tests.

Splash erosion

You may wish to extend these observations by some outdoor studies of splash erosion. Right after a rain look along the base of the school buildings where rain may have splashed mud against the walls.

Feel along the clapboards of wooden bungalows or frame buildings for soil splashed up during a rain. Make splash sticks (Fig. 8-12) and drive into the ground in such selected areas as the lawn, under deciduous or evergreen trees, under the eaves of buildings, in the school garden, on the ball diamond, under shrubs. Simulate rain by using a watering can at the same height and distance from each stake. Verify by checking for splash marks just after a rain.

Try also a pie tin study of splash erosion. Punch holes in the bottoms of several old tins or aluminum foil pie plates. Cover the bottoms with paper toweling. Then fill almost to the top with fine, dry soil. Just before a rain set out in the same areas you chose for the splash sticks. Compare the effect of a watering can with that of rain.

Wind, plants, and animals as agents of erosion

The earth's surface is worn down not only by rain and running water, but by wind, plants, and animals. Sandpaper different kinds of rock to gain a concept of wind erosion. Lead children to the generalization that it is not moving air itself that does the wearing but rather what the moving air carries in the way of dust and grit. The same is true of moving water. Some children may have watched city buildings being cleaned by sand blasting. Others may have seen the family automobile so pitted by desert sand storms as to require a new paint job. A few may have seen the grotesque desert rock formations believed to have been carved by the abrasive force of wind-driven sand. Fill two shallow boxes with soil; cover one with grassy sod. Place both outdoors in front of an electric fan (with help of extension cord). Note how wind moves soil from the bare box.

Inconspicuous lichen and moss, which

one often finds on the cool side of old buildings near the ground, are also eroding agents (Fig. 8-13). Scrape off enough of expose the rock or brick underneath. It should show marks of etching by the root-like structures of these plants. Make an inch-thick slab of plaster by pouring into a Vaseline-lined cardboard or wooden box. When hardened, remove from mold. Place bean or other seed sprouts on the smooth surface of the slab. Cover with moist paper toweling; keep in a terrarium or other humid container. After a few days, notice what the rootlets have done to the slab surface. If it is possible to secure a small piece of polished marble, cover with about one inch of soil, plant bean seeds, and water. After a few weeks, exhume the marble and examine the surface. The chemicals from root hairs will have dissolved a pattern on the polished surface.

Sidewalks cracked and heaved by roots growing under them are additional evidence of plants as erosion agents.

To illustrate the power of germinating seeds, fill a small glass jar with bean seeds. Fill to the brim with water, screw cover on securely, and leave overnight. Because the expanding seeds will crack the jar, it must be placed in a cardboard or wooden box or a canvas sack for safety.

Look for evidence of erosion along the joints of stone or brick steps. Compare weathered surfaces of old stone buildings with those of new construction. New polished headstones as compared with weathered or lichen-covered cemetery markers also illustrate the continuous, ever-present process of erosion.

Earthworms by sheer numbers are probably the most important animal agents of erosion. They are continually pulverizing lower layers of soil and bringing it to the surface for use by plants. What happens to coarse soil particles passed through their gizzards is illustrated by what they can do to certain hard foods

Fig. 8-13 Lichen growing on the surface of a fallen tree. Note the "fruiting" cup-like stalks which appear during the reproductive process. A lichen is a combination of two types of plants—fungus and alga—closely intergrown; neither plant can live alone under natural conditions, but together they survive on bare rocks and dead trees. Their association is an excellent example of symbiosis. (American Museum of Natural History.)

on earthworm farms. In some sections they are fed walnut shells and olive pits which, in a surprisingly short time, are transformed into the finest garden soil. Other burrowers such as woodchucks and gophers also aid in the total amount of soil overturn. In digging, they bring rocks and coarse soil to the surface for further erosion by weathering and fragmentation.

Expansion and contraction as erosion aids

Alternate expansion and contraction due to heat and cold are important forces of erosion. On motor trips children may have noticed the expansion joints or spaces between concrete slabs on the highway. A few may have noticed the spaces between railroad rails or at each end of a bridge. If there are cracks in the school sidewalk not caused by frost or tree roots, the cracks may have been caused by heat expansion. Make an experimental sidewalk and see for yourself how a sudden cold rain might affect a sun-baked sidewalk. Mix cement with equal parts of sand and water. Cast a 2" layer in a shoebox which can be peeled off when the cement hardens. Make enough cement mix for three slabs. Next day place one slab outdoors for a "control." Heat one with candles, Sterno, or other heat source. Then sprinkle with *cold* water. Cracking should result. Heating ordinary glass such as tubing and then plunging it into cold water also demonstrates the fracturing forces of sudden contractions.

The third slab is used to illustrate the force of fracturing due to sudden expansion. When the slab has been thoroughly chilled in the refrigerator, pour hot water over it.

A way to show the expansive force of freezing *water* is to freeze water in containers with push-up tops, such as milk cartons. Just as milk on a very cold morning pushes up the top of the bottle, so the water will push up the top of the container.

Such experiments should help children see that water as a solid occupies more space than it does as a liquid. This too may help them understand why freezing water can split great trees with the crack of a pistol shot on a still cold night. Ice crystals occupy about one tenth more space than do water molecules. Children may wish to measure the height of the frozen milk above the bottle, and so forth. If you have a heavy canvas bag or other safe container for glass splinters, freeze a jar full of water whose cover is screwed down tightly.

If you live in a climate where freezing temperatures occur, the children can find places where the sidewalk has heaved or been raised by water freezing and expanding below. This may raise the sidewalk enough to crack it. If the children observe cracks in the sidewalk or street paving in autumn, they may see in spring that these cracks have been enlarged or extended by winter frost.

In the mountains the water which seeps between rock layers or cracks expands as it freezes and loosens fragments, which sometimes accumulate to start a rock slide.

Anyone who has seen and heard the dust and roar from a rock slide has seen a combination of several erosive forces at work.

Water in the soil

Secure several glass jars of the same size and an equal number of tin cans which will just sit in the top of the jars. Baby food jars and frozen juice cans are a good combination. Make half a dozen holes in the bottom of each can with a slender nail or nail punch. Fill each can half full of soil from selected areas around the school. Add half a cup of water to each can and note what seeps through. From which sample did water start to drop first and finish dripping first; from which sample, last? Try the same procedure with sand from the kindergarten sandbox, clay from a local clay bank or from pieces of an old clay pot pulverized by hammering, loam from a garden, and humus or leaf mold from the woods. The children will see that water slips rapidly through sandy soil, and such soil is therefore apt to erode quickly. Water drips steadily through humus or organic matter, showing the importance of such material in the soil to retain rainfall and release it slowly with a minimum of erosion.

The low permeability of clays makes rain run off, tending to wash areas below. Soil samples acting like clays may come from an area which may reveal sheet erosion and incipient gullying.

The children may mix the sand, clay, and humus in different proportions and combinations, and retest for water retention. Try adding sawdust in place of humus.

STUDYING THE SOIL

Soil moisture

Secure several half-pint or pint covered paper containers. Weigh and number empty containers. About 2 days after a rain, fill containers with samples of soil from a grassy plot, from beneath shrubbery or trees, from a weedy area, from the school garden, from a bare section of the ball diamond.

Cover containers as soon as filled, weigh as accurately as possible, remove covers, and set in a warm dry place. Stir soil every day and reweigh. Where there is no change in weight for a few days, the soil may be considered dried out. Note the order in which the soils from various locations dried out. Then calculate the per cent of moisture by dividing the loss of weight by the dry weight of soil and multiplying by 100. If available, try also soil samples from pasture, crop land, or woods.

The related factor of water penetration may be studied in soils about the school with the help of some soup cans. Remove both ends of the cans with the help of a cutter, leaving smooth edges. Imbed in the ground to the same depth in selected spots. Fill to the brim with water and watch the time required for the water to sink into the ground.

Soil compaction

Your efforts to imbed the soup cans illustrate the fact that soils differ markedly in compaction of their grains or particles. Recheck by testing with a pencil or pointed length of doweling. How far can you push into the ground. Is it easier if the ground is wet? Is there any relation between the amount of organic material in the soil and the ease or difficulty you experienced in pushing into the ground? Is there any relation between plant cover and soil compaction, between erosion and compaction, between water retention and compaction?

Soil aggregates

A lump of moist garden soil or florist's potting soil breaks into smaller lumps very much like bread crumbs. Like bread crumbs, soil aggregates have holes or pores big enough to see with a magnifying glass. These holes or spaces are very important to soil because they permit the passage of water and air. Often house and garden plants die or do not flourish because these all-important spaces become pushed together, preventing the free flow of air and water to the roots of the plants Sand facilitates good drainage and the maintenance of spaces between soil aggregates.

What's in soil?

Careful examination of a cubic foot of soil from the school grounds is apt to reveal a surprisingly varied composition. Use a gardener's flat spade in order to make a straight-sided hole. Spread out each shovelful on paper and make separate piles of pebbles, roots, sticks, and the like. Have a collection of plastic pill bottles or other small containers handy for sowbugs, earthworms, or other animal life of the soil. When the soil is partly dried out, sift it through sieves of increasing fineness. A square of hardware cloth, sieves ½", ¼", or 1/16", or other wire mesh may serve. Make separate piles of each screening. Place partly disintegrated plant or animal debris in separate piles. Try the same process in another area and compare.

Soil profiles

If there is any spot near the school where the soil has been dug away three feet or more, as for a road cut or an excavation, you can distinguish at least two natural layers—the darker topsoil and the lighter subsoil. Often we miss seeing the topsoil layer because it is so thin or because it is overhung and disguised with the roots of plants and fallen debris.

Soil scientists test soil texture by the

feel, rolling it between their fingers or pressing it between the palms of their hands. By testing many soils in this way, they have come to divide soils into four kinds according to the predominant size of the particles. These four are gravels, sands, loams, and clays. Loams, mixtures of sand, silt, and clay in fairly equal proportions, are good for plants.

In order to decide what kinds of soils you have in your vicinity, try to make all the soil samples about equally moist. There should be enough moisture for all the particles to stick together when you squeeze a handful, but no water should drip out (above). Roll a ball of each sample the size of a big marble. Experiment until your samples are just moist enough to roll successfully into a snake-like or cigar-shaped roll. Put together all those "cigars" which make smooth stick rolls and hold their shape. They are probably clay soils. If you have rolls which crack in several places, you are probably working with a very silty soil. If you have soil which will scarcely roll into a small cigar, you are probably working with sandy soil.

Soil scientists tell us it takes about 300 years to make an inch of really productive topsoil. Let the children measure local topsoil in nearby road cuts or excavations. Let them calculate the probable time required for its formation and deposit. Perhaps they may wish to relate this topsoil chronology to their history studies. Scrape this away so you can see and measure the thin dark layer which grows virtually all the plants on earth. Subsoil is usually too poor in organic material and mineral elements and too coarse to support plant growth. Test this for yourselves by sprouting seeds in samples of topsoil and subsoil from the same location. In many parts of the country the U.S. Soil Conservation Agent (U.S. Dept. of Agriculture) is most willing to show the children colored slides on local soil erosion and answer questions on local problems.

Distinguishing soil by its feel

As you have tested and examined the soil around school, you have come to realize that most surface soils are mixtures of particles of various sizes. Probably there are large stones and small. Usually you can see sand grains with a magnifying glass. There are probably fine silt particles which you cannot see except through an ordinary microscope. A soil composition analysis might also show such things as plant and animal remains and bits which become humus. All of these soil elements have a special job to do in the soil and each has a certain feel. For example, *sand* grains feel gritty, dry *silt* feels like flour or talcum powder which becomes smooth and slippery when wet; dry *clay* feels harsh; wet clay is sticky. Clay cements larger silt and sand particles together. *Humus* not only cements larger particles together but also prevents clay particles from packing too closely.

Making soil

Try rubbing rocks together to make soil. Try growing plants in soil made this way. Compare with plants grown in soil made of equal parts of sand, loam, and humus. In which type of soil do the plants do better?

Place an assortment of rocks in a half-filled jar of water. The jar should be "stout" and the rocks neither too numerous nor too heavy. Every day the children can shake the jar and watch to see how fast they are making soil. Ask the local nurseryman or soil conservation agent how to make soil.

8-1 Encourage every child to make a small rock collection, say, one half or one dozen samples of common rocks labeled and/or displayed in a cigar box or egg carton.

8-2 List earthy materials in or around school. Some of these might be chalk, clay pots, graphite, copper, iron and steel, porcelain, china, glass, aluminum, slate, etc.

8-3 Examine sand with a hand glass. Examine quartz or calcite crystals. Look at the cleavage planes in common feldspar crystals. Look at snowflakes in season. If possible let them fall on dark cloth. Snowflakes, of course, are water crystals, and water is a mineral. Use refrigerator ice crystals as a substitute in warm climates.

8-4 Look at salt under magnification. It, too, is a mineral. Rock is made of mineral crystals "packaged" together. Some rocks have but one mineral, some have several. Visit a gravel pit or recent road cut where rock is exposed and collect rocks of each kind.

8-5 List local industries depending primarily or secondarily on earth materials; use a classified telephone book. Then visit some of them for samples to use in display. Make a field trip, if possible, to a local quarry or builders' supply store.

8-6 Make a map of land classifications for the nearest hill. Your Soil Conservation Service or Department of Agriculture might help.

8-7 Let a group of children get a bucket of earth from a pasture or vacant lot. Examine it bit by bit on white paper or toweling. One group of children found a total of 115 insect invertebrates in a rectangle of earth $6'' \times 12'' \times 4''$ deep.

8-8 Let children discuss and develop a chart showing the cycle of change from rocks into soil and vice versa.

8-9 How vacant is a vacant lot? Make an approximation of what college science students call *quadrate* studies of the area. This involves dividing the children into small teams, each team being responsible for making a close study and detailed report of everything they can find in their sector. You might give them a common

background by taking them on a preliminary trip to a typical part of the lot or similar area. Ask, "What do you see?" Identification is of less importance here than keen observation. Which children later remember and which make new observations on a return trip will be an interesting way of evaluating children's abilities.

8-10 An urban environment is less of a desert than we think. John Kieran's *Natural History of New York City* is a case in point. You may find the world in microcosm close at hand. For example, look for miniature examples of major geographical land forms on the school grounds. Local building stones, sidewalks, and curbstones often provide a geology field trip. There is much to be observed by close study of the area between sidewalk and curb. For a wealth of creative ideas developed by teachers, see *Operation New York*.

8-11 Fill a quart screw-top container about ⅔ full. Add soil until water just overflows. Cover and shake well. As contents settle, lay a card against the side of the container; sketch the proportions of different layers (sand, gravel, loam, clay). Secure samples from different locales and compare? Which layer has the largest particles? The finest? What is the major component of your sample? Many other interesting suggestions for investigating soil may be found in *Conservation: A Handbook for Teachers,* by E. L. Palmer.

8-12 To gain some partial concepts of the importance of organic material in soil, secure dry leaves, pine needles, and grass. Weigh together in a metal bucket, burn in the bucket, then reweigh. For further interesting suggestions, see *Suggested Activities for the Teaching of the Conservation of Natural Resources,* Montana Conservation Council, p. 15.

8-13 Older children may profit by some simple surveying around the school ground. The equipment they will need consists of a carpenter's level, a 6' rod or pole marked off in inches, and a plane-surface table made of a platform nailed to a broomstick handle not quite 4' long.

BIBLIOGRAPHY

Adler, Irving, *Dust,* Day, 1958. For upper grades. Source and structure of particles in air. Economic value of dust.

——, *Rocks, Minerals, and the Stories They Tell,* Knopf, 1956.

Allan, David, and Vinson Brown, *An Illustration Guide to Common Rocks and Rock-Forming Minerals,* Naturegraph Co., 1956.

Baumann, Hans, *The Caves of the Great Hunters,* Pantheon, 1954. For upper grades. Photographic illustrations accompany true story of boys who discover Ice Age cave.

Brown, Vinson, and David Allan, *Rocks and Minerals of California and Their Stories,* Naturegraph Co., 1957. For middle grades. Guide to galvanize the amateur rock hound.

Buehr, Walter, *Underground Riches,* Morrow, 1958.

Casanova, Richard, *Illustrated Guide to Fossil Collecting,* Naturegraph Co., 1957. For middle grades. Interesting handbook for fossil identification.

Colby, C. B., *Soil Savers,* Coward-McCann, 1957. For upper grades. Illustrative story of the U.S. Soil Conservation Service.

Conservation Activities for Elementary Schools, State of California, Dept. of Natural Resources (n.d.).

Cormack, Maribelle, *First Book of Stones,* Watts, 1950.

Dana, Edward, *Minerals and How to Study Them,* Wiley, 1949.

Darby, Gene, *What Is a Rock?,* Benefic, 1958.

Elementary Science Project: Earth and Its Resources, Board of Education of the City of New York (n.d.). 48 pp. Teachers reference. Approaches to teaching, guide to selection of materials, curriculum outlines, and suggested activities for kindergarten through sixth grade. Designed for use in metropolitan-suburban area. Excellent.

Fenton, Carroll L., and Mildred A. Fenton, *Rocks and Their Stories,* Garden City, 1951. For middle grades. How to study, identify, and collect most important kinds.

Geologic Guidebook: Along Highway 49, Sierra Nevada Gold Belt Bulletin 141, Mother Lode Country 1948 Division of Mines, San Francisco, Calif. 164 pp. Many photographs and accurate text to help the sight-seer view the landscape with greater insight.

Geology, Boy Scouts of America Merit Badge Series, 1953. 83 pp. For upper grades. A great deal of information and ideas adapted to children. Very inexpensive.

Hamilton, Elizabeth, *The First Book of Caves,* Watts, 1956.

Hogner, Dorothy, *Earthworms,* Crowell, 1953. For middle grades. Contains background information and suggestions for rearing.

Holsaert, Eunice, and Robert Gartland, *Dinosaurs,* Holt, Rinehart and Winston, 1959. For primary grades. Beginners can read the ever-fascinating story of the thunder lizards.

Jensen, David, *My Hobby Is Collecting Rocks and Minerals,* Childrens Press, 1958. For upper grades. Provides identification and classification, collection and display, sources of equipment, and reference material.

Kieran, John, *Natural History of New York City,* Houghton Mifflin, 1959.

Lauber, Patricia, *Dust Bowl: The Story of Man on the Great Plains,* Coward-McCann, 1958. For middle grades. Changes on the plains before and since the first settlers. Present conservation practices.

Let's Collect Rocks, Shell Oil Co., 1960. 17 pp. Amusing and attractive basic information for the casual tripper.

Livingston, Alfred, Jr., *Geological Journeys in Southern California,* Brown, 1949. 154 pp. Written originally for his junior college students, Dr. Livingston's manual is a treasure house of practical applications of the principles of geology, providing many examples of the geology of his locale.

Martin, Charles, *Monsters of Old Los Angeles,* Viking, 1950. For middle grades. Authentic account of Pleistocene animals trapped in the La Brea tar pits.

Miner, Opal, *The First Book of the Earth,* Watts, 1958.

Montana Conservation Council, *Suggested Activities for the Teaching of the Conservation of Natural Resources,* Reporter Printing and Supply Co., Billings, Mont., 1956.

Moone, Patrick, *The Earth Our Home,* Abelard-Schuman, 1957.

Operation New York: Using the Natural Environment of the City as a Curriculum Resource, Board of Education of the City of New York, Bureau of Curriculum Research, 1960. 117 pp. Like John Kieran's *Natural History of New York City,* an eye opener to science all around us.

Palmer, E. L., ed., *Conservation: A Handbook for Teachers,* Cornell Rural School Leaflet, Vol. 45, No. 1, Sept., 1951. 64 pp. Contains many interesting ideas and suggestions for activities, as, for example, simple mapping, recording ground temperatures, and the like.

Parker, Bertha M., *Soil,* Row, Peterson, 1952. 36 pp.

Pearl, Richard, *Popular Gemology,* Wiley, 1948.

Philips, Alfred W., *The Value of Soil Conservation,* University Publishing Co. (1126 Que Street, Lincoln 1, Neb.). 64 pp. Problems of conserving soil, water and wildlife.

Pistorius, Anna, *What Dinosaur Is It?,* Follett, 1958. For upper grades. Describes many kinds and several fossil beds. Comparison with everyday animals. Colored pictures and guide to pronunciation.

Podendorf, Illa, *True Book of Pebbles and Shells,* Childrens Press, 1954.

———, *True Book of Rocks and Minerals,* Childrens Press, 1958.

Pough, F. H., *All About Volcanoes and Earthquakes,* Random House, 1953.

———, *Field Guide to Rocks and Minerals,* Houghton Mifflin, 1953.

Reed, W. Maxwell, *The Earth for Sam,* Harcourt, Brace & World, rev. ed., 1960. An old favorite, edited by Paul F. Brandwein. Comprehensive survey of earth science. Up to date. Many exceptional illustrations.

Riedman, Sarah R., *Let's Take a Trip to a Cement Plant,* Abelard-Schuman, 1959. For middle grades. Source, manufacture, and uses of cement.

Schneider, Herman, and Nina Schneider, *Rocks, Rivers, and the Changing Earth,* Scott, 1952. For middle grades. Story of the earth, accompanied by suggestions for interesting activities.

Shannon, Terry, *Among the Rocks,* Sterling, 1956. For middle grades. Colored illustrations with simple, informative text on rocks and minerals.

Shuttlesworth, D. E., *The Story of Rocks,* Garden City, 1956.

Stamp, L. Dudley, *Earth's Crust,* Crown, 1951. For middle grades. British geographer uses drawings and photographs of models to explain physical geography.

Sterling, Dorothy, *Story of Caves,* Doubleday, 1956. For middle grades. Cave sculpture, writings, and stories of cave animals, including ancient legends.

Swenson, Valerie, *A Child's Book of Stones and Minerals,* Maxton, 1955.

Ware, Kay, and others, *Let's Read About Mountains and Volcanoes,* Webster, 1957. For upper grades. Volcano formation, uses of volcanic rock, problems. Suggestions for additional study.

Waugh, Dorothy, *Warm Earth,* Oxford, 1943. Chapters on rock-soil cycle, soil types, soil horizons, humus, liquid diet, microorganisms, soil capillarity, underground water, etc. Good.

Weaver, Dolla Cox, *For Pebble Pups,* Chicago Natural History Museum, 1955. A collecting guide for junior geologists.

White, Anne T., *Rocks All Around Us,* Random House, 1959.

Worbs, D. E., and E. W. Gordon, *Underfoot,* Cornell Rural School Leaflet, Vol. 49, No. 4, Spring, 1956. 32 pp. The world, animate and inanimate, under our feet. A wealth of challenging ideas and information.

Wyler, R., and G. Ames, *The Story of the Ice Age,* Harper, 1956.

Zim, H., *What's Inside the Earth,* Morrow, 1953.

———, and E. K. Cooper, *Minerals,* Harcourt, Brace & World, 1943.

———, and P. R. Shaffer, *Rocks and Minerals,* Simon and Schuster, 1957.

The air

AIR TAKES UP SPACE

Children, especially the younger ones, are usually unaware of the air around them. Because air is invisible, they do not realize that it is a real substance, just like solids and liquids. And just like any other real substance, air takes up space.

Obtain a large, sturdy plastic bag. Do not use one that holds onions or potatoes because these bags have small holes in them. Press the bag flat. First fill the bag with blocks of wood, or marbles, or any other bulky solid material (Fig. 9-1). The children will see the bag bulge out, owing to the solid material in it. Have the children feel the bag and its contents. Let them come to the conclusion that when something real is put into the bag, the bag will bulge.

Now empty the bag and refill it with water. The bag will bulge out again because of the water in it. Call the children's attention to the fact that as they feel and

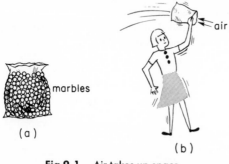

marbles

(a)

air

(b)

Fig 9-1 Air takes up space.

poke the bag, the water in the bag pushes back on their fingers.

Empty the bag again. This time grip the bag at one side of its mouth and move the bag quickly through the air. When the bag fills up, hold it tightly at the neck so that the air will not escape. Call the children's attention to the bulging appearance of the bag. It bulges out just as it did with the other real and visible materials. Have the children feel and poke the bag again, and note how the air in the bag pushes back and feels springy.

Obtain a square of cardboard, the size of a newspaper. (If the cardboard is not available, use a double sheet of newspaper opened up to make one sheet.) Have one of the children hold the cardboard in front of his body and run across the playground. Have the child run across the playground again, but this time without the cardboard. Point out that the child has to push air out of his way when he walks or runs. When he is holding a big sheet of cardboard in front of him, he has a lot of air to push out of the way. This is not easy, and the air slows him up.

Crumple a paper napkin or paper towel and press it into the bottom of a glass tumbler. Make sure the napkin is pressed firmly against the bottom so that it will remain there even when the tumbler is turned upside down. Now fill an aquarium or large glass jar almost full of water. Then lower the glass tumbler, mouth down, into the water all the way down to the bottom of the aquarium. Let the children look at the tumbler while it is in the water. The water will rise up into the tumbler, but not all the way.

Now lift the tumbler straight out of the water. Keep it upside down while you dry the edges. Then pull out the paper napkin and show it is still dry. Help the children understand that initially the tumbler is not empty but filled with air—a real substance. When the tumbler is pushed into the water, the air has no way of getting out. The water pushes against the air, and even squeezes, or compresses, the air a little; thereby the water rises somewhat in the tumbler. But the air does not let the water travel all the way up the tumbler and reach the napkin. As a result, the air in the tumbler keeps the napkin dry.

"Seeing" air

Take an "empty" bottle and lower it mouth down into an aquarium or glass jar that is almost full of water. Now tilt the bottle on its side and watch the air come out in bubbles. The children are now really seeing air. You can also obtain bubbles of air from a hollow rubber ball with a hole in it or from a rubber syringe bulb. Hold the ball under water and squeeze it gently.

Another way of "seeing" air is to fill a tall glass jar full of water. Place a piece of cardboard or glass over the mouth of the jar and invert the jar into a pan or dish containing water. Do not remove the cardboard until the mouth of the jar is below the surface of the water. Now remove the cover and let the jar stand inverted in the pan. Tilt one end of the jar a little and place the tip of a medicine dropper under it. Squeeze the bulb of the medicine dropper and watch the bubbles of air move up to the top of the jar. Remove the medicine dropper from the water to allow more air to enter in the dropper. Then repeat the

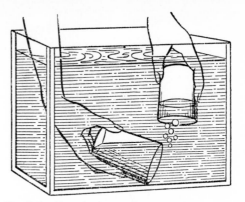

Fig. 9-2 Transferring air from one glass tumbler to another. (From *UNESCO Source Book for Science Teachers*, UNESCO, 1956.)

process. Do this several times. Call the children's attention to the fact that as more and more air enters the jar, it must occupy space. To do this, the air forces some of the water out of the jar.

The children might like to transfer air from one glass tumbler to another. Obtain two glass tumblers of the same size. Put one tumbler into an aquarium or large glass jar almost full of water. Let the tumbler fill up with water. Then invert the tumbler mouth downward and hold it so that the tumbler is half in and half out of the water. The water in the tumbler will remain there as long as the mouth of the tumbler remains below the surface of the water.

Now, holding the tumbler in this position, lower the second tumbler into the aquarium with its mouth downward (Fig. 9-2). Bring the edge of the tumbler of air under the edge of the tumbler full of water. Then slowly tip the tumbler of air so that the bubbles of air rise directly into the tumbler of water. The bubbles of air push the water out of the tumbler. Soon the tumbler of water becomes filled with air, while the tumbler of air now becomes filled with water.

"Feeling" air

Now that the children know that air is

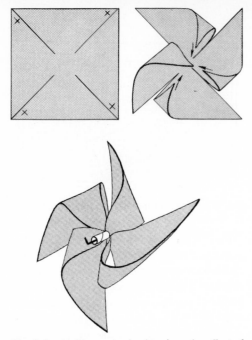

Fig. 9-3 Making a pinwheel to show the effect of moving air.

Obtain a piece of heavy paper or cardboard six inches square. Draw two lines joining the opposite corners. These lines are called diagonals. Put an X in each of the four corners, as shown in the diagram (Fig. 9-3). Now cut along each diagonal to within an inch of the center. Bend each corner containing the X (every other corner) so that all the corners lay over the center. Push a pin through the center; then push the pin into the eraser of a pencil. Let the children blow on the pinwheel or place it in front of an electric fan. Let them run up and down the schoolyard with the pinwheel in front of them.

Obtain an empty paper milk carton. Push the pencil which holds the pinwheel through the carton. Place the carton in front of an electric fan or an open window. The wind makes the toy windmill turn.

Call the children's attention to the wind as it rustles the leaves, causes the flag to fly, and makes clothes on the line flutter and flap.

AIR HAS PRESSURE

As you know, we are living at the bottom of an ocean of air that is at least 500 miles deep. The gravity of the earth pulls the air down, just as it pulls down everything else on earth. Therefore, the air has weight. Although air doesn't seem to weigh much when compared to other materials, an ocean of air 500 miles deep weighs a great deal. Everything that has weight can and does exert a pressure. Consequently, the great weight of air above us also exerts or causes pressure. Scientists tell us that the pressure of air at sea level is approximately 15 pounds (14.7) on each square inch of surface.

Lead the children to associate weight with pressure. Have them stretch their arms straight out, and pile books on their hands. Let them recall the experience in the playground when there was a pile-up

real and takes up space, it is time for them to "feel" air. Let the children lift a book cover and, holding their faces near the book, close the cover suddenly. They will feel a wind on their faces. Help them understand that there is air all around the book. When the book cover is closed, it pushes the air. This moving air is called wind.

Crumple a small piece of tissue paper and place it in front of the book. Lift the book cover and close it quickly. The moving air will cause the paper to fly away.

Make a paper fan by folding a piece of typing paper into narrow strips, first one way and then the other as in the folds of an accordion. Have the children fan themselves. When fanning, they are moving air and thus creating a wind. Point out that the blades of an electric fan cause the air to move quickly and thereby create a strong wind.

Have the children make a pinwheel.

of children. Certainly the ones at the bottom felt the pressure from the weight of those on top.

To show that air exerts pressure, place a heavy book upright on an empty paper bag. Blow hard into the bag. The pressure of the air will cause the book to topple over. Repeat the experiment, using a long balloon and a tin can.

The children might like to see how air pressure blows water out of a bottle. Fill a pan half full of water. Also fill a large wide-mouthed bottle full of water. Cover the bottle opening with a piece of cardboard or glass, and invert the bottle into the pan of water. Do not remove the cardboard or glass until the mouth of the bottle is below the surface of the water in the pan. Then remove the card and let the bottle stand inverted in the pan. Now tip the bottle a little and insert one end of a rubber or plastic tube only a short way up into the bottle. Blowing into the other end of the tube will cause the water to be blown out of the bottle. Point out that by blowing air through the tubing, you are forcing air into the bottle. This air exerts pressure on the water and pushes the water out.

Children are quite familiar with the pressure of moving air. When the wind blows strongly, the children feel its pressure on their faces and bodies. When driving in an auto with their hands out the window, they feel the pressure of the air. The air in front of an electric fan also exerts a pressure.

Obtain a bicycle pump. As you work the pump, have one child place his hand in front of the outlet nozzle. He will feel the pressure of the air as it is forced out.

Air exerts or causes pressure even when it is not moving. A demonstration very commonly used to show this involves the use of a large can. An empty duplicator fluid can or any other large can with a screw-on cap is just fine. Make sure the

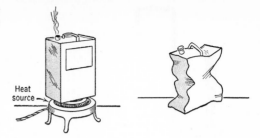

Fig. 9-4 Air pressure causes a can to collapse. (From R. W. Burnett, *Teaching Science in the Elementary School*, Holt, Rinehart and Winston, 1953.)

can is clean inside before you use it. Pour a glass of water into the can and, keeping the can's cap off, heat the can on an electric hot plate. Boil the water vigorously until steam can be seen coming from the top (Fig. 9-4). Now remove the can from the hot plate (*Caution: It is hot.*) and quickly screw on the cap before the can has a chance to cool. Have the children watch the can as it cools. It collapses and twists out of shape. If you are pressed for time, you can obtain the safe effect quickly by pouring cold water over the hot can.

Point out that before the experiment was begun there was air inside the can. Because the pressure of the air inside and outside the can was the same, nothing happened to the can. The heating serves to remove the air inside the can and thereby lower or reduce the air pressure inside the can after cooling. This is done as follows. When the water boils in the can, steam is formed. The steam pushes out some of the air. When the cap is replaced and the can allowed to cool, the steam is changed back to water. Now there is less *air* in the can than there was originally, and therefore the *pressure* of this air also is less. As a result, the greater air pressure exerted on the outside of the can causes the can to crumple. (The purpose of pouring cold water on the can is to make the

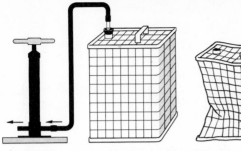

Fig. 9-5 Using a bicycle pump to make a can collapse. (From A. Joseph et al., *A Sourcebook for the Physical Sciences*, Harcourt, Brace & World, 1961.)

steam condense back to water more quickly.)

You might like to use a simpler method of accomplishing the effect described above, without having to deal with the concepts of boiling, formation of steam, condensation, etc. If so, obtain a one-hole rubber stopper that fits the opening in the can. Insert a short piece of glass tubing into the stopper. Fit the stopper tightly into the can. Use heavy rubber or plastic tubing to connect the glass tubing to a bicycle pump that is to be used as a vacuum pump (Fig. 9-5).[1] Now simply pump the air out of the can. With less air in the can, the air pressure inside becomes less and the can will collapse.

If a vacuum pump is not available, there is still another demonstration that is quite effective. Insert a short piece of glass tubing into a one-hole stopper that fits the hole in the tin can. Attach a piece of rubber or plastic tubing about 15–20' long to one end of the glass tubing. Fill the can with water and stopper the can. Now pour water into the rubber tubing until it is also filled with water (Fig. 9-6). Then fold back the free end of the rubber tubing so that the water will not run out. A spring-type clothespin serves as a clamp to prevent the water from running out.

Place the can on the window sill of the second floor of the school. Let the rubber

[1] Every scientific supply house sells the bicycle-type pump that can be used as a vacuum pump. You may also be able to borrow such a pump from a high school science department.

tubing hang down to the ground below. Have one of the children release the clamp. Enough water will run out of the rubber tubing and the tin can to cause the can to collapse. Point out that as the water leaves the can, an empty space is left in the can. This "empty space" is called a vacuum. Since, by definition, there is virtually no air in a vacuum, there is consequently no air pressure in the inside of the can. Therefore, the pressure of the air on the outside of the can causes the can to collapse. This, in turn, allows more water to flow out, thereby creating a new vac-

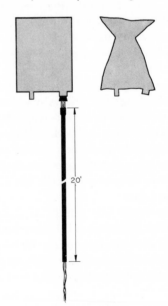

Fig. 9-6 Water running out of a can creates a vacuum, causing the can to collapse. (From A. Joseph et al., *A Sourcebook for the Physical Sciences*, Harcourt, Brace & World, 1961.)

uum which causes the can to collapse a bit more.

Obtain a thin flat stick about 2′ long and 1–2″ wide. The stick should be no thicker than a wooden ruler. Lay the stick flat on the table with about 8″ extending beyond the table. Cover the part of the stick that is on the table with two or three sheets of newspaper. Be sure to smooth the paper down as flat as possible. With a hammer or a baseball bat, strike the end of the stick sharply. The stick breaks in two. Help the children understand that when the stick is hit, the other end tries to push up like a see-saw. But the air on top of the spread-out newspaper is pushing down on the wood. This air pressure holds the wood down and, instead of flipping over, the wood breaks into two pieces.[2]

Equal in all directions

Under ordinary conditions air pressure is exerted equally in all directions. Blow a few soap bubbles. Detach the bubbles and note that they are always shaped as spheres. This shows that the pressure of the air inside the bubble is acting equally in all directions. The same holds true for the air outside the bubble.

Here is another way of showing equal air pressure in all directions. Cover the wide opening of a glass or plastic funnel with a piece of rubber from a balloon. If the rubber does not fit tightly, glue or tie it down. Remove some air from the funnel by sucking at the narrow end. The rubber will then curve downward because the pressure of the air outside the funnel is greater than the air pressure inside the funnel. Quickly slip your finger over the narrow end of the funnel. This will prevent air from coming back into the funnel. The rubber thus stays pulled inward. No matter which way you hold the funnel-

upward, downward, or sideward—the rubber stays in the same position. This is due to the fact that air pressure is exerted equally in all directions.

Increases with increasing volume

The children might be interested in using air pressure to make a milk bottle blow its cover off. Fill a milk bottle half full of hot water and quickly put the cover back on. The hot water heats the air above it. The air becomes warm and expands. This expanding air causes the air pressure inside the bottle to increase. As a result, the increased air pressure makes the bottle cover pop off.

Like most solids, liquids, and gases, air will expand when heated and will contract when cooled. Experiments showing this effect, together with convection currents, are taken up in detail in Chapter 18.

The pressure of the air can be measured. Experiments on how this may be done, together with the use of air pressure in predicting weather, are taken up in detail in Chapter 6.

THE EFFECT OF AIR PRESSURE ON WATER

Air pressure has some interesting effects on water. Fill a glass tumbler or bottle completely full of water. Place a square of cardboard over the mouth of the tumbler. Hold the card with your hand while you turn the tumbler upside down. You will be able to hold the tumbler upside down and yet the cardboard will not fall. This demonstration should be performed over the sink or a pan, just in case it doesn't work the first time.

The children would expect the water to fall out, especially since it has weight and gravity is pulling on it. However, point out that the air is pushing up on the cardboard. It is pushing up harder than gravity is pulling on the water. Therefore, air

[2] In actuality, this is an oversimplified explanation. When the stick is struck, inertia also exerts some force in the stick.

pressure prevents the water from running out.

Stretch a double layer of cheesecloth over the mouth of a bottle and fasten it securely with a rubber band or string. Fill the bottle with water by pouring it through the cheesecloth. Quickly turn the bottle upside down. The pressure of the air prevents the water from flowing out of the bottle. It is interesting that you can fill the bottle through the cheesecloth, yet cannot empty it through the cheesecloth when you hold the bottle upside down.

Place a bottle or glass tumbler inside an aquarium or large pan almost full of water. Let the bottle fill with water. Now turn the bottle upside down and lift up the bottle with its mouth down until the bottle is nearly out of the water. The water will not run out of the bottle because it is held up by air pressure pushing down on the surface of the water.

There are other demonstrations to show that air pressure interferes with pouring water or liquids. Obtain a narrow-neck bottle and a glass or plastic funnel. Place the funnel in the neck of the bottle, leaving some space to be filled with modeling clay. Be sure to pack the clay tightly in the neck of the bottle. Now pour water slowly into the funnel. The water will not run into the flask. Have the children recall that air takes up space. The water cannot flow into the bottle because the tube of the funnel is small and therefore does not provide enough room for the air to go out of the bottle at the same time that the water is going in. As a result, the air pressure inside the bottle prevents the water from running in.

With a nail or pencil carefully punch a hole through the modeling clay into the inside of the bottle. The water can run in freely now because there is room for the air in the bottle to come out.

The children should now be able to explain why water gurgles when it is poured out of a narrow-neck bottle and also why the water comes out in spurts. As the water pours out, air is trying to get in. When air does get in, it gurgles as it goes through the water. While the air is coming in, it slows up or stops the water that is coming out. As a result, the water comes out in spurts.

Punch a hole in a can of fruit juice. Because of the air pressure outside, the juice either will not pour out or will pour out with difficulty. Punch a second hole in the can. The juice will now pour out easily. As the juice pours out of one hole, the air comes into the second hole. The air in the second hole is pressing down on the juice with just as much force as it is pushing on the juice in the first hole. This allows the juice to pour of its own weight.

This effect can also be shown quite clearly by making a dip tube. Hold your finger over one end of a glass tube or transparent straw and lower it into a glass of colored water. Very little water will enter the tube because the tube is filled with air that cannot escape, and the pressure of the air inside the tube prevents the colored water from rising in the tube. Now remove the finger. The air inside the tube escapes as the water in the tumbler rises up the tube. Replace your finger over the tube and then lift the tube out of the water. Air pressure at the bottom of the tube prevents the water from running out. Now remove the finger once more and the water will run out. The air is now pressing down on top of the tube with just as much force as the air pressing up at the bottom of the tube. The water then falls of its own weight.

Diving bell

Air pressure enables men to work under water. To show this, float a cork in an aquarium or a large jar half full of water. Place a glass tumbler mouth down over the cork and press the tumbler down until

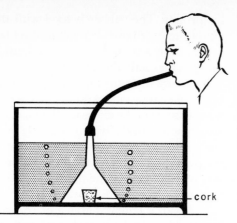

Fig. 9-7 How fresh air can be supplied to men working under water.

cardboard or glass or your finger over the mouth of the vial when you place it into the jar of water. Then release. If the vial sinks to the bottom, it has too much water in it. If the vial floats with the bottom above the water, it has too little water in it. The idea is to have the vial float upside down so that its bottom is just about level with the surface of the water in the jar. Keep on adding and taking away water in the vial until the vial floats in the desired position.

Now stretch a sheet of rubber from a balloon over the mouth of the tall jar and hold it securely in place with a rubber band or string. When you press on the sheet of rubber, the vial will sink to the bottom of the jar (Fig. 9-8). When you remove your hand, the vial rises up again to the top. Help the children understand that when you press on the sheet of rubber, you compress the air in the tall jar. The compressed air presses on the water which in turn compresses the air in the vial. When the air in the vial is compressed, more water enters the vial, which now becomes heavier and sinks. When you remove your hand, the pressure on the jar and water is released and returns to normal. The air in the vial is no longer compressed and pushes out the extra water that entered. The vial then rises up again to its original position. It is possible to adjust the balance finely so that the pressure

it reaches the bottom. The pressure of the air in the tumbler will prevent water from filling the tumbler and wetting the cork. Such a device on a large scale is called a diving bell or caisson. It looks like a steel tumbler upside down. In it men can work safely and be kept dry at the bottom of a lake or ocean.

To show how the men can be supplied with fresh air while working in a diving bell, obtain a large funnel and a rubber or plastic tube. Connect the tube to the funnel and place the funnel over the floating cork (Fig. 9-7). Push the funnel down to the bottom of the aquarium. While holding the funnel down, blow air into the rubber tube. As long as air is blown into the tube, the men are safe and dry and are supplied with a constant source of fresh air. Excess air will leave at the sides of the funnel.

A Cartesian diver

The children have a lot of fun playing with a Cartesian diver, a bottle within a bottle that moves up and down mysteriously. Obtain a tall glass jar and a small glass vial with straight sides. Fill the jar almost full of water. Then partly fill the vial with water and turn it upside down in the water in the jar. Hold a piece of

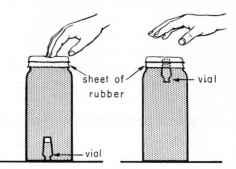

Fig. 9-8 Changes in air pressure make a Cartesian diver go up and down.

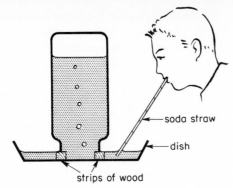

soda straw

dish

strips of wood

Fig. 9-9 How a drinking fountain for chickens works.

against the glass sides of a capped bottle completely filled with water will cause the vial to sink.

Drinking fountain for chickens

Have the children ever made a drinking fountain for chickens? Air pressure is responsible for the way it functions. Put about an inch of water in a deep pie dish. Fill a widemouthed jar with water. Cover the top with cardboard, invert the jar, and place it face down into the water in the dish. Obtain two small strips of wood about ¼–½″ thick. Place the wood in the dish and support the jar on the strips of wood (Fig. 9-9).

Now suck some of the water out of the dish with a straw. Water will leave the jar and move into the dish to take the place of the water that is drawn out. At the same time large bubbles of air will occasionally move up into the jar. The air takes the place of the water that flowed out of the jar. The children may have noticed the same effect with the air bubbles in office water containers.

THE EFFECTS OF REDUCING AIR PRESSURE

Stretch a piece of rubber from a balloon over the top of a tobacco or clay pipe. Tie the rubber securely around the pipe bowl with a rubber band or string so that it will be airtight. The rubber is level with the top of the pipe bowl. It remains level because air pressure both outside and inside the pipe is exactly the same.

Now suck in on the pipe stem. The rubber immediately curves downward. By removing some of the air inside the pipe, the air pressure inside is consequently lessened. The air pressure on the outside of the pipe is now greater than the air pressure on the inside of the pipe. As a result, the rubber is forced downward.

When air is removed from a space, leaving nothing in its place, the resulting "empty space" is called a vacuum. If *all* the air were removed, the space would be called a *complete* vacuum. However, because it is almost impossible to remove all the air, only a *partial* vacuum is created. Whenever a vacuum is produced, a difference in air pressure results. This difference in air pressure causes things to move and creates interesting effects.

In 1650 Otto von Guericke, mayor of Magdeburg in Germany, performed an ingenious experiment demonstrating the effects of a vacuum. He made two iron hemispheres, each one resembling one half of a rubber ball, that fitted closely together to form a hollow iron sphere. The hemispheres were so constructed that air could be pumped out of them when they were joined together as a hollow sphere. When von Guericke removed most of the air from the hemispheres, thereby creating a considerable vacuum within the sphere, teams of eight horses on each side were unable to pull the hemispheres apart!

It is not hard to understand why the horses could not pull the hemispheres apart. When the air was removed from the hemispheres, there was very little air pressure on the inside of the hemispheres. Yet on the outside there was approximately 15 pounds of air pressing on each square inch of surface. No wonder the horses were unable to overcome the tre-

egg →

burning paper

Fig. 9-10 Making an egg pop into a bottle.

mendous force pressing on the hemispheres! However, when air was re-admitted into the hemispheres, the air pressure on the inside and outside became the same. As a result, the hemispheres came apart very easily.

The children will enjoy watching you put a hard-boiled egg into a milk bottle. Obtain a small hard-boiled egg that is slightly larger than the mouth of a milk bottle. Peel the egg. Make a twist of paper and light it with a match. While the paper is still burning, drop it into the milk bottle and quickly set the peeled egg into the mouth of the milk bottle (Fig. 9-10). Almost as soon as the flame goes out, the egg goes through the neck of the bottle with a loud pop.

Point out that the burning paper uses up some of the oxygen from the air in the bottle and also drives some air out through expansion. This means there is less air in the bottle and, consequently, less air pressure. The air pressure on the outside of the bottle is now greater than the air pressure inside the bottle. The air on the outside thus pushes the egg into the bottle.

To get the egg out of the bottle, tip the bottle mouth down so that the egg rests in the neck of the bottle. Lean your head all the way back, and press the mouth of the bottle against your own mouth until it is airtight. Now blow hard into the bottle. This will force much air into the bottle until the air pressure inside the bottle is greater than the air pressure outside. The air inside will now push the egg out.

The same experiment can also be done with a partially peeled banana (Fig. 9-11). Select a banana that fits snugly into the bottle mouth so that it will be airtight. The banana will end up in the bottle, completely peeled.

The sink plunger, or "plumber's helper," illustrates the effects of a partial vacuum and differences in air pressure. You can borrow one from the school custodian. Moisten the rubber cup and press down firmly on a stool or chair until most of the air in the cup is expelled. You will now be able to lift the stool with the plunger. Help the children understand that by forcing the air out of the cup, a partial vacuum was formed inside. The air pressure on the outside is greater than the air in the cup and holds the cup firmly to the stool. Coating the cup with water helps seal out the air.

If you can, obtain two small-sized plungers. This experiment works better with the smaller ones. Moisten the surfaces of both cups. Have a child hold one handle against the floor or the wall, while you push one cup against the other to force the air out of both cups. Now have two children try to pull the plungers apart (Fig. 9-12). The children are actually repeating von Guericke's experiment with the hemispheres. They should now know that there is a partial vacuum inside the cups. The air pressure on the outside holds the cups firmly together.

Many toys and gadgets use suction cups. One such common toy is the dart gun which shoots darts that have suction cups

burning paper

Fig. 9-11 Air pressure peels a banana.

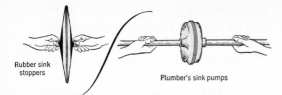

Rubber sink stoppers

Plumber's sink pumps

Fig. 9-12 A partial vacuum makes it difficult to pull two pumps apart. (From R. W. Burnett, *Teaching Science in the Elementary School,* Holt, Rinehart and Winston, 1953.)

instead of points. A common gadget using the suction cup is one that attaches an ash tray to the dashboard of the car. If you can obtain one, demonstrate it in class. Do not use water to seal out the air, because water evaporates soon after and the suction cup falls off. Try mineral oil or Vaseline instead, and the suction cup will stay for a very long time.

Open up a bottle of soda water, preferably one that is colored. You might like to use colored lemonade in a bottle instead. Insert a glass or plastic straw and have one child drink some of the soda through the straw. When the child sucks on the end of the straw, he removes some of the air in the straw. This creates a partial vacuum inside the straw. The air on the surface of the soda in the bottle now has a greater pressure than the air inside the straw. Consequently, the air pressing on the surface of the soda pushes the liquid up the straw.

If the child wishes, he can put his tongue quickly to the top of the straw while he is drinking. His tongue will make the straw a dip tube (see p. 136).

Now obtain a one-hole rubber stopper that fits the mouth of the soda bottle. The bottle should be full or almost full of soda or lemonade. Insert the glass or plastic straw into the stopper and fit the stopper tightly in the bottle. If a stopper is not available, pack modeling clay tightly around the straw instead. The child will now find that he cannot drink the soda

because it will not go up the straw. This phenomenon takes place because no air can enter the bottle to push the soda up the straw. Loosening the stopper or punching a hole in the clay will make it possible for the child to drink again.

Have the children manipulate a medicine dropper. Point out that when the bulb is squeezed, some of the air is forced out of the dropper. You can show this by squeezing the bulb while the dropper is in the liquid. There is now a partial vacuum in the dropper. The pressure of the air inside the dropper is less than the pressure of the air on the surface of the liquid. Therefore, the air on the surface of the liquid pushes the liquid up the dropper.

Fit a test tube with a one-hole rubber stopper. Insert a glass or plastic tube into the stopper so that one end of the tube is just below the stopper (Fig. 9-13). Pour a small amount of water into the test tube. Stopper the test tube tightly and heat the test tube in the flame of an alcohol lamp or Bunsen burner. The water soon begins to boil, driving some of the air out of the test tube. After the water has boiled a short while, invert it so that the open end of the glass tube is in a tumbler of colored water. As the test tube cools, the steam inside the test tube condenses. This leaves a partial vacuum in the test tube. The air pressure on the surface of the water in the tumbler is greater than the air pressure in-

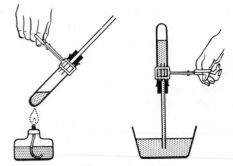

Fig. 9-13 A difference in air pressure causes colored water to rise into a test tube.

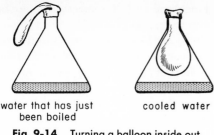

water that has just been boiled   cooled water

Fig. 9-14   Turning a balloon inside out.

Fig. 9-15   Making a balloon larger by reducing the air pressure around it.

side the test tube. Therefore the air on the surface of the colored water pushes the water up into the test tube. Recall the experiment with the boiling water in the duplicating fluid can (p. 133). The partial vacuum is formed in the same manner in each case.

Differences in air pressure can turn a balloon inside out. Obtain a Pyrex flask and a rubber balloon. If the flask is not available, a Pyrex baby bottle will serve as well. Pour a small amount of water in the flask. Heat the flask on a hot plate until the water boils vigorously. Then remove the flask and quickly stretch the opening of the rubber balloon over the mouth of the flask (Fig. 9-14). As the flask cools, the balloon will turn inside out in the flask. The children should now be able to understand that a partial vacuum has been formed. The air outside the flask pushes hard enough to turn the balloon inside out and even blow it up.

Obtain a large bottle and a one-hole stopper to fit the mouth of the bottle. Insert a short piece of glass tubing through the stopper and connect a piece of rubber tubing to the outer end of the glass tube. Blow up a balloon, but not all the way. Prevent the air from escaping by twisting a rubber band around the neck of the balloon. Place the balloon in the jar and stopper the jar tightly. Now have a child suck air repeatedly from the jar (Fig. 9-15). When the child stops for breath each time, remind him to squeeze the tubing tightly. This will prevent air from going

back into the jar while the child catches his breath. The balloon will become larger. As a partial vacuum is formed in the jar, the air inside the balloon pushes the balloon out in all directions. When you let air inside the jar again, the balloon returns to its original size.

Reducing the air pressure in the lungs enables us to breathe. When you breathe in, your diaphragm moves downward and makes the lungs expand. The air already present in the lungs spreads out to occupy this larger space. This reduces the air pressure in the lungs. The higher air pressure outside now pushes air through your nose or mouth into your lungs. How we inhale and exhale is explained more fully in Chapter 14.

HOW MOVING AIR BEHAVES

Obtain an electric fan and hold a long narrow strip of paper first in front of and then behind the fan (Fig. 9-16). Held in

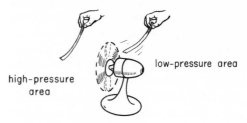

low-pressure area

high-pressure area

Fig. 9-16   Effects of high and low air pressure.

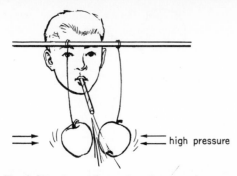

Fig. 9-17 A rapidly moving air stream between two apples makes the apples come together.

front, the paper strip blows away from the fan because the whirling blades create moving air with a high pressure. Held in back of the fan, the paper strip bends toward the blades. This indicates low air pressure. The blades push the air in front of it away, creating a partial vacuum behind the fan. A fresh supply of air is then pushed into this low-pressure area in back of the fan.

A vacuum cleaner has a motor which runs a fan. The high-pressure area is in the region of the bag which collects the dirt. The low-pressure area is in the nozzle and the hose. Fresh air rushes into the low-pressure area with such force that it carries the dirt with it.

When air is moving rapidly, the air pressure is affected. Where the forward speed of the moving air stream is high, the air pressure at the sides is low.

Tie strings to two apples (or thread two ping-pong balls) and suspend them from a support so that they hang side by side about an inch or two apart (Fig. 9-17). Ask one of the pupils to blow air through a straw between the apples in order to try to blow them farther apart. However, the apples will come together instead. The fast moving stream of air between the apples creates an area of low pressure on the facing sides of the apples. The greater air pressure on the outer surfaces of the apples pushes the apples together.

Place one end of a sheet of paper between the pages of a book. Hold the top of the book level with your mouth and blow over the top of the book (Fig. 9-18). The sheet of paper rises up. Point out that here again the fast moving air stream over the top of the paper creates a low air pressure on the top side of the paper. The greater air pressure underneath the paper pushes the paper up.

The wing of a plane is curved so that when air streams move over the wing, the same lifting effect is produced on the wing. See Chapter 27, for many demonstrations on the principles of flight and for a discussion of kites, gliders, and balloons.

There are many more experiments the children can perform to show the effect of fast-moving air streams. In each case, the fast-moving air stream creates a low air pressure on one side. The greater air pressure on the other side then pushes toward the side with the lower air pressure.

The following activities illustrate this principle of moving air streams, discovered by the scientist Bernoulli and called Bernoulli's principle. Have the children explain the action in each case.

Obtain a piece of paper about 8″ long and 4″ wide. Bend down each end of the paper about an inch, so that the paper forms a bridge. Now place the bridge on

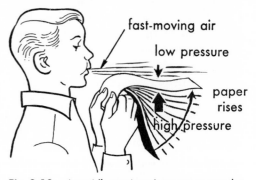

Fig. 9-18 A rapidly moving air stream across the top of a paper makes the paper rise. (From Paul F. Brandwein et al., *You and Science*, Harcourt, Brace & World, 1960.)

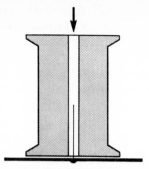

Fig. 9-19 Using Bernoulli's principle to keep an index card from falling. (From A. Joseph et al., *A Sourcebook for the Physical Sciences,* Harcourt, Brace & World, 1961.)

the table and blow hard under the bridge. The bridge, instead of blowing over, will cling tightly to the table.

Cut a 3″ square from a filing card. Draw diagonals to find the mid-point and put a pin through it. Now place the pin in the hole of an empty thread spool, so that the card is resting at the bottom of the spool (Fig. 9-19). Hold the card lightly with the finger and blow through the spool. Then remove the finger, continuing to blow. The card will cling to the spool. Have the children note that the air you are blowing flows out rapidly between the bottom of the spool and the card, as shown in the diagram. This produces a low pressure in this space, and the air below the card pushes up against the card.

Place a ping-pong ball in a glass or plastic funnel. Bend your head back and blow hard into the stem of the funnel (Fig. 9-20). The ball will not blow out of the

funnel but cling closely to it. Now invert the funnel so that its mouth faces downward. Hold the ping-pong ball in the funnel and blow hard. Now remove your hand, continuing to blow into the funnel. The ball will remain in the funnel.

Hold your hand flat outside the window of a moving auto. Then tilt your hand slightly so that the front end is raised. The fast-moving air stream will cause your hand to lift.

Tilt an electric fan so that it is facing straight up. Blow up a rubber balloon and tie the neck tightly with a string. Then place the balloon in the air stream. The balloon will remain in the stream. The pressure of the surrounding air is greater than the sidewise air pressure of the stream.

Obtain two soda straws and flatten one end of each straw slightly. Place one straw in a tumbler of colored water. Place the other straw at right angles to the first straw, with both flattened ends together (Fig. 9-21). Now blow hard through the horizontal straw. The water level in the vertical straw will rise. If you blow hard enough and carefully enough, the water will reach the top of the vertical straw and spray out.

Point out that blowing a stream of air rapidly across the top of the straw lowers

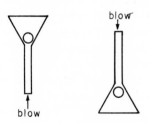

Fig. 9-20 Keeping a ping-pong ball inside a funnel.

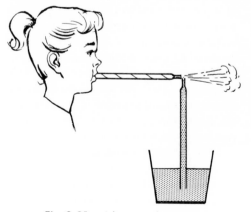

Fig. 9-21 A homemade sprayer.

(a)

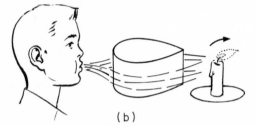

(b)

Fig. 9-22 (a) Making a low-pressure area; (b) the effect of streamlining.

the air pressure inside the straw. The air on the surface of the water in the glass then pushes the water up the straw. When the water comes out at the top of the straw, the fast-moving air stream breaks the water up into a spray. This is the way an atomizer or insect and paint spray gun works.

Obtain a piece of cardboard about 2″ or 3″ square. Hold the cardboard in front of a lighted candle (Fig. 9-22A). Blow hard toward the cardboard. The flame will move toward you. The air stream will be directed over, under, and around the card. This fast-moving stream around the edges of the card will produce a low-pressure area behind the card. The air behind the flame then pushes the flame toward this low-pressure area and toward you.

Now prepare a "tear-drop" shaped cardboard (Fig. 9-22B). Place the cardboard in front of the candle and blow on the blunt side of the cardboard. This time the air flows smoothly along the sides of

the "tear-drop," meets at the candle, and blows the flame away from you. If you blow very hard, the flame will be extinguished.

Point out that autos, trains, and planes are now shaped into this "tear-drop" design. We call it streamlining. This helps to remove low-pressure areas, with the resulting "dragging" effect. Streamlining enables the air to flow smoothly along the sides and then away from the moving object.

AIR CAN DO WORK

Air is very helpful to us. The wind not only helps dry our clothes but also runs windmills. The electric fan keeps us cool. The auto fan helps cool the engine.

When air is compressed, it can do many things. We have already shown how it can be useful in caissons or diving bells. It also enables deep sea divers to work far down in the water. Compressed air is also used in air brakes, submarines, tires, footballs and basketballs, door checks, and whistles. It is used to operate pneumatic tools such as the riveter, hammer, drill, and sand blaster.

Gusher

The children might like to make a gusher using compressed air. Obtain a soda bottle and a one-hole rubber stopper to fit the mouth of the bottle. Push the narrow tip of the glass tube from a medicine dropper through the stopper. Lubricate by wetting with water. Then attach a rubber or plastic tube to the large end of the glass tube. The rubber tube should be long enough almost to reach the bottom of the bottle (Fig. 9-23). Now fill the bottle about half full of water and stopper it tightly. Have a child blow as hard as he can into the bottle. When he removes his mouth from the top of the dropper, the water gushes out of the tube. Point out that the child blew air into the bottle and compressed it. When he removed his mouth and thus released the pressure, the compressed air pushed against the water and forced it up the rubber tube and medicine dropper.

We have already seen what partial vacuums and differences in air pressure can do. The soda straw, medicine dropper, atomizer, and spray gun operate because of these differences, as does the lift pump in a well.

Siphon

The children will love watching a siphon empty a container of water for them. Obtain two large glass jars and a piece of rubber tubing about 15–20″ long. Fill one jar with water and place it on the table. Place the second jar on a chair, so that the empty jar is lower than the jar with water. Now fill the rubber tube with water. To do this make the tube U-shaped. Place one end of the tube under the faucet. Let the water run until water flows out of the other end of the tube. The tube is now full of water.

Pinch both ends of the tube tightly and bring the tube to the jars. Place one end of the rubber tube in one jar, and the other end in the second jar (Fig. 9-24). Now release the ends of the tube. Water will flow from the jar on the table to the jar on the chair.

Point out that there is more water in the long arm of the rubber tube than in the short arm. Consequently, gravity pulls more on the water in the longer arm and the water runs out. As the water runs out it leaves a partial vacuum in the rubber tube, with lower air pressure. The pressure of the air on the surface of the liquid pushes the liquid up the short arm of the rubber tube and over into the longer arm. In this way, the water is transferred continuously from one jar to the other.

If it is inconvenient to get at a water

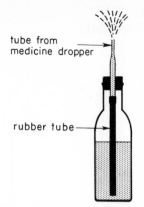

Fig. 9-23 A gusher fountain.

faucet to fill the rubber tube, you can start the siphon another way. Simply place one end of the tube in the jar of water and the other end in the empty jar. Kneel down and suck the air from the lower end of the tube. This will create a partial vacuum in the tube, with a lower air pressure, and the water will begin to flow.

Siphon fountain

Try making a siphon fountain. Fit a glass quart bottle or flask with a two-hole rubber stopper. Through one hole insert the glass tube of a medicine dropper. Through the other hole insert a short piece of glass tubing that extends about an inch above the stopper. Connect two

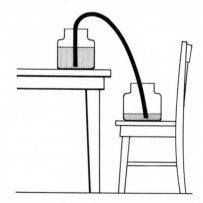

Fig. 9-24 Transferring water from one container to another with a siphon.

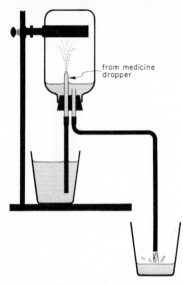

from medicine dropper

Fig. 9-25 A siphon fountain.

pieces of rubber tubing to the glass tube and medicine dropper, as shown in the diagram (Fig. 9-25). One rubber tubing should be about 1' long, and the other about 3' long.

Obtain two large glass jars. Fill one with water colored deep red with vegetable coloring. Put one rubber tube in the jar of colored water on the table. Put the other rubber tube in the empty jar on the floor. Pour a little water into the bottle, invert the bottle, and set it up as shown in the diagram.

To start the siphon, kneel down and suck on the long rubber tubing until water begins to flow into your mouth. Quickly take the tube out of your mouth and drop it into the jar. A beautiful colored fountain will play up against the bottom of the bottle. If the fountain will not start, try putting a little less water to begin with in the bottle.

Help the children understand that when the water runs down the long rubber tube, a partial vacuum is formed in the bottle. The air pressing on the colored water in the jar pushes the colored water up into the bottle. The colored water then runs

down the long rubber tube and the process is repeated. This keeps the fountain going.

AIR IS EVERYWHERE

We already know that air is all around us. However, the children may be surprised to learn that there is air in water and soil as well.

In water

The air is dissolved in the water. To show that water contains air, draw a glass of cold water from the faucet or drinking fountain. Let the glass stand in a warm place for an hour or so. Tiny bubbles of air will appear on the sides of the tumbler.

Heat some cold water in a beaker over a hot plate. Bubbles of air will appear and rise to the surface long before the water begins to boil. Heating the water, then, will drive off the air dissolved in it.

Many animals and plants that live in the water get their air directly from the water. Fish have gills, which serve to take the oxygen from the water. Water lilies get air from both the water and the air above the surface. The surface leaves get their air above the water. The underwater leaves get their air from the water.

In soil

Soil also contains air. Fill a wide-mouthed glass jar about half full of soil. Then add water to it. Bubbles of air will appear and rise to the surface. The air was originally present between the soil particles.

There may be a few skeptics who will remind you that water also contains air. Consequently, the air may have come from the water rather than from the soil. If this happens, repeat the experiment using cold water that has been recently boiled. Boiled water, on standing, will not give off tiny air bubbles. All the air was driven off by the boiling.

Place a building brick in a large container of water. Air bubbles will be given off. Point out that many materials are porous and contain air.

AIR IS A MIXTURE OF GASES

Air is a mixture of many gases. However, air is composed mostly of oxygen and nitrogen. Together these two gases make up about 99% of the air. Air contains about 21% oxygen and about 78% nitrogen.

The remaining 1% of the air contains some very interesting gases. These include carbon dioxide and the inert gases helium, neon, argon, xenon, and krypton. Helium is a very light gas used in dirigibles and balloons. It is also mixed with oxygen in place of nitrogen to make "artificial air" used in hospitals and by deep sea divers. Neon is well known to the children because of its use in colored electric signs. Argon is used in electric light bulbs. The air in the bulbs is replaced with argon. Argon is not an active gas, and so helps prevent the filament in the bulb from decomposing or burning away.

The air also contains varying amounts of water vapor, depending upon weather conditions. There are also tiny solid particles in the air such as dust and pollen.

Oxygen

Oxygen is necessary for burning. Wrap some soft wire around a candle and bend the free end of the wire so it will serve as a handle. Obtain a large glass jar and a square of glass or cardboard large enough to cover the mouth of the jar. Light the candle and lower it into the jar. Then cover the jar with the glass or cardboard square. The flame will go out when so much oxygen is used up that it can no longer support combustion. Remove the candle, light it, and lower it in the jar again. The flame will go out immediately, showing that without sufficient oxygen the candle will not burn. The gas remaining in the jar is mostly nitrogen, though there are measurable quantities of carbon dioxide and water vapor—the products of combustion.

Obtain a long narrow olive jar. Pack moist steel wool washed in detergent and thoroughly rinsed, firmly into the bottom of the jar so that it will remain in the jar when inverted. Now place the jar, mouth down, in a shallow pan of water. (See Fig. 13-2 in Chapter 13.) Then let the jar stand for a day or two. Have the children notice that the water has risen in the jar. Measure the height of the water and compare it with the height of the jar. The water will have risen one fifth up the jar. This means that the volume of water in the jar is about 20% of the total volume of the jar. This corresponds quite closely with the volume of oxygen in the air.

Pull out the wad of steel wool and examine it. Notice how some of the steel has become brownish. This is rust, or iron oxide. Iron combines with oxygen in the air to form this brown iron oxide.

Many more experiments on the presence of oxygen in the air, burning, and rusting are described in Chapter 17.

Carbon dioxide

Carbon dioxide is a colorless gas that can be very quickly and easily identified. When carbon dioxide gas is bubbled in limewater, the limewater becomes milky. Limewater, simple to make, can be purchased very inexpensively at the drug store.

Place some limewater in a shallow dish and leave it exposed to the air for an hour or so. The carbon dioxide in the air combines with the limewater to form a thin milky crust.

Pour some fresh limewater in a test tube

or narrow bottle. Place a straw in the test tube and bubble air from your lungs into the limewater. The limewater quickly turns milky, showing the presence of carbon dioxide in the air you breathe out. (If this bubbling is prolonged, the water will clear again.)

The children can make carbon dioxide out of simple household materials. Obtain a large pitcher. Put half a cup of baking soda into the pitcher. Now pour vinegar in a glass tumbler until it is half full. Fill the rest of the tumbler with water and stir thoroughly. Then pour the vinegar solution into the pitcher. The mixture will foam, giving off bubbles of carbon dioxide. Hold a candle in the pitcher. The flame will go out. Carbon dioxide is used to extinguish fires, since it does not support burning.

Many more experiments on carbon dioxide and its use as a fire extinguisher are described in Chapter 17.

Water vapor

Water vapor is in the air in varying amounts. Have the children recall the droplets of water that accumulate on the sides of a pitcher of cold water or a bottle of cold soda. Obtain a shiny tin can. Fill the can half full of water at room temperature. Make sure the outside of the can is dry. Now add several ice cubes to the can and stir. Soon a film of water will form on the sides of the can. Adding a little salt to the mixture of ice cubes and water will make the film appear much sooner.

The film of water comes from the air. The air contains water vapor. When the air comes in contact with the cold sides of the tin can, the air cools and contracts. The cold air now cannot hold as much water vapor, because the air has contracted and become smaller. As a result, some of the water vapor condenses out on the sides of the can.

There are many activities on condensation of water vapor from the air as well as on evaporation of water into the air. These are well described in Chapter 18. Material showing the relation of the water vapor in the air to weather and precipitation is given in Chapter 7.

Dust

There is always dust in the air. To show this, either darken the room or take the children in a room that can be darkened. Turn on a flashlight or the filmstrip projector. The children will see dust particles in the beam of light. A ray of sunlight will show this just as well.

Have one of the children ruffle his hair vigorously with his hands near the beam of light. Many more dust particles will appear. Shake a child's jacket, sweater, or coat near the beam. Clap two chalkboard erasers together. Dust particles appear in each case.

Let a sheet of white paper stand for several days in a quiet part of the room. Then examine the dust that accumulates on the paper. Examine the dust particles with a hand magnifying glass or with a microscope. The dust may consist of particles of ash, fiber from clothing, pollen, plant spores, etc. How many kinds can the children identify?

CAPSULE LESSONS

9-1 Show the class an empty bottle. Ask the class if the bottle is really empty. Lead into the question of whether or not air is real and occupies space.

9-2 Ask the children to help you originate and set up an experiment to prove that air has weight.

9-3 Make a hole with a nail near the bottom of a small frozen juice can. Fill the can with water. The water will start flowing out of the hole. Now hold the palm of your hand tightly over the top of the can. The water will stop flowing from the hole. Remove your hand and the water begins to flow again. Lead into a discussion of the air pressure and its effect on water.

9-4 Manipulate a medicine dropper. Lead into the study of the effect of differences in air pressure and their effect on water.

9-5 Obtain a suction cup from a dart or some other gadget. Lift an object with the suction cup. Use a sink plunger to lift a stool. Lead into the study of air pressure and partial vacuums.

9-6 Suspend two ping-pong balls side by side and about an inch or two apart. With a soda straw blow a stream of air between the ping-pong balls. After the balls come together, discuss and study the effect of rapidly moving air streams on air pressure.

9-7 Blow up a basketball or football with an air pump or at a gasoline station. Discuss and study the compression of air and its uses.

9-8 Condense some water droplets on a tin can containing water and ice. Then blow through a straw into a test tube containing limewater. Discuss and find out what happened in each case. Lead into a study of the gases that make up the air.

BIBLIOGRAPHY

Bruce, Guy V., *Experiments with Air,* National Science Teachers Association, 1950.

Carlisle, N. V., R. M. Cleveland, and J. Wood, *Modern Wonder Book of the Air,* Holt, Rinehart and Winston, 1945. Detailed treatment of the air around us, its properties, and uses. For advanced students.

Fisher, James, *The Wonderful World of the Air,* Doubleday, 1958. Description on an advanced level of the atmosphere, aeronautics, and astronautics. Brief history of man's study of the atmosphere. Includes climate and the different kinds of winged animals and insects.

Friskey, M. R., *The True Book of the Air Around Us,* Childrens Press, 1953. Simple but effective treatment of air and its properties.

Larrick, Nancy, *See for Yourself,* Aladdin Books, Dutton, 1952. Simple experiments on air and water.

Leyland, Eric, and T. E. Scott-Chard, *Boy's Book of the Air,* Roy, 1958. Good treatment of air, its properties, and uses.

Newell, Homer E., Jr., *Window in the Sky,* McGraw-Hill, 1955. Discusses the upper atmosphere, with special emphasis on its composition, density, pressure, temperature, and radiation.

Parker, Bertha M., *Air About Us,* Row, Peterson, 1941. Comprehensive description of properties of air.

Pine, Tillie S., *Air All Around,* Whittlesey, 1960. Primary.

10

The stars and seasons

A friend of one of the authors teaches first grade. In the year of the first Sputnik, the children wanted to study about the solar system, and the teacher had the wisdom to let them. She was later looking through a collection of elementary science texts. There was little or nothing about astronomy in texts for children below the third grade. Yet here was great interest on the part of the children and a teacher willing to find ways to meet it.

It is our experience that astronomy has a fascination for young children. They ask such fundamental questions as "What holds the moon up in the sky?" Your college astronomy course probably is too advanced to help you here. Perhaps you have been teaching yourself about astronomy by skimming children's science books. In any case you should avoid killing the child's interest by giving a long detailed answer to the question.

At one time the teaching of astronomy in elementary science was limited to learning the names of constellations and their legends. This study does not go far enough today. Current interest in space travel and the ever-widening frontiers of space force us to go further. Even young children are intrigued by interesting facts to be learned about our neighbors in space. Some writers imply there is a lack of activities for children in the area of astronomy. We have found that the children's interest and the possibilities of integration with experiences

in language, reading, art, and construction fully occupied all the time we could spare for the unit.

THE SOLAR SYSTEM

The sun, its nine planets and their satellites, and the planetoids, comets, and meteorites make up the solar system. Its name—*solar system*—derives from the dominance of the sun in size and mass as compared to lesser members of the system. The solar system, we now know, is located toward the edge of the Milky Way galaxy, which is off the center of the universe of galaxies so far discovered through the giant telescopes.

However, this picture of the "heavens" has not always been held as true. At one time, the early peoples who lived near the Mediterranean Sea regarded the sea to be the center of the earth which, in turn, was thought to be the center of the universe. And they therefore named the sea Middle-of-the-World Sea. This attitude is reflected in the world picture by the famous Alexandrian astronomer, Ptolemy (c. 150 A.D.), who believed that the earth was stationary and was the center of the universe around which the sun, moon, and planets revolved. His view of the solar system, called the Ptolemaic system, is shown in Fig. 10-1A. Help the children to consider how well he did with the available instruments and information. With only

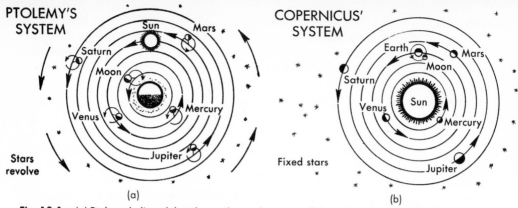

PTOLEMY'S SYSTEM

Sun, Mars, Saturn, Moon, Venus, Mercury, Jupiter

Stars revolve

(a)

COPERNICUS' SYSTEM

Earth, Mars, Moon, Saturn, Venus, Sun, Mercury, Jupiter

Fixed stars

(b)

Fig. 10-1 (a) Ptolemy believed that the earth was the center of the universe and that the sun, moon, and planets revolved around it; (b) Copernicus believed that the sun was the center of the universe and that the earth, moon, and stars revolved around it. (From R. Brinckerhoff et al., *The Physical World*, Harcourt, Brace & World, 1958.)

our naked-eye observations might we have noted all but the two outer planets? Our present-day knowledge could well appear a little quaint tomorrow unless others, too, are tolerant and understanding.

Almost 1500 years later, the Polish astronomer Nicoluas Copernicus (1473–1543) revived a theory suggested by the Greeks but abandoned under the tremendous influence of Ptolemaic thought. Copernicus wrote (1540) that the sun—rather than the earth—was the center of the universe and that the earth rotated daily in its revolution about the sun (Fig. 10-1B). He could not offer any proof of his hypothesis, and it remained for Johannes Kepler (1571–1630) and Galileo Galilei (1564–1642) to establish direct experimental evidence of the truth of Copernican theory. In one of the exhibit cases of the Mt. Wilson Observatory in California is a photostatic copy of the journal of Galileo. The journal entries show his observations of the planet Jupiter upon which his telescope was trained. Noticing Jupiter's moons changing position each successive night, he realized that they were revolving around the planet. By analogy earth and Jupiter and the other planets could revolve around the sun.

Children who will become acquainted with a model of the solar system should first be encouraged to learn that the whole system is in motion. They will grasp this fact if you start them off with a study of the earth's motion in relation to the sun—that is, the rotation and revolution of the earth.

The earth's rotation

Very young children can be led to observations of such celestial phenomena as the sun's apparent daily motion or path across the sky. At first you might draw their attention to the sun's position in the sky during morning recess and again at afternoon recess. On a walk through the school, draw their attention to rooms with morning sun and those with afternoon sun. Encourage them to make similar observations at home. This may be another opportunity for good home-school interaction. Have the children notice their shadows on the playground at recess times. Mark the path of sunlight in your classroom. It may take several successive experiences until the majority of the class can point out the sun's path through the sky.

At this point you are ready to develop the concept of direction. With young children this should be limited to east and west. On a sunny morning, take the class out on the playground and point to the sun. Point east. Which way do the shadows point? Point west.

Things are not always what they appear to be. Sky study may be children's first real opportunity to check their senses against the accumulation of scientific knowledge. Little children are apt to state that the sun moves. And so it does appear in relation to them. You need not make categorical denial. Let the evidence accumulate and speak for itself. This may take considerable time. Once children believe that the sun moves in an east-west path, they are ready for another step. Use the moving train analogy to explain to them that it is really the earth that is in motion relative to the sun. A train sitting in the yards may appear to be moving as we pass it in another train. Have children recall that a train alongside appears to move backward when their train moves forward; if their train is standing still and a train passes, they will feel as if their train is moving backward. Point out, however, that it is really our train—the earth—not the sun which is moving. When children ride in the merry-go-round, stationary objects appear to be moving because the merry-go-round is turning.

Shadows. Young children have a very strong egocentric sense, even in regard to their shadows.

> I have a little shadow
> that goes in and out with me . . .

Children sometimes draw shadow portraits for a Mother's Day or Christmas present. By this we mean tracing the shadow cast by a profile of a child sitting in front of a projector lamp. Children will be equally interested in tracing a full-length shadow made outdoors in sunshine. Try doing some in the morning and afternoon as well as at noon and compare with the child's actual size. Let the children discuss the possible reason why the child's shadow portrait is taller or shorter than his real height. If sunlight comes into your classroom, mark the edge of a shadow on the floor and check it at 10-minute intervals. The children will see that the shadow moves. Eventually they may understand that the position of a shadow continuously changes because the earth continuously turns in relation to the sun.

Constructing a sundial. If the school flagpole stands free, watch the shadow it casts. In the morning the shadow points west, at noon, north, in the afternoon, east. You can make a giant sundial out of such a flagpole. Collect a jump rope and 12 flat sticks the same size. Mark each stick with one of these numbers, 8, 9, 10, 11, 12, 1, 2, 3, 4, 5, 6. At 8 A.M. measure a jump rope length or any rope length along the shadow cast by the pole and drive in the stick at the end of the rope. Do this every hour. By sundown you will have a semicircle of sticks at equal intervals, much like half of a clock face.

Another kind of sundial is made by outlining a child's feet as he stands in the sun on the school sidewalk. At hourly intervals mark the direction of his shadow with lines radiating from the center where he stands.

A more traditional sundial can be made of wood or metal, painted to withstand weather. The vertical or inclined rod that casts the shadow is called the *gnomon*. The base angle should be the same as the latitude of the locality where the sundial is to be set up (Fig. 10-2). The hypotenuse should point to the North Star. Then you are ready to mark off the hours on the baseboard as the shadow falls. It may be advisable to experiment with cardboard models while calibrating the baseboard markings at the proper intervals. A temporary sundial can be made with a pencil stuck into a lump of clay. The Egyptians

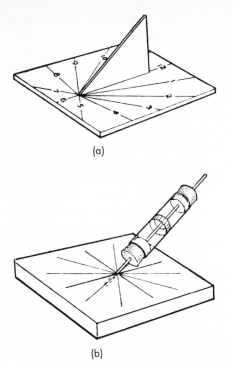

(a)

(b)

Fig. 10-2 (a) Sundial. The gnomon is a right triangle. The hypotenuse points north. Numbers indicate hours. (From *UNESCO Source Book for Science Teachers*, UNESCO, 1956.) (b) A more elaborate sundial, made with a metal wire or knitting needle inserted into the base at the correct angle. The middle band is the time scale, divided into 24 parts, one for each hour of the day. The shadow of the rod on the scale tells the hour. (From *UNESCO Source Book for Science Teachers*, UNESCO, 1956.)

used obelisks as gnomons for enormous sundials in ancient times.

Night and day. It is our experience that middle-grade children love to pore over a globe of the world in their spare time. Ask a child to mark the approximate place where he lives with a small paper flag on a match stick imbedded in a lump of modeling clay. Set the globe on the window sill in the noon sunlight. Give the globe a half turn and the children will see that the flag is in shadow. Some will guess that this means darkness at midnight for their part of the world. Repeat, this time

using quarter turns (90°) to signify six-hour intervals and a corresponding difference in daylight. Some children may have traveled across the country and experienced different time zones caused by the earth's turning.

Pupils may want to make their own globes. These may be made from plaster of Paris and newspaper with a solid metal curtain rod as the axis. First obtain an apple box or one of a similar size. A pupil removes one side of the box as indicated and cuts a semicircular opening in one side as shown in Fig. 10-3. Use a compass or keyhole saw for cutting. The semicircular hole should be 10–12″ in radius to make a 20–24″ globe. Set the curtain rod at the edge of the box to close the open semicircle. Secure the rod with staples loose enough to permit its rotation. Have a pupil wrap newspaper in the shape of a ball around the rod, using cord to hold the paper in place. Next mix plaster of Paris to a thick consistency by slowly adding water and mixing with a trowel or spatula. Apply the plaster by hand to the paper shape to form a roughly shaped ball. Allow this to set for 20 minutes. Then slowly add layers smoothly by rolling the ball on its axis so that excess plaster is scraped off by the semicircular cut. A perfect sphere will form. Allow it to set for several days. Then mount the axis in a thick block of wood at an angle of 23½°. The pupils may use water color paints to show continents, oceans, etc.

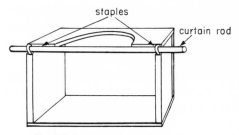

staples

curtain rod

Fig. 10-3 Form for making globes.

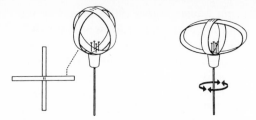

Fig. 10-4 The effect of centrifugal force on the earth's shape. This is the same force that holds the water in a pail which you swing in an arc around your head. (From G. Blough and M. Campbell, *Making and Using Classroom Science Materials in the Elementary School,* Holt, Rinehart and Winston, 1954.)

Using different models let the children work out their own explanation of the earth's diurnal motion.

One consequence of the earth's rotation is the slight flattening at the poles and the slight bulge at the equator. Recent IGY measurements show that the earth tends to bulge just below the equator.[1] To illustrate this, let the children paste and pin two paper loops as shown. Spinning the spindle on which the cork is mounted will flatten the poles and bulge the middle of the circle (Fig. 10-4).

The concept of rotation will need to be reinforced by many experiences. For instance, young children can illustrate rotation by twirling around in space. A child might hold a light in his hand while another walks a globe in a circle about the light.

If the room can be darkened, use a globe with a projector or large three-cell flashlight or gooseneck lamp as light source.

Let a child pretend he is the earth and face a lamp, though not looking directly at the light but just below it. Facing the light, his nose or where he lives is in full daylight as at noon. If he stands sideways, the light falls slantingly on his nose as in early morning or late afternoon. Standing

[1] In fact it is very slightly pearshaped, being 23′ wider just below the equator.

with his back to the light, his nose is in shadow as at night.

Foucault's proof of rotation. In 1851, a little more than a century ago, the French physicist J. B. L. Foucault proved by a simple experiment that the earth really turns. Foucault hung a long pendulum from the dome of the Pantheon, a public building in Paris. Foucault's pendulum seemed to swing in an arc, indicating that the earth rotated under it. You can see the same phenomenon in many public buildings where heavy lamp fixtures are suspended by a long wire from the ceiling. Watch closely and you will see that the heavy weight at the bottom swings in a slight arc. It doesn't swing straight.

Use a C-clamp. Then glue or solder a ball bearing to the inner surface of the jaw (Fig. 10-5). This will provide a free-swinging attachment for a long cord and "plumb-bob" weight at the bottom. Mark the direction of the swing at the start and note change of course after a few hours.

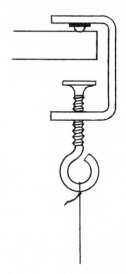

Fig. 10-5 C-clamp attachment for free-swinging weight. Many schools use C-clamps in elementary construction or woodwork. (Redrawn from *UNESCO Source Book for Science Teachers,* UNESCO, 1956.)

The earth's revolution

The fact that the earth makes an annual revolution about the sun is not directly perceived by our senses. Nor do we notice the tremendous speed with which the earth travels in its orbit, whirling along to cover over 500 million miles in 1 year! Both the speed of rotation and the speed of revolution are great. As the earth rotates on its axis, a person living at the equator moves 24,000 miles each day (since the earth's equatorial waistline is 24,000 miles). Approaching this as an elementary problem in division, the children can figure out that the speed of rotation is about 1000 miles per hour. (In northern latitudes we are rotating at the speed of about 800 mph, even though we seem to be standing still.) In 1 hour, we move on our orbit 66,600 miles in our annual journey about the sun. On this journey, our speed of revolution is about 18½ miles per second. (To find the hourly rate, the children can multiply by 60 and again by 60 to arrive at the breakneck speed of 66,600 mph.) In one day, therefore, the earth whizzes along 1,580,000 miles.

The concept of the earth's annual journey and its orbit around the sun can be reinforced for children as they study other members of the solar system, the planets. The concept of causes of seasons may also be reinforced as children learn about the zodiac and the change in star groups at different seasons.

Children can perform experiments to show that the changes in daylight and dark and the changes of season are the result of the earth's revolution.

Changing daylight. Children watching shadows over a period of days may notice the shift in position. To verify this or to bring it to their attention, make a hole the size of a pencil in a piece of cardboard or paper. Scotch tape the cardboard in a sunny window where the sunlight will come through the hole and fall on a piece of paper on a shelf or window sill. Trace the outline of the shaft of light and record the time and date within the outline. Repeat this daily at the same time and note the shift in the outline.

Daily weather reports in the newspaper and almanac provide evidence of changing daylight and dark.

Charting the changing hours of daylight and dark is a useful and graphic illustration that helps explain seasons.

Changing seasons. The seasons are the result of both the earth's revolution about the sun and the fact that the earth's axis is tilted at an angle (23½°). First let the children illustrate the positions of one place (their locality) on the earth in relation to the sun during the four seasons. Set up a gooseneck lamp (sun) and four apples (earth during four seasons). Mark your locality with a crayon, and put colored rubber bands around the apple to show the equatorial line. Place the apples at four points in a circle around the lamp, and tilt them; notice that the light strikes your locality at different angles during each season.

Because of the earth's tilting on its axis, the angle that the sun's rays make with the earth at various positions in its orbit is different. A simple demonstration can show children how this determines the intensity of the sun's rays during seasons. Darken the room and point a large flashlight through a mailing tube directly at the blackboard or on the floor. Let the children trace the outline of the circle of light. Repeat at the same distance, but holding the light source at an angle to the surface. They will see that the oblique rays are much less bright and spread over a larger area than those pointed directly at the board or floor. If you have a photographic light meter, compare readings in the two positions. In the same way when the sun is high overhead as in summer, it gives much more heat than in winter

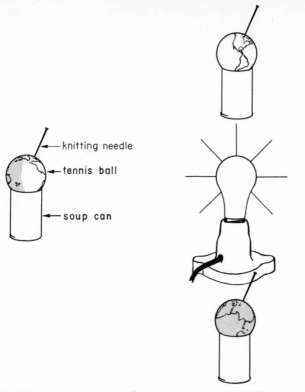

knitting needle

tennis ball

soup can

Fig. 10-6 Demonstration of seasons. For greater stability, screw a porcelain light socket to a wooden base. A short-necked lamp can also serve as light source.

when it describes a low arc in the sky at northern latitudes. Note the difference between a map of the United States at the angle of summer light and again in winter.

Let the children develop ways to record differences in length of daylight and angle of the sun's rays. Using symbols to represent the earth and a light source to represent the sun sometimes confuses elementary grade children. Often children do not make the connection between the models and the actual phenomena. Nevertheless, direct observation may be reinforced secondarily by the use of models.

Whiten four old tennis or other balls with water paint or tempera, and mark the poles with knitting needles. You also want to sketch in roughly the continents on each of the balls. Set each at the earth's approximate tilt on top of a soup can or

milk bottle to keep the ball from rolling. Make a circle on the floor (Fig. 10-6). Place the light source in the middle of the circle. The light must be from an unshaded lamp to simulate the sun shining in all directions. Place balls at four points of the circle so tilted to show the seasons. If you have a globe, set it at the earth's tilt and move it about the light source, thereby showing how the sun's direct rays shift during the seasons.

Bring in a toy house or doll house. When the room is darkened, let the children use a flashlight to show the angle of the sun's rays as they observe it in their own homes at different seasons. If a child holds the flashlight under the table, it may help some children visualize that the sun is shining on the other side of the world when it is dark here.

Compare a globe which is tilted to 23½° with one which is not tilted. Help the children see that we would not have seasons if it were not for this tilting of the globe on its axis.

Some children may think our summer season is warmer because we are nearer the sun. Help them to understand why Australia and parts of South America have summer during our winter. In actuality the earth is more than 3 million miles nearer the sun in winter than in summer.

The sun—our nearest star

The kindergartener who observes the sun is moving is not really in error. You have calculated that the earth moves in its annual orbit around the sun at the rate of about 66,000 mph. Scientists have estimated that our whole solar system is moving at about 43,000 mph. While the earth rotates once a day, the sun rotates every 25 days. While the earth rotates about 18½ mps, the sun rotates 13 mps as it and we with it move along a huge path through the galaxy.

Studying and watching the sun's daily path will bring questions and discussion from the children. The sun is very big, so big it could hold a million earths. If a model of the earth had ¼" diameter, the sun on the same scale would be 27". The sun is so hot it could boil steel easily.[2] It is so bright you should never look at it directly. It is warm enough to heat the whole earth. In parts of the country where it snows, remind the children how quickly the sun can melt snow. The sun is shining all the time. Even on a gray day, an airplane flying above the clouds is in sunshine. And when it is night in our side of the world, the sun shines on the other side of the earth. It even makes the moon shine by reflected light. Can you imagine getting all your heat and light from a power plant 93 million miles off in space? For a discussion of the sun's light and the colors of its spectrum, see Chapter 16.

Use an ordinary unshaded household light bulb to represent the sun. A pinhead across the room represents earth. The amount of light falling on the pinhead is roughly proportional to the amount of sunlight falling on the earth. Hold a thermometer for 2 minutes about 2' away from an unshaded light bulb. Check temperature. Repeat at 1', and at 2". The relative distances at which you held the thermometer represent the relative temperatures of Pluto, Earth, and Mercury, in that order.

Light years. The sun is our nearest star; yet it is 93 million miles away from us. By traveling at 50 mph it would take nearly 200 years to reach the sun. It would take about 12,000 earths in a row to cover the distance (about 3700 times the distance around our equator). Light from the sun reaches us in about 8 minutes. Our next nearest star neighbor is more than 24 trillion miles away. So many stars are still so much farther out in space that astronomers save time and trouble by using the term *light year* as a measure of distance. Light traveling 186,000 miles per second will travel about 6,000,000,000,000 miles in a year. This is 1 light year. At the speed of light we could cross the United States 75 times in 1 second! So we may find it more convenient to say that our next nearest star, Alpha Centauri, is 4 light years rather than 24,000,000,000,000 miles away from us.

star	light years from sun
Vega	37
Pollux	33
Arcturus	40
Castor	45
Regulus	77

[2] The temperature of the sun is believed to be 11,000° F at the surface and 100,000,000° F or more in the interior.

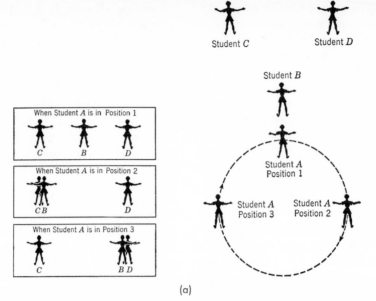

Fig. 10-7 (a) A demonstration of parallax. As student A actually changes position, he notes an apparent change in the position of student B in relation to students C and D. (From R. W. Burnett, *Teaching Science in the Elementary School*, Holt, Rinehart and Winston, 1953.)

Parallax. Children sometimes wonder how astronomers measure distance to bodies far out in space. The method is to measure the apparent annual back and forth shift of stellar bodies. This phenomenon is called parallax. The parallax method was first suggested by a Greek mathematician, Aristarchus (c. 250 B.C.), when he tried to measure the solar parallax directly by geometrical means.

Let the children try a simple visual experiment in order to understand Aristarchus' brilliant concept. Cover one eye with your hand and look at the vertical lines of a nearby window frame against the light. Now cover your other eye. The lines of the frame will appear to have shifted in relation to the background. Of course they have not. What has changed is the angle of observation. To make it even clearer, position pupils as in Fig. 10-7A. Student B is the one who seems to shift in relation to C-D as A moves. For older children you may want to measure the angles formed

at positions 2 and 3 and the distance between the two positions, and thus directly show how stellar parallax leads to a measurement of stellar distances.

As we revolve about the sun, our angle of observation of the stars changes so that certain stars seem to shift in relation to the stars near them (Fig. 10-7B). This shift can be measured, and from this the distance can be computed by triangulation.

To measure the distance to the sun or moon, astronomers at observatories across the world agree to measure at the same time the angles of their lines of sight to the center of the sun's or moon's disk. They compute the distance between them (straight line through the earth, not over its surface). With this distance for a baseline and the angles of their observations as two angles of a triangle, they compute the solar distance geometrically.

To measure distances to the stars, a star's apparent position in relation to nearby stars is photographed and studied

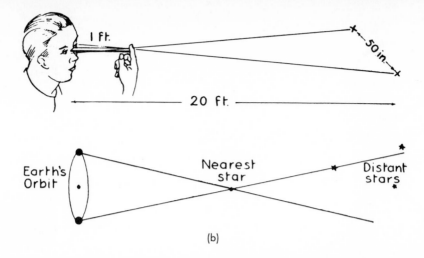

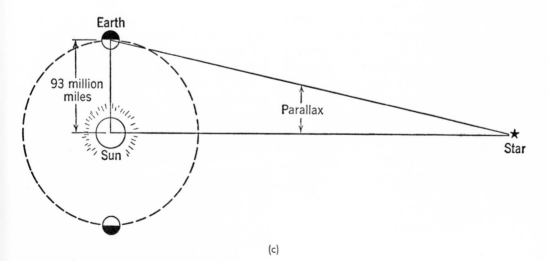

(b)

(b) Stand about 20' away from a blackboard. Hold a ruler between the forehead and the index finger. Close one eye and sight across the fingertip to one end of a 50" horizontal line on the blackboard. Without moving, use the other eye. Ask someone else to mark on the horizontal chalk line the point lined up by your "second look." Erase the remainder of the chalk line. Measure the distance between the eyeballs. This is usually about 2½". Use this figure as divisor, the remaining chalk line as dividend. The quotient should work out to be the approximate distance between the blackboard and the observer. (From *General Science Handbook, Part III,* New York State Education Department, 1956.)

(c)

(c) Determination by means of parallax of the distance to a star. (From R. W. Burnett, *Teaching Science in the Elementary School,* Holt, Rinehart and Winston, 1953.)

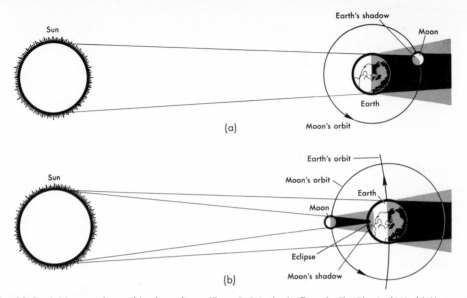

Fig. 10-8 (a) Lunar eclipse; (b) solar eclipse. (From R. Brinckerhoff et al., *The Physical World*, Harcourt, Brace & World, 1958.)

under magnification. Six months later when the earth is on the opposite side of the sun, the star is again photographed and studied. Microscopic measurements will now show that the star has apparently moved in relation to the stars nearest it in the pictures. Again, knowing the angles of observation, the length of the baseline (186,000,000 miles—diameter of earth's orbit), and the angular displacement of the star in question, astronomers compute a triangle (or two right triangles) that will determine the star's distance from the earth (Fig. 10-7C).

Solar eclipses. A few times during one's lifetime one may see an eclipse of the sun. A total eclipse lasts only 7 minutes. Birds and animals act just as though it were night and start to go to bed or wake up, as the case may be. Scientists are always interested in an eclipse because it gives them a chance to study gaseous eruptions from the face of the sun. Sometimes these are 3000 to 4000 miles high. By studying the colors of gases in these solar prominences, scientists have identi-

fied the elements in the sun. As you discover by experiment with flame tests (Chapter 12), elements have characteristic colors when heated. Elements in the sun are the same as many found on earth. For this reason scientists think that the earth was once part of the same material that made up the sun. Present theory speculates that the solar system was a huge gas and dust cloud which gradually condensed under gravitational stresses to form the planets and the sun.

A solar eclipse occurs when the moon comes between the earth and the sun. This happens at least twice a year. The shadow of the moon is round like that of the earth, but smaller. The area of deep shadow is called the *umbra;* the area of partial shade is called the *penumbra.* The umbra is about 240,000 miles long and cone-shaped. Since the moon is 240,000 miles away, the tip of its shadow will barely reach the earth. It is never near enough to cover a spot more than 160 miles in diameter on the earth—one reason why we see a total eclipse so infrequently. Let the children use an unshaded light to represent the sun, a tennis ball for the moon and a small globe. Let them work out relative positions of these three objects to illustrate both solar and lunar eclipses (Fig. 10-8). Because solar eclipses are rare, astronomers will travel thousands of miles to see one. They always hope weather conditions will allow them to study the corona. This circle of light around the sun is visible above the rim of the eclipsing moon. Most almanacs give dates and areas where eclipses may be observed. For example, July 20, 1963, Maine, late afternoon; March 7, 1970, southeastern United States; February 26, 1979, Idaho and Montana; August 21, 2017, entire United States. Even during an eclipse you should not look at the sun except through film negative or dark glasses. Near the edge of the moon's shadow you may be able to see a reddish ring. This is the chromosphere, the colored layer of gas close to the sun.

Let the children hold a small disk or coin a few inches in front of them. Squint one eye and sight with the other. Hold the coin in the line of sight between your eye and a ceiling light so that the coin completely hides the light. The coin represents the moon and the ceiling light represents the sun. Other children will note that the coin casts a shadow on the eye of the viewer.

A more elaborate demonstration of a solar eclipse involves the use of a cardboard box, a light bulb, and stiff wire or a bicycle spoke. A small wooden or clay ball mounted on a knitting needle represents the moon (Fig. 10- 9A).

Make a 2″ circular hole through a piece of cardboard painted or colored black. Draw a red crayon mark around this hole to represent the corona. A light bulb shining through the 2″ hole is the sun. The corona cannot be seen until the "moon" totally eclipses the "sun." The wire is used

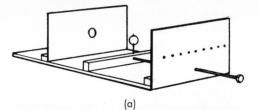

(a)

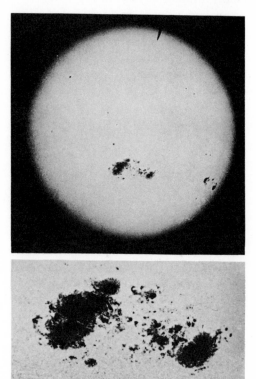

(b)

Fig. 10-9 (a) "Solar eclipse." The viewer should be at the right, looking through one of the small holes. The light source representing the sun should be at the left end of the box. The red corona is around the large circle at the left end of the box. (From *UNESCO Source Book for Science Teachers,* UNESCO, 1956.) (b) The entire solar disk, showing sunspots, and an enlargement of the great spot group of April 7, 1947, taken at Mt. Wilson Observatory. (From the AMNH.)

to adjust the moon's position with relation to the viewer and the sun. The eclipse is viewed through one of the pinholes made in the cardboard behind the ball that represents the moon. Read aloud the story of how the "Yankee in King Arthur's Court" saved his life, thanks to an eclipse.

Observing sunspots. If you have a simple telescope, point it at the sun and focus so that a bright clear image of the sun appears on a white paper placed a short distance beyond the eyepiece. (*Under no circumstances should you look at the sun through a telescope.*) If you do this during a time of sunspot activity, you may be able to see images of sunspots reflected as small dark blobs on the paper. Sunspots come and go on the sun's surface. Astronomers make systematic observations and records of them (see Fig. 10-9B).

The moon

Even young children who go to bed early can see the moon in the daytime. Sharpen their observations by asking if it has the same shape as the sun. Is it smaller or larger? Which looks bigger, a penny held close to your eye or one held at arm's length? A bird flying low overhead may look bigger than a plane in the distance, but which one is really bigger? Which is brighter, the sun or the moon? Let the children compare the light from a very small flashlight and a large one in a darkened room. Sunlight is always bright enough for reading, moonlight rarely. Moonlight is of course "secondhand" (reflected) light. In a darkened room, let the children look at a picture or book by lamplight. Then use a chalk smeared mirror and control the light source so that they look at the same material by reflected light. Which is brighter, direct light or light reflected from a rough surface? Which is warmer?

Phases of the moon. Young children will notice that the moon changes shape. Ask the children to draw or cut out the shape they see. The first time they will probably have very different ideas. Or prepare a set of cutouts, ranging from a thin crescent through quarter and half moon up to a full moon. They may pick out the shape they saw. Then let them arrange these in order. They are beginning to gain a concept of the waxing and waning moon. Make a picture record of the moon's phases on different dates. Make cutouts of the local skyline to help children relate the pictures to their environment.

Depending on the age and maturity of the group, the children may profit by demonstrating the phases of the moon with balls, papier mâché models, held in relationship to a light source. A playground ball scrubbed clean or painted with yellow water paint works well. All of the lunar phases can be shown.

Another method requires an old tennis ball and a steel knitting needle or piece of stiff wire. The needle or wire is the axis for the tennis ball moon. Let a child stand with his back to a strong light source such as a projector lamp. Holding the ball at arm's length, the child revolves slowly eastward (earth's motion). Thus he will see the shape of moon shadow change as the earth changes position in relation to it (Fig. 10-10).

Let children who have a pencil-box compass impale a small fruit or ball on the point and revolve it about themselves in relation to a light source.

Another method to demonstrate phases of the moon to a group of children involves setting a globe on a box in front of a light and letting one child hold a small ball suspended by a string from the end of a ruler or dowel rod (Fig. 10-11). This represents the moon. Watch the "moon" from the direction of "earth" as it is swung slowly around the globe. (Incidentally this can also be used to demonstrate the nature of eclipses—lunar and solar.)

Or try making a large chalk circle on the floor. Darken the room and let one child hold a clean white playground ball, another a strong flashlight. Let the rest of the class sit on the floor in the middle of the circle while the child holding the ball walks around the circle. In this manner the seated children in the center get an "earth's-eye" view of the moon moving about them.

Motions of the moon. Demonstrations with lights and balls should never take the place of actual observations of the moon. The children will tell you that the moon moves like the sun. It rises in the east and sets toward the west. Suggest they note the position of the moon with respect to the nearest bright star and watch over a period of days how it moves in relation to that star. They will find the moon really moves eastward. It is the earth's rotation which makes the moon appear to move in a false direction. Some children may have the misconception that the moon does not progress during the daytime. Let three children act out the moon's two motions as earth moves around the sun. Since the moon's speed of rotation and revolution are the same (28 days), it always presents the same side to us. This slow rotation means long days on the moon; i.e., about 1 moon day equals 15 earth days, 1 moon night equals 15 earth nights. To illustrate how the moon makes just one turn

Fig. 10-10 Illustration of the moon's phases. Challenge the class with the question, "What could you show about orbits with a ball and a light?" Accumulate enough spheres and lamps for children to work in small groups. Pool results and draw generalizations about the movements of celestial bodies in orbit.

(rotation) as it travels around the earth ask the school custodian to lend you his "dolly" for moving heavy objects. Lacking a "dolly," you might borrow a child's wagon. Let one child draw another around the room. The child riding should be facing out. While circling the room, he has turned around (rotated) once, has he not? If he faces in while being drawn around in a circle, he will always keep his

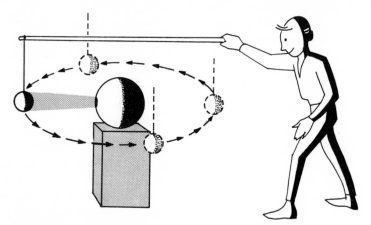

Fig. 10-11 Another method of demonstrating the moon's phases. This is one of a related group of investigations through which children gradually develop a concept of the movements of the solar system. Such a concept is basic to understanding the causes of seasons.

face to the center of the circle while making one rotation.

Surface of the moon. Some children may have been told to look for "The Man in the Moon." The apparent face is caused by shadows cast by its mountains and craters. Looking at the moon through a telescope or even through binoculars will show that the moon's surface is very rough. Let the children make clay balls with deep holes in the surface. Shine a strong light across the balls and the children will see how the resulting shadows assume all kinds of shapes. Astronomers have found there are high mountains on the moon by measuring the shadows cast by the mountains.

Not many years ago books told us that we would never see the other side of the moon. Now the Russians have photographed it by TV camera. The possibility of traveling to the moon is coming closer. Astronomers are collecting information about the moon so that earth visitors can land there safely. The first moon visitors must bring their own oxygen supply because there is none on the moon. They will need protection from the extreme heat and cold of the moon's bare surface. They will need special training for moving under condition of low gravity. A 72-pound boy would weigh about 12 pounds. He could easily jump a height of 24'. Acting out conditions on the moon would provide excellent motivation for research reading and listening.

Size and distance of the moon. Children find many facts about the moon which are related to its size and distance relative to the earth. For example, you could put about 50 moons inside the earth. The moon's diameter is ¼ that of earth (2000/8000). The moon is 240,000 miles away from earth—10 times the earth's circumference. It is our nearest neighbor in space. That is, of course, why scientists are thinking of "shooting the moon." You may want to look at the Popular Science filmstrip *Rocket to the Moon* or the Harbrace *Neighbors in Space.*

The sun is 388 times farther away from us (93,000,000 divided by 240,000). Let the children find a place they know which is about 400 miles away. If the sun were located there, then, proportionately, the moon would be about 1 mile away.

Apparent distortion of the moon. The moon, like the sun, usually looks bigger when it is just rising or setting. They *look* big in comparison to objects on the sky-line, and look smaller when they are high in the sky. This is a good example of optical illusion (see refraction, Chapter 16). Let children check by sighting (Fig. 10-12). Bend a paper clip so that it fits over a yardstick, and holding the stick beneath the eye, slide the clip until its prongs encompass the moon. Do this when the moon rises and also later; compare the two sightings. Again, the moon and sun look redder when close to the horizon. There are always dust particles in the air. When we look at the moon or sun close to the horizon, we are looking through more dust than when we look overhead. The dust particles absorb most of the colors that make up light; only the red rays penetrate.

Lunar eclipses. Dramatic play and manipulation of balls, lights, and globes to show phases of the moon and solar eclipses have already been suggested. From such activities the children may also develop understanding of the causes for lunar eclipses. They may now understand why the moon can be eclipsed only when it is full. A solar eclipse must fall at the dark of the moon. They may well ask why solar and lunar eclipses do not occur once a month. From the start, the limitations of models should be made clear; i.e., they do not present a wholly true picture of the situation. For example, the relative sizes and distances of sun, moon, and earth would

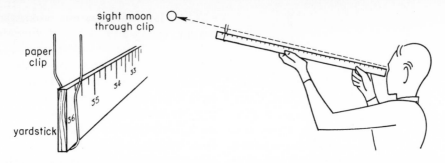

sight moon
through clip

paper
clip

33
34
35
36

yardstick

Fig. 10-12 Sighting the moon. This investigation is one of many we should use with children to illustrate the need of verifying appearance vs. reality. (Redrawn from *General Science Handbook, Part II*, New York State Education Department, 1952.)

be hard to demonstrate. Therefore the proportions of the actual shadows cast are much narrower and smaller than would appear from working with models. For example, the moon's shadow never covers more than a spot 160 miles in diameter during a solar eclipse. However, it can be shown with models why lunar eclipses occur more often than solar eclipses— namely, the earth casts a much larger shadow than the moon. Again, the almanac should give dates for lunar eclipses. The full moon looks dark red when in

total shadow ("moon turned into blood," Joel 2:31). Another factor which prevents more frequent lunar eclipses is the difference between the plane of the earth's orbit and that of the moon's. The plane of the moon's orbit is inclined 5° to that of the earth's, and so only occasionally does the moon happen to pass through the earth's shadow. Mounting balls of clay on the ends of stiff wire as in Fig. 10-13 and holding them in the beam of a flashlight is a simple way to demonstrate eclipses and the influence of different or vital planes.

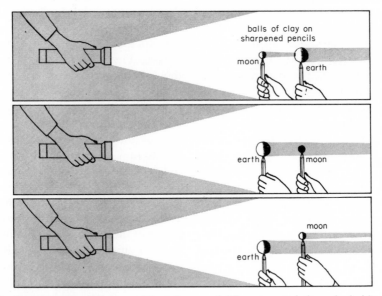

balls of clay on sharpened pencils

moon   earth

earth   moon

moon

earth

Fig. 10-13 Demonstrating eclipses and the influence of different or vital planes by holding clay balls in the beam of a flashlight.

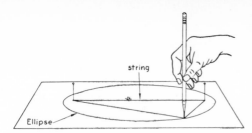

string

Ellipse

Fig. 10-14 Drawing an ellipse. The elliptical orbits of planets and satellites, natural or artificial, are important for children of the space age to "learn by doing." Call attention to the triangle within the ellipse. See parallax (p. 158). (From *General Science Handbook, Part II*, New York State Education Department, 1952.)

Lunar proverbs and superstitions. A study of the moon is not complete without some study of the folklore about the moon. See Bartlett's *Dictionary of Familiar Quotations* for sources in the literature, e.g., Shakespeare.

The planets

Very early in man's history, sky watchers noticed that certain celestial bodies remained in approximately the same part of the sky night after night, while others kept changing position. Sometimes these appeared to go backwards, and were thus called "planets" (wanderers); the stationary points of light are stars. Even without the aid of telescopes, the ancient astronomers were able to see and observe the motions of the five planets nearest the sun. These they called Mercury, Venus, Mars, Jupiter, Saturn. Mercury, being nearest the sun, is less often visible, and being smaller, it is harder to see. The three outer planets, Uranus, Neptune, and Pluto, can be observed only through telescopes. Pluto was not discovered until 1930, when it was located by the American astronomer, Percival Lowell. His observations of the behavior of Uranus and Neptune led him to suspect there must be another planet "out there" that was disturbing their motion.

There is a definite family resemblance among the planets. All of them are spheres, spinning on their own axes. All travel in elliptical orbits around the sun. All are made from the same group of elements. All of them follow a definite pattern of spacing in their orbits except for the space between Mars and Jupiter. A German astronomer, Bode, noticed the gap in this pattern and concluded that a planet was missing. In the search for the "lost planet," an Italian astronomer in 1801 discovered Ceres—a tiny "planetoid" less than 500 miles across. Since then more than 1500 planetoids have been found in this region. Such minor planets or planetoids are often called asteroids.

Orbits. The nine planets move in orbits which are all approximately on one plane. Illustrate the plane of orbit by swinging a weight at the end of a string. In first studying the sun's family with young children, it is appropriate to make a chalk reproduction of the Copernican system on the classroom floor. (See Fig. 10-1B.) With older children, the next step would be to learn that the orbits of the planets are slightly elliptical. Let children practice drawing an ellipse with the aid of a loop of string and two pins (Fig. 10-14). The relative sizes of these orbits should be developed at a later stage in the study.

By dramatic play, little children act out the basic concepts of orbits and motions of the sun and its planets. For instance, ask a child to walk to the classroom door; he will see that his feet leave no mark. Every day children move in and out of the door, yet they leave no visible path on the floor. Then ask one child to sit or stand in the center of the room. This child is the sun. Another child—the earth—walks around the first. Then, depending on the age and mental maturity of the children, the teacher gradually adds to the dramatic play. Whereas the first time the children

Table 10-1
The solar system

planet	diameter[1] (in miles)		distance from sun (in millions of miles)	revolution in orbit	number of moons
Mercury	3000	(⅓″)	36	3 months	0
Venus	7575	(¾″)	67	8 months	0
Earth	8000	(1″)	93	1 year	1
Mars	4215	(½″)	141	2 years	2
Jupiter	88,000	(11″)	483	12 years	11
Saturn	75,000	(9″)	886	29 years	9
Uranus	31,000	(4″)	1786	84 years	4
Neptune	33,000	(4½″)	2792	165 years	1
Pluto	3000	(½″)	3680	249 years	0
Sun	864,100	(108″)			
Moon	2160	(¼″)			

[1] Figures in parentheses are diameters of scale models (1″ = 8000 mi).

may work in pairs, playing sun and earth, another day they may work in threes, the third child representing the moon. Eventually the children may play at being the solar family of sun and nine planets. In developing the concepts of orbit and motion the teacher relates it by discussion and outdoor observation to the earth's revolution in orbit and the change of season.

Often children enjoy choosing one of the planets and making a special study of it. They may like to work in teams to do the necessary reading and writing, art, and construction on their planet. They will need such information about their planet as is given in Table 10-1.

Relative sizes. Building a scale model of the solar system provides good experience with reading large numbers and reducing them to scale. Some teachers make clay models formed around a paper clip suspended at the end of a string. Each string is eventually suspended from a wire hung across a room. We find it more practical to make paper or tagboard disks cut out to a scale of a 27″ sun or, if space permits, a 9′ sun. Proportionate diameters of the planets are listed in Table 10-1 where the sun is shown as 108″ (9′). You can reduce or increase these proportions

to suit your purposes and facilities. For instance, a 27″ sun would reduce all the proportions to one fourth of those listed. Using these paper patterns, next blow up balloons to the right size. For the sun we use a large meteorological balloon usually available at army surplus stores. Some teachers like to use these balloons as forms over which to mold papier mâché models. When the papier-mâché is dry, the balloon is deflated. Either the balloons or the light papier-mâché balls are easy and safe to hang overhead in the classroom.

The sun is so enormous with respect to its planets that one can usually show only a segment of it if the smaller planet models are to be seen.

Relative distances. With respect to relative distances between the planets, the enormous distances between the four outer planets make them difficult to include in a correct reduction to scale of these distances. The usual schematic diagram of the planets often gives a distorted idea—namely, that the planets move in concentric rings spaced at regular intervals. By examining Table 10-1, you will see that the four inner planets are relatively close to the sun. The outer four are really in the outfield. No scale model of the solar system "tells a true thing" unless it shows this wide gap between the inner and outer four.

Most scales of linear planetary models do not give children any sense of the enormous distance in space, one of the important concepts of any astronomy study. If you use a scale let 1' equal 1 million miles. If you measure interplanetary distances on the playground and beyond, your children come closer to the concept of space than if you try to measure the distances in the classroom. The whole activity will be smoother and more effective, and you will have some excellent reasons to use arithmetic if the distances are measured ahead of time. Collect kite string and yardsticks or, if possible, 50' tapes. Let the children show you they know how to wind and unwind one of these tapes without snarling it. Let the children work in teams, using the hallway to measure the amount of string necessary, say, to show the distance from Venus to Mars. It takes much less work and string to measure this distance than to measure the distance from the sun each time. Show the children how to wind their string around a folded newspaper or box core.

Start at the nearest corner of the playground. Leave one child here to represent the sun. The Mercury team stretches its 36' string out from the "sun," and one child remains at the spot where the string ends. The group continues outward on the diagonal for greatest distance. By the time the Jupiter team has measured off the correct distance, the children will see that the four outer planets are well beyond the playground. In view of this you may only have pre-measured distances as far as Saturn. At this point, ask the class to turn and see how far off and small the children marking the sun and inner planets appear. The children may suggest that the other planetary distances be measured by means of a car with parental cooperation. The children may also wish to hold their size scale models as they stand in position.

In addition, the children may want to make a mural to illustrate relative distances in the solar system. Using a scale of about 6" as the distance between Earth and the sun, Pluto would be about 20' from the sun. A strip of mural paper about 8 yards long should be about right. Some first graders had a wonderful time making a Milky Way by spatter painting on their sky mural. The children will want to include the planetoids, Jupiter's moons, Saturn's rings, the canals on Mars, phases of Venus, and so forth. Adding a comet will provoke research and discussion to explain why the tail always points away from the sun. Using a light source for the sun, a small ball for Mercury, and a globe for Earth, let them figure out why we seldom see Mercury except close to sunrise or sunset.

If there are enough boys in class who own toy electric trains, they can set them up in concentric ellipses with each track representing an orbit and each train carrying the name of its planet. The speeds of the planet trains should be roughly adjusted to the year length for each planet (see Table 10-1).

An almanac can be a very useful tool in astronomy. It gives a timetable for the visible planets: Mercury, Venus, Mars, Jupiter, Saturn. Sometimes these are morning, sometimes evening "stars." The almanac will tell where to find them and when.

Life on other planets.   Children often raise the question of life on other planets. Their own research will eventually answer their questions. In capsule form, according to our *present* knowledge, Mercury has no atmosphere. The distant planets are too cold and too small to hold an atmosphere. There is no evidence of oxygen on Venus. Mars's atmosphere contains CO_2 and traces of oxygen. It should be able to support plant life. Jupiter's atmosphere includes ammonia and methane gases which would be poisonous for humans. There has been much speculation about life on Mars but no one knows for sure. Perhaps with larger telescopes or observations from space satellites, we shall come closer to finding out. The possibility of life as we know it on Earth being duplicated on Mars is highly doubtful.

Comets, meteors, and meteorites

Comets and meteorites also travel around the sun along with the rest of its family.

Comets. Whether a comet is approaching or going away from the sun, the tail is always pointed away from the sun. The tail does not show until close to the sun. The tail is composed of gas so thin that Earth and other planets have passed through without effect. The heavier the particles of gas, the more curvaceous the tail of a comet. "Comet" means "long haired" in Greek. The tail is longest when the comet is nearest the sun because the sun's light pushes gases out of the comet's head. The pressure exerted by light on the comet's gases creates an effect much like wind blowing flame away from a fire. Most comets are small, but some have heads thousands of miles across and tails millions of miles long. Like the tail, the head of a comet is made of particles of dust and gases.

Over a thousand comets have been seen, some regularly. Few are visible except through the telescope. The most famous is Halley's comet. The English astronomer for whom it is named studied this comet in 1682 so thoroughly that he was able to predict its orbit and return— once every 75–76 years. It will provide good arithmetic practice to calculate its return on schedule, 1758, 1835, 1910, and its next appearance, about 1985.

Meteors. How can you tell a comet from a meteor? A meteor makes a sudden, thin streak of light across the sky as it falls. A comet shows as a steady streak of light during the nights it is visible. Almost everyone has seen a "shooting star" and enjoyed its brief display. These are meteors, not stars at all. Meteors are much more common than comets, and as many as five to ten meteors per hour are visible to the naked eye at night. Meteors, the smallest members of the sun's circus, are caused by tiny fragments of stone or metal striking the earth's atmosphere and burning up by friction as they plunge to earth. They then fall as dust.

Meteorites. Some solid particles get through the atmosphere without being totally consumed. Such solid particles are called meteorites, and many land on the earth. These odd-shaped lumps often resemble burned-out cinders. Some are much heavier than coal, however, because they consist mainly of nickel, iron, and cobalt; others are of lighter materials and are called stone meteorites.

In the American Museum of Natural History in New York you can see the 14-ton meteorite which fell near Willamette, Oregon. Here also is the 36-ton meteorite brought from Greenland by Admiral Peary. The Eskimos called it Ahnighto (the tent). They used fragments of it to make metal arrow points and tools.

At one point about a mile south of U.S. Highway 66 in Arizona is a crater about ¾ of a mile across. Meteorite craters look exactly like those we see on the moon. Some believe this one was made by a giant meteorite which buried itself so far below the surface that it has not yet been found. Cedars growing around the rim have been found by tree ring dating to be over 700 years old.

Recently aerial explorations in northeastern Canada revealed the Chubb meteorite crater, 2½ miles in diameter. It con-

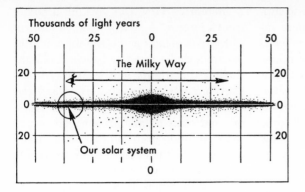

Fig. 10-15 The Milky Way. The relatively minor position of our huge solar system within our galaxy is a humbling piece of essential information. (From R. Brinckerhoff et al., *The Physical World*, Harcourt, Brace & World, 1958.)

tains a lake 2 miles across. In 1908 a meteor which landed in Siberia burned the forests for 25 miles around.

Children can see meteorites on almost any clear night, but especially during the Perseid meteorite showers about August 11th, and the Leonid meteorite showers in November. A monthly star map usually tells when the earth will pass through such areas of meteorite activity.

Children who have done no thinking about friction may not understand how a chunk of black inert meteorite could once have been bright and shining. Let them rub their hands together first slowly, then fast. Which generates the most heat? Jet pilots have refrigerated cockpits to counteract heat of friction due to high speeds. The thousands of tiny rocks pulled around by the sun's gravity meet earth's atmosphere at 20–40 miles per second. They begin to burn or glow about 100 miles up. Most of them turn into gases before they ever reach the ground. The few which are not entirely burned up are full of holes just like a furnace clinker. It is hard to imagine a heavy piece of black rock being hot enough to glow. The minerals in it melt and even turn into gas just as water boils into steam.

OUTSIDE THE SOLAR SYSTEM

As we have seen, earth and planets belong to the solar system, and we have learned that this whole system rotates slowly in space. But the solar system occupies but one small region in the huge galaxy known as the Milky Way—a whirling mass of hot gases, billions of stars, and interstellar dust (Fig. 10-15). Even the Milky Way is only one such galaxy in the universe of galaxies sighted and studied by astronomers. (Of the many million comparable systems, astronomers have thus far determined the distance of about 100 galaxies—a relatively small number.)

The stars

Most of the stars that we observe individually are in the Milky Way galaxy. It is somewhat like a fried egg or filled cookie in cross section. Naturally, from inside the stars will look closer together toward the rim. With binoculars you can see another great galaxy in the beautiful autumn constellation of Andromeda. Through the glasses this Andromeda galaxy looks hazy —like light shining through tissue paper. With your naked eye locate the approximate position that the galaxy should occupy within the constellation; then bring your glasses up between your eyes and the star points chosen. This galaxy is one of the closest, a mere 2,800,000 light years away. With binoculars you can also see the nebula in Orion's sword. Orion is a fall and winter constellation, within our own galaxy. The Orion nebula is also a fuzzy patch rather than the twinkling pinpoint of light it would be if it were a single star. Small as it appears, it takes 15 years for light to cross it.

With binoculars you can also see the star clusters that are associated with our galaxy. There is one in the summer constellation, Cancer the Crab. This is a rather faint group of stars, usually rather low in the southeastern skies in northern latitudes. The star cluster is called the Beehive because the close group of stars is supposed to look like a swarm of bees. In the winter constellation of Hercules is a star cluster which looks like a single star to your naked eye. Telescopic photographs have revealed over 30,000 stars. Despite their seeming closeness, they are separated from each other by billions of miles.

Color of stars. Let the children heat iron wire, say picture wire, until it glows red hot. Hold the wire with pliers. As the wire gets hotter, it glows orange, then yellow. If you could get it hot enough, it would turn *white*. The hottest stars have a bluish white light. Our sun is medium hot. Rigel, 14,000 times brighter than our sun, is blue-white. Betelgeuse is a red giant, one of the biggest stars known. Capella is yellow like our sun. Aldebaran is orange, cooler than our sun.

Table 10-2 shows the relationship between star color and temperature.

Star trail photography. A child and a parent interested in photography can have an interesting experience taking time exposures of stars. Point the camera toward the North Star. Expose for several

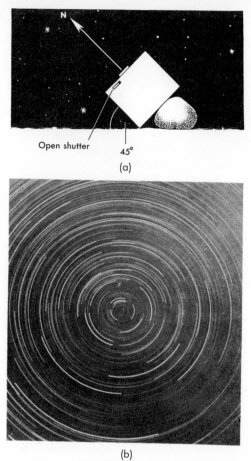

Open shutter   45°

(a)

(b)

Fig. 10-16 (a) Camera in position for a star trail photograph. Select a clear moonless night and make the camera aperture as small as possible. (b) Star trails around the North Star. (From R. Brinckerhoff et al., *The Physical World*, Harcourt, Brace & World, 1958.)

hours but with a small aperture to keep out stray starlight. Your photography should show one apex of the axis on which our earth turns (Fig. 10-16). Try also with shutter wide open. Protect from headlights, etc. (See also Harbrace filmstrip, *Neighbors in Space.*)

The zodiac

Ask children to watch and decide if the sun, the moon, and the planets appear anywhere in the sky or follow a broad path. Eventually they should agree that

Table 10-2
Star color and approximate temperature

star	color	surface temperature
Rigel	blue-white	above 36,000° F
Procyon	yellow-white	13,500° F
Sun	yellow	11,000° F
Arcturus	orange	7,500° F
Antares	red	5,500° F

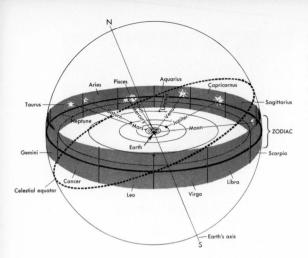

Fig. 10-17 Since all the planets move in nearly the same plane, from the earth we see them along the zodiac. For example, as the drawing indicates, we would see Jupiter among the stars of the constellation Capricornus, and Saturn in Aries. (From R. Brinckerhoff et al., *The Physical World*, Harcourt, Brace & World, 1958.)

these bodies follow roughly the same path. At our latitude this broad band arches high across the southern sky (why we see planets along the zodiac, Fig. 10-17). Most of the constellations parade along an imaginary equatorial line called the ecliptic. This belt which is 16° wide is divided into 12 sections each extending 30°. Each section includes a constellation which is called a sign of the zodiac. The 12 signs of the zodiac are given in Table 10-3.

Signs of the zodiac. When people say, "The sun is in Taurus," what do they mean? Copy the 12 signs of the zodiac on large cards or white paper. Lay them in a circle on the floor around an unshaded lamp (Fig. 10-18). Let a tennis ball represent the earth. The children will then quickly see why at different seasons we see different constellations. It will also be seen that the "sun is in Taurus" because looking from "Earth" toward the sun, the observer is facing Taurus's section of the circle.

Constellations

Start children with the names and legends connected with the best-known constellation, the Big Dipper. Be sure to include some of the American Indian legends. For instance, relate the one that explains the stars in the handle as the robin, the bluejay, and the chickadee. The double star in the middle is the chickadee carrying the pot in which the birds hoped to cook their quarry, the Great Bear. The robin is the star in the handle nearest the Bear. Since he was right up in front, he was covered with blood when they shot the Bear with their bows and arrows. Ever since, the robin's breast has been red.

Sometimes we put a purposely misaligned row of dots on a board and let the children help correct our design for the Dipper. Then the children use small squares of black or dark blue construction paper. Let them use chalk to draw the Dipper and the point of an ordinary pencil to poke small holes where the stars should be. Held up against daylight the design can be checked and redrawn until satisfactory. Taken home, it can serve as a check for observation of the Dipper at night.

Some children may wish to make a star box, using a flashlight inside an oatmeal or

Table 10-3
Signs of the zodiac

spring signs	*month*
Aries	March
Taurus	April
Gemini	May
summer signs	
Cancer	June
Leo	July
Virgo	August
autumn signs	
Libra	September
Scorpio	October
Sagittarius	November
winter signs	
Capricorn	December
Aquarius	January
Pisces	February

Fig. 10-18 Demonstration of why at different seasons we see different constellations and why the sun appears in different signs of the zodiac. (From *General Science Handbook, Part II*, New York State Education Department, 1952.)

shoe box (Fig. 10-19). Then let the children prick out the design of each dipper, then both together, through a piece of thick black (or other opaque) paper which slips over the end of the box or in through a slot near the end with a flashlight shining behind it. The children will notice that the Big Dipper has sloping sides and a curved handle. The Little Dipper has vertical sides. One appears to be pouring into the other. Polaris, the Pole Star or North Star, is important for all to be able to locate through the pointer stars in the Big Dipper. The North Star does not rise or set. It is brighter than our sun but appears insignificant because it is 470 light years away. The North Star is the pivot for the five circumpolar constella-

tions: the two Dippers; Cassiopeia, the Queen; Cepheus, the King; and Draco, the Dragon. After the two Dippers have become familiar, the children should have no trouble finding Cassiopeia. It looks like a battered M or W, and lies opposite the Big Dipper, across the North Star.

The Big Dipper has been called the Clock in the Sky. The position of the Dipper handle changes not only with the hour of the night but also with the seasons. For example, on a clear wintry night, the handle of the Dipper hangs down. In summer, about the same time of evening, the handle is high. But in any position, the two end stars in the bowl always point to the North Star. If the children are not sure where to look north, remind them it

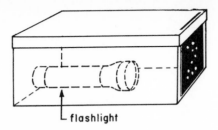

L flashlight

Fig. 10-19 A star box. There are many ways to show the constellations, based on shining a light behind a pattern of holes pricked in a plane or curved surface. Here as elsewhere let your own and the children's creativity have full play.

will be to the right of where the sun sets. If they begin star gazing at home, ask them to watch and decide whether the sky grows dark at once. Ask them as they watch twilight ("twixt light and night") fade into night to decide whether the stars are of equal brightness. Later in a darkened room, with different size light sources, help them to understand why astronomers list stars as first, second, third, etc., magnitude. Let them look at a flashlight at close range and at a distance. This is more effective if done outdoors at a greater distance. Help them to understand that stars are present in daytime though we do not see them. Hold a lighted flashlight near the window. Let them compare the light when the room is darkened and when the shades are lifted.

Although the North Star has been our chief guide to navigation for centuries, astronomers tell us that it is drifting through space together with the other stars. Even the shapes of constellations are changing imperceptibly.

Umbrella planetariums. An ancient umbrella provides an excellent way of learning the patterns and the paths of the circumpolar constellations. Let the tip of the umbrella where the ribs converge be the North Star. This is also the end of the handle of the Little Dipper. On the inside make the outline of the Little Dipper with squares of masking tape or adhesive disks.

Then place the Big Dipper with the pointer stars in its bowl pointing toward the North Star. Opposite this design place Cassiopeia. Add Cepheus and Draco in the appropriate positions (see Fig. 10-20). Let the children work under the raised umbrella. When the umbrella is held overhead, the star groups should look much as they do outdoors. It may encourage direct observation of the constellations if the children are asked to find out and reproduce with their umbrella planetarium the correct position for each constellation at a given time of evening.

To show the relationship between the constellations and the rotating earth, you can take an old globe and after making holes at the North and South Poles, slip it over the rod of the umbrella. On many umbrellas the handle screws off; if it doesn't, the holes through the globe must be big enough to accommodate the handle. In position the globe can be turned. Take a piece of modeling clay or other marker and put it on the globe to indicate where you are. Ask the children to pretend they are standing on the globe looking up at the sky, that is, at the inside of the open umbrella. Now turn the globe to demonstrate why the constellations each night appear to move about Polaris.

Star charts. For a large star chart procure a sheet of Masonite and drill holes for stars in several constellations, for instance, those grouped about Polaris. Behind the sheet mount a flood lamp and drape the sheet with cloth to keep extraneous light from escaping.

Divide the children into teams for studying the constellations. When each team is familiar with the outline of a particular constellation and its neighbors, you may then gather for an evening of star gazing. Each team should be accompanied by a parent or other adult and should have a good strong flashlight and chart of their constellation and its neighbors. Each team

Table 10-4
Stars and their constellations

star	constellation	star	constellation
Algol	Perseus	Regulus	Leo
Arcturus	Bootes	Pollux	Gemini
Antares	Scorpio	Rigel	Orion
Deneb	Cygnus	Betelgeuse	Orion
Vega	Lyra	Sirius	Canis Major
Capella	Auriga		

About 200,000 stars have been seen and catalogued with the aid of telescopes. Of these we can see 2500–3000 with the naked eye. This number probably includes the total number to be seen whether one looks from the northern or southern hemisphere. The larger stars have been known and observed since ancient times. Most of them have Arabic names. Several begin with the Arabic prefix *al* meaning "the"; for example, Algol, the Demon, in the constellation of Perseus; Altair, the Flier, in Aquila, the Eagle; Aldebaran, the follower (because it follows the Pleiades), the "eye" of the constellation Taurus, the Bull. In Arabic, Arcturus means "the star of the shepherds of the heavenly herds." Planes and ships navigate with respect to the positions of these and other brighter or first magnitude stars. There are about 90 named constellations. Table 10-4 gives some of the constellations and the great stars found in them.

should bring a star map for the sky at that season. Such a map is often published once a month by the newspaper or nature or science magazine. Urge the children to select maps which are relatively simple. Many star maps are useless for young children because they are drawn to show too much detail, that is, too many stars and minor constellations.

A flashlight with a strong beam is useful in pointing out the general direction of the constellation being studied. Each team could point out its constellation and give some interesting information about it to the other children. It will be much easier to see the constellations if the flashlight lens is covered with red cellophane. Red light does not affect the eye's adaptation to the dark.

Constellations are stars which seem to move as a group around the North Star, or more or less along the ecliptic. Of the 90-odd named groups, some are not visi-

Table 10-5
Constellations visible in northern latitudes

spring	summer	fall	winter
Leo, the Lion (or the Sickle)	*Lyra, the Lyre	*Andromeda, the Maiden	*Orion, the Hunter
*Auriga, the Charioteer	*Cygnus, the Swan	Pegasus, the Horse	Canis Major, Big Dog
*Gemini, the Twins	Scorpio, the Scorpion	*Perseus, the Knight	Canis Minor, Little Dog
Corvus, the Crow	*Aquila, the Eagle	*Hercules, the Hunter	*Taurus, the Bull
*Cancer, the Crab	*Boötes, the Herdsman		*The Pleiades, Seven Sisters
	Delphinus, the Dolphin		Lepus, the Hare
	*Northern Crown, the Corona Borealis		*Aries, the Ram
	*Draco, the Dragon		*Cepheus, Andromeda's Father
	*Serpens, the Snake		*Cassiopeia, Andromeda's Mother

* You will find these constellation positions in Fig. 10-20. The stellar constellations shift a little every night as the earth, tilted on its axis, proceeds about the sun. At any particular time many of the constellations in the partial list above are below the horizon. However, what does remain constant is the relationship of the constellations to each other.

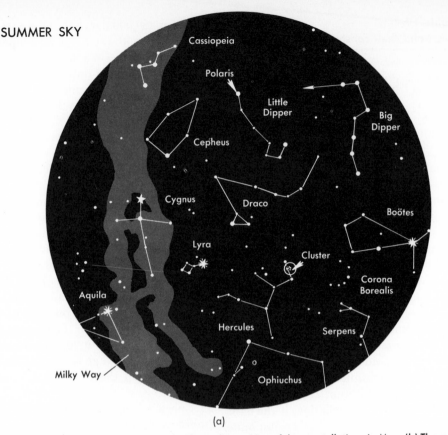

Fig. 10-20 (a) The map of the summer sky shows the position of the constellations in May. (b) The map of the winter sky shows them in January and February. (From R. Brinckerhoff et al., *The Physical World*, Harcourt, Brace & World, 1958.)

ble in both hemispheres. The circumpolar constellations are visible at all seasons, although some are below the horizon at different hours. The other constellations are visible at different seasons. Table 10-5 gives those visible in northern latitudes at the seasons indicated (see also Fig. 10-20).

Most children can find the Big Dipper. If they extend a line through the two stars which form the top of the Dipper, it will run right into Auriga, the Charioteer. If the line from the top two stars of the Big Dipper is continued beyond Auriga, it passes close to Taurus, the constellation which encompasses the Pleiades (off to one side) and Hyades, a V-shaped cluster of stars in the middle of the constellation.

Follow the line out further and you come upon Orion, a prominent and easily identified winter constellation with a bright line of stars in his belt (Orion's belt).

The Andromeda family is that group of constellations which circles about Polaris. All three constellations are not always visible. Take a line from the two end stars of the Big Dipper to find Polaris. Continue the line and you will find Cepheus (shaped like a child's drawing of a house), Andromeda's Father. Clockwise about Polaris is Cassiopeia (shaped like an askew M or W). Going clockwise about Polaris is Andromeda herself, often low on the horizon.

The other nearby constellation, which

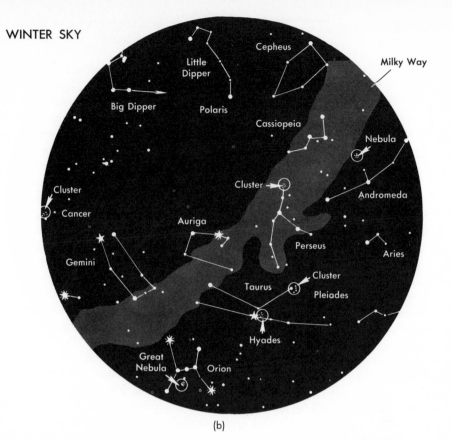

(b)

has the Milky Way as a background, is Perseus. Clockwise from Perseus about Polaris is Auriga; a line from Polaris which runs between Perseus and Auriga will come upon Taurus.

Here are the constellations about Polaris going clockwise from the Big Dipper: Little Dipper (closer in and fainter than the Big Dipper), Cepheus, Cassiopeia, Perseus, Auriga. If you extend a line from Polaris through the end or the next to the end star of the Little Dipper's handle, you will come upon Draco, a summer constellation located between Cepheus and the Big Dipper about Polaris.

You and the children can make up other guide lines of interrelationship among the constellations. Eventually you can become so familiar with them that you need to see only a portion of the sky

to know in what direction Polaris lies. In the long run the best way to study the geography of the heavens is to go out at night and look upward with a star guide in hand and a flashlight whose lens has been covered with red cellophane. You'll be surprised how quickly it all becomes like your own backyard, which, in a sense, it really is.

INSTRUMENTS AND TECHNIQUES IN ASTRONOMY

Astronomers throughout the ages have been aided in their study of the heavens and celestial phenomena by many devices and techniques that are continually being improved. From the crudest sundial of early times to the modern radio telescope, astronomical aids extend our frontiers of knowledge.

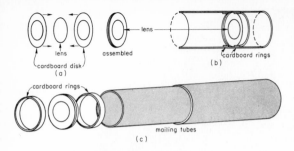

Fig. 10-21 Making a refracting telescope.

Telescopes

Refracting telescope. Essentially making a refracting telescope comes down to placing one lens (the objective) with a fairly long focal length (8″ or so) so that it focuses a little in front of an eyepiece lens (focal length 1″). The distance between should be adjustable. This simple two-lens arrangement inverts the image at the eyepiece so that you see things upside down (Fig. 10-21).

It is easy to measure the focal length of a lens. Stand next to a wall 30′ or more opposite a window. Hold the lens up and focus an image of the window onto the wall. Move the lens until you get the smallest *sharp* image. The distance from the center of the lens to the wall will be the lens's focal length.

The better the lenses the better your telescope. A stamp magnifier (focal length about 1″) makes a good eyepiece. A high school laboratory or optician's lens (focal length about 8″) makes a good objective. Both lenses, of course, are convex like a hand glass. (Let the children feel the shape of the glass in a hand magnifier.) With achromatic lenses you will have a better instrument than that with which Galileo discovered the moons of Jupiter. These lenses should be set into tubes which slide back and forth one inside the other. Once you have your lenses, you might go to a stationery store and buy some mailing tubes, one for the objective

lens and one, slightly smaller in diameter so that it just fits inside the larger tube, for the eyepiece.

Next mount the lenses in the ends of their respective tubes (Fig. 10-21B). Cut two disks of cardboard exactly the inside diameter of the mailing tube. Out of the center of each cut a circle whose diameter is a little less than that of the lens. Glue the overlap to the glass edge and also glue the two rings to each other. Once dry, the lens may be set into the tube by being anchored with cardboard rings, one on each side of the mounted lenses.

Reflecting telescope. A reflecting telescope consists basically of a concave mirror (surface curved inward) with an eyepiece lens a little beyond its focus. A 45° mirror is often used to reflect the light being focused by the concave mirror into the eyepiece (Fig. 10-22). The famous 200-inch mirror at the Palomar Observatory is used in a reflecting telescope.

To find the focal length of a concave mirror, let strong sunlight follow it. Make a cloud of chalk dust over the mirror. You will see the conical shape of the focused light rays.

Reflecting telescopes can be made larger than the typical refracting telescope through which visitors to an observatory may look. Most astronomical observation today is done by photography (long exposure). This method is much more exact and more sensitive than the human eye. It also provides accurate records from which modern astronomers may work.

Radio telescope. One of the newest and most interesting developments in astronomy today is what is being done with radio telescopes. These pick up radio signals from stars so distant or indistinct their light cannot be seen.

Science and timekeeping

Startime. The bigger our telescopes, the farther the universe seems to stretch out before us. The more man finds out about the stars, the more infinitesimal our world becomes. At the same time astronomy has many practical uses. One of the most important is to give us correct, or sidereal (star), time. When the earth rotates once on its axis, like a merry-go-round, the stars appear to turn once. A star day or sidereal day is the amount of time it takes for the earth to make one full turn. A star will travel 360° or 24 star hours in a star day. If we observe a star at the highest point of its circle in the sky, we know it will travel west 15° every hour (360 divided by 24).

If we sight on a star at 6 P.M. and at 7 P.M. find it has moved, say, 16°, we know our clocks are fast. If it has moved 14°, we know our clocks are slow.

The amount of time from sunup to sunup is called a solar day. Our clocks and watches are adjusted to keep solar time, but we check them by sidereal time or against our star signposts in the sky.

Sundial, hourglass, and water clock. The children may already know that the first timekeeping was done by means of shadow sticks and stones and other kinds of crude markers. From such activities evolved the sundial, used up to modern times (see p. 152). It is believed that Egyptian obelisks, such as Cleopatra's Needle, were the shadow sticks, or gnomons, of giant sundials. But sundials were of no use at night and in cloudy weather. Consequently, men worked on other timekeepers, such as the water clock (clepsydra). In the eighth century an enterprising monk invented the hourglass, the protoype of our modern 3-minute egg timer. Time was an all-important factor in computing distance at sea, out of sight of land, and the hourglass, which was possible aboard ship where the sundial and water clock were not, was an important aid to early navigation.

Pendulum clock. It is said that the

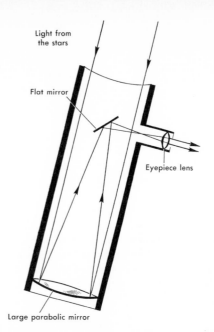

Fig. 10-22 A reflecting telescope. (From R. Brinckerhoff et al., *The Physical World*, Harcourt, Brace & World, 1958.)

modern clock is due to Galileo's mind's wandering in church. He noticed the swinging of a lamp suspended from the ceiling by long chains. Timing it by his pulse, he discovered that the swings were regular. After Galileo's keen observation of everyday phenomena, watchmakers added a swinging weight to the large, heavy egg-shaped timepieces carried on their rounds by watchmen. We call these swinging weights pendulums. Let the children suspend a weight from the top of a door opening. If the string is about 39" (one meter) long, the pendulum should "bob" about once every second. Let the children discover that shortening the string quickens the beat, and lengthening it slows the swing. (See also the discussion on the Foucault pendulum, p. 154.)

Finding positions on the earth

Finding your latitude. Finding your way at sea or in the air is quite a different matter from finding your way on *terra*

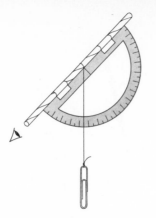

Fig. 10-23 Working model of astrolabe. Sight in the direction of the North Star through the drinking straw taped to the protractor. The weighted string should fall across the figure corresponding to the latitude of the observer.

firma. The saying "all at sea" is not an idle expression. Even on one of the Great Lakes, being out of sight of land or at night or in bad weather, one has only the sun or stars by which to steer. At sea or in the air, time is inseparable from distance. The intrepid Vikings and other early navigators who sailed without benefit of compasses or accurate timepieces have our respect and appreciation for their fearlessness in pushing the frontiers of knowledge even a little farther.

The most serious handicap to early navigation was the lack of accurate time-keeping devices. In the days of sailing vessels, sailors tried to figure how far they had sailed by using a 28-second hourglass and a "log line." The line had a log chip at one end to carry it out and knots at intervals of 47′ 3″. By counting the number of knots slipping through his fingers in 28 seconds, the sailor could tell the ship's speed. Thus were derived the terms *ship's log* and *speed in knots.* Knowing the ship's heading from the compass and speed figured by the log line, sailors could, by *deduced reasoning,* figure their new position even in cloudy weather. Shortened to

"ded. reckoning," the expression has come to be called "dead reckoning."

The great voyages of exploration during the fifteenth century were undertaken by men better equipped with courage than with instruments of navigation. By the next century it became clear that accurate navigation was out of the question without more accurate ways of keeping time at sea. During the same period mapmaking had become a real art.

The mercator map projections still used today were invented by the famous Flemish geographer, Gerardus Mercator. Just as we map the land with a grid of streets and roads, early cartographers marked off the globe with east-west (latitude) and north-south (longitude) lines. These establish one's position with reference to the nearest parallel of latitude and meridian of longitude. These lines might be regarded as imaginary world streets or highways. Sailors first learned to find their latitude with the help of an astrolabe, a crude instrument for measuring the height (altitude) of the sun and stars. Try making one with the aid of a protractor and other simple materials (Fig. 10-23). More accurate latitude positions were possible when the sextant was invented.

If you estimate how much your arm is raised (what angle it makes with the earth's surface) when you point to the North Star, you can estimate your latitude. If you were standing at the North Pole, your arm would be straight over your head (latitude 90°). If you were at the equator, your arm would be out straight in front of you (latitude 0°). Hinge two rulers together with adhesive tape. Touch a world globe at any point with the hinge. Let one ruler point to the North Star, the other to the horizon at the point selected (i.e., at right angles to globe surface as if it were someone standing on the earth's surface). Just as the person pointing at the North Star creates an angle between his arm and the earth's surface equal to his latitude, so do our pair of rulers indicate approximate latitude at the point selected. For accurate latitude, measure the angle with a simple protractor.

Latitude vs. longitude. To understand the difference between latitude and longitude, children need to become aware of the difference between *parallel* lines and those which *converge* to a point (i.e., the poles). It may be helpful here to illustrate the difference by drawing lines around a tennis ball—they stay parallel though the circles get smaller and smaller; then draw lines through the poles—these spread out and come together always crossing at the poles. Once they knew the world was round, the early mapmakers divided the globe into parallel slices. Starting at the equator, they drew a parallel of latitude every 10° until they reached the poles.

10°	=	700 miles
1°	=	70 miles
1 min	=	6000 feet (1 nautical mile)
1 sec	=	100 feet

Many children know from playing with protractors that 90° makes a right angle. Remember this was the angle of the man's arm as he stood at the North Pole pointing at the North Star.

The mapmakers then divided the globe along its axis longitudinally, producing in this way pie-shaped segments much like the sections of an orange or grapefruit. The mapmakers called the convergent lines dividing the globe's segments *meridian* lines or meridians. Since it takes the earth 24 hours to turn full circle or 360°, they divided 360 by 24 and drew a meridian line every 15°. Here is a good case of time equaling distance (1 hour equals 15° of longitude east or west). Which was

to be the starting line? After considerable confusion, in 1884 by international agreement they recognized the *prime meridian* or 0° as that which passed through the Royal Observatory in Greenwich, England. Starting at the prime meridian, the meridian lines go both east and west up to 180°. The 180th meridian is directly opposite the prime meridian and is the same for both east and west. Illustrate to the children with a peeled orange or grapefruit.

Finding your longitude. To find your longitude, you need to know about time around the globe. As the earth turns, it becomes noon successively around the world. It is noon when the sun is highest overhead. You "shoot the sun" with a sextant to determine when it is "high noon" where you are. At the same time you need to know the time at a given meridian, which is generally the prime meridian. Every ship has an accurate clock (chronometer) set at Greenwich time.

Suppose it is 3 P.M. Greenwich time when it is noon sun time in your location. This means you are 3 hours or 45° west longitude.

Use a flannel board, some ships' outlines, and some grid lines to give the children a deeper understanding of the applications. Assume it is noon aboard each ship. Given different Greenwich readings from the ships' chronometers, let the children work out the ships' longitude positions by simple arithmetic.

Finding longitude is simpler than finding latitude. However, it was very difficult for the early navigators because they lacked accurate timepieces. The story of Harrison's chronometer, or the man who worked 50 years to win a prize, is worth knowing. The children might wish to dramatize the story of his life.

CAPSULE LESSONS

10-1   Accumulate a number of balls or spheres. Take the children outdoors at high noon of a sunny day. Let them work in teams and observe shadows on the balls as they stand still or rotate. Repeat at morning or afternoon recess and compare.

10-2   To illustrate a solar eclipse, close one eye and with the other look at a ceiling light. Hold a small disk or coin a few inches in front of your line of sight. The light source represents the sun, the disk the moon. Note how the "moon" can completely hide the "sun." A friend will note also the "moon" shadow cast on the eye of the observer.

10-3   To study latitude and longitude lines, a third grade teacher and his children invented the idea of pinning a grid of strings to the ceiling. The strings were attached in true N–S, E–W directions.

10-4   If you can secure a Florence flask from a high school science teacher, you can make a model celestial globe. Half fill the flask with water colored for visibility. Tape around the middle with a narrow band to represent the celestial equator. With a protractor, measure and mark a point 23½° above the first band. Beginning at this point and using different colored tape, tape straight around the flask at its greatest circumference. This band represents the *ecliptic,* an imaginary line made by the plane of the earth's orbit extended to cut the sky. The intersections of your two tapes are astronomers' reference points, the vernal equinox and the autumnal equinox. Except for the circumpolar constellations, most constellations are spaced along the ecliptic line. Note, for example, the angle at which the great autumn constellations of Scorpio and Sagittarius appear to roll up from under the horizon. A dowel rod run through a one-hole stopper in the flask should be aimed toward the North Star.

10-5   Challenge the children's creative thinking by encouraging arithmetic problems and diagrams which come out of any study of astronomy.

10-6   Make a brightness scale for observing stars. The method is adapted from *Discoveries in Science,* by Violet Strahler and Clifford Nelson, Harcourt, Brace & World, 1960. You will need a strip of cardboard about 12″ long and 2″ wide. Draw a line down the center of the long dimension, and measure the strip into 2″ sections along this line. Using each of these points along the line as a center, draw five 1″ circles. You may use a half-dollar to trace the circles. Cut them out carefully with a pair of pointed scissors. Now obtain some clean, clear, unwrinkled cellophane. Try to make sure that there is no difference in thickness or clearness of the cellophane you use. Leave the first hole in the strip uncovered. Cover the second hole with a single thickness of cellophane, fastening it with transparent tape. Cover the third hole with a double thickness of cellophane. Cover the fourth hole with four thicknesses and the fifth with eight thicknesses.

Now select a bright star in the sky to observe. Look at it first through the uncovered hole and then through the others. Is there a hole which shuts off all light from the star? This instrument does not give a mathematical measure of brightness, but you will be able to say that a star which can be seen through hole three but not through hole four is brighter than those which can be seen only through holes one and two. You can also say that it is not as bright as those which can be seen through holes four or five. To make a more finished instrument, cut out a second piece of cardboard just like the first and seal it over the side which has the cellophane.

10-7   Make this investigation, adapted from Paul E. Blackwood's *Experiences in Science,* 3rd ed., Harcourt, Brace & World, 1960, to discover why some stars appear brighter and larger than others. You will need two candles and two smoked glass plates 4″ square or two pieces of waxed paper. Place two lighted candles about 8′ apart. Stand about 2′ away from one candle so that the second candle is 10′ away. Look at the nearer candle through the smoked glass (or waxed paper) and mark on the glass where the top and bottom of the flame appear. Standing in the same spot, look at the other candle through the second smoked glass and mark the top and bottom of the flame. Compare the size of the markings. Which flame seems to be larger? If both flames are the same size, how do you account for the apparent difference in sizes? Are the brightest stars necessarily the largest? Then what are the two causes of the brightness of stars?

10-8 You do not need a telescope to study stars. There are over a dozen star clusters, variables, and nebulae which can be seen through binoculars. Encourage children and their parents to check such references as *Astronomy with an Opera Glass,* by Garret Serviss, *A Field Book of Stars,* by W. T. Olcott, and *Discover the Stars,* by Gaylord Johnson and Irving Adler. The last comes in an inexpensive paperback edition.

10-9 Observe and map the position of one constellation over a period of several weeks. Make a star sighter by mounting screw eyes at each end of a T-shaped stick. Record the time and date of each observation. The observations are more valuable if made at regular intervals.

10-10 Check the references to find out how they represent the solar system. To date many show the planetary orbits as concentric rings spaced at regular intervals. In reality, the orbits are elliptical, and the outer planets should be spaced at much wider intervals than the inner planets. Let the children work this out to scale to see for themselves (see p. 168).

BIBLIOGRAPHY

Baker, Robert H., *Introducing the Constellations,* Viking, 1957. Upper. Revised, expanded edition of old favorite. New chapter on telescope making and amateur astronomy organizations.

Bischof, George, and Eunice Bischof, *Sun, Earth and Man,* Harcourt, Brace & World, 1957. Upper. Interrelations and adaptation of men to their planet, Earth, and their star, the sun.

Boeke, Kees, *Cosmic View: The Universe in 40 Jumps,* Day, 1957. Upper. Develops concept of immensity of universe by showing object from different points, each ten times farther from the object.

Branley, Franklyn M., *Mars,* Crowell, 1955. Upper. Scientific hypothesis about the "red" planet. Techniques in presenting astronomy data.

Freeman, Mae, *Fun with Astronomy,* Random House, 1953. Middle. Observations and activities, instructive descriptions.

Goodwin, Harold L., *Real Book About Stars,* Garden City, 1954. Middle. Methods of astronomy. Causes of night and day, seasons, and eclipses. Information on heavenly bodies. How to locate constellations. Fascinating exploration of solar system and other stars.

Lewellen, John B., *True Book of Moon, Sun, Stars,* Childrens Press, 1954. Primary. In large text for young readers.

Meyer, Jerome S., *Picture Book of Astronomy,* Lothrop, 1945. Middle. Clear, satisfying explanations of typical astronomy questions raised by young children.

Newell, Homer E., Jr., *Window in the Sky,* McGraw-Hill, 1959. Upper. Story of upper atmosphere. Latest information on characteristics of various zones in our atmosphere.

Orr, Clyde, Jr., *Between Earth and Space,* Macmillan, 1959. Upper. Weather, climate, and other aspects of our atmosphere.

Popular Science magazine, eds., *Everybody's Guide to Astronomy,* Grosset & Dunlap, 1949. Illuminating introduction. Many simple, practical do-it-yourself activities.

Rey, H. A., *Find the Constellations,* Houghton Mifflin, 1954. Middle. Clear, accurate, intriguing illustrations.

Schealer, John, *This Way to the Stars,* Dutton, 1957. Middle. Lively discussion of our solar system.

Schloat, G. Warren, Jr., *Andy's Wonderful Telescope,* Scribner's, 1958. Middle. Observable phenomena of optics of telescopes.

Schneider, Herman, and Nina Schneider, *You Among the Stars,* Scott, 1951. Middle. Excellent beginning method of learning about the sky.

Wolfe, Louis, *Let's Go to a Planetarium,* Putnam, 1958. Middle. Typical planetarium show and building.

Zim, Herbert S., *Shooting Stars,* Morrow, 1958. Middle. History and study of meteors.

———, and Robert Baker, *The Sun,* Morrow, 1953. Middle. Excellent information on sun's spectroscope, solar energy, tides, sunspots, and eclipses. Some experiments.

11

Water

If you have a sink in your classroom, there are a surprising number of science experiences which you will want to keep from "going down the drain." Even if your classroom does not have a sink, the children can enjoy many of the following activities with the help of a bucket and/or dishpan and some rubber tubing.

Perhaps you could begin by giving children the chance to see what goes on inside a water faucet. Most hardware or plumbing shops are glad to give you an old spigot. Have the parts loosened so the children can take the faucet apart and put it together again as many times as they wish.

Turn on the water in your sink and let the children watch carefully to learn all they can about the shape and direction of running water, the way it runs out of the drain. Does the water flow in any particular pattern? Does it drain any faster when an air hole appears in the middle of the draining water? Observation will answer these and other questions. Tack clean paper to cardboard and hold it close to the sink in order to find out the height and distance of splash marks. Are these the same when the water runs slowly as when it runs fast? Pour water from a pitcher into the sink and observe the shape and fall of the flow. Pour water from one container to another, again observing closely. Watch the pattern of water flow from a dish drainer at home.

If you have running hot water, turn it on and listen for a change in sound when the water begins to run hot. Compare the sounds of variously shaped containers being filled. If a hot plate is handy, listen to the change in the sound of a pan beginning to boil dry.

PROPERTIES OF WATER

There is a great deal to consider about water. Let the children note its color, taste, and feel. Compare the colors of water from different sources if these are available. Try tasting water after it has been boiled and cooled, after it has been frozen and then melted. Taste water just run from a tap and water which has stood (covered) for a time.

Boiling and freezing points

At standard atmospheric pressure, water freezes at 0° C (32° F) and boils at 100° C (212° F). However, for water that contains dissolved impurities the boiling and freezing points may vary slightly. Your children are more apt to remember this if you make it possible for them to take thermometer readings while boiling and freezing pure water. Compare these temperatures with those of boiling and freezing salt water.

Let the children observe how heat is transferred to water, thereby causing the temperature of water to rise. One activity which interests children very much requires a piece of iron with a wooden handle. An old soldering iron is excellent. Heat the iron and plunge it into a pan of water whose temperature you have read from a floating baby's bath thermometer (bathometer). Watch the temperature of the water rise. Watch it drop when you remove the iron.

Volume and density

Children are aware that alcohol is "thinner" than water and that molasses is "thicker" than water. Each of these liquids has a different *density;* that is, the weight of a volume of one liquid differs from the weight of an equal volume of another liquid. The density of water (taken as 1) is used as the standard for measuring densities of other substances; therefore, alcohol is less dense or lighter than water and molasses is denser or heavier than water.

Compare the weights of a gallon (or pint or quart) of water and a gallon of syrup, oil, kerosene, milk, etc. How much water does it take to weigh a pound?

HOW WATER BEHAVES

Water is one of the few substances which occurs commonly in three different forms—liquid, solid, and gas. In each of these guises it exhibits interesting behavior which we can study in our sink laboratory.

Water, the great dissolver

Let children experiment with dissolving small quantities of such household staples as sugar, salt, soda, cocoa, flour, and others. Dissolve the same amount of each substance in hot water. Compare the rate at which solution takes place in each case. Now try dissolving substances in other liquids such as oil, vinegar, milk, alcohol, and kerosene. The children will soon decide that water is the most universal solvent.

Learn about saturated solutions by adding sugar or salt to a small quantity of water until no more will dissolve. Pour into shallow dishes, across which you have laid short lengths of white cotton grocery string. Watch crystals form along the string as the solution evaporates. If your local druggist has copper sulfate, alum, or hypo in small crystals, you can dissolve them and grow larger crystals as described above. Try suspending a piece of string in a deeper container such as a peanut butter jar. See Chapter 8, Fig. 8-7. The children will undoubtedly enjoy growing their own rock candy crystals. To a cup or more of boiling water, add double the amount of sugar. Stir until dissolved, and cool. Suspend a clean string in the solution and leave undisturbed until crystals have grown large. Add a string of rock candy to another sugar solution and watch the crystals grow larger.

Perhaps you live in a limestone region where water has dissolved out caves or potholes in the rocks. Nearly all parts of the country have some rock which shows evidence of the dissolving action of water. The accumulation of salts dissolved out of the rocks answers the question, "Why is the sea salty?" Classroom chalk is a powdered form of a kind of rock which is usually a combination of limestone and gypsum (plaster). Dissolve chalk in water and filter it through filter paper. (Use coffee filter paper or secure filter paper from the drug-store or from a high school science teacher.) The water will appear clear. Put it in a flat pan or pie tin and boil away the water or allow it to evaporate naturally. A residue of white powder will remain.

Dissolve lime tablets obtained from the drugstore. Filter until clear. Also procure from the drugstore a small quantity of phenophthalein solution. Add a few drops of this to the clear liquid. Note that it turns red. Nothing happens when the test-

seal made of raw potato, clay, etc.

Fig. 11-1 A simple still, illustrating the principle of evaporation and condensation useful in so many processes. It also illustrates the water cycle of such importance in weather. Finally, it illustrates matter-energy interchange and changes in the state of matter.

ing agent is added to some pure tap water.

Speed of dissolving. Use a hammer or some heavy object to crush a sugar lump. Put particles into glass jar. Put whole lump in another container. Add equal amounts of water to both. Which dissolves faster? More surface of particles is exposed in the crushed lump. Hence it dissolves faster.

Distilling water. How could we get water from the sea? Use natural salt water if available, or make your own brine. Add red food coloring, just to complicate the problem of pure water. Now you need a small teakettle, rubber tubing, an electric hotplate, a pan of ice cubes, and a pint jar or jelly glass. Set up your "still" (Fig. 11-1) and start the water boiling. Before long clear, uncolored water drops should begin to collect in the glass. The steam which boiled off the teakettle solution became water as it cooled in the jar, leaving the impurities behind.

Getting solids out of water. Put some muddy water in a tall glass bottle. Add a few crystals of alum plus ammonia. Stir and let settle. Alum forms a jellied mass which entraps and carries dirt particles downward with it. This coagulation process is used by many municipalities for purifying water.

Set up a miniature filter plant by filling a large glass or plastic funnel with a layer of clean pebbles, a layer of coarse gravel, and a layer of fine sand (Fig. 11-2). Point out that this unit and the coagulation process make water cleaner but not always safe to drink.

Evaporation

The fact that water can "disappear into the air" is just another example of its extraordinary behavior. Draw two squares or circles of the same size on the blackboard. "Paint" them with water. Time the difference in evaporation between the figure you fan and the figure which is not fanned. Be sure that your circles or squares are not too close to each other. Perhaps your children will have already learned something about the rate of evaporation in connection with other investigations. Boil a nearly empty pan to dryness. Where did the water go?

Expansion on freezing

Scientists tell us that if water did not expand as it freezes and if the resulting ice did not float, our climate would be so cold that the earth would be uninhabit-

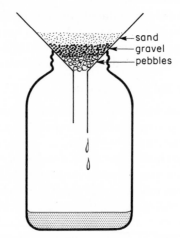

sand
gravel
pebbles

Fig. 11-2 Water filtration. The possibilities of introducing variables with relation to filtration agents are endless.

able. Ice is less dense than water and therefore floats on the oceans where, exposed to the air, it is melted. If ice did not float but sank to the bottom, it would never be melted. Ultimately the oceans would fill with ice, and the surrounding climate would be very cold. The fact that water expands upon freezing causes the resulting ice to be less dense than the same volume of water.

If you do not have a school refrigerator, perhaps the children can do the following at home. Rinse out a paper milk container, fill to the brim with water, and close the cap as firmly as possible. As the water inside freezes, it will expand and push up the cap. In case the children are not sure that ice floats, recall how ice cubes float in lemonade. Let them float ice in their home sink.

The work of water in solid form is evident in those parts of the country which have been glaciated. Draw attention to the work of running water in smoothing pebbles and boulders, in carving canyons and valleys, in those parts of the country which have not been glaciated.

Surface tension

Partly fill with water a tall, thin glass container such as an olive bottle. Looking carefully, you should note that the water climbs slightly higher on each side than in the middle. Water molecules adhere better to glass than to water molecules. This makes the water climb the sides of the jar. The attraction between unlike molecules is called *adhesion*.

In explaining a magnetic compass to children, we often let them make their own by magnetizing a needle (p. 342). In order to permit it to swing freely, we float it on water with the help of a drinking straw or a bit of cork. Sometimes, if we drop it very gently and carefully on the water, it will float without help other than from the surface tension of the water. The

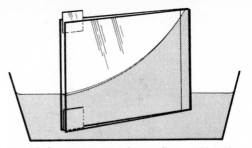

Fig. 11-3 Water rising by capillarity. When the plates are wet, the film of water between them replaces the air. The tags separating the plates should be no thicker than two layers of Scotch tape. (From A. Joseph et al., *A Sourcebook for the Physical Sciences*, Harcourt, Brace & World, 1961.)

surface tension is the result of the attraction or *cohesion* between water molecules.

Capillary attraction

Another one of water's interesting characteristics is involved when we make water disappear with the help of a sponge or blotter. Use colored water and a white blotter or sponge so that you can observe how the water is taken up. Wipe up water with a dry cloth and with a cloth of the same material that has been wet and wrung out. Which works best and why?

To find out how water rises in the soil, you can use glass plates or squares such as those used in seed germination experiments. Bevel the edges for safety with emery or sandpaper. Spread a film of water all over one plate. Lay another plate on top and secure with rubber bands. Separate at one edge with cardboard tags (Fig. 11-3) and set in a saucer of water. Note how water rises highest where glass is closest together.

Water does not rise with equal speed through all kinds of soil. To find out which local soil moves water fastest, fill one lamp chimney with sandy soil and one with clay soil (Fig. 11-4). Keep dirt from falling out the bottom of chimneys with netting or cheesecloth. Set in a container of colored water and observe. Lamp chim-

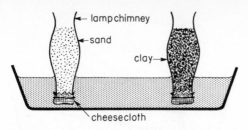

Fig. 11-4 Water rising through sand and through clay.

neys are usually available from hardware stores.

Buoyancy

Another bit of water's magic which we are apt to take for granted is its ability to transport objects. Primary children love to find out what things float and what do not. Older children may wish to review this experience and consider possible reasons. It may help them to understand if you can secure some tinfoil or some very light sheet tin. (Aluminum foil is too light.) Make some miniature boats of tinfoil by bending up the sides of the sheet or pieces of tin. Then crumple the tin and watch it sink.

For the next step you need household scales, a dishpan, and a pan that can be set into the dishpan and yet is big enough to float a toy boat. Set the smaller pan inside the empty dishpan. Fill the small pan to the brim with water. Float the toy boat. Some water will be displaced and overflow into the dishpan. Collect this carefully and weigh. Now weigh the boat. The weights should be very close. Repeat, adding some "cargo" or "ballast."

Older children and sometimes younger ones ask what makes a steel ship float. One way to explain this is to secure a piece of tin and a spring balance. Place the sheet in water and it sinks. Tie the sheet to the hook of a spring balance and note its weight. Now lower the sheet into water and again note its weight, which will be less. With pliers bend up the sides

of the sheet to form a tray and set it on water. Now it floats (Fig. 11-5). Obviously some force is counteracting the weight. Notice the position of the water line on the outside of the tray. Mark this level with a crayon inside and out. Remove the tray from the water and fill the inside with water up to the level which you marked. Pour off the water and weigh it. Its weight equals the force that held up the tray when it floated. It should also equal the weight of the sheet when weighed in air. A giant ocean liner like the Queen Mary displaces or pushes out as much water as it weighs. That is why a ship is said to have so many tons of displacement. When a child in the class swims, he or she displaces as much water as he weighs. Help the children to see that the upward force called buoyancy is equal to the weight of the floating object. Recall that the amount displaced by the tin sheet was much less than when it was made into a tray. Thus an object which is heavier than water can float if it is shaped so as to displace water equal to its own weight. An object which is lighter than water sinks only far enough to displace its weight in water. Weigh a block of wood, then the amount of water it displaces. The weights should be nearly equal.

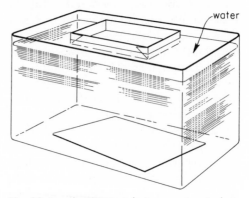

Fig. 11-5 Floating metal. An aquarium is desirable but not essential for visibility. The children should come to the conclusion that water pushes "up" against the floating object.

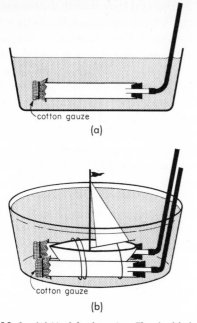

cotton gauze

(a)

cotton gauze

(b)

Fig. 11-6 (a) Model submarine. The double layer of cheesecloth provides a layer of air which prevents water from re-entering the model submarine. When a tumbler of water is covered with a double layer of ladies' nylon hose and inverted over a pan or sink, the air layer provided by the mesh fabric permits outside air pressure to keep water from falling out. (b) Raising a sunken boat by using pontoons.

A classroom submarine. Submarines are always fascinating to children. To make one which will dive and surface you need the following: a wide glass or plastic tube stoppered at one end with a one-hole cork, a plastic tube to fit the hole in the cork, and rubber tubing to fit the plastic tube. The other end of the large tube is closed with cheesecloth secured with rubber bands. Place the "submarine" in an aquarium or widemouthed glass jar or dishpan (Fig. 11-6A). It will sink as soon as water enters through the cheesecloth. When a submarine dives, the ballast tanks fill with water and air escapes. To make this "submarine" rise or "surface," blow into the rubber tube. In a real submarine, compressed air is pumped into the tanks

to drive out the water; in your simple apparatus, air compressed from your lungs is accomplishing the same thing. You may want to try raising your "submarine" with air pumped by a basketball or bicycle pump. A submarine-shaped hull or a toy model submarine fitted around the plastic tube may make the device more realistic to children. Help them to see the principle of reducing the weight of the "submarine" by forcing out enough water to equal the weight of the "sub."

Pontoons for raising ships. Raising sunken ships depends on the same principle. An experiment to illustrate this requires two of the "submarine" tubes. A small nonfloating model boat or a hollow plastic one with a hole in it may be the sunken ship. Sink the two pontoon tubes one on each side of the "wreck" (Fig. 11-6B). Attach the tubes to the wreck with string to simulate the steel cables used in real life. Blow the water out of the tubes. As they surface, they will bring the "wreck" with them. Keep the rubber tubing pinched with a clothespin or your fingers to retain air in the plastic tubes.

Pressure

Water goes upstairs. Young children often verbalize their wonder at how water climbs hills or goes upstairs in their houses. Older children take it for granted and do not ask, although they usually don't know. Near the bottom of a quart milk carton punch a hole into which you can squeeze an end of some rubber tubing. Use a plastic or glass container to collect water from the other end of the tube. Fill the carton with water. Watch the rate at which the water flows into the collecting jar as you hold it at different levels. The children will see that the water runs "uphill" as long as your milk carton "reservoir" is held at least as high. Some children may now bring up observations about hilltop municipal water towers and

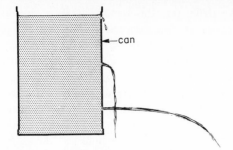

Fig. 11-7 Water pressure increases with depth. (From A. Joseph et al., *A Sourcebook for the Physical Sciences*, Harcourt, Brace & World, 1961.)

reservoirs. Gravity flow will permit water to flow at least to the same height as its source. The greater the height, the better the water pressure.

Let the children repeat, humping the tubing in the shape of a hill. Water left to itself always flows downhill, but constricted into pipes it can be made to flow uphill. The same principle holds true for water pressure in a house. Children who live in apartment houses will better understand why the water pressure may be better downstairs than several flights up.

Pressure increases with depth. A simple device for showing that the depth of water affects the pressure can be made. Punch three equidistant holes in the side of a milk carton or tall tin can (Fig. 11-7). Use a 1-quart or 2-quart milk carton. Fill with water and note that the stream of water flowing from the bottom hole is longest

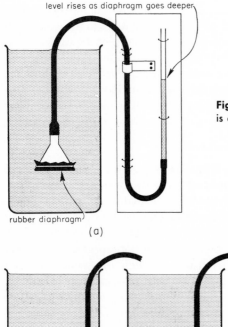

Fig. 11-8 (a) Water depth indicator; (b) water pressure is exerted equally in all directions at the same depth.

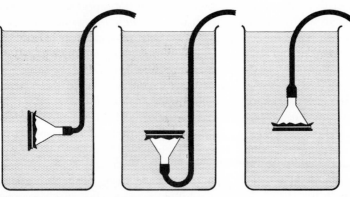

and swiftest. The middle hole has about half the flow and force, while the top hole is barely a dribble. This is a good experiment for children to repeat.

Homemade depth gauge. Another simple device for measuring water pressure requires a small plastic funnel, a toy balloon, rubber tubing, and a clear glass or plastic drinking tube (Fig. 11-8A). First, cover the mouth of the small funnel with a layer of rubber from the balloon. Stretch the rubber and fasten it securely with plastic tape. Next attach one end of about 3′ of rubber tubing to the funnel opening and attach the other end to the clear glass or plastic tubing. Anchor the tubing to white cardboard with thin wire or cord. Now bend the rubber tubing to form one leg of a U, with the glass or plastic tube as the other leg, and tie it down with cord or thin wire. (For greater permanence the tubing can be mounted on wood.) Temporarily remove the funnel from the rubber tubing and add water containing red ink or vegetable coloring to the glass tube until it is half full. Now slip the rubber tubing back on the funnel. Fill an aquarium or bucket with water. With arms bare, lower the funnel. As it descends, the water pressure will push against the rubber sheet; the rubber sheet, in turn, will push the air which will make the column of colored water rise in the plastic tube. As you go deeper, the level in the tube rises in direct proportion. Submarines use a device working on the same principle to find their depth below the surface.

Equal pressure in all directions. Using the same equipment as for the depth gauge, try the following test midway and at the bottom of the container (Fig. 11-8B). Hold the funnel mouth to the left, to the right, upward, and downward. At the same depth the "depth gauge" will register the same pressure in the tube (manometer.). If the school has a supervised swimming pool, the pupils might be able to test the same device on a larger scale in 3-4′ of water. For this you will need longer rubber tubing and a longer plastic tube. It would be best to check with the principal in case any of the students should take an unexpected plunge in the pool.

THE WATER CYCLE

One concept about water you will surely want your children to have is that of the water cycle—condensation to evaporation to condensation to evaporation and so on. You will need a teakettle with a spout, a small hot plate, a few ice cubes, and a kitchen gravy tablespoon with a wooden handle or very long metal handle which will not conduct heat too quickly to your hand. Bring the water in the teakettle to a boil so that a good jet of "steam" (water vapor) is coming from the spout. Place an ice cube in the bowl of the spoon, hold the underside of the spoon in the steam, and watch drops of water form on the spoon.

Instead of a spoon, many teachers use a metal plate in which are placed several ice cubes. The plate bottom collects and forms more "rain," but it is more difficult to hold the heated plate than the spoon. Pot holders or gloves are needed.

How a well works

Water falling on the earth as rain becomes available to us from such sources as springs, rivers, streams, and wells. An aquarium or other container full of sand or soil can be used to illustrate a simple well. Countersink a tin can open at both ends in the soil. Generously water the surrounding soil. The level to which the water rises in the can shows the level of water in the soil. Measure the depth of the "well" at intervals (after 1 hour, 6 hours, 24 hours). The artesian well was described earlier (pp. 117–18).

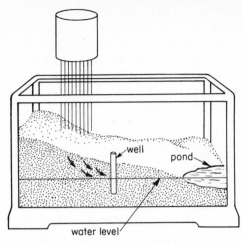

Fig. 11-9 Marsh and lake formation.

How lakes and marshes are formed

An aquarium may also serve to illustrate how lakes and marshes are formed. Mold the sand or earth so that there is a hollow or depression at one end or in the middle. Water sprinkled generously on the higher ground will eventually collect in the low spot first as a miniature marsh and then, when more water collects, as a lake (Fig. 11-9).

If a garden hose and a school garden are available, they are useful accessories to the sink in constructing and experimenting with the flow of water in model irrigation ditches or along model contours. Otherwise, the aquarium or other large container can serve on a smaller scale to help children understand contouring and irrigation. They may wish to build a model dike of modeling clay to understand how people live below the level of the water, as is the case in many scattered parts of our own country as well as in Holland. They may wish to make a sluice in the dike or a lock in the canal.

PUTTING WATER TO WORK

Water, like fire, can be one of the most useful as well as destructive forces in na-ture. Man early discovered that water could work for him in many ways.

The breast wheel

The oldest type of water wheel is the breast wheel or wheel on its side. Start with a Tinkertoy hub. Next insert a 2″ or 3″ Tinkertoy stick into each hole. Cut blades about 2″ × 2″ from the walls of milk containers. Slip the blades into the slots on the Tinkertoy stick ends (Fig. 11-10A). A thick nail through the center

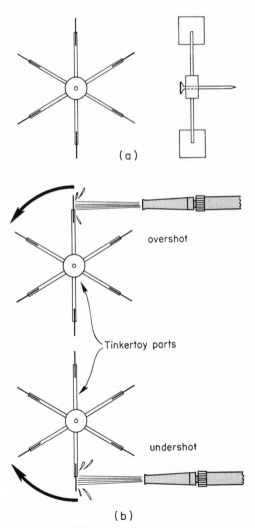

Fig. 11-10 (a) Simple water wheel; (b) overshot and undershot water wheels.

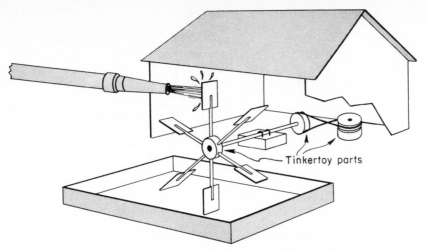

Fig. 11-11 Water wheel-operated model grist mill.

hole of the hub serves as a vertical axle for the horizontal wheel. Immersed into a stream of running water, as in the sink or overflowing from a pan into the sink, the wheel will spin. Because the blades on one side fight the water, the breast wheel is the least efficient type.

The undershot wheel

With the same equipment, hold the axle horizontally with the wheel in a vertical position. Hold the wheel so that only the bottom blades are impelled by the water.

More efficient undershot and overshot wheels

Use the same simple wheel with water power from the downflow of a faucet or rubber tubing. If the stream is directed vertically at the top of one side of the wheel, the pressure of the water will make the wheel spin rapidly.

The overshot wheel (Fig. 11-10B) takes maximum advantage of water pressure and gravity to spin the wheel. It was the type frequently found in old-fashioned grist (or flour) mills—the type that powered New England textile mills before the days of steam power. Using the same toy

wheel as before, direct the stream of water horizontally through a rubber tube.

Model grist mill

To build a working-model grist mill, mount the water wheel used above to turn two Tinkertoy pulleys (Fig. 11-11). These last represent the millstones. A mill shed or building can be made from the waterproofed sides of milk cartons, sewn together with thread and needle.

High-pressure turbine

To build an efficient high-pressure turbine, you and your pupils need some thin sheet aluminum or zinc. Using a pattern (Fig. 11-12A), lay out a 6″ wheel with a sharpened nail as a scribing tool. A ¼″ hole is drilled or punched in the center. Then cut out the shape with tin snips or tinners' shears. Jewelers' snips may also be available through the school arts and crafts shop. Shape the blades into half cylinders (Fig. 11-12B). Use a ¼″ bolt as an axle and use washers to keep the turbine wheel clear of a skate wheel which will provide a low-friction base. Oil the skate wheel bearings and the bolt to prevent rust. A clear plastic container is now needed to house the turbine wheel. A

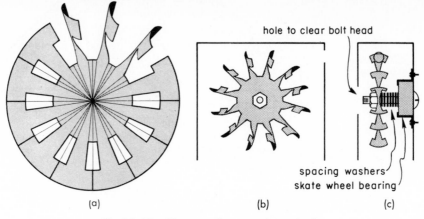

Fig. 11-12   Sheet metal water turbine wheel.

hole to clear bolt head

spacing washers
skate wheel bearing

(a)   (b)   (c)

shallow covered refrigerator storage container will do if it is large enough. Now cut out one side of the tray. Drill ¼" holes in the center of the cover and bottom of the plastic case (Fig. 11-12C). Remount the bolt (use a longer one if necessary). Attach the skate wheel to the bottom by using bolts and washers. Drill a hole with a hand gimlet or pointed nail for a glass nozzle and rubber tubing in one end of the plastic case.

To use the turbine, connect the rubber tubing with a faucet and hold the turbine in position (Fig. 11-12). The wheel will rotate at an extremely high speed. Waste water will fall out of the bottom opening previously cut out of the side of the plastic tray. A 12" water wheel of this type can spin a bicycle generator and light a small flashlight bulb (1.1 volt).

CAPSULE LESSONS

11-1   Boil 2" of water in a saucepan. Cool and measure again. Heat and carefully remeasure the depth of the water. Set in ice and again remeasure.

11-2   The principle of surface tension permits the delightful pastime of blowing soap bubbles. Encourage children to discover whether different kinds of soap or differences in strength of solution make any difference in the size of the bubbles.

11-3   There is a host of delightful experiments with floating objects. See E. Hone and L. Raphael, *Science Around the Harbor* (pamphlet to be published fall 1961).

11-4   Make flannel board drawings to illustrate the water cycle.

11-5   Study a globe or world map and decide what proportion is covered with water.

11-6   Drop an egg in fresh water; then add salt until the egg floats. Would the load or Plimsoll lines on ships be the same for fresh as for salt water? Encourage children to do encyclopedia research and other readings on Samuel Plimsoll.

11-7   Study labels on household bleach bottles. Encourage children to find out about municipal water purification. How do good campers determine safe drinking water? What chemicals or procedures insure pure water?

11-8   Is water a chemical? Is water a mineral? Let children discuss and do research to reinforce their ideas and conclusions.

BIBLIOGRAPHY

Bate, Norman, *Who Built the Dam?*, Scribner's, 1958. For middle grades. Concept of current and control; construction of hydroelectric dam—in picture story.

Black, Irma S., *Busy Water,* Holiday, 1958. For primary grades. Water cycle explained for young children.

Blough, Glenn, *Not Only for Ducks: The Story of Rain,* McGraw-Hill, 1954. For primary grades. Water cycle, seed germination, and frog life cycle.

Boys, C. V., *Soap Bubbles and the Forces Which Mould Them,* Doubleday Anchor, 1959. A gem of science literature by one of the most colorful of the nineteenth-century English scientists. Reprinted as part of a fresh approach to the study and teaching of physics.

Bruce, Guy V., *Experiments with Water,* National Science Teachers Assn., 1950. 48 pp. For upper grades. Simple and carefully tested experiments restricted to home equipment.

Clymer, Eleanor, *Make Way for Water,* Messner, 1953. For primary grades. Interdependence of town and country in story of building a dam and reservoir.

Cocannouer, Joseph A., *Water and the Cycle of Life,* Devin, 1958. For upper grades. Information in story form on the importance, use, and control of water. Extensive glossary.

Green, Ivah, *Water: Our Most Valuable Natural Resource,* Coward-McCann, 1958. For upper grades. Water—its sources, movements, benefits, and problems.

Pine, Tillie S., and Joseph Levine, *Water All Around,* McGraw-Hill, 1959. For primary grades. All kinds of water in various forms. Simple experiments.

Riedman, Sarah R., *Water for People,* Abelard-Shuman, rev. ed., 1960.

Schloat, G. Warren, Jr., *The Magic of Water,* Scribner's, 1955. For middle grades. Simple experiments to help children understand the source and uses of water.

Tresselt, Alvin, *Rain Drop Splash,* Lothrop, 1954. For primary grades. Raindrops to puddles, to ponds, to rivers, to the sea.

Van Dersal, W. R., and E. H. Graham, *Water for America,* Walck, 1956. For upper grades. Picture story of water conservation.

12

Chemistry for children

CHEMICALS AS ELEMENTS, MIXTURES, OR COMPOUNDS

Everything in the world is made of chemicals. Of course, with the word "chemical" we mean something different from "thing" or "stuff" or "matter." Generally, a chemical is matter whose nature and elemental substance are identified, that is, we know what it is. In some instances such as certain very complex chemicals found in living things we might not know just what elements make up a chemical. Then it is identified by what it does, by its properties. Every day in your kitchen or bathroom you use such common chemicals as water, sugar, and salt. Some chemicals such as copper, silver, and gold are made of only one substance. Any chemical made of only one substance is called an "element." There are at least 103 elements, but some of them are very rare and others have been produced only in a laboratory. Most of the things we use are mixtures of elements or compounds of elements. Encourage the children to make an exhibit to show some of the following:

elements	compounds	mixtures
lead	salt	baking powder
iron	sugar	paper
aluminum	water	soil
mercury	glass	cement
sulfur	cooking oil	cake

What is the difference between compounds and mixtures?

If you mix dry sand and sugar, the children can see these are two kinds of grains. With patience one can be separated from the other because they are different kinds of substances. However, if you sprinkle out some salt and ask that the sodium and chlorine be picked out, of course no one can do it because these two elements have combined to make one substance.

The elements in salt

As noted above, common table salt is a compound, not a mixture, of two elements —sodium, a metallic solid, and chlorine, a greenish gas. To see this for yourself, secure several dry cell batteries or portable radio A batteries. You will also need a tumbler, two glass or plastic vials or test tubes (available from the druggist), insulated bell wire from a hardware store, and two carbon rods from dead flashlight cells. Dismantle the cells until the black carbon rods in the center are free. Hold the rods with tongs or pliers and heat until slightly red to drive out residual wax. They may be heated on the open flame of a kitchen stove's top gas burners. When cool, attach a battery clip (available from an electrician or a radio shop) to each rod. Attach copper wire to each clip. Mix a tumbler of saturated salt solution (Fig. 12-1). Fill the

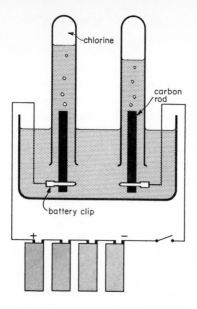

Fig. 12-1 Electrolysis of water.

test tubes or vials with the salt solution and immerse the carbon rods. Holding your thumb over the mouth of each tube or vial, invert it into the tumbler. Attach the wires leading from the clips to a series of at least four dry cells. Note carefully (Fig. 12-1) how the cells are connected.

Chlorine gas will form in the tube inverted over the carbon rod connected to the positive (center) pole of a battery. There is no danger from the minute amount of gas formed. The sodium combines with water to form a weak solution of sodium hydroxide (household lye). A few drops of phenolphthalein (from the druggist) produces no color change in plain water or the salt solution. Added to the sodium hydroxide, it turns pink, showing that a different substance has been produced by the electrolysis of brine.

The elements in water

Water, our most important household chemical, can also be separated into its two gaseous elements—hydrogen and oxygen. Use the same equipment (with eight instead of four batteries) as for the electrolysis of brine (above). Add as much sodium sulfate as will dissolve in a glass of cold water. (Sodium sulfate is much safer than the sulfuric acid usually recommended for this experiment.) If possible, secure stainless steel knife blades as substitutes for the carbon rods. With the current on, you will notice that gas bubbles up twice as fast in the tube connected to the minus battery terminal (edge of the battery) as it rises in the tube connected to the positive terminal (center of the battery). The electrode connected to the negative terminal generates hydrogen, while that connected to the positive terminal generates oxygen. To test for oxygen, light one end of a slender wooden stick or swab stick; then blow out the flame. While the tip is still glowing, put it into the tube where oxygen has been collected. Pure oxygen will make the glowing tip burst into flame (Fig. 12-2).

To test for hydrogen, plug the mouth of the tube under water with your thumb. Remove the inverted tube. Hold a match near the tube mouth as you remove your thumb. The small "pop" is the typical hydrogen explosion. There is no hazard involved. Many children are already familiar with the chemical symbol or formula for water—H_2O. They may then wish to repeat the electrolysis experiment to see

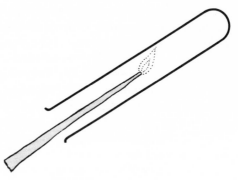

Fig. 12-2 Test for oxygen.

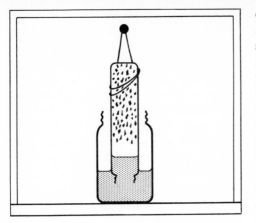

Fig. 12-3 Slow oxidation of iron.

or two the water level will rise. Since air is about one fifth oxygen, the water column should have risen about one fifth the height of the tube. Stopper the tube with your thumb and remove from the water bath to measure more exactly. Less than this may indicate there were not enough iron filings to combine with all the oxygen present. To prove that oxygen has been used up or nearly used up in the tube, remove your thumb and quickly insert a flaming match or splint. The flame will go out owing to lack of oxygen.

CHEMICAL TESTS

Certain chemicals provide telltale clues to their identity or presence. For example, you might wish to motivate a study of the chemistry of common substances by a parlor trick with starch and iodine.

Iodine and starch color reaction

Unobtrusively prepare a glass jar of cornstarch or laundry starch and hot water. Use relatively little starch so that the solution will appear clear. Set out in plain view on your desk or table, with iodine bottle nearby. Parry the inevitable questions of the more observant children. Without comment drop a little iodine in the solution and stir. The "water" turns blue. The children's curiosity will no doubt lead them (with your guidance) to filling another jar with tap water and adding iodine themselves. The characteristic blue color produced when iodine forms a complex with starch is very different from the brown tinge that results when iodine is dropped into "plain" water.

Flame colors of elements

In testing laboratories chemists asked to determine which elements are found in certain substances often begin by holding some of the material in a flame. For instance, any substance containing the ele-

if hydrogen collects twice as fast as oxygen.

Preparing oxygen—an element

Using common 3% peroxide from the drugstore provides a safe and easy way to separate the element oxygen from some of its compounds. The formula of peroxide, H_2O_2, indicates that each molecule contains one more atom of oxygen than does a molecule of water, H_2O. To extract this extra oxygen, drop iron rust into a test tube or pill bottle of peroxide. Lower the container into hot water. Oxygen bubbles should be released from the peroxide.

Pour peroxide on a cookie sheet or other sheet of metal. Watch oxygen bubbles form. To test again for oxygen (p. 197) lower a glowing, not flaming, match or splint into the air space above warmed peroxide in a tube (see above). The glowing wood should rekindle into a flame.

Oxygen and oxidation. Wet the inside of a test tube or bottle so that iron filings will stick when scattered into it. Invert and hang in a jar of water to prevent gas from escaping (Fig. 12-3). Mark the water level inside the test tube with a rubber band or wax crayon line. The rusting or oxidation of the iron filings will use up some of the oxygen in the container, and within a day ment *sodium* produces a bright *yellow* flame. To show this, dip the end of a wooden stick (e.g., swab stick) in water and then in salt. Hold over a Sterno flame and note the yellow color when the salty tip kindles. Boric acid produces a green flame, while that of powdered copper nitrate is blue-green. Nitrates of strontium give off red color; potassium kindles reddish-purple flames (often masked by the presence of sodium or other impurities).

Your children may have already made candles from old candle ends or from paraffin melted and poured into double paper cups or half-pint milk cartons to cool. Using the same method, add crystals of nitrates of copper, potassium, sodium, or strontium while the wax is still warm. Use one kind per cup or container. When placed in a fireplace fire, these give off driftwood colors. Straining the wax before pouring makes for clearer colored flame.

SOLIDS, LIQUIDS, AND GASES

The same chemicals in different forms often have a "Now you see it, now you don't" quality. For example, the children see that the familiar liquid, water, also exists as a gas—steam—or as a solid—ice. It may be important to let children watch a kettle boil. Steam is really invisible. What we see is water vapor condensing from the steam. Note space between the spout and the water vapor.

The dry ice used to pack ice cream and other perishables is carbon dioxide *gas* pressed into solid form. Secure some and let it evaporate in a glass jar covered with a piece of cardboard. (Dry ice should be handled with tongs.) Do not screw on the jar's cover. Twist a pipe cleaner around a birthday candle (Fig. 12-4). Lower it lighted into the jar immediately upon removing the cardboard cover. The carbon dioxide gas formed in the covered jar will put out the candle. Later in this chapter

and especially in Chapter 17, you will read how this gas is made from other substances.

Two gases form a solid

Fasten a small wad of cotton or paper toweling to one end of each of two paper clips or pipe cleaners. Dip one wad in dilute hydrochloric acid, the other wad in ammonia (ammonium hydroxide). Hang the clips or wires on opposite sides of a glass. A white cloud of ammonium chloride should form and eventually deposit a visible salt on the inside of the glass.

Precipitating chalk to form a solid

An example of chemical precipitation can be made with washing soda from the kitchen and calcium chloride from the hardware store. Children may already have seen calcium chloride used to melt snow and ice on the sidewalk, to settle dust on gravel roads, or to dry out damp cellars and closets. Dissolve about an ounce in a tumbler of water. Dissolve the same amount of washing soda in another glass. Pour the solutions, one after the other, into a milk bottle or quart jar. The heavy white solid which forms is precipi-

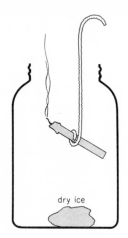

dry ice

Fig. 12-4 Flame-extinguishing action of carbon dioxide.

tated chalk. This is used as a base for face powder, toothpaste, and metal polish.

The hardening of cement and plaster of Paris is another example of chemical reactions forming solids. Make a small batch of each to illustrate the need for water in this as in many other chemical reactions. The children will also note the generation of heat.

Emulsions and colloids

Many common chemicals such as liquid soap, paint, mayonnaise, and the like are strictly neither liquid nor solid in form. Some of these substances, the so-called emulsions or colloids, can be made in class.

Making soap. Children who are studying the pioneers will be reliving one activity of early days in helping to make soap. It is generally very easy for a class to collect enough bacon grease and other fats to make a batch of soap.

To wash the grease, melt and strain into a kettle with 2–3 quarts water. Bring to a boil, stirring frequently. Cool until you can lift off the fat. Repeat once or twice more. This removes salt and other sediments.

Select only enamel ware, crockery, or iron vessels of about 2 gallons capacity. Aluminum is not recommended. Use a wooden or stainless steel tablespoon or stick for stirring.

Place the container on the ground and let the children watch the process from a standing position. This obviates any risk of their being splattered by the lye as you pour the contents of a can *very slowly* into 2 pints of cold water. Stir until all is dissolved. You may wish to use rubber gloves and apron for extra safety. The solution becomes very hot because of the reaction between the sodium hydroxide and water. The children should be prepared for this part of the operation by a careful study of the label on a commercial lye can. One teacher reproduces these directions and

uses them as the basis for discussion on Home Safety as well as science. With due precautions and a responsible group of children, the activity is well worth undertaking.

As soon as the lye and water solution feels lukewarm through the bottom of the container, slowly add melted *lukewarm* grease. Stir constantly until the mixture becomes as stiff as honey. Add perfume if desired and stir about 20–30 minutes until the soap becomes the consistency and color of divinity fudge.

Pour into a mold such as a large flat Pyrex dish or a box lined with waxed paper. Leave until hard enough to cut into pieces about 3″ square. Then turn out on a clean surface to dry in the sunshine. Turn daily and allow to harden for about 3 weeks before using. Cut the soap so that each child can take home a piece.

Detergents. The purpose of soap in laundering is really to emulsify or to surround dirt particles with a film or emulsion. Detergents make washing easier by speeding up the wetting process. This can be very simply illustrated. Fill two jelly glasses or tumblers partly full of water. To one add a teaspoon of liquid detergent and stir. Into the clear water cut pieces of white cotton grocery string (Fig. 12-5). They float around on the surface. The children may suggest recording the time necessary for the string to become watersoaked and sink. Lengths of cord cut into the detergent solution become watersoaked and sink to the bottom almost at once.

Mayonnaise. Common mayonnaise is another kind of colloid or emulsion. Into a tall thin container such as an olive jar pour 3 parts salad oil to 1 part vinegar. Shake vigorously and let stand. Very shortly the oil and vinegar will separate. Add an egg white and shake again. This time the mixture remains in suspension.

House paint. Ordinary oil paint is another example of emulsion. From a paint or hardware store get a small tube of ferric oxide or other pigment. From the high school science teacher borrow a round-bottomed mortar dish and pestle, or substitute similar containers. Grind a very small amount of pigment with a few table-spoons of linseed oil. Add a little turpentine to make the paint spread. When the mixture is thoroughly ground and emulsified, apply your homemade paint where needed.

Nicotine spray for plants. Indoor plants sometimes do poorly because they become infested with pests such as aphids and the like. Empty tobacco from a cigarette into about 2 tablespoons of water in a tin can. Boil for 5–10 minutes; then filter out the tobacco. Add a few drops of liquid soap and dilute to make about a cupful of spray solution. The colloidal property of soap helps spread the spray and clogs the spiracles of sucking insects such as aphids. Use an old spray gun or aspirator and observe the effect on aphids. Repeat if more aphids develop.

Volatile liquids—solvents

Make some grease spots on paper toweling, blotter squares, or cloth squares. Use different kinds of household cleaning fluids according to the directions (often a good reading lesson). Compare chemical contents according to the labels. Try using talcum powder or chalk dust on some spots. Observe how powder absorbs most of the grease. Compare results of *immediately* cleaning spots with removal after 24–48 hours.

Draw a pair of identical circles or squares on the blackboard. Moisten one with plain water and one with cleaning fluid. Which dries faster? Why use cleaner instead of waer? With a medicine dropper place the same number of drops of such solvents as kerosene, turpentine, nail polish remover, alcohol, and white gas in the

Fig. 12-5 Wetting action of detergent on cotton string.

centers of squares of blotting paper. Compare the speeds of evaporation of various chemicals. Be sure to have windows open and no flame in the room. (Relate speed of evaporation to danger of explosive mixtures.)

The question of safety in the choice of cleaning solvents may arise. Place a teaspoon of carbon tetrachloride cleaner in a metal jar top or painting dish. Try igniting with a match. Taking necessary precautions, repeat using only a drop or two of a flammable naphtha-type cleaner. Such experiments may motivate careful reading and comparison of labels of many other chemicals used around the house, for example, insecticides which, because of their base, should not be sprayed near open fires or hot surfaces. (It might not be out of place to discuss precautions for keeping ant paste and other poisons out of the reach of younger brothers and sisters.)

Volatile solids—naphtha crystals and moth flakes

Place some crystals, flakes, or mothballs in an open dish or box. After a few days a reduction in size and amount is noticeable. Some children may have watched their mothers replace the moth killers which have gradually become volatilized. If a Pyrex tube is available, heat some naphtha crystals over a Sterno or candle flame. (*Caution: These materials are inflammable.*) Hold the tube with kitchen tongs or forceps and rotate slowly to keep the glass from becoming overheated in one spot and cracking. Watch how large, shining fern-like crystals are deposited upon the cooler parts of the tube.

ACID OR ALKALI?

Another way of grouping or identifying chemicals is to find out whether they are acid, alkali (base), or neutral. Most drugstores carry small strips of pink and blue paper dipped in litmus solution. The blue paper turns reddish if dipped in acids such as vinegar, lemon juice, and so forth. The pink paper turns bluish when dipped in such bases as ammonia, borax, washing soda, and the like. Often we use an alkali to neutralize an acid. For example, a strip of blue litmus paper dipped in vinegar will turn red, but if it is then dipped into ammonia, it will turn blue again. This is the principle involved in neutralizing the weak acid of insect bites or bee stings by dabbing with ammonia (dilute). Some chemicals such as certain salts will not change the color of either kind of litmus paper. Litmus paper dipped in a solution of table salt, for example, will not change color.

Most households include some dry acids, such as boric acid powder. Dissolve any of these in water and test with litmus. Test again, using only the dry acid. The children will conclude that water is necessary in these as in most chemical reactions.

The juices of certain fruits and flowers can be used as acid-alkali indicators. Leaves and petals or fruit peelings are soaked in water to remove the color. When red cabbage is in season, shred some in water and heat until the water is deep purple. Pour off the liquid into a container and add more water to the cabbage. The liquid is again drawn off when colored and added to the first batch of solution. Saturate paper toweling or filter paper with the solution and let dry. Repeat the cycle of wetting and drying times; then cut in small strips and use as litmus paper. Or shred some red cabbage in rubbing alcohol. As soon as the alcohol turns purple, add some vinegar and the solution should become deep red. Pinches of baking soda or ammonia make the solution turn green. Vinegar turns it back to red.

Test the school drinking water with litmus. Test soil samples in solution. Test a solution of alum water. Dissolve soap in water and test. If the school serves hot lunches, the children will be interested to observe and certainly to sample the results of neutralizing acid (tomato soup) with a base (soda). To keep the soup from curdling, we add a pinch of soda. If at all possible, make a sour milk chocolate cake in a school oven or portable oven in the classroom. The children will be intrigued by making sour milk from evaporated milk (diluted with water 1:1) with the addition of vinegar (acid). Most good recipes show a proportion of 1 tablespoon vinegar to a cup of milk. The children will also note that the recipe you write for them on the board or chart probably calls for a small amount of soda, whereas most cakes use baking powder. The section which follows may help children understand this.

Before leaving this section, however, it may be useful to point up the acid reaction of many foods with high sugar content. Yeast cells working in a sugar solution (as in breadmaking) give an acid reaction to litmus. The way acid can erode bone structure may be shown by soaking clean chicken bones in concentrated vinegar for several days. Children's teeth have enamel which is resistant to vinegar. However, if a tooth is left in a glass of cola drink, it may dissolve very quickly because of the drink's acid content.

Many of our daily activities in home and classroom are made possible by the interaction of chemicals. We tend to take these activities for granted, and do not think of the individual chemical reactions that take place when we use various substances.

Carbon dioxide

Makes bread rise. Very often a chemical reaction is necessary to produce a substance which is important in our daily lives. We depend on the release of carbon dioxide gas to make bread rise. Crumble a yeast cake in a glass jar. Add a tablespoon of sugar and ⅓ cup of water. Stir until smooth. Within an hour a spongy mass full of carbon dioxide bubbles will form. The fermented smell is due to the formation of alcohol.

If the glass jar is kept covered and rubber tubing leads out through a one-hole stopper into another jar, you can test the gas being formed to see if it is carbon dioxide (Fig. 12-6). As we saw (p. 69), the test for carbon dioxide is whether it will turn clear limewater milky. If it is not easy for you to secure or make a one-hole stopper, use a milk bottle and make a hole in the cardboard cap just big enough to accommodate the tubing.

Baking powder, since it contains bicarbonate of soda, will also release carbon dioxide. As a result it is often used instead of yeast for breads. Mix dry 1 tablespoon of flour and ½ teaspoon of baking powder. Add just enough water to make dough. Put some of the dough in a cooking spoon with long, preferably wooden, handle. (A plain wood handle does not transmit heat as readily as metal). Hold over a heat source, such as Sterno, a hot plate, or even a candle. Soon the dough will rise to double its size. Take off the top layer of dough and notice how soft and puffy the mass has become as carbon dioxide bubbles formed through the mass. In class the children may like to make their own baking powder. Mix dry 1 teaspoon of soda, 2 teaspoons of tartaric acid, and 1 teaspoon of cornstarch. Pour in some vinegar and test with a lighted match. If carbon dioxide gas is being given off, the flame will be put out.

Making CO$_2$ gas. Another way to make carbon dioxide gas is with vinegar and baking soda. You will need a pop bottle, a cork to fit, and a piece of paper to make a funnel. The funnel is to help you pour a handful of baking soda into the pop bottle. Add ½ cup of vinegar and cork quickly but not too tightly. Give the bottle a shake or two and then set inside a tin can to prevent tipping or breaking. Stand back and await results. Very shortly the pressure of the carbon dioxide released by vinegar from the soda makes the cork fly out with a sharp pop. This demonstration may well be done out on the playground.

Carbon dioxide may be collected by the water bath method (p. 225) from any of the above experiments and tested with limewater.

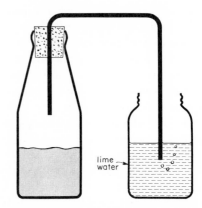

Fig. 12-6 *Carbon dioxide production by yeast. If the children say the limewater turns milky because of CO$_2$ in the air, set up another, identical container. Its solution may indeed turn slightly milky but only after several days' exposure to the air.*

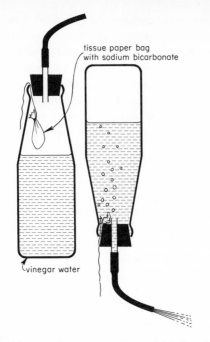

tissue paper bag
with sodium bicarbonate

vinegar water

Fig. 12-7 Model soda-acid fire extinguisher. Salvaged teabags are good containers for the soda.

Extinguishes fire. Light a candle and hold it so that a few drops of wax will fall in the center bottom of a coffee can. While the wax is still soft, immediately shove the butt of the candle into the soft wax and let the mass harden, anchoring the candle upright. Light the candle and pour in a glass of saturated solution of bicarbonate of soda. Slowly add vinegar. If the candle is not too far above the solution level, the flame will be smothered. To help the children be sure that the invisible gas—carbon dioxide—is responsible, repeat using only vinegar or only bicarbonate of soda. Of course, the flame will not be extinguished.

Somewhere in your school the children will have noticed one of the large brass fire extinguishers which operate because of a reaction between soda and acid. Perhaps the custodian or local fireman will open the extinguisher to show the children what is inside—a bottle of acid and a solution of baking soda (Fig. 12-7). For other model fire extinguishers (soda acid and foam) see Chapter 17.

Carbon dioxide and mothballs. Put ¾ cup baking soda in a gallon jar about ¾ full of water. Stir until dissolved. Slowly add a cup of vinegar. Soon the water is full of bubbles of carbon dioxide released from the soda. A couple of handfuls of mothballs dropped in sink to the bottom. Here they become coated with a layer of CO_2 bubbles which makes them rise. When they reach the surface, the bubbles break, and the mothballs sink to become recoated and rise over and over again.

Bases, or alkalies

Ammonia. Ammonia's basic reaction has already been mentioned (p. 202). In common with most alkalies, it is apt to be harmful to painted surfaces. With a medicine dropper try some on samples of different paints and set aside to observe results. However, ammonia is very effective in other ways. For example, compare the effectiveness of ammonia, plain water, and soapy water in cleaning a classroom windowpane. Note that ammonia water leaves no residue on the glass.

If children carry pocket combs, they may wish to watch the emulsifying effect of ammonia on natural hair oil and dust particles in the comb. Set a comb in a pan of water to which a teaspoon or two of ammonia has been added. After 20 minutes remove and rinse in clear water.

Bleaching action

The chemical change caused by various bleaching agents is something which goes on around us all the time. For example, have you noticed how tea, iced or hot, becomes light in color when you add lemon?

Removing stains. On a household stain chart, lemon is a frequent suggestion for stubborn stains. Such a chart is a gold mine of ideas for introducing chemistry at the elementary level. Very often cookbooks include a chart at the beginning or end of the book. Let children write their names in ink on paper and cloth and try removing the ink stain with such substances as lemon, vinegar, milk, onion, or household bleach. (Use care with bleach. Brush on with an old paint brush and avoid splashing.) Color a jar of water with a few drops of ink. Note color changes when you add a few drops of chlorine bleach.

Old-fashioned ink. Dissolve ¼ teaspoon tannic acid in 1 teaspoon water. Dissolve ¼ teaspoon iron sulfate in a like quantity of water. Note the color of each solution; then observe when you pour the two together. The new substance you see is old-fashioned ink. Use it to do some writing.

If iron sulfate is not easily available, use any iron compound soluble in water. The sulfate is the compound that contains both sulfur and oxygen. If you add strong tea to iron sulfate solution, you will be correct in judging from the result that tea contains tannic acid. So does hemlock bark, used in quantities in the tanneries of pioneer days.

Magic writing. Let the children use the end of a used match or a nurse's swab stick to write their names in milk or lemon juice on squares of bond paper. Try some of the various bleaches mentioned above. When dry, the name becomes invisible until held over a heat source. (A hot plate or light bulb is safer than open flame.) The writing turns brown. The problem, of course, is not to ignite the paper while heating to produce the desired chemical change.

Bleaching colored cloth and paper. Watch what happens to swatches of colored cloth or paper soaking in dilute household bleach. Make a solution of 1 cup peroxide and ½ cup of water. Add a few borax crystals to make a basic solution

(test with litmus). Boil some bright colored wool for about 10 minutes in this solution. Compare color with sample of same material unbleached and wet. Compare with another sample bleached in chlorine-type laundry bleach. Review safe ways of handling household bleach. Useful when treated with respect.

Chemical reactions and metal stains

A consideration of household stain removal may have led the children to mention, for example, how aluminum pans look almost new after cooking rhubarb or tomatoes. Try cleaning aluminum by heating water in it to which a little vinegar is added. The acid dissolves the thin film of stain on the metal.

Children whose home chore is cleaning silver know only too well how egg stains silver. Rub a clean, bright silver coin or piece of silverware first with the white, then with the yolk of hard-boiled egg. The children may be able to tell you without much help that the yolk makes the most stain because of the sulfur in it. To verify, bring some powdered sulfur in contact with silver. Put elastics around a silver coin for a few days and then remove. The sulfur used in vulcanizing the rubber forms a sulfide film on the silver.

Clean silver coins with a salt and soda solution. Dissolve a teaspoon of each in enough water to cover the silver. Use an aluminum pan or some pieces of aluminum foil in an enameled or glass pan. Bring to a boil and let stand. After a few minutes rinse and dry with a cloth. Compare with results from various commercial cleaners.

Observe the action of brass and copper cleaners on these metals. Scrape or sandpaper a penny to reveal fresh, clean copper. Undertake your own copper plating. Get an ounce of copper sulfate from the druggist and mix with 9 parts water by weight. Allow plenty of time for it to

blow

Fig. 12-8 Dust explosion. Scattering the particles permits each fragment to be surrounded by air for combustion in a high-temperature atmosphere.

dissolve. Suspend a thoroughly clean iron or steel key or old knife blade in the solution. If metal is absolutely clean, it will be coated with a thin layer of copper when removed in about 10 minutes. If the crystals of copper sulfate are large, break them up using a milk bottle as a rolling pin. Small crystals dissolve much more rapidly than large ones.

Chemical change due to heat (cooking)

Ordinary toast is a good illustration of changing something chemically by heating. Recalling the iodine-starch test (above), dip a slice of toast in a dish of iodine water. Then slice in strips so that the cross section will show the blue inner portion (starch) and the brown surface layer of dextrin. Does this show anything about the relative digestibility of bread versus toast?

Combustion and chemical change

Burning wood chips in a tin pie plate produces heat, smoke, ashes—all very different from the original wood.

Gas, another useful product of combustion, may be safely made on a small scale in the classroom. Punch a nail hole in the center of a coffee can cover. Cut some pine

blocks into thin chips. Put them into the can and close the lid securely. Set the can on an electric hot plate or other heat source for 15–20 minutes. Try lighting the smoke or gas escaping through the hole. It should ignite and burn. When the can has cooled, you should find charcoal formed in the can. Charcoal is almost pure carbon.

Dust explosions. Fill a drinking straw with ¼ teaspoon of fine cornstarch. Light a candle set in a candlestick. Aiming away from the children, blow the cornstarch at the flame (Fig. 12-8). For a fraction of a second the cornstarch particles ignite. The particles are so small and the flame so brief that the experiment is quite safe. Here in miniature you have reproduced the type of explosion which can occur in flour mills and grain elevators. Coal dust in the mines may explode in the same way.

Combustion and carbohydrates. We began this chapter talking about common chemicals such as sugar, salt, and water. We took salt and water apart and found each was composed of two elements. To find out what is in sugar, let us "turn the heat on." Put ½ cup of sugar in an old skillet over low-medium heat. Watch the sugar bubble and then turn black. Compare the black residue with the charcoal you made in a coffee can (above). Try writing with fragments of charcoal and the burnt sugar. Heating cornstarch the same way produces the same black residue. The children will begin to realize that many common chemicals contain carbon, hydrogen, and oxygen, and are thus called carbohydrates.

Water—a product of combustion. Remembering that water is composed of two of the same elements as in the carbohydrates, some children may wonder if you can get water out of sugar, starch, and wood chips. Heat a teaspoon of sugar in a small tin can. Invert a glass over the can.

Look for condensation. Invert over a candle. Heat more sugar, this time holding a cool object such as a cold flat iron over the can. Especially if you have momentarily refrigerated the flat iron, you should be able to see drops of moisture condensing on the metal. Repeat with cornstarch. Flour is 95% starch. Heat flour or a slice of bread until it is scorched. Hold close to a cool mirror or blackboard. The moisture given off shows that water is present in starch. Hold a cold iron above a candle and note the moisture condensing. Draw a parallel with cloud formations which often build up over forest fires. Another illustration within the experience of many children is the white "smoke" seen coming out of automobile tail pipes or factory smokestacks. Some may have noticed water dripping from tail pipes on cold days. This water is condensed moisture from the combustion of gasoline.

Your children have no doubt already discovered some of water's interesting abilities as a solvent (see Chapter 11). Experimenting with other chemicals soon leads them to see how often water is required for chemical action. For example, when one mixes cream of tartar and baking soda, nothing happens until water is added.

CHEMICAL SUPPLIES

Most supplies needed for elementary science can be bought at the grocery or drugstore. Science supply houses generally sell cheaper grades of common chemicals than those available at drugstores. Sometimes local doctors or hospitals have available surpluses of common harmless chemicals. Also children's chemistry sets can be a source of supply. Here is a list of household substances and their chemical names.

alum	aluminum potassium sulfate
ammonia	ammonium hydroxide (a mixture)
baking powder	
baking soda	sodium bicarbonate
cream of tartar	potassium bitartrate
Epsom salts	magnesium sulfate
household lye	sodium hydroxide
iodine	iodine tincture
peroxide	hydrogen peroxide
rust	iron oxide
rotten eggs	hydrogen sulfide
silver tarnish	silver sulfide
slaked lime	calcium hydroxide
sugar, starch	carbohydrate
table salt	sodium chloride
tea	tannic acid
vinegar	dilute acetic acid
washing soda	sodium carbonate

Blueprints

Blueprinting leaves illustrates chemical change while developing awareness to differences in plants. If you live in an urban area, check the classified telephone directory for blueprinting or drafting firms. The paper comes in wide rolls. Perhaps the supplier will cut it for you in small squares to match the smallest standard window glasses. Secure enough panes for the children to work in teams of not more than three each. Let the children bevel the edges of glass with steel wool or emery paper or bind the edges with tape. Cut cardboard to match the glass. Bind the glass and cardboard together along one edge with adhesive. Insert blueprint paper, sensitive or emulsion side up toward the light. Spread material to be printed on top, let the glass fall, and set in the sun until the paper darkens and turns blue. Remove and wash thoroughly in cold water. The print will remain more permanent if you fix it by one rinse in a pan of dichromate solution. Add a pinch of crystals to a glass of water to make the solution. Rinse the print in clear water and pin or hang up to dry.

Ozalid prints

If ozalid paper is available at your blueprint suppliers, you can make interesting brown prints in much the same way. The only difference is that the paper is developed by rinsing in weak ammonia water rather than plain tap water.

Photography

The whole process of developing and printing pictures involves a great deal of chemistry. The child who has an interest in chemistry and the child who has photography as a hobby may sometimes join forces to their mutual enrichment and enjoyment.

CAPSULE LESSONS

12-1 This recipe will make enough toothpaste for two dozen children for a week.

    8 oz precipitated chalk
    2 oz magnesium carbonate
    2 oz powdered sugar
    2 oz sodium bicarbonate
    1 oz sodium lauryl (dodecyl) sulfate
        (ingredient in some detergents)
   20 drops wintergreen or peppermint for
        flavoring[1]

12-2 A health study including the skin might conclude with children making their own hand lotion. One recipe includes

    2 oz powdered gum tragacanth
    6 oz ethyl alcohol
    1 medium size crystal of menthol
    pinch of salicylic acid
    2 oz tincture of benzoin
    4 pints water
    perfume[1]

12-3 Individuals or teams may wish to make their own wall size table of the elements with models of simpler elements attached. Chemistry and elements also become more meaningful to children when they set up a display of common elements such as iron, copper, and aluminum tied to a chart with colored yarn.

12-4 Make individual crystal gardens as follows: 4 tablespoons each of salt (noniodized), water, liquid bluing, household ammonia. Pour slowly over brick, coal, clinker, or other porous matter. Add food coloring, mercurochrome, or red ink for color.

12-5 If available from the druggist or high school chemistry lab, these chemicals coming out of solution grow colored crystals as follows:

    blue—nickel nitrate or cobalt nitrate
    brown—ferric chloride
    white—mercurous nitrate
    green—ferrous sulfate

12-6 These chemicals provide a characteristic color when heated in flame tests:

    sodium chloride—orange-yellow
    calcium chloride—violet-red
    strontium chloride—red
    copper sulfate—green

12-7 If you can secure Michael Faraday's *Chemical History of a Candle,* encourage "science-prone" child to read and demonstrate some of the ideas and experiments described.

12-8 Chemistry is involved in the operation of every flashlight battery and car battery. A child interested either in chemistry or electricity might produce interesting reports and demonstrations for the class on the transfer of chemical energy to electrical energy.

12-9 Chemistry is also involved in many aspects of photography. Many children are becoming interested in photography as a hobby. Alone or teamed with a friend, these children interested in chemistry could also do a useful and interesting piece of investigation and exposition to their classmates.

[1] *Science Guide,* Schenectady Elementary Schools, Schenectady, N. Y., 1953. p. 32.

BIBLIOGRAPHY

Asimov, Isaac, *Building Blocks of the Universe,* Abelard-Schuman, 1957. For upper grades. Origins, properties, and uses of elements.

Beeler, Nelson, and F. M. Branley, *Experiments in Chemistry,* Crowell, 1952. For middle grades. Chemistry of everyday objects by observation and experiment.

Blackwood, Paul, *Push and Pull: The Story of Energy,* McGraw-Hill, 1959. Sources and uses of energy in various forms. Simple experiments.

Cooper, Elizabeth K., *Discovering Chemistry,* Harcourt, Brace & World, 1959.

Freeman, Mae, and Ira Freeman, *Fun with Chemistry,* Random House, 1954. For upper grades. Simple chemistry experiments.

Gallant, Roy, *Exploring Chemistry,* Garden City, 1958. For middle grades. Historical development. Practical applications and future problems.

General Science Handbook, No. 2, Bureau of Curriculum Development, Division of Secondary Education, New York State Education Department, 1952. Excellent section, including six everyday chemical problems and exploratory investigations.

Milgrom, Harry, ed., *Matter, Energy, and Change: Explorations in Chemistry for Elementary School Children,* Manufacturing Chemists' Association, 1960. 50 pp. General directions for experimentation. Explorations appropriate to both lower and upper grades on common chemistry phenomena. Glossary, table of elements, and bibliography.

Morgan, Alfred, *First Chemistry Book for Boys and Girls,* Scribner's, 1950. For upper grades. Sixty-four activities using household equipment.

Newcomb, Ellsworth, and Hugh Kenny, *Miracle Fabrics,* Putnam, 1957. For upper grades. Research and development on synthetic materials.

Schloat, G. Warren, Jr., *Magic of Water,* Scribner's, 1955.

Schneider, H. and N. Schneider, *Plants in the City,* Day, 1951.

Schwartz, Julius. *It's Fun to Know Why: Experiments with Things Around Us,* McGraw-Hill, 1952.

Swezey, Kenneth, *Chemistry Magic,* McGraw-Hill, 1956. For upper grades. Activities and common tests. Laboratory techniques and apparatus explained.

White, Anne, *Rocks All Around Us,* Random House, 1959.

Wyler, Rose, *First Book of Science Experiments,* Watts, 1952.

13

Food and nutrition

All of us who have worked with elementary school children will agree that they possess one outstanding characteristic—energy, boundless energy. They never walk if they can run; they seldom speak softly (unless they have secrets to communicate). Even sitting at their desks, they are in motion—chewing a pencil, tapping on the desk, wiggling a foot.

All this energy implies fuel. Fuel implies burning or oxidation. And fuel for all living things—both plants and animals—is food. An objective study of foods and what they can do is a real contribution to learning. For if learning is a change in behavior, there is ample need for Americans to learn better food habits. Many thousand Americans starve in the midst of plenty because they eat an unbalanced diet. Family food preferences are often more of an obstacle than a budget to wise food selection. Food preferences and prejudices may be illustrated by asking each child to list three or four favorite foods and three or four of the opposite. A blackboard compilation of the lists will show some of the same foods on both sides. The children will immediately see that food likes and dislikes may have a shaky foundation of prejudice or habit. You are also aware that a study which may produce evidence counter to the family customs must be strictly objective and scientific. Here is a golden opportunity to practice the scientific attitude of open mindedness, the scientific method of solving problems on the basis of many observations and much research.

There is much evidence to indicate that proper nutrition requires that we eat some foods of the Basic Seven food groups every day.

1. Milk: One pint or more a day.
2. Eggs: One or more a day; at least four each week.
3. Meat, cheese, fish, or fowl: A serving a day.
4. Vegetables and fruits: A serving of one yellow and one green vegetable and a potato a day.
5. Citrus fruits (whole or in juice): One serving a day.
6. Cereals and bread (especially bread made from whole grain; spread with butter or with margarine which contains vitamins): Two or three servings a day.
7. Liquid: The equivalent of six to eight glasses of water.

You may wish to use a grouping involving these four food groups:

1. Milk group: You need 3 to 4 cups of milk a day.
2. Vegetable-fruit group: You need 4 or more servings a day.
3. Meat group: You need 2 or more servings a day.
4. Bread-cereals group: You need 4 or more servings a day.

Many of the large food processors have developed excellent colored charts and other free materials which you can use in a study of foods. For instance, one of these companies produces pictures of foods ready to cut out and set up to illustrate three balanced meals. One bulletin board illustrates the *Four Corners of a Square Meal*, with cutouts of foods rich in proteins, calories, minerals, and vitamins. In either case, children might make cutouts and set up exhibits of a day's meals. Then check what the exhibits show they ate vs. the Basic Seven chart. Asking *all* children to keep a daily diet record may put at a disadvantage those whose families have poor food habits. And it creates problems for those whose vocabulary and spelling are weak. Checking the diets of those with high attendance records does not always prove these children eat the right foods. Recall with children how keeping classroom pets healthy (Chapter 2) was also related to a variety of food offerings.

Keeping weight records may have possible disadvantages in the middle grades where the girls grow faster than the boys. Girls who are overweight sometimes overeat because they are emotionally disturbed. Any emphasis on their obesity only aggravates the difficulty.

Nutrition experiments with white rats offer children valuable experiences with animals and an object lesson in proper nutrition. Rats from a hospital laboratory are used to being handled and are apt to be free from disease. Try to get rats of the same sex, age, and litter for your experiments. Keep animals warm and away from drafts. Cover the cage overnight and over weekends. Feed milk to a control group of animals and plain water to experimental subjects (plus a regular food diet, of course). Weigh food and water daily. Keep a careful weight record of each rat from the time it comes in until you return it to the laboratories. There are some excellent free pamphlets with de-

tails on animal feeding experiments. (See also Chapter 2.)

Of all the substances found in foods, the following are ones about which elementary children should learn: carbohydrates (sugars and starches), fats, proteins, vitamins, minerals, and water. Proteins ("grow foods") are for growth and repair; sugar, starch, and fats ("go foods") are for energy; minerals build bones and promote general health. Different vitamins have different functions in health and growth. These will be recapitulated in the section on tests for vitamins.

Plants are our source of starch and sugars. Plants also make vitamins (A, B, C, E). Minerals such as calcium and iron which we get from eating fruits and vegetables are taken by plants from the soil. Animals are our source of proteins, fats, and other vitamins. Animals get minerals from the soil via plants. Animals also get some vitamins from eating plants. Here we see some of the steps in food chains. Help the children see that animals use more energy than plants and can store less.

As we have seen (Chapter 11), water is the great solvent. Our food has to be liquefied before our bodies can use it. Our chopping box (the mouth) mixes saliva with our food as we chew it into small bits. There are many juices in our body which keep food moist and also dissolve it. Saliva, which is partly water, is just one of these juices. Our bodies are, in fact, 66% water. When our food reaches our stomachs, it could not get to our fingers and toes if it were not carried through the blood, which is 90% water. We can live for a month without food, but not more than 3 or 4 days without water.

DIGESTION

Most children can understand they need to eat to *go* and *grow*. But most chil-

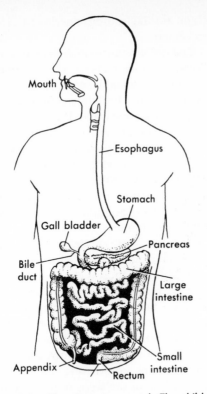

Fig. 13-1 The alimentary canal. The children should note the number of different organs involved in digestion and the arrangement permitting lateral and horizontal churning of food. (From G. Simpson et al., *Life*, Harcourt, Brace & World, 1957.)

other things doctors discovered that the man's emotions had a great deal to do with the digestive process. If he was angry or upset, his stomach reacted in such a way that food might be only partly processed or not at all, thus causing indigestion. They found that the stomach has no way of grinding food. Food is churned by two kinds of muscle motions—lengthwise and crosswise.

Thus the children can see how hard a time their stomachs will have if food is not ground into small pieces in the mouth by the teeth. Let children try grinding some food, as between stones Indian-fashion. Compare the rates of changing starch to sugar in ground starch lumps dissolved in saliva solution and in whole starch lumps dissolved in saliva solution.

The usual stomach temperature is 100° F. The temperature goes up during exercise and down during sleep or rest. Let the children discuss the relation of stomach temperatures to activity and rest. Let them conclude why food should not be too hot or too cold when it passes into the stomach.

Let the children deduce the role of different organs in food intake and digestion.

the mouth takes in food	the hopper
the teeth grind	the grinders
the tongue mixes food with saliva	the mixers
the muscles push food through esophagus into stomach	the conveyor belt

Food cannot be digested until it is ground up and liquefied. Recall with children that not all parts of food can be digested. Some food leaves the body in solid form, some in liquid form. (See Fig. 13-1.)

As we have seen, food is physically changed by chewing and liquefying in the mouth. Chew a soda cracker slowly and

dren don't really understand why parents and teachers are forever trying to keep them from wolfing their food and from rushing around or swimming right after eating. Perhaps a little applied science will make life easier for both adults and children.

No one has ever been able to build a machine which duplicates all the complex processes of digestion in the body. For a long time doctors could only guess what went on inside the stomach. Then a hunter, with his stomach wall accidentally shot away, was taken to a doctor who persuaded his patient in the interests of science to permit observations of what happened inside his stomach. Among thoroughly. The cracker gradually becomes sweet as the saliva converts the starch to sugar. Starches begin to be chemically changed to sugars by the action of saliva. When they reach the stomach, starches continue to change and proteins begin to be chemically changed also. If you can secure small amounts of dilute hydrochloric acid and pepsin, you may wish to demonstrate chemical changes in proteins. Place samples of different types of protein foods in hydrochloric acid and pepsin and observe the results after 24 hours. The protein is broken down, changed and in part liquefied.

OXIDATION OF FOOD

Robert Frost's poem about the woodpile describes the "slow smokeless burning of decay." This is the poet's way of describing slow oxidation. We can illustrate slow oxidation with the aid of some steel wool (plain, not a treated scouring pad) and an olive jar. Wash the steel wool in detergent and rinse well; shove it to the bottom of the jar. Invert the bottle and set in water (Fig. 13-2). In about a week the iron in the steel wool will have rusted. This combination of iron and oxygen from the air is called iron oxide or rust. Since air is about one fifth oxygen, water should have risen about one fifth the height of the bottle. At the start of the experiment mark the water level with a rubber band or crayon mark on the glass. Compare with the water level after rust has formed. Invert the same size container over a burning candle standing in water. The candle will use up oxygen inside the jar until it goes out, and water will rise to replace the oxygen.

If the place and the season permit, secure a bushel or so of fresh grass clippings, fresh cut hay, or fallen leaves. Pile in a warm moist place. Feel with your hand and notice that the temperature inside the heap is usually warmer than the outside air. Better yet, take some temperature readings. Put the thermometer into the middle of the pile. Recheck the temperatures in about a week. Perhaps the children will have noticed condensation of water vapor above a pile of leaves or grass cuttings. Why does this happen? Farmers know that heat is formed inside a pile of fresh manure. Sometimes if hay is put in the barn too green and without proper curing, the heat generated is sufficient to cause spontaneous combustion and set fire to the barn.

The body is an unusual machine in its ability to oxidize or use fuel at relatively low temperatures. The slow oxidation of sugar produces a temperature higher than normal in the body. However, evaporation of moisture through the sweat glands keeps the body near 98.6° F (normal body temperature). This varies a few tenths of a degree. It is usually higher with children.

A simple experiment will show slow oxidation of food at low temperatures. Secure two clinical or laboratory thermometers to insert in one-hole stoppers that fit two small Thermos bottles. Be sure to shake down to a low reading. Put ½ cup of dried vegetable seeds (peas, beans, squash, radish) in one bottle, the same amount of soaked seeds in another (Fig. 13-3). Each Thermos should be about one fourth full of seeds. The thermometers

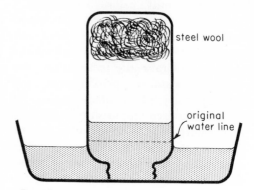

steel wool

original water line

Fig. 13-2 Slow oxidation of steel wool in air.

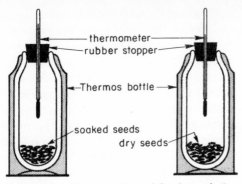

Fig. 13-3 Slow oxidation of food, producing heat.

should not touch the seeds. Do not stopper tightly, as germinating seeds expand. The temperature reading for the Thermos of soaked seeds should be higher because of the oxidation process started by soaking the seeds. Read at the start and again at intervals of a few hours for 24–48 hours.

CALORIES

A study of foods is sure to bring up the term *calories*. A calorie is a unit of measure to indicate the energy value of different foods. Scientists define a calorie as the amount of heat needed to raise the temperature of 1 gram of water 1 centigrade degree. One centigrade degree equals 1.8 Fahrenheit degrees. Heat 1 gram of water so that its temperature is raised just less than 2 Fahrenheit degrees; you have thereby demonstrated how one scientist's calorie is expended.

The nutritionist's calorie is a "giant" unit equal to 1000 of the scientist's calories. Hence to show one *food* calorie you will need to raise the temperature of a quart of water (approximately 1000 grams) nearly 2 Fahrenheit degrees.

Some children may wish to make their own calorimeter. This requires two tin cans, a laboratory thermometer, a butter candle, and a stone or weight to hold down the inner can. (See Fig. 13-4.) For the butter candle use any kind of fat

(butter, suet, lard, meat fat) in a frozen orange juice can or similar container. Use soft cotton string for a wick. Ignite the candle and measure the rise in water temperature. If you use a quart of water, every 2-degree (F) rise indicates a calorie of energy given off by the little candle. If you measure the water with a graduated cylinder or other container marked in milliliters (ml), the children can more accurately measure the number of giant or food calories given off by the candle. For instance, if the quart of water reaches a temperature 10 F° higher, they know that the candle released approximately 5 giant calories. However, this total heat loss is difficult to measure with simple apparatus. What our calorimeter really indicates is the amount of heat being absorbed by the water.

Sixth graders are estimated to need 1 calorie per hour per pound body weight. Let each child figure his daily (24 hours) caloric need. For example, a 100 pound boy would need $24 \times 100 = 2400$ calories.

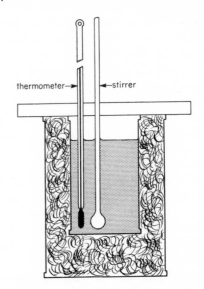

Fig. 13-4 Simple homemade calorimeter. Insulation surrounds the inner can, which contains the water. (From A. Joseph et al., *A Sourcebook for the Physical Sciences*, Harcourt, Brace & World, 1961.)

(This, of course, varies with the individual.) Using tables showing the number of calories in different foods, let children figure the total daily intake from foods eaten.

THE HUMAN BODY AT WORK

One of our over-all objectives for elementary science is to develop appreciation for the world and the living things in it. Using a study of foods as a vehicle, we hope to come out with children having greater understanding of their own bodies and more knowledge of how to take care of them.

You may initiate such a study by asking children to count the different things their bodies do in one day. For example, we may *hear* the alarm clock in the morning, *open* one eye, and *look* at the clock, hoping it may be a mistake. It is not. We *lift* off the covers, *slide* one foot out, and *step* into a slipper.

Some teachers like to use the analogy of a machine to initiate the study. For example, you may ask the children to guess a riddle patterned after the following lines:[1]

I am the best machine in the world.
I can lift things.
I can remember things I do.
I can change a glass of milk into part
of me.
I need something to make me go, and I
can get it myself.
I can repair myself.
I can think and figure.
There are millions of machines like me.
What am I?

While the human body is like a machine in some ways, it can do many things a machine cannot. It can guide itself. It can think. It can repair itself. Although both require air to burn their fuel,

[1] Beauchamp, W. I., et al., *Discovering Our World*, teachers ed., Book I, Scott, Foresman, 1952, p. 67.

and both give off wastes, perhaps our bodies are more unlike engines than like them. For example, our fuel is burned at fairly low rather than high temperatures. Our fuel is burned in cells all over the body, not in one place. Our bodies can grow larger. Engines cannot. Scientists still do not wholly understand how our bodies repair themselves.

Our bodies are always at work. For example, even when we are asleep, our hearts keep pumping, our diaphragm and chest muscles keep us breathing, and our digestion continues. Even in a machine age, our bodies do a surprising amount of work in a day. By work we mean motion, and every motion means using muscles.

Let the children double up their fists to illustrate the approximate size of their hearts. Let one of them demonstrate heart action by immersing his fist in water and, by squeezing, squirting water between his thumb and forefinger. At the rate of 60 to

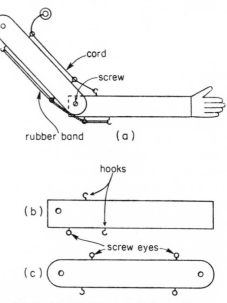

Fig. 13-5 Model of the arm. Halloween cutouts of the body skeleton may also be used. Tendons in a chicken leg can be pulled or relaxed to show how claws open and close. (From *UNESCO Source Book for Science Teachers*, UNESCO, 1956.)

70 times per minute, how long is it before the hand get tired? Yet the heart does much more work night and day, and its only rest is the pause between pulses.

We have all watched boys invite their friends to feel their arm muscles. And junior "muscle men" are often the acknowledged leaders through the middle grades. Some of these boys may enjoy making a model of the arm and its muscles (Fig. 13-5). Muscles get tired because of too much lactic acid, a waste product. Rest permits the excess wastes to be carried away, broken down, or absorbed. Muscle is rebuilt by eating foods rich in protein, minerals, and water. Diet for athletes in training is often rich in such protein foods as meat, eggs, cheese, fish, yogurt, and milk. Elementary grade children are still growing, and protein foods help children grow.

FOOD TESTS

Proteins

The bad odor (burnt hair, burnt feathers) produced by burning proteins is a simple but not wholly desirable test for proteins in common foods. Another test involves making a very dilute (3%) solution of copper sulfate. Use it with household ammonia. You will need to add only a few drops of each to some milk in a tumbler or jar. The chemical reaction should produce violet milk. Other foods to be tested for protein will first have to be made into a water solution before the copper sulfate and ammonia are added. Cooked foods test more readily than raw foods. A variation of the test described uses a medicine dropper of household ammonia.

Here is how to detect the presence of starch in wheat flour. Make a stiff paste using about a pint of flour. Knead for about 10 minutes and then put into an old sugar bag or piece of cheesecloth.

Continue kneading under water, rinsing until little milkiness remains. The milky water should turn blue with the addition of household iodine, showing the presence of starch. The gluten remaining inside the bag should show protein when tested with copper sulfate and ammonia.

Show that lean meat (muscle) is mainly protein. Test a candy bar for protein. Show by high school science charts of musculature that our bodies, other than bone and water, are mainly protein. Lead the children to conclude the importance of enough protein foods for adequate muscle growth and general development.

Older children may separate a bottle of milk into its component nutrients as follows. Secure a pint bottle of raw or non-homogenized milk. Let it stand in the refrigerator until all the cream has come to the top. Remove this carefully. It contains the fat which was in the milk. Heat the rest of the milk until lukewarm. Add white vinegar, a few drops at a time, stirring until the milk curdles. Remove the solid part (curds) from the liquid (whey) by filtering through paper toweling fitted inside a funnel (Fig. 13-6). The curds, called casein, should be tested for protein. Casein has many commercial uses. It is used in glue and in making plastics and buttons (most buttons are casein plastic). Now bring the whey to a boil. Light curds called milk albumin should appear. These also can be filtered off and should be tested for protein. Next the filtrate (the liquid that passes through the filter) from the milk albumin should be evaporated. Use a double boiler and leave the top off. As the water boils off the solution, milk sugar is deposited on the bottom of the vessel. It tastes sweet. Test it for sugar by heating it with water. Drop in a sugar test tablet such as Clinitest. Clinitest tablets provide an easy way to test for sugar. Try also match-like Clinistiks. The tips turn color in the presence of simple (glucose) sugars.

Druggists sell these together with color charts for diabetics to do their own sugar testing. The tablets make a blue solution. In the presence of sugar, the solution turns brick red. This color means a 2% sugar content; yellow means 1%; greenish means ¼%. No heating is necessary.

It is interesting to note that these experiments show milk is indeed the perfect food. It contains fats, proteins, and carbohydrates (sugars) in about the proportion needed for proper nutrition. It lacks only iron and vitamin C.

Fats

Athletes may need protein for muscle growth and repair, but they do indeed need other nutrients from food for energy. Carbohydrates (sugars and starches) and fats are our best sources of energy. For energy we must eat foods that will produce heat in the body. Everybody knows that fats produce heat when they are burning. Fill metal bottle caps with a variety of fats and oils, using soft cotton string for wicks. You may be surprised how long these will burn and how much heat they will give off. Secure a 100-watt bulb and let the children hold their hands near it to feel the heat radiated. The body as a whole releases energy at about the same rate.

One of the commonest tests for fat may be illustrated by placing a dab of lard on some paper. Warm the paper over the radiator or other heat source. Notice how the oily spot becomes more and more translucent. In general, oils come from plants, and solid or semisolid fats come from animals (although some commercial fats are made from plant oils). Anything leaving a translucent grease stain on paper contains fat or oil.

A more interesting test, which actually recovers fats or oils, requires carbon tetrachloride (Carbona). (*Caution: Do not inhale fumes.*) Do this test outdoors. Pulverize

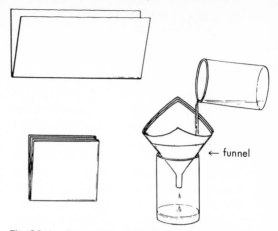

Fig. 13-6 Separation of milk into its components. Fit the folded paper inside a funnel, and pour between the first and second folds.

some nut meats and immerse in solvent. Leave for several hours or overnight. Filter the solution and pour the filtrate (liquid) into a shallow dish to evaporate. The residue will be oil or fat. A variation involves crushing the food and placing it in a tumbler of water. Watch for the oil film on the surface.

Nuts will provide another interesting illustration of energy in food. Secure butternuts, walnuts, or whole peanuts. Mount each on a long needle. Imbed the eye of the needle in a cork to hold the needle upright. Place all on a metal pan for safety. Ignite each nut with candle flame. If you use a Brazil nut, it proves its high fat content by burning longest with the largest flame.

Look at a drop of milk mixed with water under the microscope. You should be able to see the small ball-like droplets of fat. These collect to form cream.

Sugar and starch

Sugar and starch are also regarded as energy foods. If this is so, they must give off heat. Here is a way to find out. Lay a stiff piece of paper across the open end of a tin can. Do this near the sink. Put a teaspoon of sugar on the paper and light the paper. First the sugar will look as though it were boiling. Then it will make a blue flame. Do the same thing with cornstarch. Both sugar and starch burn and both give off energy (heat). Or place a sugar lump in a cooking spoon with a long wooden handle. If you coat the lump first with fine ash as from a cigarette, it will ignite more easily. Hold the spoon over heat (candle, Sterno, alcohol lamp). The sugar will melt and then ignite. All carbohydrates (e.g., wood) release water vapor when they burn. To see this, hold a mirror above the flame. If cool enough, the mirror will condense the water vapor released in burning. Repeat the experiment with dextrose obtained from a drugstore.

Burn bread (in the same manner), and again test for water vapor. Have children breathe against a cool mirror. The slow burning of energy foods in our bodies also releases water vapor and carbon dioxide.

The simplest test for sugar is tasting. Dip a toothpick in sweetened water and touch various parts of your tongue. You will find that your taste buds are not equally distributed over the surface. Locate with the aid of a mirror the most taste-sensitive regions.

The chemical tests for sugar are, in general, effective only with simple sugars such as are found in raisins, fruit juices, and brown sugar. In the body, complex sugars are reduced by saliva in the mouth and enzymes in the intestines. Compare the rates of reducing complex sugars in ground sugar lumps dissolved in saliva solution and in whole sugar lumps, dissolved in saliva solution. Apply saliva to a sugar lump, and after an interval test for sugar as described above.

Test lemon juice for simple sugars. It will show as much color reaction as a sweet orange. Lemons are sour because the sugar flavor is screened by the high citric acid content of the lemon.

To remove sugar from foods, boil and filter. When the filtrate evaporates, a small residue of sugar will be left.

Drop some household iodine on a cracker. The iodine immediately turns from brown to blue. Try the iodine test on other foods. Dip a matchstick in iodine and write a name on a slice of raw potato. Note how the name becomes dark blue. Test fruits for starch content. In many fruits the starch changes to sugar as the fruit ripens. Illustrate this by assembling some fruit such as apples in different stages of ripening. The apples which show most starch in reaction to iodine are the green apples.

Try dissolving some sugar in water. Of course, it does so easily. Help the children relate what they see to the use of sugar for "quick energy" and for that purpose only. Because sugar dissolves easily, it is quickly carried to parts of plants or animals where energy is needed.

Starch tests will show the children what a large number of foods contain starch. Does starch dissolve as well as sugar? Compare a teaspoon of starch in a tumbler of water and a teaspoon of sugar in a second tumbler of water. Stir well in each case; then let stand. Filter some of each solution into other tumblers. Did the sweet taste go through from the sugar solution? Test the filtrate from the starch solution with iodine.

Make a starch paste by following directions on the cornstarch box or as follows. Mix a tablespoon of cornstarch with a cup of water. Heat to boiling, and then cook for 10 minutes. Stir constantly to prevent burning. Put a tablespoon of the very thin paste in two jars. Add saliva to one jar; add a teaspoon of water to the other. Set in a warm place for an hour and check. Saliva changes the starch to sugar and the paste dissolves. The paste with plain water remains the same.

Let some pieces of cracker stand for 20

minutes in saliva. Add Benedict's solution (obtainable from druggist or scientific supply house). Boil. You should have an indication of sugar in the color reaction. Saliva contains an enzyme, *ptyalin,* which changes starch to sugar. Other enzymes in the small intestine continue changing starches to sugars. Secure from a druggist inexpensive digestant tablets containing such enzymes as *papain* and *pepsin.* Papain is also found in meat tenderizers (e.g., Adolph's). Add a crushed tablet to one solution of food, e.g., some ground beef in water. Compare in a half hour with a control solution of the food being tested in water. By the next day the ground beef in solution with enzyme will be nearly liquefied.

In the same manner, plants that store starch in their roots have to change the starch into sugar before they can use it. For example, parsnips dug in the fall are rather tasteless. By spring they are sweet and tasty. During their first summer, parsnips store starch in their fleshy roots. Toward the end of winter, this starch begins to change to sugar so that by spring the sugar can be carried up into the stems and leaves. Parsnips use this energy food to make flowers and seeds. Parsnips are biennials, plants that make enough food during the first year of their lives to bloom the second season before they die.

Dissolve cornstarch in water. Add a drop or two of iodine. You should get a blue solution. Make your own starch from raw potatoes. Grate several and make a bag around the pulp with a piece of old sheet or sugar bag. Dip the bag several times in a little water to wash out the starch. Filter the milky liquid. Starch will be retained by the filter. Spread this out to dry in a flat pan near heat.

Vitamins

You could eat all the food you could hold and still starve. Everyone needs the different vitamins found in different foods. This is another reason we spend so much time helping children learn by heart the Basic Seven food groups. Let children practice making cutout meals which include foods containing each of the four vitamins—A, B, C, and D. The children will discover that no one food contains all the vitamins. They will note which vitamins are listed on the wrappers of cereal and other foods and will begin to look carefully at the labels on bottles of vitamin pills. Such an activity will soon show them that vitamin pills differ considerably in the relative amounts of different vitamins and minerals (e.g., iron).

Testing for vitamins helps children understand that vitamins are real substances—are chemicals. For vitamin C, use ordinary iodine diluted in 100 parts of water. Dilute 1 drop of 10% ascorbic acid (from the druggist) in 20 drops of water. Add iodine. The brown color disappears completely, leaving the liquid clear. The more vitamin C contained in the substance you are testing, the quicker the iodine color will disappear.

Or mix 10 drops of boiled starch and 1 drop of iodine in a half glass of water. Add forms of citrus foods until the blue color disappears. Be sure to have the children test some foods which you know do not contain vitamin C, as, for example, proteins or fats.

Testing for vitamin A should be done only by the teacher. Dissolve a pill containing vitamin A in ¼ ounce of carbon tetrachloride. (*Caution: Do not breathe the fumes.*) Then with tweezers drop in one crystal of antimony trichloride obtained from a high school science laboratory or chemistry set. (*Caution: Do not handle crystals except with tweezers.*) If much vitamin A is present, the white crystal will turn deep blue; if there is only a small amount of the vitamin, the crystal will turn light blue.

Minerals

Burn a small square of bread until it turns to ash. Notice how the black carbon turns to light grey, indicating the presence of minerals in bread. Most foods contain minerals that are important to the body.

Many children know that iodine is needed for proper functioning of the thyroid gland. To make up the deficiency of iodine in the water and soil in certain regions (the "goiter belt"), salt companies sell iodized salt. Show the children how to test for iodine in salt. Fill a test tube one quarter full of dry cornstarch; add the same amount of salt. Wet the salt by adding a little household bleach. If the salt is iodized, a dark blue-black dividing line will form between the salt and the starch.

Calcium and phosphorus are necessary minerals for bone growth. Using the caption *How Are These Alike?*, pin up to your bulletin board an outline of the human skeleton (of the kind often sold for Halloween decoration) and a picture or sketch of the framework of a modern building. Children who want to be tall athletes or airplane pilots should know what foods are needed to build a good body frame. Ask the children to bring in some poultry bones. Chicken drumsticks are fine. If necessary, boil and scrape them clean of any adhering muscle tissue or ligaments. Place in a jar. Cover with concentrated vinegar, screw cap on tightly, and let stand. After several days the bones should be rubbery enough to tie into knots. The vinegar, of course, has dissolved the calcium in the bones. Some children do not think of bone as living or growing tissue. Ask the butcher to saw off for you a cross section of bone which will show marrow with blood vessels. Let the children plan make-believe meals or list the foods rich in calcium and phosphorus. They will soon find that milk is the best source of both these minerals. Review the feeding experiment in which milk was given to the experimental rat(s) and no milk was given to the controls. Make a bulletin board of pictures of animals which should eat calcium and phosphorus foods. The children will find that all animals with bony skeletons need such diet. The invertebrates do not. Help the children understand why the first food of young mammals is mother's milk.

Since your children probably listen to radio and watch TV, encourage them to do so with discrimination. Ask them to listen for food advertising and to write down the claims, the slogans, and propaganda for each brand. The children's findings can then be evaluated in class discussion. Some of the fantastic appeals are revealed for what they are in the cold light of objective analysis.

CAPSULE LESSONS

13-1 What animals have no teeth (e.g., hen, earthworm)? How do they pulverize food for digestion and absorption? If possible, let children see the teeth of different animals and relate them to food habits, e.g., grinding teeth of herbivores (plant-eaters), tearing teeth of carnivores (flesh-eaters).

13-2 To show how bile emulsifies fats and oils in the intestine, let children observe the action of soap on mixtures of water with household fats and oils. Shake the fat or oil together with soap solution, and note how fat globules are surrounded and separated by the emulsifying agent, soap.

13-3 Do you really eat calories? Not any more than you eat inches, another kind of measure. One and one-half lb of sugar or 4 lb of eggs would supply the daily calorie needs of many. Let children prepare an exhibit to demonstrate this and explain why neither would make a good diet. They may wish to investigate and explain sex differences and occupational differences in calorie needs.

13-4 Let children dramatize Dr. Lind's discovery of the cure for shipboard scurvy and why British sailors are called "limeys."

13-5 Let children report on an exhibit of supplementary vitamins. Discuss the importance of reading the labels with care and comparing the relative proportions of various vitamins (arithmetic and reading). Let children show the right and wrong ways to cook with respect to preserving vitamins.

13-6 Clarify differences between vitamins and minerals in food by following up 13-5 with an exhibit of minerals necessary for health, e.g., iron, calcium, sodium, potassium, sulfur, magnesium, iodine, fluorine.

13-7 To show the importance of soil minerals for *growing* food plants, wash an amount of soil five or six times in hot water to leach out the minerals. Plant bean or tomato seedlings in the soil when dried. Use an equal amount of unwashed soil and the same number of plants as a control. Divide both lots of soil into at least two containers before transplanting seedlings.

13-8 Encourage children to study seed catalogs and note the number of *new* vegetable hybrids or improved strains due to the work of plant and animal geneticists.

13-9 Consult with the school nurse on various aspects of nutrition.

13-10 Arrange for a committee of children to visit the school dietitian to discuss the planning of school lunches.

13-11 Investigate foods produced by the growth of nonflowering plants, e.g., bread mold, cheese and butter bacteria, etc. Discuss with the cafeteria manager measures used to inhibit growth of harmful molds and bacteria in the school kitchen.

BIBLIOGRAPHY

Burnett, R. W., *How Long Do You Want to Live?*, SRA Modern World of Science Series, 1954. 48 pp. Upper. Modern scientific facts about good health.

Callahan, Dorothy, and Alma S. Payne, *The Great Nutrition Puzzle*, Scribner's, 1956. Upper. Scientific techniques and experiments to discover facts about food and nutrition.

Carlson, A. J., and V. E. Johnson, *Machinery of the Body*, University of Chicago, 1953. Teacher reference. Most complete reference for teacher with some science background.

Cosgrove, Margaret, *The Wonders Inside You*, Dodd, Mead, 1955. Middle. Excellent presentation of human anatomy. Very useful index.

Glemser, Bernard, *All About the Human Body*, 1958, Random House. Middle. Meaningful descriptions of body structure and function.

Mabee, Elsie, *Young Nutritionists in Action*, Teachers Lesson Unit Series, No. 103, 1942. Bureau of Publication, Teachers College, Columbia. 26 pp. Record of year's activities with fifth grade children.

Novikoff, Alex, *From Head to Foot*, International, 1946. Upper. First-rate presentation of functional physiology. Vivid diagrams.

Parker, Bertha M., *Foods*, Row, Peterson, 1948. Middle. Basic food needs of the body. Food groups, values, and content.

Ravielli, Anthony, *Wonders of the Human Body*, Viking, 1954. Middle. An anatomical artist has produced a simple, clear anatomy book for children.

Schneider, Herman, and Nina Schneider, *How Your Body Works*, Scott, 1949. Upper. Imparts sense of wonder at our amazing body machinery.

Schneider, Leo, *Lifeline: The Story of Your Circulatory System*, Harcourt, Brace & World, 1958. Middle. Story of blood function and circulation.

Selsam, Millicent E., *How Animals Eat*, Scott, 1955. Middle. Simple explanation of food chains.

Turtox Service, *Laboratory Experiments in Nutrition*, General Biological Supply House, Chicago, Ill. 38 pp. Detailed suggestions for teachers prepared by one of the leading science supply houses.

Zim, Herbert S., *Your Food and You*, Morrow, 1957. Middle. Function of food and digestion.

Breathing

Like any other machine which does work, our bodies need fuel, and that fuel is food which is converted into energy by burning. Burn a teaspoon of sugar or starch on a piece of stiff paper. The heat and light are energy from the sugar and starch.

Burning requires air, specifically the fraction of air we call oxygen. In our bodies this burning or oxidation of the food we eat takes place slowly. Even in cold-blooded animals such as frogs and toads the body sugars are oxidized into glucose at body temperatures even below 50° F.

HOW ANIMALS BREATHE

Before children understand what it is we take from air when we breathe, they

Fig. 14-1 Mosquito wigglers (larvae of Culex mosquitoes) breathing through tubes at the surface of the water. (Hugh Spencer.)

first will want to know *how* we go about the business of breathing. We have a much easier time of it than do many creatures. The nymphs or larval form of many water insects must breathe through gills in their tails. Mosquito wigglers breathe through tubes they stick up above water (Fig. 14-1). Fish have gills (Fig. 14-2A). In order for the interchange of fresh and used air to take place through the gills, the fish must continually open its mouth. One interesting little water spider breathes underwater by carrying an air bubble down with it. When this is used up, the creature comes up for more.

Frogs literally spend their lives swallowing air. They have nostrils (Fig. 14-2B), but their throat pulsation, which reminds one of a nervous boy's Adam's apple, is part of the breathing mechanism. Although tadpoles breathe through gills, frogs breathe through lungs. A slit in the mouth connects the mouth to the lungs through a windpipe. We draw air into our lungs as our rib case expands. Frogs cannot do this. By lowering the floor of the mouth, they draw in air through the nostrils. The nostril flaps close, the floor of the mouth rises, and air is forced into the lungs. Encourage children to watch this action in a frog. The children should now see why both fish and amphibians would smother if their mouths were kept closed.

To help children understand how a fish breathes, run a glass of water from the tap

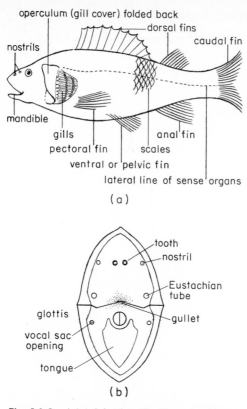

operculum (gill cover) folded back

dorsal fins

caudal fin

nostrils

mandible

gills

pectoral fin

ventral or pelvic fin

scales

anal fin

lateral line of sense organs

(a)

tooth

nostril

Eustachian tube

glottis

gullet

vocal sac opening

tongue

(b)

Fig. 14-2 (a) A fish. The gills, like animal lungs, are bright red because of blood vessels close to the surface to permit absorption of oxygen. (b) Frog mouth. Do not confuse frog breathing motions with the expansion of the throat resonator sac during spring "vocalizations." Air can be pumped into this resonator sac through the vocal sac opening. (From Ella Thea Smith, *Exploring Biology*, 4th ed., Harcourt, Brace & World, 1954.)

and let children count and time the bubbles which collect inside the tumbler. These bubbles are formed from air dissolved in the water. Fish gills are always bright red because the blood is just beneath a thin skin. Oxygen from air dissolved in water moves through this thin membrane into the blood stream.

PLANTS BREATHE TOO

Animals need much energy in order to move about as well as to maintain body processes. Plants need less energy because they do not move about. But like animals, they also need the oxygen in air to convert their food supply into energy. That plants cannot ultimately live without air may be demonstrated by germinating seeds with and without air (Fig. 14-3). Soak seeds such as peas, beans, bird or grass seed overnight. Fill two bottles half full of cotton or soil. Put in seeds so they can be seen through glass. Add a little water. Tightly cork one bottle and seal with candle wax or paraffin. Leave the other bottle open. Put in a warm dark place for 2 or 3 days. Check daily and replace water evaporated from the open bottle.

Which bottle shows first seed germination? Which bottle shows best germination? How long until the airless seedlings die? (See also pp. 213–14.)

LUNG MODELS

In order for children to understand the mechanism of breathing, it may be useful to construct some simple models of the lung cavity and diaphragm. You will need a lamp chimney, a one-hole stopper, a plastic feeding tube, a rubber balloon, rubber sheeting or Pliofilm, and some elastic bands. Attach the balloon with rubber

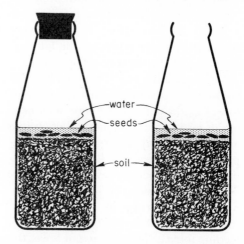

water

seeds

soil

Fig. 14-3 Seed germination with and without air.

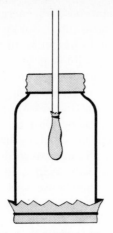

Fig. 14-4 Simple breathing model.

Half fill a pan with water and fill a jug with water. Hold your hand over the jug mouth and invert it in the pan (Fig. 14-6). Insert rubber tubing. Have a child

bands to one end of the feeding tube. Insert tube into stopper and stopper into top of chimney. If a one-hole rubber stopper is not available, make one from a Thermos cork. The tubing will slip into the stopper hole more easily if wet. The rubber sheeting stretched across the base of the chimney simulates your diaphragm in breathing.

To illustrate inhaling, pull on the rubber sheeting (diaphragm) (Fig. 14-4). The balloon, like lungs, will inflate as air is sucked in due to differential in air pressure. When you release the diaphragm or push it up a little, the balloon collapses.

With a two-hole stopper inserted into a lamp chimney (Fig. 14-5 A), your model may better represent the bilateral character of our breathing apparatus.

A more lifelike model may be made if equipment is available. Remove the bottom of a cider jug with hot wire (see Chapter 28 for the hot-wire method of cutting glass). The Y-tube represents the windpipe, the balloons the lungs, the open-bottom jar the thoracic cavity (Fig. 14-5B). Air pressure inside the jar (chest) is reduced by lowering the rubber bottom (diaphragm). Close the tube (windpipe) leading into the jar and raise or lower the diaphragm.

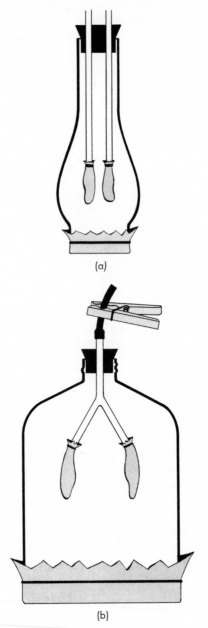

(a)

(b)

Fig. 14-5 (a) Two-lung breathing model; (b) large two-lung breathing model.

take a deep breath and see how much water he can blow out of the jug. Mark with wax crayon or elastic (or measure by the amount of water needed to refill the jug). Dip the tube in rubbing alcohol to sterilize (check with school nurse), rinse thoroughly in water, and let another student measure his lung capacity by water displacement. The children may soon realize that the biggest child in the room does not necessarily have the largest lung capacity. Repeat after some strenuous exercise. Let children discover how exercise affects breathing.

Older children can estimate and then measure the amount of air inhaled per hour.

1. Count number of normal exhalations necessary to empty a gallon jug of water.

2. Count number of exhalations per minute in normal breathing (18–20 per minute). This number divided by the number of exhalations required to empty the jug equals the approximate number of gallons per minute. This number times 60 equals the number of gallons of air breathed per hour.

WHAT HAPPENS WHEN WE BREATHE?

Just as in the lamp chimney or cider jug model, your diaphragm moves up and down when you breathe. However, because your chest cavity is flexible, the size of the cavity increases. Let children check this by tape measurements around the upper chest as they inhale and exhale.

Let children use a watch with a second hand to count the number of times they breathe in and out in 1 minute. Multiply by 60 for the hourly rate of respiration. Let children see if there are individual and sex differences in breathing rates.

Put your hands on your ribs to check lung space changes in breathing. Press your hands *hard* against your diaphragm and try to inhale—impossible. What happens when we breathe?

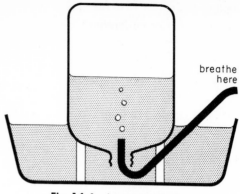

breathe here

Fig. 14-6 Lung capacity test.

As in the lung tester, fill a dish or pan half full of water. Fill a quart jar full, cover its mouth with something to keep water in (e.g., a small piece of glass, invert into the dish, and remove top. Now insert rubber tubing and blow water out of jar. Upon questioning, the children should be able to state that the "empty" jar is full of exhaled air.

Re-cover the jar under water, remove, and set upright in plain view. Twist pipe cleaner around a small candle. Uncover the jar just enough to lower the lighted candle into it. The candle goes out quickly. Secure a similar jar and lower a lighted candle into it. This time the candle should stay lit. The children should be able to deduce that the difference in air determines the outcome of each test. Some may be able to tell you the jar full of exhaled air lacks O_2 but has more CO_2, which smothers fire. The second jar is a "control," an experiment that duplicates all aspects of the experiment to which it is being compared except one—in this case the variation in the presence or nonpresence of exhaled air in a jar. (See Fig. 12-4.)

AIR PRESSURE

Why does air move into our lungs simply by a slight lowering of the diaphragm? The answer is that air is every-

Table 14–1
Air pressure on our bodies*

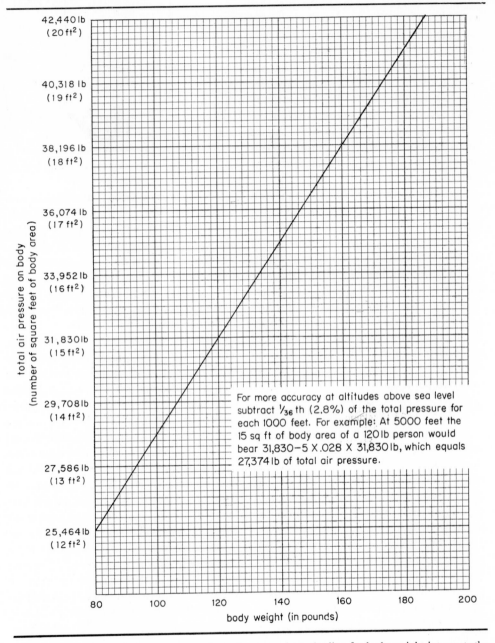

For more accuracy at altitudes above sea level subtract $\frac{1}{36}$ th (2.8%) of the total pressure for each 1000 feet. For example: At 5000 feet the 15 sq ft of body area of a 120 lb person would bear 31,830–5 X .028 X 31,830 lb, which equals 27,374 lb of total air pressure.

*To calculate the total air pressure on the body, note where the line for body weight intersects the diagonal. Multiply the nearest number of square feet of total area by 144 to yield the approximate number of square inches of body area. Multiply again by 14.7 or 15 to yield the approximate number of pounds of pressure.

where, about 15 pounds of it pressing on every square inch of our bodies. We don't notice the pressure because it is exerted equally on the inside and outside of the body. Our bodies don't collapse from the weight of air because there are many air spaces within our bodies. For example, beef or chicken lungs from the butcher shop will float in water because of air trapped in tiny lung *alveoli* (air sacs).

To lead children to understand the concept of air pressure, offer graphic illustrations of a square inch and of 15 pounds. For example, paste a square inch of colored paper in the middle of a large white sheet of paper. Let children estimate a 15-pound weight, say of books. Then let them check on household scales.

Carry the analogy further by letting children figure the amount of air pressure on an outstretched hand (about 200 pounds on the hand of an average sized, middle-grade child). Pressure is equal in all directions—up, down, and sideways—and is balanced by pressure within the hand. The child is accustomed to this weight of air, but if he holds a pound weight in his hand, he feels the additional weight at once since it is not balanced by pressure within the hand and so must be sustained by an increase in muscular tension and the resistance of tissue.

Table 14-1 enables the children to calculate the approximate total air pressure on their bodies. For further discussion of air pressure, see Chapter 7 and Chapter 9.

OUR RESPIRATORY SYSTEM

Respiration is the name for the exchange of oxygen and CO_2 by the blood cells. Notice how the heart and lungs lie close together in the chest cavity behind the flexible yet tough protection of the ribs. This protected closeness allows for quick exchange of blood between heart and lungs at minimum cost in energy. In the lungs carbon dioxide diffuses out of the blood into the tiny lung chambers called alveoli while oxygen moves in the opposite direction to be picked up by the blood.

The heart is really a double pump. Into the left side is pumped blood oxygenated by the lungs. The red oxygenated blood is sent throughout the body. Every bit of tissue must have oxygen to live. The maroon venous blood returns to the right chamber of the heart which pumps it into the lungs for aeration. Some children may have seen aeration of water at a municipal water purification plant. Thus the blood might be likened to a conveyor belt, carrying life-giving oxygen to all tissues and collecting waste, the CO_2, which is always an end product of burning. In the slow burning inside of us, some oxygen we breathe is combined with carbon from our food to form CO_2.

Observations show our rate of breathing to be 18–20 times a minute or around 1000 times an hour. Yet we are as casual about the condition of the air we breathe as our forefathers were about the purity of their water supply. Anyone who has watched particles floating in a beam of light is aware of some of the normally invisible burden of air. We should be concerned much less about the nonliving soot and dust particles than about the living particles—microbes and their spores. Bacterial counts differ greatly in different environments. An average inhalation of 1/3 cubic foot of air per minute in the high mountains would take in only one microbe about every 20 minutes. In a crowded theatre an average man would inhale about 60,000 microbes per breath. Samplings have shown an average of 50 million microorganisms (not all harmful) in a gram of dust from city streets. In the same amount of indoor dust, samplings yielded about 4 million bacteria.

The structure of the nasal passages fortunately provides a three-way air condi-

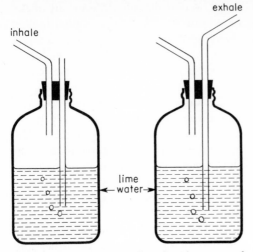

Fig. 14-7 Comparing carbon dioxide content of inhaled and exhaled air.

Let children blow through straws into ⅓ tumbler of limewater. How soon will they notice a cloudy precipitate forming? This is calcium carbonate, the same chemical compound which makes up most of the body skeleton. Place a shallow glass saucer of limewater in a paper sack. Pucker the sack around your mouth and breathe into the sack 15 times. Examine the limewater. Set up a control by placing another dish of limewater in another sack. Pin the sack closed for 10 minutes. Compare the amounts of precipitate in the dishes. Let children open a bottle of soda pop in a bag containing a dish of limewater.

tioning system. The nose, the chief filtering agent, does preliminary screening by means of fine inner hairs. Furthermore, the nose is divided by bony shelves into a labyrinth of passages. These are lined with tissue full of glands constantly secreting a mucus, which catches particles passing the first screens. Some special cells in the nasal membranes have fine whip-like projections called cilia on their free surface. The continuous lashing of these cilia keep in motion the fluid secretion covering the cell. All of this should impress upon children the reasons for breathing through one's nose. The trachea or windpipe is also covered with cilia and mucus for entrapping any particles which get past the nasal hairs and the sticky nasal passages. The whole nose and windpipe structure also provides for warming and moistening air.

WHAT WE PUT BACK INTO THE AIR

Stir a handful of builder's slaked lime into a gallon of water. Allow to settle, siphon or pour off 1–2 quarts clear liquid, and discard the remaining liquid. The clear liquid is limewater, used in chemical tests for CO_2.

THE AMOUNT OF OXYGEN IN THE AIR

Let children set a candle in the middle of a glass saucer or dish half full of water. Invert a jar over the candle. Mark water level inside the jar. Remove the jar long enough to light the candle. Observe water rising in the jar. Mark the new level when the candle goes out. Let children repeat and observe several times. The candle goes out every time after about the same time interval, during which about the same amount of water is pulled up into the jar to occupy a little less than one fifth of the jar's volume. All of the O_2 will not have been used, but enough so that the candle can no longer burn. Ordinary materials won't burn with less than 15 per cent oxygen in the air.

The candle going out illustrates the purpose for taking a lighted candle into a cave or mine. If the flame goes out (except from a gust of air), there is not enough oxygen for breathing. Often before descending into an old well or mine shaft, men will test the air by lowering lighted candles.

For demonstrations on oxidation in our bodies (slow burning), see Chapter 9 and Chapter 13.

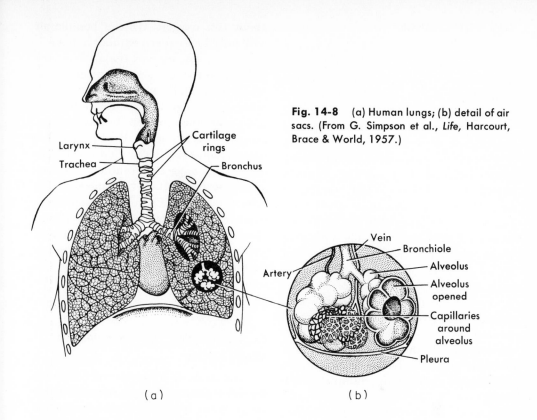

Fig. 14-8 (a) Human lungs; (b) detail of air sacs. (From G. Simpson et al., *Life*, Harcourt, Brace & World, 1957.)

Larynx

Trachea

Cartilage rings

Bronchus

Vein

Bronchiole

Alveolus

Alveolus opened

Capillaries around alveolus

Pleura

Artery

(a)

(b)

BREATHING EXHALED AIR

Let children breathe in and out several times through a rubber tube at least ¼″ in diameter into a quart or half-gallon milk bottle. What sensation do they note from breathing exhaled air? It usually speeds up the breathing rate. Test air in this bottle with a glowing match splint or candle. Since the flame is extinguished, children will deduce breathing has removed some oxygen from air.

COMPARING EXHALED AND INHALED AIR

Secure a Y-tube from a high school science teacher. Connect the two ends of the Y to lengths of rubber tubing. Through two-hole stoppers insert one long and one short piece of glass or plastic tubing. Insert the stoppers into two flasks or into ordinary bottles. In each bottle pour some limewater. Squeezing one rubber tube and then the other, inhale through one bottle and exhale through the other. When the breath bubbles through the limewater, cloudiness results, showing the presence of carbon dioxide. The liquid in the bottle through which the air bubbled while being inhaled remains clear. If you lack a Y-tube, use separate tubes, holding your breath as you move back and forth. (See Fig. 14-7.)

Children should see from this that inhaled air contains little or no carbon dioxide, while exhaled air has a considerable amount, that is, more than we breathe in. You may at this time recall that plants give off oxygen and use carbon dioxide during photosynthesis, while animals do just the opposite.

GAS INTERCHANGE

If these demonstrations have helped children understand how we inhale O_2 and exhale CO_2, they should be ready to understand the continual exchange of these gases in the lungs. This exchange is made possible by the related structures of the respiratory and circulatory systems. The bronchial tubes continue to branch and redivide, leading into fine channels, *bronchioles,* less than 1/100″ in diameter (Fig. 14-8). These minute air channels permeating the lungs open into little clusters of hemispherical bags. These *alveoli* or air sacs are thin-walled structures bounded by an extremely thin layer of flattened cells. Pressed close against this cell membrane is a tangled mass of thin-walled capillary blood vessels. The interchange of oxygen from fresh inhaled air and CO_2 carried back to the lungs as waste from combustion, takes place here by a process of diffusion through the damp thin cell walls.

SMOG

Many thousands of times a day we breathe air which is loaded with foreign bodies, dust, soot, bacteria, and spores.

You can show as follows that smog may be produced by condensation of moisture in the air on dust particles. Blow as much air as possible into a gallon jug. Note that there is little or no vapor in the jar as you let the air escape.

Invert the jug and thrust a lighted match into the mouth of the jug. Again blow into the jar and release the air quickly. A thick smog should show.

OXYGEN CONTENT

The ocean of air which surrounds our planet is about 500 miles deep. Half of all air is below 18,000′. About 21% of a cubic foot of air is oxygen. The air we exhale is about 16% oxygen. We can breathe air with only 17% oxygen without noticing a difference. The air we exhale mixes very quickly and soon regains its normal 21% oxygen content. Even indoors enough fresh air seeps through the cracks around windows and doors to keep the oxygen percentage close to normal. Even poorly ventilated rooms rarely show a drop of more than ½% in oxygen percentage. The constant absorption of CO_2 by plants keeps the concentration of CO_2 in the atmosphere to 3 to 4 hundredths of 1%. There is evidence that the CO_2 percentage has been very gradually rising since 1800. It is the amount of water vapor in indoor or outdoor air that makes us conscious of poor ventilation.

ROOM TEMPERATURE AND PROPER VENTILATION

Good air for breathing should be neither too warm nor too cold with respect to what we are doing. Experiments suggest the following:

50–59°	doing heavy shop work
54–59°	asleep in bed
60°	playing in the gym
61–64°	doing light shop work
61–64°	"spectator sports"—indoors
68°	resting or studying at home
68–72°	taking a bath

Note particularly that a bedroom at night need not be as cold as often thought. Good air for breathing also contains moisture. A relative humidity of 50–60% is best for health.

See Table 7-1 (Chapter 7) in order to measure the relative humidity of your classroom. Repeat outdoors. On what kind of days do you notice greater difference?

The air near the nose and next to the body is the air which affects health. Circulating air keeps it from forming a layer which contains too little oxygen or too much CO_2. More important, moving air prevents too high a temperature or too much moisture close to the body. The body maintains a constant temperature by constant evaporation through the skin. If the surrounding air is too moist or too hot, the body is not able to maintain its temperature regulatory function. Study the sources of heat and air motion in the classroom. Make a smoke box (see Chapter 18) to illustrate convection currents. Such observations and experiments should soon lead children to conclude that the usual method of ventilating a room by opening a window at the bottom only can be useless and ineffective in a completely closed off room.

AIR TRAVEL AND ALTITUDE SICKNESS

Anyone who normally lives near sea level and travels into the mountains may notice slight symptoms related to lower air pressure and less oxygen content. Because of lower pressure there are fewer oxygen molecules per cubic inch of air. At 18,000' there are only half as many as at sea level. The following table tells the tale.

altitude	blood hemoglobin level of oxygen
sea level	96% capacity
10,000'	81% capacity
15,000'	71% capacity
25,000'	58% capacity

A candle flame which burns lower and lower as we ascend goes out at 25,000'. Humans "black out" at this point unless they are wearing oxygen masks or are flying in pressurized cabins (some black out at lower altitudes). At 12,000' breathing is two times faster than at sea level. At 12–15,000' there is an impairment of vision, hearing, capacity for movement, ability to think clearly. At 63,000' air pressure is so slight that the body fluids of mammals, if unprotected, would vaporize ("boil"). The sudden distention would cause instant death. These are some of the problems in space travel that are being solved by research into space medicine and physiology.

CAPSULE LESSONS

14-1 Ask Red Cross representatives, firemen, policemen, or lifeguards to demonstrate new methods of artificial respiration.

14-2 Let children demonstrate principle of diver's helmet by pumping or blowing air into a funnel inverted on the bottom of an aquarium or glass pickle jar. (For other illustrations of the use of air pressure underwater, see Chapter 9.

14-3 Children may wish to make an exhibit of underwater breathing apparatus used by skin divers.

14-4 There may be one youngster in the group who would wish to plan and collect articles and pictures on problems of breathing in high-altitude flying or space travel. An airline may be willing to lend an oxygen mask such as those kept on hand in commercial jet planes.

14-5 Children whose parents are connected with the air-conditioning industry may wish to bring in illustrative materials and set up experiments on the principles of air conditioning.

BIBLIOGRAPHY

Turner, E. T., and C. L. Fenton, *Inside You and Me,* Day, 1961. Middle. A child's introduction to the human body.

Wells, H. G., *The Science of Life,* Doubleday Doran, 1934. Upper. Covers all aspects of biology. Easy reading.

Sound

WHAT CAUSES SOUND?

Sound is produced by vibrating objects. There are many things children can do to understand that vibrations cause sound.

Remove the cover from a cigar or chalk box and put a rubber band around the box. Pluck the rubber band. Notice how it moves back and forth, or vibrates, rapidly. These rapid vibrations of the rubber band produce the twanging sound.

Have the children put a thumb and forefinger to the larynx and say "ah," hum, or sing. They will feel the vibrations of their vocal chords, which are producing the sounds.

Many familiar objects can be used to show that vibrating bodies produce sound. Place a blade of grass (or a thin strip of plastic material of the same thickness) between your thumbs. Hold the grass securely with the balls of your hand and the upper part of your thumbs. Now place your lips at the base of the gap between your thumbs and blow. With a little practice a shrill sound will result.

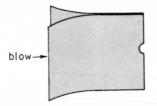

blow→

Fig. 15-1 *Making paper vibrate rapidly enough to produce sound.*

Fold a strip of paper 2″ × 5″ in half. Tear a small semicircle from the center of the fold. Place the folded paper between your forefinger and middle finger. Make sure your fingers do not cover the semicircle. Now insert your lips between the open ends of the paper as close to your fingers as possible and blow hard. The vibrating paper will squeal (Fig. 15-1). Make a small hole in one end of a 12″ wooden ruler or a thin piece of wood the same size. Tie a piece of strong string to the hole and swing the ruler in a circle. The harder you swing, the more the ruler will vibrate, and the louder will be the groan produced by the ruler.

Make a tom-tom out of a large tin can. Stretch thick rubber from a heavy toy balloon or old inner tube across the mouth of the can. A rubber band or tightly tied string will hold the rubber sheet in place. Make a rubber hammer by inserting the sharpened end of a stick or pencil into a rubber stopper or a small solid rubber ball. Now pound the tom-tom and feel the vibrations. Strike the tom-tom and drop a cork or small pieces of cork on the rubber head. Note how the cork bounces up and down as the rubber vibrates.

Objects that produce sound vibrate rapidly

When an object produces sound, it is usually vibrating so rapidly that either you cannot see the vibrations or you can see only a faint blur. Borrow a tuning fork from a music teacher, a high school science teacher, or a piano tuner. Strike the tuning fork sharply against your knee-cap or the rubber heel of your shoe. You will hear the sound produced, but the motion of the prongs of the tuning fork will at most be a blur.

You can show the children that a tuning fork does make vibrations by first striking it, then quickly dipping the prongs into a full glass of water. The vibrations of the prongs will cause the water to spray. Repeat this procedure, this time touching the prongs to a sheet of paper held in your hand. The paper will rattle.

If a tuning fork is not available, use a dinner fork. However, strike the fork as hard as possible and perform the experiment as quickly as possible. The tines of the fork do not vibrate as easily or as long as those of the tuning fork. Instead of striking the dinner fork, you might try plucking two of the tines, then bringing the tines quickly to your ear.

Have the children repeat the experiment at school or at home. At the same time they can pluck the tines of the dinner fork and listen to the musical tone produced. Ask them to note what happens to the sound when they touch the vibrating tines.

There is a limit to the sounds we can hear. This depends upon the number of vibrations that are produced. An object must vibrate at least 16 times a second to produce audible sounds. However, if the object vibrates more than 20,000 times a second, most people cannot hear the sounds produced. Sounds produced beyond the range of our hearing are called ultrasonic.

HOW DOES SOUND TRAVEL?

Vibrating objects produce sound *waves,* each vibration producing *one sound wave.* These sound waves move away from the vibrating body just as ripples or water waves spread out from the spot where a stone has been thrown into the water. However, sound waves differ from water waves because sound waves travel in all directions from the point where the sound begins; also sound waves cannot be seen.

Travels in waves

Refresh the children's memory of water waves by dipping a finger in and out of water in a wash tub or bath tub. Waves are produced which spread out rapidly in increasing circles.

You may want to investigate sound waves. Obtain a new or used hacksaw blade. (Borrow or buy one from your hardware store.) Attach a small firm piece of broom straw to the free end of the blade, using liquid cement or Scotch tape. Smoke a small sheet of glass by holding a candle flame against the underside of the glass and moving the flame around slowly. Attach the hacksaw blade to a block of wood with scotch or cloth tape. Place the hacksaw blade on the block so that the broom straw just touches the layer of soot on the glass (Fig. 15-2). Set the hacksaw vibrating. As it vibrates, pull the smoked glass under the broom straw. A wavy track of the sound waves will be left under the soot. Make the hacksaw blade vibrate

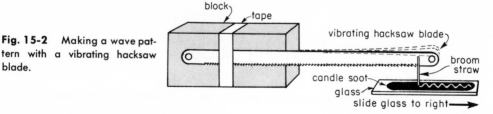

Fig. 15-2 Making a wave pattern with a vibrating hacksaw blade.

block tape vibrating hacksaw blade broom straw candle soot glass slide glass to right ⟶

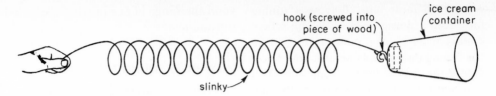

ice cream container

slinky

Fig. 15-3 A Slinky illustrates how sound travels.

harder, and the waves produced will be larger. If you have a tuning fork, perform the same experiment by attaching the broom straw to one tip of the tuning fork. If you vary the length of the vibrating part of a hacksaw blade or use tuning forks of different frequencies, you will get waves of different sizes.

Compression and rarefaction of waves

One way of helping the children understand how sound travels is to show how waves move in a coiled spring. Borrow a Slinky from one of your pupils or buy it at a toy store (see Fig. 15-3). Any coiled spring will also do, such as the spring from the roller of a window shade. Screw a cup hook into the top of your doorway. Fasten one end of the spring to the cup hook. To every fifth coil attach a piece of paper, using scotch tape. Attach a block of wood to the bottom of the spring to give the spring some tension. Now press together several coils of the spring near the bottom end, then quickly let the coils go. The coils first compress then expand. In so doing,

these coils cause the neighboring coils to compress and then expand. Thus, the impulse travels from coil to coil with a back-and-forth motion, that is, by a series of alternate compressions and rarefactions.

Sound waves travel in much the same way. When an object vibrates, it moves back and forth rapidly. This movement presses the particles or molecules of the gases in the air closer together—compression. The molecules now spring back, then spread farther apart—rarefaction. When they do this, they push against their neighboring molecules in the air and press them closer together. These, in turn, spring back and then spread farther apart, pushing against other molecules. Thus, sound waves are produced. These waves have been transmitted by the molecules in the air; yet the molecules themselves have traveled back and forth only a very short distance.

Let two children spread the Slinky across the room. Now have one child strike the coil of the Slinky with a pencil at

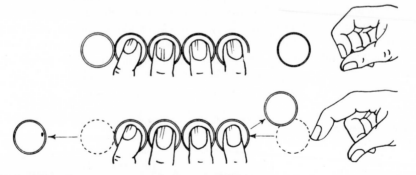

Fig. 15-4 Compressions can be transmitted. (From *General Science Handbook, Part II*, New York State Education Department, 1952.)

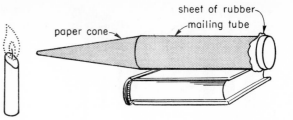

Fig. 15-5 Sound waves help put out a flame.

a point just beyond the fingers holding the coil. Note how the impulse travels with a back-and-forth motion along the coil, in a series of compressions and rarefactions.

With the four fingers of your left hand, press down firmly on four checkers placed side by side. Place a fifth checker to the left of the four checkers. Make sure all five checkers are touching. Now place a sixth checker a few inches to the right of the five checkers. With the right hand snap the free checker against the end of the row (Fig. 15-4). The end checker on the left quickly moves away. This happens because the checker first struck was compressed slightly. This compression was passed on or transmitted to the other checkers until it reached the last checker, which was free to move. Help the children understand that sound vibrations travel through air in much the same way.

Travels in all directions

Obtain a mailing tube about 2′ long. Stretch tightly over one end of the tube a sheet of thin rubber from a toy balloon. Fasten the sheet of rubber to the tube with a rubber band or tightly tied string. Make a paper cone with an opening of about ¼″ in diameter at the smaller end of the cone. Fasten the cone to the other end of the tube with Scotch tape (Fig. 15-5). Support the tube on a book and place the small end of the cone as close to a candle flame as possible without setting fire to the paper. Now clap your hands sharply together close to the rubber sheet. The candle flame will flicker and flutter. Whistle with your mouth close to the

rubber sheet, and the candle will flicker again. Sound waves produced by the clap of the hands or whistle cause the rubber sheet to vibrate. This, in turn, causes the molecules of air in the tube to vibrate. This vibration is passed on until it reaches the flame and then pushes the flame about.

Arrange four rows of dominoes in the shape of a cross. Leave a space in the center of the cross slightly smaller than the diameter of a rubber ball. Now push a rubber ball into the center of the cross, causing the four nearest dominoes to tip over (Fig. 15-6). Each domino, in falling, will cause its neighbor to tip over. These, in turn, will strike their neighbors. This toppling over travels down all four lines until the last domino falls over. If there were enough dominoes to make rows the length of the room, this disturbance would travel all that distance. Sound waves travel in all directions also, the molecules in the air transmitting the impulses to their neighboring molecules.

WHAT MATERIALS CARRY SOUND WAVES?

You have already shown that air can carry sound waves. One further example would be to take a long garden hose, open at both ends, and have two children speak to each other very much as through a telephone. Let one child speak while the other child listens.

Liquids transmit sound waves

Liquids also carry sound. The drop of

Fig. 15-6 Sound waves travel in all directions.

the water faucet in the bath tub can be heard very clearly when the ears are submerged in the water. Have a child strike two rocks in air while another child notes the sound produced. Then fill a large battery jar with water. Let the child with the two rocks strike them again, but this time under the water in the battery jar. At the same time have the other child put his ear against the side of the jar and listen. The sound will travel through the water and can be heard, and the sound will be louder than it was in air. Water carries sound better than air.

Solids transmit sound waves

Solids also carry sound waves. Have a child place his ear against one edge of a table top while another child scratches the opposite edge lightly. Place the base of a vibrating tuning fork at one end of a yardstick; the vibrations will be audible to a child whose ear is placed at the other end of the yardstick.

A tin-can telephone is very popular with the children. Two juice cans, each with one end removed, are used. Punch a hole through the bottom of each can. Run a string at least 25′ long from the bottom of one can to the bottom of the other can. The string can be prevented from slipping out the bottom of each can by tying large knots at each end of the string inside the can. Or you can tie each end of the string to a nail or button which will not slip through the punctured holes in each can. Now wax the string with paraffin or can-

dle wax. The children using the phone must go far enough apart to stretch the string taut. The cans are used like telephones, with one child talking and one child listening. If thin wire is used instead of string, the children will hear even more clearly since metals carry sound better than string does. Let children discover that the sound will be muffled unless they hold the can by its rim.

Beautiful sounds are heard by taking a piece of string 3–4′ long and tying a tablespoon at the mid-point of the string. The ends of the string are looped once or twice around the forefingers, and then a forefinger is placed in each ear. Now make the spoon swing so that it strikes the edge of the table. The sounds produced are like chimes. This can be repeated with different spoons and forks and with pairs of spoons or forks. Using fine wire instead of string will improve the quality of the sound produced.

Metals transmit sound waves best

Sound travels through metals even better than it does through string, wood, or water. Have one child hold a long curtain rod against his ear. Place a loud-ticking wrist watch or an alarm clock against the other end. The base of a vibrating tuning fork may be substituted for the watch.

Have the children make up a code. Then let one child go to another classroom and send a message by tapping a radiator. If the radiator is hot, the child who is listening can press a metal rod against the radiator and put his ear to the rod instead. Messages can be sent back and forth this way. If pupils place their ears against their desk tops and the teacher taps on her desk gently with a pencil, the sound will be carried from the desk through the floor to the children.

Strike the prongs of a tuning fork or dinner fork; then touch the handle of the fork against the bone just behind your ear.

You will hear a distinct sound. Repeat the procedure touching other bones of your head. The loudness of the sound you hear will depend upon the amount of flesh between the handle of the fork and the bone. The more flesh there is, the greater the amount of insulation and the softer the sound. Now set the prongs of the fork vibrating and place the handle firmly between your teeth. The sound will be most distinct.

Sound waves, then, must have a solid, liquid, or gaseous medium by which they can travel. The loud ticking of an alarm clock, heard even when placed under a large glass bell jar, would soon fade out if the air were pumped out of the jar.

SYMPATHETIC VIBRATIONS

Obtain two tuning forks that have the same frequency of vibration or pitch. You can borrow them from your music teacher or high school physics teacher. Secure two cigar boxes. Knock out one end of each box. In the center of each box make a hole slightly smaller than a one-hole stopper or plug. Push the handle of a tuning fork into each stopper. Then insert the stoppers into the holes of the cigar boxes so that the tuning forks are firmly erect. Place the boxes end to end, with open ends facing each other, and adjust the position of the tuning forks so that they are in direct line with each other (Fig. 15-7). Strike one tuning fork with a rubber hammer made by inserting a sharpened stick or pencil into a rubber stopper. After a few seconds stop the fork from vibrating by touching it with your hand. You will now hear the second fork vibrating even though it was not struck.

When the first fork was made to vibrate, it caused the molecules of air around it to vibrate. Sound waves were produced with a definite frequency of vibration. But the second fork is also capable of producing

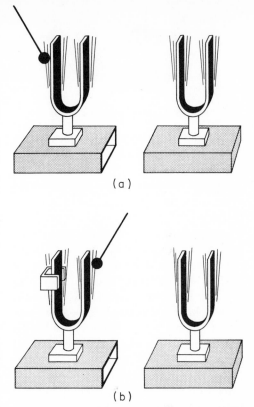

Fig. 15-7 Producing sympathetic vibrations: (a) the forks vibrate in complete resonance, producing no beats; (b) one fork is a little out of phase, and beats are heard. (From A. Joseph et al., *A Sourcebook for the Physical Sciences*, Harcourt, Brace & World, 1961.)

the same frequency of vibration as the first fork. Thus, the molecules of air pushed against the prongs of the second tuning fork with a frequency that corresponded to its natural frequency of vibration. This caused the second fork to vibrate in unison with the sounding body and thereby produce sound as well.

Have the children recall how they were able to push their friends higher on a swing just by timing their push to coincide with the natural vibration rate of the swing. Note that the vibrations of the first tuning fork coincided exactly with the natural vibrations of the second tuning

Fig. 15-8 Making sounds louder.

fork. Once you started the first fork vibrating, the vibrations helped the second fork to vibrate.

Obtain two milk bottles or soda bottles of the same size. Have a child blow across the mouth of the bottle until he produces a strong, clear note. At the same time let him hold the mouth of the other bottle close to his ear. Make sure the bottle is not so close as to obstruct the opening. Whenever the child blows a note with the bottle, he will hear a similar, but weaker, note in the second bottle. Because the bottles are the same size and have the same air columns, they will vibrate at the same frequency. Consequently a noise produced by one bottle will set up sympathetic vibrations in the second bottle.

This explains why often, when music is played on the piano, radio, or television, whenever a certain note is sounded, a vase or some other object in the room begins to vibrate. The natural frequency of vibration of the vase is exactly the same as the frequency of vibration of the musical tone.

MAKING SOUNDS LOUDER

Have a child strike a tuning fork and hold it up in the air for the rest of the class to hear. Now let the child strike the tuning fork again, but this time have the child put the base of the tuning fork to a table top or to the chalk board. This sound is much louder because the tuning fork makes the table top or chalk board vibrate also. This larger vibrating surface or area sets a greater amount of air vibrating, so

that the sound is greater as well. The table top or chalk board thus acts as a sounding board or *amplifier*.

Obtain a quart ice-cream container, a brass cup hook, and a small flat piece of wood or mortarboard. Screw the cup hook into the sealed end of the container and through the piece of wood as well (see Fig. 15-3). This prevents the cup hook from pulling out. Now repeat the experiment with the Slinky (above), but this time attach the cup hook of the container to one end of the Slinky. When the wire is tapped with a pencil, a loud whine comes from the container. This happens because the end of the container sets a large amount of air vibrating, and the sound is thereby amplified.

Take a needle or rounded toothpick and put the point into the groove of a revolving phonograph record. The sound will be quite faint. Then put the needle through one end of a 3″ × 5″ card (Fig. 15-8), and repeat the procedure. The sound will be louder because the card also vibrates, causing a much larger volume of air to vibrate. Make a cone out of heavy wrapping paper, fold the small end, and force the needle through the entire thickness of the paper (Fig. 15-9). Put the needle in the groove of the revolving record. The sound will be heard all over the room.

STOPPING SOUND

When sound waves hit solid objects such as a wall, ceiling, or cliff, they bounce back. These rebounding sound waves are

Fig. 15-9 A phonograph megaphone. (From *UNESCO Source Book for Science Teachers*, UNESCO, 1956.)

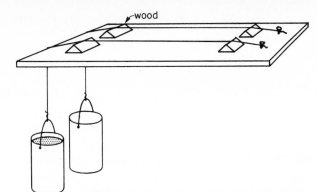

Fig. 15-10 A sonometer shows how the pitch of vibrating strings can be changed.

called *echoes*. To stop unwanted echoes in a large room or auditorium, sound-absorbing material is hung on the walls and window frames. Carpets also help. When the auditorium is filled with people, the clothing and bodies of the persons will also absorb some of the sound waves.

To show how sound waves can be absorbed, place an alarm clock in a cardboard box with the open side facing a child who is listening. Have the child walk away from the box in a straight line until the ticking is barely audible. Note the distance. Now fill the space in back of the alarm clock with cotton and have the child move back to the box until the ticking is audible again. Note the change in distance.

HOW WE MAKE MUSIC

The number of sound waves produced per second by a vibrating body determines the pitch of the musical sound produced. Thus, the more vibrations per second, the higher the musical tone produced. The fewer vibrations per second, the lower the musical tone. The number of vibrations produced per second is called the frequency, and the "highness" and "lowness" of a musical sound is called the pitch.

Rub your fingernail lightly across the cover of a cloth book. Note the sound produced as your fingernail vibrates when moving across the threads of the book. Now rub your fingernail across the cover several times, moving a little more quickly each time. Because you increased the number of vibrations per second, you increased the pitch. That is, you made the sound higher and higher. If you move your fingernail more slowly, you decrease the number of vibrations per second and the sound becomes lower. You can also get the same effects by rubbing your fingernail across the teeth of a comb.

How string instruments produce tones

Make a two-string guitar (sonometer). Obtain a board or piece of plywood about 3' long, 6" wide, and at least ¾" thick. Drive a nail into each side of one end of the board. Loop a thin steel wire about 4' long firmly around one nail and loop a similar length of thicker wire around the other nail. Let both wires extend across the board to the handle of a pail half full of water hanging at the other end of the board (Fig. 15-10). Instead of water, one or two bricks may be added to the pail. Place a spring-type clothespin or small triangular block of wood under each wire near the nail. Put another clothespin or block of wood under each wire two thirds of the way across the board.

Pluck each section of wire between the clothespins and note the musical sounds produced. The thinner (lighter weight) the wire, the higher the musical note. Now

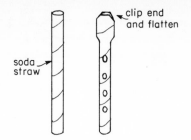

Fig. 15-11 A soda straw saxophone.

move each clothespin placed two thirds of the way across the board closer to the clothespin near the nail. The shorter the section of vibrating string, the higher the musical note will be. Let the children produce the musical scale this way.

Return the clothespins to their original positions. Now add more water or bricks to the pail. This will make the strings tighter. Pluck the strings each time you add more water or bricks. The greater the pull on the string, the higher the musical note produced.

Another way of showing the effect of thickness and tension would be to place two or more rubber bands having the same length but different thicknesses around an open cigar or chalk box. The thicker (heavier) rubber bands will produce lower tones. Increasing the tension on each rubber band by stretching it will make the musical tones higher.

String instruments such as the violin and harp depend upon these properties of vibrating strings to produce their musical sounds. How would the children classify the piano? The sound is produced by vibrating strings (characteristic of string instruments) while the emitter of sound waves is hit with a hammer (characteristic of percussion instruments). A visit to the school piano helps show these properties clearly. How would you classify the organ and harpsichord?

Have the children make lyres or harps by stretching rubber bands of different thicknesses across open cigar boxes with lids removed. If necessary, use tacks to adjust the tension on the bands and thereby produce the desired musical tones.

How wind instruments produce tones

Wind instruments such as the flute, trombone, French horn depend upon vibrating columns of air for their musical tones. Take a piece of glass or metal tube about 12″ long and ½″ in diameter. Fill a bottle nearly full of water and insert the tube. Blow across the top of the tube while you move the bottle of water up and down. As you change the length of the column of air in the tube, different musical notes will be produced. Help the children understand that the shorter the air column, the higher the note produced.

The effect which the length of air column has on the "highness" or "lowness" of the musical tone can be shown in many ways. Blowing across the tops of different size bottles all having the same size neck is one way. With a little practice the children can place different amounts of water in eight tall, thin drinking glasses (same size) and reproduce the musical scale. A medicine dropper will help adjust the exact amount of water necessary for each note. Tapping the glasses with a pencil or ruler will set the different lengths of air columns vibrating. This musical effect can also be produced by using bottles or test tubes of the same size.

A most popular musical toy is the soda straw saxophone. Flatten one end of a soda straw about ½ inch. The plain white soda straw works best. Then cut both corners of this flat end. Place the flattened end (the reeds) into your mouth, close your lips around the straw, and blow very hard. If you have trouble producing the sound, moisten the flattened end somewhat. If it becomes so moist that it sticks together, start over. Once the sound is produced, shorten the straw quickly with a pair of scissors, cutting off about an inch at each time. The ever-shorter vibrating air columns will produce a musical scale, while the flattened end acts as a reed to set the air column vibrating (Fig. 15-11).

If you like, you may cut small holes in the straw about 1″ apart. Cover the holes with your fingers, blow into the straw to produce a musical note, and then release various fingers. The nearest open hole determines the length of the vibrating air column and, consequently, the musical tone produced (Fig. 15-11).

✗ Make a tambourine by punching holes in the edge of a pie tin with a hammer and nails. Then sew or tie bells around the edge. You can also make chimes by hanging various lengths of metal tubing from strings. Use a rubber hammer made by inserting a sharpened stick or pencil into a rubber stopper or a small solid rubber ball.

Quaker Oats Box Drum

How we speak and sing

Hold one end of a rubber band between your teeth. Now stretch the rubber band and pluck both lengths of the band. The rubber band vibrates rapidly and a sound is produced. Now stretch the rubber band further. Note that the increase in tension of the band brings an increase in pitch of the sound.

Show the pupils a drawing of the larynx as seen from above (Fig. 15-12). Point out that the larynx makes sounds exactly the same way. Instead of the rubber band there are two flat cords called vocal cords. Tiny muscles on each side can stretch these cords. Air from the lungs causes these vocal cords to vibrate and produce sound. The tiny muscles control the amount of tension on the vocal

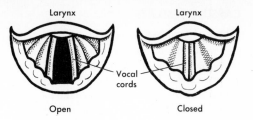

Fig. 15-12 The vocal cords of the larynx vibrate and produce sounds. (From R. Brinckerhoff et al., *The Physical World*, Harcourt, Brace & World, 1958.)

cords. This changes the highness and lowness, or pitch, of the sound which the vocal cords make.

Have the children press a thumb and forefinger against the larynx and sing a low note. Let them note the sound vibrations produced by the vocal cords. Now tell them to sing the musical scale and observe the different vibrations and the changes in tension. Make artificial vocal cords by stretching rubber pieces held by tape across the top of a tube. Blow air at the rubber "vocal cords." Point out that men have longer vocal cords than women. This is why their voices are lower than women's.

✳ Blow up a balloon. Now grasp each side of the balloon with the thumb and forefinger of each hand just below the balloon's opening. As the air escapes from the balloon, pull on each side of the balloon. The stretched rubber will vibrate and produce a sound. Point out that this is very much like the way the vocal cords operate in speaking and singing. Increase the pull on each side of the balloon. This increases the tension of the rubber membranes and the sound becomes higher. Decrease the tension and the sound becomes lower.

CAPSULE LESSONS

15-1 Try to obtain a model of the ear. If one isn't available, perhaps a student will make a large chart of the ear from a drawing of one in a science textbook. Study the different parts of the ear and their functions. Trace the path of a sound wave from the outer ear through the middle and inner parts to the brain.

15-2 Do the same for vocal cords. Show the position of the vocal cords during breathing and when sound is being produced.

15-3 How well can your children recognize noises? Prepare a list of things that make noises which the children should be able to recognize. Go to the back of the room so the children cannot see which noise producer you are using, and see how many sources the children can identify.

15-4 Have those children who are members of the school band or orchestra or who have musical instruments bring in their instruments. Show how the sounds are produced in each case. Develop the concept that sounds having the same number of vibrations per second also have the same pitch.

15-5 Start your own orchestra, using toy musical instruments such as the tin whistle, fife, ocarina, harmonica, xylophone, and triangle. Trace the source of sound in each case. Add to it such humming instruments as the kazoo and the paper and comb.

15-6 Does one of your students have a dog whistle? Show how this whistle differs from regular whistles, and develop an understanding that objects have a wide range in the number of times they vibrate per second.

15-7 Place a 6″ flexible plastic ruler on the table, with 2″ of the ruler extending beyond the table's edge. Hold the ruler firmly with one hand and start the extended portion vibrating with the other hand. Repeat, using extended lengths of 3″ and 4″. Develop the idea that the greater the frequency of vibration, the higher the pitch.

15-8 Mention each of the following sounds to the class. In each case have the pupils tell what did the vibrating: (a) a door slamming; (b) the sound of raindrops on the window; (c) the rustling of cloth; (d) a boy whistling; (e) a book falling on the table; (f) a boy scratching his arm; (g) the screech of automobile brakes; (h) the wind blowing. (*Note:* The wind blowing against telephone wires will make the wires hum.)

15-9 If you have a sink in your room, let children listen to the pitch change as you fill a bottle of water. Ask them to listen at home to the changes in pitch as water from the "hot" faucet begins to run warmer.

BIBLIOGRAPHY

Baer, Marian E., *Sound,* Holiday, 1952. Describes experiments showing the various properties of sound.

Brandwein, P., et al., *You and Science,* Harcourt, Brace & World, 1960. A junior high school survey of science, with many simple demonstrations suggested.

Brinckerhoff, R. F., et al., *Exploring Physics,* Harcourt, Brace & World, 1959. Principles of physics on the high school level.

———, *The Physical World,* Harcourt, Brace & World, 1958. A general survey of the physical sciences on the high school level.

Bruce, G., *Sound,* National Science Teachers Association, Publication Sales Section of N.E.A., 1951. A discussion of the principles of sound, accompanied by experiments.

Geralton, J., *The Story of Sound,* Harcourt, Brace & World, 1948. Information on sound at children's level.

Irving, Robert, *Sound and Ultrasonics,* Knopf, 1959. Describes the nature of sound, different kinds of sound, recording and transmitting sound, and sounds we cannot hear. Special section on high-frequency sounds.

Kettelkamp, Larry, *The Magic of Sound,* Morrow, 1956. Offers a variety of experiments on the nature of sound.

———, *Singing Strings,* Morrow, 1958. Discusses stringed instruments and gives clear instructions on how to make simplified versions of the harp, piano, violin, and guitar.

Knight, David C., *The First Book of Sound,* Watts, 1960. Gives a basic introduction to the nature of sound and its properties.

Lynde, C. J., *Science Experiences with Ten-Cent*

Store Equipment, Van Nostrand, 1950. Includes many experiments on sound and music.

Parker, Bertha, *Sound,* Row, Peterson, 1950. The nature of sound and music, including experiments.

Pine, Tillie S., and Joseph Levine, *Sounds All Around Us,* McGraw-Hill, 1958. Simple explanation of the principles of sound, including experiments using materials in the home.

Posell, Elsa, *This Is an Orchestra,* Houghton Mifflin, 1950. Pictures of orchestral instruments and explanation of their functions.

UNESCO, *UNESCO Source Book for Science Teachers,* UNESCO Publications Center, 1956. A sourcebook of experiments for the classroom teacher.

16

Light and color

Light is another phenomenon of the physical world which is usually taken for granted, but without which life would be very different. Without light there would be no color. Without light there would be no plants and, therefore, no animal life on earth. Our sun is the original source of all forms of energy on this planet. Some people who move to Alaska find it most difficult to get used to the long nights—children going to and from school in darkness, no outdoor recess during the long night. Not only recreation but also entire industries such as photography and motion pictures depend on the controlled use of light. The same holds true for modern scientific instruments such as microscopes and telescopes. The bending of light rays in modern medical diagnostic tools is another illustration of the importance of light and the utilization of its properties.

HOW LIGHT TRAVELS

Take three of the regular 3″ × 5″ index cards. Find the exact center of each card by drawing two diagonals; the point of intersection is the exact center. With a paper punch or a pencil point, make a hole at this point. Now tack each card to a small wooden block so it will stand upright. Place a lighted candle on the center of the table and have one of the children line up the cards so that he can look through all three holes and see the candle flame (Fig. 16-1). Make sure the candle is just the right size so that the center of its flame will be level with the holes. Call the children's attention to the fact that the holes are all in a straight line. Now move any of the cards a little to one side. Can the children look through the holes and still see the candle flame? Point out that the candle flame is seen only when the cards are lined up so that light can pass through the holes in a straight line. This can only happen because light itself travels in a straight line. Students can also do this individually at their desks, sighting at a lamp on the teacher's desk. You may want to compare light's straight path with the path sound can take.

Move the cards over to other parts of the table. Repeat the above experiment each time you move the cards. The children will soon realize that a source of light will send out the light in all directions, but always in straight lines.

Have the children look at a candle

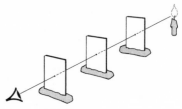

Fig. 16-1 Light travels in a straight line. (From A. Joseph et al., *A Sourcebook for the Physical Sciences,* Harcourt, Brace & World, 1961.)

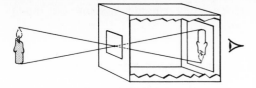

Fig. 16-2 A pinhole camera.

flame or a lighted electric bulb through a soda straw. They will see the light through the straw because light travels in a straight line. Now have the children bend the straw a bit. They will not see the light this time because it cannot make the turn.

Pinhole camera

A striking example of light traveling in straight lines is the pinhole camera. Get a small cardboard box. In the center of one end cut an opening about 2″ square. Cover this opening, using either glue or Scotch tape, with a piece of aluminum or tin foil. With a fine sharp needle puncture a tiny hole in the center of the foil. In the center of the opposite end of the box cut an opening at least 3″ square. Cover this opening with waxed paper or tissue paper, again using either glue or Scotch tape. Now blacken the entire inside of the box with flat black paint or ink.

Darken the room and point the pinhole end of the camera at a lighted candle about 6″ away (Fig. 16-2). Note the image which forms at the other end of the camera. If it is difficult to darken the room, you can cover your head and the rear part of the camera to see the image clearly.

Call the children's attention to the fact that the image is inverted. This could only happen if light travels in straight lines. Rays of light from the top part of the candle pass through the pinhole and fall on the bottom of the square of wax or tissue paper. Similarly, rays of light from the bottom part of the candle pass through the pinhole and fall on the top of the waxed or tissue paper. You can make this quite clear to the children by drawing a picture of the candle and pinhole camera on the blackboard. Then draw straight lines from the top and bottom of the candle through the pinhole and onto the image of the candle on the screen at the rear of the box.

Move the pinhole camera closer rather than farther away from the candle. Have the children note what happens to the size of the image in each case. Diagrams on the board will help explain the change in size in each case.

How to make a smoke box

A smoke box is an excellent device for studying light and light rays. Get a wooden box about 2′ × 1′ × 1′. Remove the top and front side of the box and replace with window glass. You may use cellophane or plastic in place of glass. A glazier will supply you with this glass, cut to proper size. Use black cloth tape to keep the glass, cellulose, or plastic firmly in place (Fig. 16-3).

Remove the rear side of the box. Over the rear place a black cloth, taping the top and tacking the sides. It is better to use two pieces of black cloth so arranged

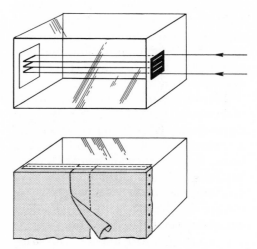

Fig. 16-3 A smoke box for studying light and light rays.

that the two halves overlap about 4" at the middle. This will allow you to put your hands in the box to move objects about.

Paint the inside of the box with flat black poster paint. Now about halfway down one end of the box, cut a hole about 3" long and 2" wide. This hole should be nearer the front end of the box. About 3" from the front end of the box should be enough. This hole is to let in light rays. All you have to do is to cut a piece of black paper or cardboard to tack over the hole. To get the kind of light rays you want, just cut the slots or slits as openings in the black paper or cardboard.

A 5" × 8" index card tacked on the other end of the box, just opposite the hole, acts as a screen. This will show up images beautifully when you work with lenses.

Now all you need is a light source. A three-cell focusing flashlight will do. This should rest on a block of wood about 2-3' from the hole you cut out. A slide projector with the front lens (objective) removed is even better. If you use the flashlight, focus it so you get a parallel beam. If it is too near the hole in the box, the light rays will be scattered or not clearly defined. Just move the flashlight back or forth until you get well-defined parallel rays of light. Your smoke box is now ready to use. Several demonstrations that employ a smoke box are described in following sections.

There are many things you can use to make smoke. Punk, incense candles, and cigarettes are all good sources. You may buy touch paper from a scientific supply house, or you might want to make it yourself. Obtain some potassium nitrate from your drugstore or high school chemistry teacher. Dissolve as much of the potassium nitrate in a small deep saucer of water as you can, stirring with a spoon. Dip strips of paper in the solution and let them dry. When you put a lighted match to these strips, they smolder, giving off much smoke.

WHAT HAPPENS TO LIGHT?

Have the children place a pane of clear glass on the page of a book. Note how clearly the material on the page can be seen. Let the children look at the filament of a lighted clear-glass electric bulb. A material such as glass through which objects can be seen clearly is called transparent. Transparent substances allow almost all of the light to pass through them readily. Cellophane, clear water, and air are other examples of transparent substances.

Repeat the experiment, using a pane of frosted or ground glass and a frosted glass electric bulb. Your school usually has some frosted glass windows. Note how much light will pass through these windows, but not enough to permit objects to be seen clearly. Substances such as frosted glass are called translucent. Translucent objects scatter or diffuse the light in all directions. Tissue and waxed paper, thin silk, parchment, paraffin, and clouds are other examples of translucent substances.

Tape some heavy black paper on one of the window panes or around a 15-watt lighted electric bulb. Do not keep the paper on the hot bulb too long. The black paper does not allow the light to pass through. Substances through which light cannot pass are called opaque. Wood, metal, and heavy cloth are examples of opaque substances.

Darken the classroom. Aim a focused beam from a flashlight first at a pane of clear glass, then a pane of frosted glass, and finally a square of wood. The children should understand the difference between transparent, translucent, and opaque objects. Incidentally, if you make a smoke box, it would be ideal for this experiment.

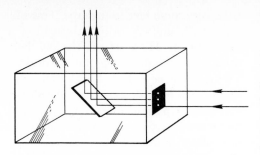

Fig. 16-4 A mirror reflects light rays.

Cut a piece of black cardboard or paper for use in the opening of the smoke box. Cut three slits in the black paper, one underneath the other. Each slit should be about ¼″ in width. Tack or tape the black paper to the opening. Fill the smoke box with smoke. Focus the flashlight down to a parallel beam and aim it at the slits in the black paper. Make sure the flashlight is far enough away so that the light rays are parallel. Note the three rays of light in the box. They are traveling in a straight line. Now hold a plane mirror at a 45° angle in the box (Fig. 16-4). Observe how the light beams are reflected and how clearly defined they are. Place your eye directly in the reflected rays leaving the top of the smoke box. Point out that the glare is almost as great as if you had looked directly in the flashlight. Help the children understand that a smooth surface reflects light with next to no scattering or reduction of the light's brightness.

If you haven't made a smoke box, you might try the following. Darken the room. Shine the focused beam of a flashlight at a slant on the mirror. The ray of light will be reflected so that the reflected beam leaves the mirror at the same angle as the incoming beam. Clap two blackboard erasers over the mirror to produce a dust. This will make the rays of light visible.

At one time most of your class have caught a sun's ray on a mirror and sent it dancing on the wall or at someone's eye.

Diffuse reflection

Take a piece of clear plastic and roughen it by scouring it with some steel wool. Scour in a circular motion until the surface is uniformly dull. Attach the plastic to the mirror either with Scotch tape or rubber bands. Now repeat the same experiment with the smoke box or in the darkened room. Observe how the rays of light are not reflected in regular beams but are scattered. Place your eye again in the reflected rays and notice the difference in brightness (Fig. 16-5). This type of reflection is called diffuse reflection.

HOW WE SEE

Most of the things we see do not have smooth surfaces. When light falls on a rough surface, the rays are spread out or diffused in all directions. When these diffused reflections reach the eye, you see the object. Help the children draw the conclusion that there are three conditions

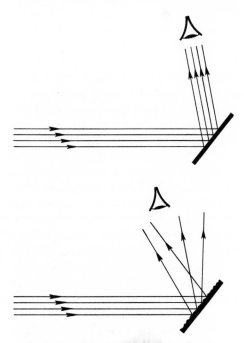

Fig. 16-5 Regular and diffuse reflection.

Fig. 16-6 Bouncing a ball up and down and back and forth illustrates how light is reflected.

needed in order to see a nonluminous object: (1) there must be a source of light, (2) the light must strike the object, and (3) the light must be reflected from the object to the eye.

Light-colored objects reflect more light than dark-colored objects. Ask your children to do this experiment. Have them enter a darkened room and note which objects are more easily visible after the eyes are adapted to the semidarkness—the light-colored objects or the dark ones? Have them comment on which rooms are brighter, those with light-colored walls or those with dark-colored walls.

MIRRORS

You can make it easier for children to understand how light behaves with mirrors by first studying reflection with a rubber ball. Throw the ball straight down, and it will bounce straight back along the same path it came from. Let two children stand some distance apart and then bounce the ball back and forth to each other (Fig. 16-6). Point out that if the ball is thrown down at a slant or angle, it bounces up at an angle, but in the opposite direction. Have the two children vary the distance between them and observe how the angle the ball makes when it strikes the ground changes accordingly.

Hang a mirror on the wall about waist-high. Darken the room. Get a strong focusing flashlight and adjust it to give a beam that is approximately parallel. You might want to cover the glass of the flashlight with black masking tape and then

cut a very small hole in the tape. This will give you a fine ray of light instead of a broad beam. Have one of the children shine a ray of light straight at the mirror. The ray will be reflected back along the same path. Now shine the ray of light on the mirror at a slant or angle. The rays will be reflected at a slant or angle, but in the opposite direction.

Angles of incidence and reflection

Get a small shoe box. Set the box on one side with the open end facing you. Cut a slit about ¼″ wide all along one end of the box. The slit should be located a short distance from the top of the box. Paint the inside of the box with flat black paint. Now place the box in bright sunlight so that the sun's rays fall on the slit. Turn the box until the sun's rays fall on the bottom of the box (Fig. 16-7). Then place a mirror on the bottom of the box just where the sun's rays strike the bottom. Note the reflected beam. Set another mirror in the path of the reflected beam and

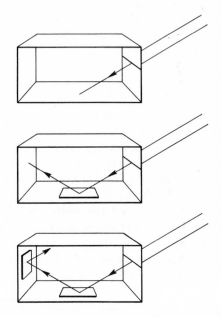

Fig. 16-7 Showing angles of incidence and reflection.

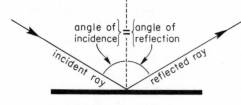

Fig. 16-8 The angle of incidence equals the angle of reflection.

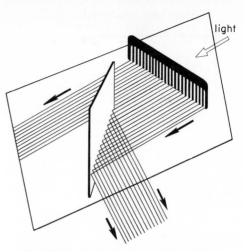

Fig. 16-9 Reflecting beams of sunlight.

note the second reflection. Draw dotted lines on the blackboard showing the paths the light takes. Draw a perpendicular line at the point where the light strikes the mirror and changes direction. Compare the angle at which it is reflected. They will be equal. The ray which strikes the mirror is called the incident ray, and the angle it makes with the mirror is called the angle of incidence. The ray which changes direction is called the reflected ray, and the angle it makes with the mirror is called the angle of reflection (Fig. 16-8). The angle of reflection equals the angle of incidence.

Hold a comb in the sun's rays so that the rays shine through the teeth and fall on a piece of white cardboard. By tilting the cardboard, you can make the rays of light on the cardboard several inches long. Now place a mirror diagonally in the path of these rays (Fig. 16-9). Point out that the beams which strike the mirror are reflected at the same angle. Turn the mirror and note how these angles change.

Using the classroom to demonstrate reflection

Line the children's chairs in the classroom in a series of equal parallel rows. Hang a large mirror from the blackboard so that it is in the center of the wall. Adjust the height of the mirror so that the children can see each other. With chalk draw a line on the floor so that the line is perpendicular to the front wall at a point directly under the mirror. Now ask pupil #1 to tell the class which one of his fellow pupils he sees in the mirror. Most likely he will name pupil #6, who will see pupil #1 in turn. Now draw chalk lines on the floor from pupil #1 and pupil #6 to the point where the perpendicular line meets the front wall (Fig. 16-10). Compare the two angles and observe how they are equal. Repeat for pupils #2 and #5, etc.

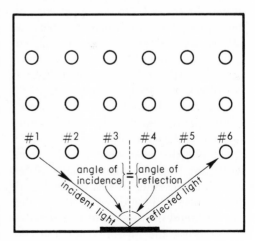

Fig. 16-10 Proving the principle of reflection in the classroom.

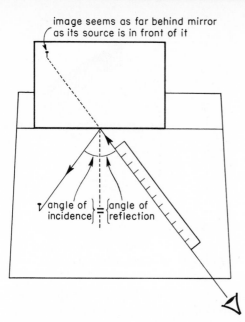

image seems as far behind mirror as its source is in front of it

angle of incidence = angle of reflection

Fig. 16-11 Constructing angles of incidence and reflection.

Reflection in a mirror

With Scotch tape attach a pocket mirror to a block of wood so that it stands upright. You can also hold the mirror upright by placing it between the pages of two books standing up and facing each other. On a piece of white paper draw a straight line parallel to the upper edge of the paper. Place the mirror so that its edge rests on the straight line. Stick a pin in the paper about 6″ in front of the mirror and a little to the left of the center of the mirror (Fig. 16-11). Now place a 12″ ruler on the right-hand side of the paper. Keep your eye level with the ruler and sight along the edge of the ruler with one eye. Move the ruler until its edge is in direct line with the mirror image of the pin. Hold the ruler in this position and draw a pencil line along the edge of the ruler. Extend this line until it meets the mirror. Push the mirror away if necessary. The parallel line you drew originally will show you where the mirror stood.

Now draw a perpendicular line at this point. Then draw another line from this point to the pin. You now have an incident ray and reflected ray, and an angle of incidence and an angle of reflection. Use a protractor to measure the two angles with reference to a line at right angles to the mirror at the point where the incident beam hits the mirror; compare these angles to see if they are equal.

Have two pupils move apart and about to various positions with relation to the mirror. They will find that one cannot see the eyes of the other in the mirror unless the second sees the eyes of the first at the same time. Some of your rapid learners may enjoy figuring out why this is so.

Plane glass acts as a mirror

Obtain a piece of window glass about 6″ square. Clean and polish the glass. Lay the glass on white paper and have the children try to see their reflections. Now lay the glass on black paper and have the children try again.

When light strikes glass, most of the light passes through, but some is reflected from the surface of the glass. When the glass is placed on white paper, the light passing through the glass is reflected back from the white paper. However, this light is diffusely reflected, and it is very difficult to see yourself clearly. When the glass is placed on black paper, the light passing through the glass is absorbed. This allows you to see clearly the light reflected from the surface of the glass. This will help the children understand why a window is a fairly good mirror at night when it is bright inside and dark outside. Common glass reflects about 10% of the light and transmits about 90% of the light.

Clean and polish a piece of window glass about 6″ square. Set the glass upright by placing it inside the pages of a book standing on edge. Make sure the glass is exactly vertical. Place a lighted

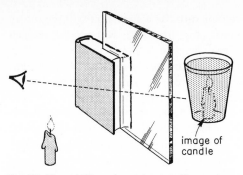

Fig. 16-12 Making plane glass act like a mirror.

candle in front of the glass (Fig. 16-12). Compare the size of the image with the size of the object. Place a glass of water in back of the glass and move it about until the image of the lighted candle seems to be burning in water. Remove the glass of water and replace it with your hand. The candle will seem to be burning in your hand.

Take a second candle exactly the same size as the lighted candle. Place the unlighted candle in back of the glass. Move it about until the image of the burning candle fits exactly with the unlighted candle, no matter from which angle you look at it. Now the unlighted candle seems to be burning. Measure the distances of both candles from the glass and compare.

The children should now readily understand that in plane mirrors the image is (1) the same size as the object, and (2) just as far behind the mirror as the object is in front of it.

Water acts as a mirror

Water can also act as a mirror. Fill a pan almost full of water. Bring a table near the window so that sunlight can fall on it. (*Warning: Do not let the children look at a direct image of the ball of the sun.*) Set the pan of water on the table in the sunlight. Look for a bright spot on the wall or ceiling. Strike the side of the pan with your hand just hard enough to cause the surface of the water to form ripples. The spot of light will dance about, but will be less bright and sharp.

Making a periscope

A periscope is a sure-fire way of arousing interest in light and how light is reflected. All you need is a wooden cheese box (a shoe box will do just as well) and two pocket mirrors, either square or rectangular in shape. Using Scotch tape, fasten the mirrors at a 45° angle across both ends of the box (Fig. 16-13). (You may want to glue the mirror to pieces of cardboard which fit into the box.) Each mirror must be at a 45° angle for the periscope to be effective. A protractor, available at any ten-cent store, can be used by the class to measure and check the angle. Or fold a square of paper along its diagonal to make two 45° angles. Now cut a window opposite the mid-point of each mirror. One window should be facing the upper mirror, the other window opening to the rear and facing the lower mirror. The dimensions of each window should be slightly smaller than the dimensions of the mirrors. Replace the cover on the box.

You can now let one child kneel beside a table and look into the periscope. If the top of the periscope is above the table top, the child can identify objects on the table

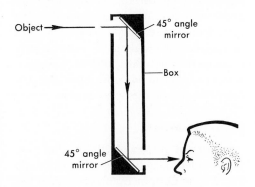

Fig. 16-13 A periscope. (From R. Brinckerhoff et al., *The Physical World*, Harcourt, Brace & World, 1958.)

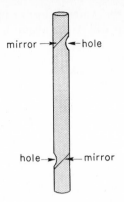

Fig. 16-14 An extra long periscope.

mirror into the other. You will see many coins (Fig. 16-15A). Repeat the experiment, using a lighted candle. Point out that you see many images because light from the coin or candle is reflected back and forth many times.

Using Scotch tape, hinge two mirrors together. Set them up so that they are at right angles to each other (Fig. 16-15B). Place a coin between the mirrors and note the number of images formed. Make smaller and smaller angles and see what happens to the number of images. Try this experiment again, using a lighted candle.

Beautiful multiple images can be obtained from a kaleidoscope. Put together three long rectangular mirrors, all of the same size, to form a triangle. The mirror surfaces should be on the inside. Metal camp mirrors, cut out with tin shears or a hacksaw, can also be used. Fasten the mirrors together with Scotch tape (Fig. 16-15C). Place a pane of glass upon two blocks of wood. Put tiny pieces of colored paper on the glass. Now set the kaleidoscope over the colored pieces on the glass. Six-sided figures will be seen. Tap the glass while you are still looking down into the kaleidoscope. The figures will change their shape and color combinations. Turn the kaleidoscope to change the patterns. Repeat the experiment, using colored beads, bits of colored glass, colored yarn, or tiny pieces of colored ribbon.

Mirror images are reversed. Let the children write their names on a piece of paper. Hold the paper to the mirror. Write your name in ink very heavily. Blot the paper with a fresh blotter, then hold the blotter to the mirror. Can you read your name now?

Place a sheet of carbon paper with its carbon side up under a sheet of white paper. Write a sentence on the white paper. Turn the white paper over and note the reversed writing on the other side.

or describe what his classmates are doing. Help the children understand that light enters the top window and is reflected by the top mirror down to the bottom mirror. The light is then reflected from the bottom mirror to the person's eye. Have the children explain why it is absolutely necessary that the mirrors be placed at 45° angles.

An extra long periscope can be made by using a cardboard mailing tube about 2″ in diameter and at least 2′ long. Mark two points, one about 3″ from the bottom and the other about 3″ from the top. At these points cut slits at angles of exactly 45°. It might be wise to mark these positions carefully in advance so that the angles will be correct. Now insert two pocket mirrors into these slits and fasten with Scotch tape (Fig. 16-14). Then cut two window holes about 2″ wide directly opposite the face of the mirrors. One window should be on one side of the tube, the other window on the opposite side.

Fun with mirrors

Stand two mirrors on edge so that they are parallel to each other. You can keep the mirrors upright by placing them between the pages of a book. The mirrors should be facing each other. Now place a coin between the mirrors. Look over one

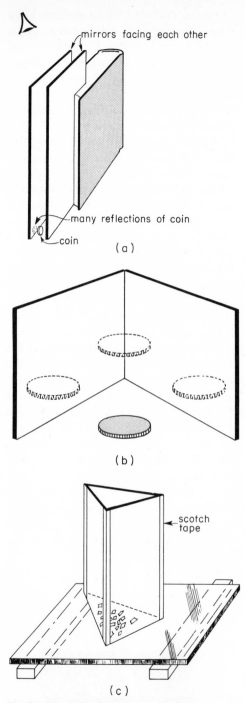

mirrors facing each other

many reflections of coin

coin

(a)

(b)

scotch tape

(c)

Fig. 16-15 (a) Making many coins from one coin; (b) decreasing the angle between the mirrors increases the number of coins produced; (c) a kaleidoscope.

Now hold the reversed writing to the mirror and try to read the sentence.

Let one child look into a mirror and raise his right hand. The mirror image will raise its left hand. If the child winks his left eye, the mirror image will wink its right eye. If the children find this hard to understand or insist that the image moves the same hand or eye as the object, try the following. Have two boys face each other. Let one boy raise his right hand. Make the second boy raise the hand that a mirror image would have raised. This hand will be the left hand.

Place an alarm clock in front of a mirror. The face will be reversed. Now hinge two mirrors with Scotch tape and arrange the mirrors so that they are at right angles to each other (Fig. 16-16). Place the clock exactly between the two mirrors. Now the face image is not reversed. In this case the image does not seem to be reversed because it actually has been reversed twice. The light from one half of the face goes to the left mirror, is reflected to the right mirror, then back to your eye. The light from the other half of the face goes to the right mirror, is reflected to the left mirror, then back to your eye. The image is reversed once at each mirror, making twice altogether, so that you see the face as it usually appears.

Obtain a thin rectangular sheet of

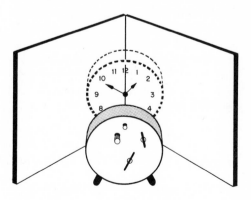

Fig. 16-16 Reversing a reversed image.

Fig. 16-17 Bending a metal mirror will produce unusual images.

smooth, polished, pliable metal from a tinsmith. Look at yourself in the metal. You see an image just like the one formed in a mirror. Now bend the sheet so that the hollow side is away from you. If you hold the sheet vertically and look into it, your face will be very long and thin (Fig. 16-17). If you hold the sheet horizontally and look into it, your face will be short and fat. Now bend the sheet so that the hollow side is toward you and look at this curved mirror vertically and horizontally again. Note the kind of images formed.

Curved mirrors which bulge outward are called convex. Curved mirrors which are hollowed inward are called concave. Have the children look at their images in a highly polished metal coffeepot or teapot. This will have both concave and convex surfaces at the same time. A shaving mirror is a good example of a concave mirror, while the rear-view mirror of a car is a good example of a convex mirror. A concave mirror forms a larger image of an object, while a convex mirror forms a smaller image of an object. At amusement parks trick mirrors that distort the shape of the body are good examples of concave and convex mirrors.

BENDING LIGHT

Rays of light will change their direction when they pass at an angle from one transparent substance into another. Fill a rectangular fish tank with water until the level of water is about 2″ from the top. Obtain some fluorescein from your pharmacist. Add just enough fluorescein to the water to make it yellow. Cover the top of tank with cardboard with a ⅛″ × 1″ slit in the cardboard as in Fig. 16-18. Now use smoke paper to fill the air above the water with smoke. You can also use chalk dust.

First shine the ray of light straight down into the fish tank. Point out that there is no change in the direction of the ray. Now shine the ray of light into the water at a slant or angle. This time the ray is bent. This bending of light is called refraction. Light travels faster in air than it does in water, so that it is bent slightly when it passes from air to water.

You might like to repeat the experiment, using only a glass of water. Add a few drops of milk to the water so that the ray can be seen distinctly as it bends.

Place a stick in a glass of water. Some of the stick should be above the surface of the water. Keep your eyes level with the surface of the water and look at the point where the stick meets the water. The stick

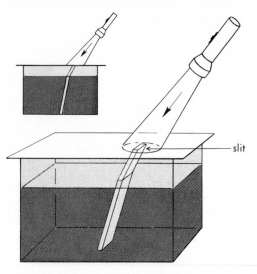

Fig. 16-18 Making light rays bend.

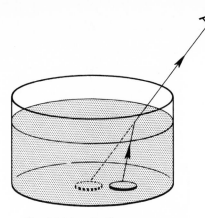

Fig. 16-19 Making a coin disappear.

appears to be broken or bent. This is because the rays of light which come from the part of the stick in the water are bent as they leave the water and go into the air. Repeat the experiment, using a spoon or a pencil. Have pupils recall the bent rowboat oar in water or the bent spoon in a glass of water.

Place a coin on the bottom of a pan or coffee can near the edge of the pan. Have one pupil step close enough to the pan to see the coin clearly. Now let the pupil step back to the point where the coin completely disappears. While the pupil is holding this position, have another pupil slowly pour water into the pan (Fig. 16-19). Pour the water carefully so it won't move the coin. The first pupil will see the coin emerge into full view. When the water was added, light from the coin was bent as it passed from the water into the air. This enabled the pupil to see the coin once again. The coin now seems to be in a different position from where it actually is.

Call the children's attention to the fact that water appears to be more shallow than it really is. Water that seems to be chest-deep in a swimming pool is often over your head. Fill a saucepan full of water. Keep your eyes about 3″ above the level of the water. Now lower a ruler into the water at the side farthest from you.

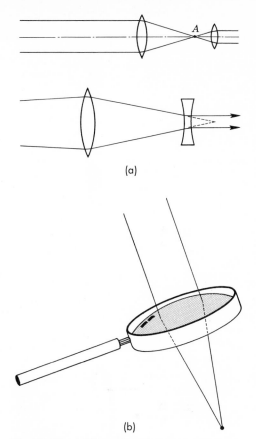

Fig. 16-20 (a) The action of convex and concave lenses on light rays; (b) focusing light rays with a magnifying glass. (From F. Miller, Jr., *College Physics*, Harcourt, Brace & World, 1959.)

The ruler seems to become shorter as it goes into the water.

Look straight down into a glass of water filled to the very top. The bottom of the glass seems to be closer to your eyes than the table upon which the glass is resting. Put your finger on the side of the glass where the bottom appears to be. The water seems to be about three fourths as deep as it really is. The children should realize that this apparent depth occurs because the light rays from the bottom of the glass are bent as they leave the water. This gives the bottom a different position, just as with the coin in the previous experiment.

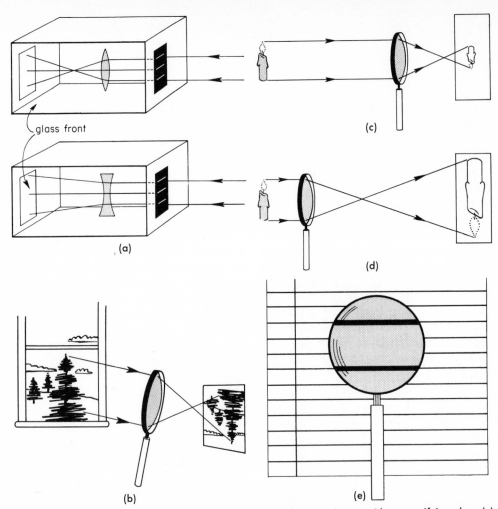

Fig. 16-21 (a) Bending light rays in a smoke box; (b) producing an image with a magnifying glass; (c) obtaining a small inverted image; (d) obtaining a large inverted image; (e) finding the magnifying power of a lens.

LENSES

Lenses are transparent substances, such as glass, which have curved surfaces. You have shown that there are two kinds of mirrors, concave and convex. The two principal kinds of lenses also have the same names. Viewed in cross section, a convex lens is thicker in the middle than at the ends; a concave lens is thinner in the middle than at the ends. The convex lens brings or focuses rays of light to-

gether. The concave lens will spread out rays of light (Fig. 16-20A). A convenient mnemonic for pupils is to remember "cave" in concave. Caves are hollow in the middle.

A magnifying glass is a good example of a convex lens. Place the magnifying glass on a piece of black paper and let the sun's rays shine on the glass. Lift the magnifying glass slowly from the black paper until you reach a position where the rays are focused on the paper. You will see a bright spot on the paper (Fig. 16-20B). This bright spot is the point where the parallel rays of the sun are brought together. This point is called the principal focus or focal point of the lens. The distance between this point and the center of the lens is called the focal distance or focal length. You may recall that you are able to set a match head on fire by focusing the sun's rays on it.

The lenses of glasses used by nearsighted persons are concave lenses. See what happens when you place a concave lens in the sun's rays and try to focus the rays on black paper.

The lenses of glasses used by far-sighted persons are convex lenses. They will focus an image like ordinary magnifying lenses. Try to obtain lenses from discarded glasses of both nearsighted and farsighted persons. You might want to visit an optometrist or optician and ask him for a convex and a concave lens.

A smoke box (pp. 245–46) is an ideal instrument for showing what convex and concave lenses do to parallel rays of light. Hold a convex, then a concave, lens in the path of parallel rays of light and see how each one bends the light (Fig. 16-21A).

Darken the room except for one window. Have a child stand with his back to the window and hold an unlined 5″ × 8″ index card up to the light. Now let the pupil move a magnifying glass back and forth until he gets a clear picture image of whatever is outside the window (Fig. 16-21B). Note that the image is smaller and upside down (inverted).

Darken the entire room. Stand a lighted candle on the table. Let one child hold a large sheet of white cardboard about 3′ away. This cardboard serves as a screen. Now have another child hold a magnifying glass (convex lens) near the screen in the path of the candle's rays. Move the lens slowly toward the candle until a clear image is seen on the screen. The image will be smaller than the object (Fig. 16-21C). By changing the flame-to-lens distance, you can also get an enlarged (inverted) image on a distant wall.

Now move the lens still closer to the candle. You will have to move the screen farther away to get a clear image (Fig. 16-21D). The image is now larger and is still inverted. The children should realize that the closer the lens approaches the candle, or object, up to a certain point, the larger the image will be.

When a convex lens is brought very close to an object, it magnifies, and the image is erect. A magnifying glass shows this to good effect. You will find the magnifying power of a lens by focusing it over lined paper (Fig. 16-21E). Compare the number of spaces you see outside the lens with the spaces you see through the lens. A magnifying glass will magnify several or more lines, depending on the curve of the lens. The greater the curvature, the greater the magnification.

Curved glass jars or tumblers will also magnify. Dip your finger or a pencil into a glass of water and look at it from the side. Observe a fish in a round fish bowl, looking at it first from the top and then from the side. Place various objects in an olive jar filled with water. Or screw the cover back on the olive jar filled with water. Now put a ruler, then a lighted candle, and then other objects behind the jar. Note how the objects are magnified.

Clear glass marbles also will magnify. Even a drop of water, which is spherical, has magnifying powers. Place a drop of water carefully on a piece of glass. Set the glass on a printed page and see how the letters of a word are magnified. The drop of water acts in the very same way as a convex lens.

Making an astronomical telescope and a microscope

Obtain two cardboard mailing tubes,

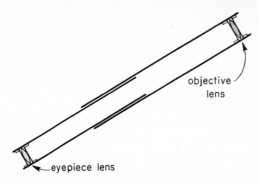

Fig. 16-22 An astronomical telescope.

each about 1' long. The diameter of one tube should be slightly larger than that of the other. This will enable the smaller tube to slide back and forth in the larger tube. From your optometrist, optician, or optical supply company (see appendix) obtain two convex lenses. One lens should have a large focal length or distance, the other a smaller focal length. The best combination is one lens with a focal length of 8″ or 10″ and one with a 1″ focal length.

Insert the lens with the larger focal length into one end of the larger mailing tube. To keep the lens firmly in place, glue cardboard rings above and below it inside of the tube. Each ring should have a slit or small hole in the center so that the top of the lens will fit tightly. You can estimate how thick the rings should be. The lens in the larger tube is called the objective.

Now insert the lens with the smaller focal length into the other end of the smaller tube. Use cardboard rings again to keep the lens in place. This lens is called the eyepiece. (For further details on the building of a telescope, see Chapter 10.)

Your telescope is now ready to operate (Fig. 16-22). Looking through the lens in the smaller tube (the eyepiece), slide the tube back and forth until you get a clear picture image. When you look at objects in the street, the image will be inverted. However, this does not matter when you look at the moon and stars. The magnification is the product of the larger focal length by the shorter. If you have a 10″ focal-length objective lens and a 1″ focal-length eyepiece lens, the magnification is 10.

You may want to use this telescope as a microscope. You will need much light to see clearly. Set the object to be magnified on a pane of clear glass resting on two blocks of wood or on two books (Fig. 16-23). A plane mirror underneath the glass will help concentrate the light. Use a small mirror on a stand. The mirror can be tilted until light is reflected directly on the object. Now slide the tube back and forth until you get a clear image. For a microscope it is best to use an eyepiece lens of very short focal length, such as ¼–½″.

HOW OUR EYES WORK

Obtain a cow's eye from the butcher. Let the children examine the tough white ball. All they can see is the colored circle called the iris, with the black pupil in the center. Now with a single-edge razor cut the eye entirely through the middle from front to back. A jelly-like liquid will flow out and the eye will collapse.

Now look at the remaining part of the eye carefully and observe how the parts

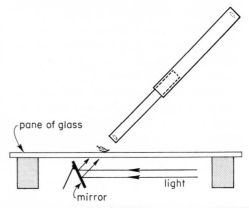

Fig. 16-23 Using a telescope as a microscope.

are arranged (Fig. 16-24A). The white of the eye, which bulges slightly, is called the cornea. Then comes the iris, which gives the eye its characteristic color, with the pupil in the center.

Obtain another cow's eye. In back of the cornea and iris is the convex lens which focuses the light that enters the eye. This time dissect the eye carefully so that you can remove the lens intact. Use the lens to focus the light from the sun or from a flashlight in a darkened room. Or set up the lens on a cardboard with a hole, and use it for focusing a candle flame onto a table top. In the back of the eye is a dark purple lining called the retina. The purple is visual purple made in the eye from vitamin A. The retina contains nerves which are sensitive to light. The lens focuses the light on the retina. The nerves in the retina are connected to the optic nerve which leads to the brain. The light falling on the retina sends impulses or messages through the optic nerve to the brain. There the impulses are changed to what we call "seeing." If the children should note that the image falling on the retina will be inverted, help them understand that the brain makes them see objects erect (Fig. 16-24B).

Try to borrow a commercial eye model from the high school biology teacher. Point out the different parts of the eye and explain how they function. You can make your own model of the eye with a rubber ball. Tape a convex lens in front. A round piece of cardboard can be painted to look like an iris and pupil. Paste the cardboard behind the lens. Tissue paper taped on the back of the ball will serve as a retina.

The iris controls the amount of light which enters the eye. This protects the retina from receiving too strong light and thereby being injured. Have a child remain in a darkened room or in a dark corner of a room. Let the children observe how wide his irises are. Because the room

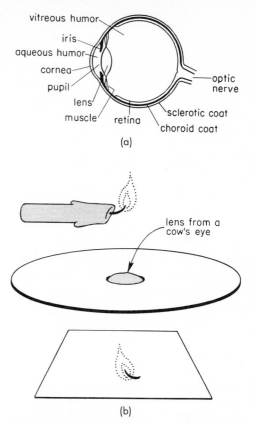

Fig. 16-24 (a) Cross section of cow's eye; (b) using the lens of a cow's eye to obtain the image of a flame.

is dark, the iris widens in order to let as much light into the eye as possible. Now ask the child to step close to the window. Observe how his irises begin to close down in order to shut out some of the light. Notice a cat's iris during the day and at night.

Comparing the eye with a camera

Bring a camera into the classroom. Show the similarities between the eye and the camera. The eyelid corresponds to the shutter. The diaphragm of the camera controls the amount of light entering the camera, just as the iris does with the eye. The size of the opening of the diaphragm corresponds to the pupil of the eye. A blink is a snapshot, while a stare is a time

Fig. 16-25 Making a lion enter a cage.

exposure. Both camera and eye have a lens. The camera has a lightproof box, while the eye has a lightproof eyeball. The retina of the eye corresponds to the film in the camera. In both cases light enters and is bent by the lens so that the image falls on the film or retina.

camera	eye
camera lens	eye lens
film	retina
lightproof box	eye socket
diaphragm to control lens opening	iris
snapshot	blink
time exposure	stare
focus by changing lens distance	focus by changing lens curvature
pictures are permanent when developed	pictures last about 1/16 second
pictures are black and white or color	pictures are in natural colors
finder is necessary	no finder is necessary

Finding the blind spot in your eye

The point at which the optic nerve joins the retina is insensitive to light. Light falling on this point will not produce an image. To find this "blind" spot, obtain a 3″ × 5″ unlined index card. Make a cross and a circle 3″ apart on the card. Close your right eye, hold the card at arm's length, and stare fixedly at the symbol on the right. Now move the card slowly toward you while you are still staring at the circle. The left-hand symbol will disappear. Repeat the experiment, this time closing the left eye and staring at the symbol on the right.

Normal vision combines two images

Each eye produces an individual image, but the brain combines these two images to form a single image. Roll a sheet of paper into a tube about 1″ in diameter. Put the tube to your left eye. Hold your right hand beside the tube, the open palm toward you. Now look through the tube with your left eye and at your hand with your right eye. A hole will appear in the middle of your hand. Repeat the experiment, holding a book next to the tube with your right hand.

On a sheet of white paper draw a cage and a lion beside it (Fig. 16-25). Place the horizontal edge of a 3″ × 5″ index card between the cage and the lion. Bend over and place your nose against the upper edge of the card. Now look at the cage with one eye and the lion with the other. The lion will seem to enter the cage. Repeat, using a bird and bird cage.

Two eyes are better than one, especially in estimating direction. Hold two pencils, one in each hand, with the erasers facing each other. Keep the pencils at arm's length and about 2′ apart. Now close one eye and try to bring the erasers together. Try again, but this time use both eyes.

Sometimes your eyes find it difficult to do two things at one time. Hold two pencils, one in each hand, about 12-18″ away from you. The point of one pencil should face the eraser of the other pencil. Bring the pencils together so that the point of one touches the eraser of the other. Now focus your eyes on a distant wall. Stare at a point on the wall just above the point where the pencils met. You will see a tiny pencil between the two you are holding. Still staring at the wall, separate the pencils slightly. The tiny pencil will shrink and be suspended in mid-air. Repeat the experiment, this time bringing your index

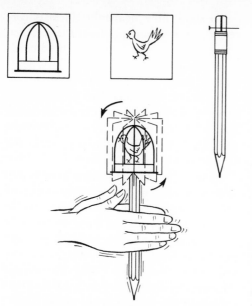

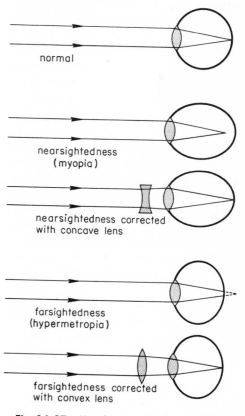

Fig. 16-26 Putting a bird inside its cage.

and hold the card firmly by pushing a short pin through the eraser and card (Fig. 16-26). Roll the pencil back and forth quickly between the palm of your hands. The bird will seem to be inside the cage. Have the children explain how this effect is produced. Another combination is a fish bowl and fish.

Obtain about 20 unlined 3″ × 5″ index cards. Arrange them in a single pile with the broad side facing you. Draw a stick figure of a man on the right-hand side of the top card. Draw the figure again on the right-hand side of the second card, but change the arms and legs slightly. Draw figures on successive cards, each time changing the position of the arms and legs. Now collect the cards into a pack. Hold the cards in your left hand and flip them rapidly with the thumb of

fingers together. A tiny sausage will appear between your fingers. When you stare beyond the pencils or your fingers, each eye makes a separate side-by-side image of them. These images overlap at the center to give you the extra pencil or finger.

Motion picture effect

An image will remain on the retina of the eye about 1/16 second after the object has been removed. This means that the eye will continue to see an object 1/16 second after the object has disappeared from view. This effect is called persistence of vision.

Darken the room. Swing the glowing end of a small flashlight or piece of punk in a circle. Persistence of vision will create the effect of a circle of fire. Try making other figures with the cigarette or punk.

Draw a bird cage on a white card about 2″ square. On the other side of the card draw a bird and color it with a bright color. With a single-edge razor, slit the eraser of a pencil down the middle as far as it will go. Insert the card in the slit

normal

nearsightedness (myopia)

nearsightedness corrected with concave lens

farsightedness (hypermetropia)

farsightedness corrected with convex lens

Fig. 16-27 How lenses correct eye defects.

your right hand. The figure of the man will seem to dance. Have the class make their own motion pictures of a boy batting a ball, shooting a basket, etc. Help the children understand how persistence in vision is used in making motion pictures and television.

How eyeglasses help us see

Many people have eyeballs of just the right size so that the eye lens focuses the light exactly on the retina. Some people, however, have eyeballs that are too long. The lens now focuses the light in front of the retina, and distant objects seem blurred. Such people are said to be near-sighted. Other people have eyeballs that are too short. The lens focuses the light behind the retina, and near objects seem blurred. These people are said to be far-sighted.

These eye defects can be corrected by using glasses with special lenses. This can be shown by the following experiment. See Fig. 16-27 for basic relationships. Find the focal length or distance of a convex lens. On a piece of cardboard draw a circle with a diameter equal to the focal length of the lens. Cut this circle out. Place the lens at the left edge of the circle and shine a beam of light through the lens. If the lens does not focus the light exactly on the other edge of the cardboard circle, trim the circle down until this effect is produced. The beam of light may be obtained from a strong focusing flashlight or from a slide projector with the front lens removed. Label this cardboard as a normal eye.

Now cut out two other cardboard circles, one slightly larger and one slightly smaller than the original circle. These are your nearsighted and farsighted eyes. Label them as such. Have the children observe how the convex lens focuses the light either in front of or in back of the right edge of the circle.

To show how nearsightedness is corrected, shine a beam of light through the convex lens across the nearsighted cardboard eye. Borrow eyeglasses from a nearsighted child. The lenses in these glasses are concave. Place one lens of the glasses between the beam of light and the convex lens. Move the concave lens back or forth until the light is definitely focused at the far end of the cardboard eye.

To show how farsightedness is corrected, shine a beam of light from the convex lens into the farsighted cardboard eye. Obtain a second convex lens, or a convex lens in a pair of glasses for a farsighted person, and place it between the beam of light and the original convex lens. Move the second convex lens back or forth until the light focuses at the far end of the circle.

TAKING LIGHT APART

Borrow a glass prism from the high school physics teacher. If a prism is not available, a three-sided crystal from a chandelier will do just as well. Perform the experiment when the sun is entering the classroom windows. Cut a narrow horizontal slit about ⅛" wide and 1" long in a piece of dark cardboard. Paste the cardboard to the window. Darken the other windows. Put a table near the window so that the sun's rays fall on the table. Set the prism in modeling clay or soft wax so that the prism rests on one edge. Place the prism on the table in such a position that the sunlight falls directly on it. Adjust the position of the prism until the sunlight passes through it and is projected on a white screen or cardboard on the opposite wall (Fig. 16-28). A beautiful band of colors, or spectrum, is formed on the screen. The white light of the sun is composed of the colors in the spectrum. As these colors pass through the prism, each one is slowed down differently, causing the colors to separate. Clap two erasers in

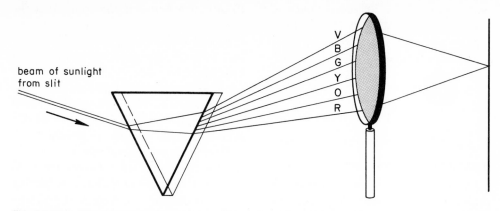

Fig. 16-28 Obtaining a spectrum. A magnifying glass placed between the prism and the screen puts the colors back together to form white light.

the path of the beam of light between the prism and the wall. Note what happens to the chalk dust.

Try making your own prism. Obtain Mortite cement from the hardware store. It comes in a long coiled strip. Unwind some Mortite and pat it into a flat cake. If the Mortite is not available, modeling clay will serve. Put three microscope slides or three $2'' \times 2''$ slide cover glasses together to form a triangle. Imbed the ends of the slides firmly into the Mortite or clay (Fig. 16-29). This seals the bottom and makes it waterproof. Make sure the edges of the slides are close together by taping them with narrow lengths of Scotch tape. Now pour water into this triangular prism

until you have completely filled it.

You can also produce the spectrum with a mirror under water. Fill a saucepan full of water. Lean a mirror against one edge of the pan. Let sunlight fall on the water and the mirror (Fig. 16-30). Adjust the mirror so that a spectrum appears on the wall underneath or beside the window. Stir the water with your finger and see what happens.

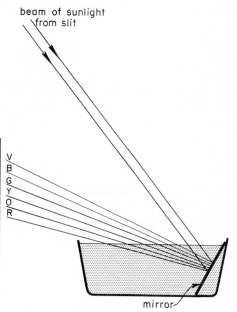

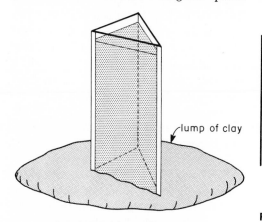

Fig. 16-29 A homemade prism.

Fig. 16-30 A mirror under water can produce a spectrum.

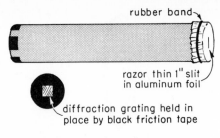

rubber band

razor thin 1" slit
in aluminum foil

diffraction grating held in
place by black friction tape

Fig. 16-31 A mailing-tube spectroscope.

Mailing-tube spectroscope

In addition to breaking up light (or producing a spectrum) by means of a prism, there are other ways of producing spectra.

Obtain a hollow cardboard mailing tube about 14-18″ long. Cover one end with aluminum foil, holding it firmly to the tube with a rubber band. With the corner of a razor blade make a slit 1″ long in the foil (Fig. 16-31).

Obtain a sheet of diffraction grating. This may be purchased from Edmund Scientific Company, Barrington, N. J. A sheet of diffraction grating about 8″ × 10″ should cost less than $2.00. Cut 1 square inch of this diffraction grating and attach it to the other end of the mailing tube. This may be done by attaching four strips of black friction tape to the other end of the tube in a criss-cross manner. First put on two of the strips of black tape. Then place the square of diffraction grating on the strips of tape, then put on the other two strips cross-wise. This will hold the diffraction grating in place. The lines of the grating should be parallel with the slit in the foil. Now look through the slit and diffraction grating at a lighted electric bulb that is not frosted. This is important. The bulb must be unfrosted so that the filament is visible. The slit in the aluminum foil must be held so that it is parallel to the filament in the bulb.

For best results, stay at least 3′ away from the bulb. The farther away you stay, the larger the spectrum produced.

Results are better if the room is darkened.

As you look straight through the grating, look for the spectrum to appear a little bit to one side.

Carefully prepare a double slit in the aluminum foil. This will produce even better results than the single slit. The slits must be as close together as possible.

Results almost as good may be obtained by eliminating the tube. Have each child hold a 1″ square of diffraction grating to his or her eye and look at the lighted unfrosted bulb. An 8″ × 10″ sheet of diffraction grating will give you 80 square inches, enough for 80 individual squares, 1″ × 1″, so that each child may do the experiment individually.

Perform the same experiment, using sunlight instead of a lighted unfrosted bulb. Pull the shades down in the room, so that each shade is 6″ from the window sill. Cover one of the window panes with black construction paper. Make a vertical slit in the construction paper. Now look at the slit of sunlight either with the mailing tube spectroscope or by holding the square of diffraction grating to the eye.

If the diffraction grating is not on hand, use some black electrical tape. This is a plastic that will stretch. Obtain a glass microscope slide and stretch a piece of the tape *tightly* over the length of the slide. Cut the tape vertically all the way through with a razor. The tape will separate slightly, producing a slit. Hold the microscope slide up to the eye so that the slit is vertical, and have the children look through the slit at an unfrosted bulb.

The result will not be as sharp as the experiments using the diffraction grating, but a spectrum will appear.

Making rainbow colors

In a rainbow, droplets of water act as prisms and break up the sunlight to form the beautiful arch of rainbow colors.

Early in the morning or late in the afternoon, stand with your back to the sun. Squirt a spray of water from a hose against a dark background of trees. A beautiful rainbow will be formed.

Place a glass tumbler on the window sill when the sun is shining brightly through the window. Adjust the position of the tumbler so that it extends a little over the inside edge of the window sill. Fill the tumbler full of water (Fig. 16-32). A rainbow will be formed on a sheet of white paper placed on the floor.

Blow bubbles using soapy water. Notice the rainbow colors in the bubbles. These colors are caused by a refraction from different molecular layers in the soap bubble which is several molecules thick. An oil film on water on the ground acts the same way. Fill a shallow plate with water. Add black ink until the solution is dark. Open a window and put the plate on the window sill where the light is very bright. However, do not put it into the sunlight. Now place yourself so that the light from the sky is reflected to your eye. While looking at the surface of the water, place a drop of oil or gasoline in the water nearest you. A brilliant flash of rainbow colors will move across the plate, away from you, and toward the opposite side of the plate.

Fill a large pan full of water. Let one drop of Duco cement fall on the water. The cement quickly spreads out into a thin sheet having beautiful rainbow colors. Slip a piece of dark cardboard or paper carefully under the sheet of cement and lift it out. Examine the permanent colors on the cardboard.

Seeing colors

A colored transparent substance will transmit only light of the same color as the colored substance. Let a single ray of light enter the smoke box. Hold a clear sheet of glass or cellophane in the path of

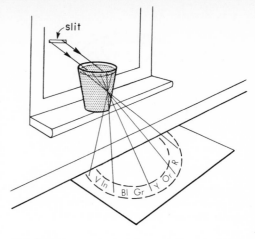

Fig. 16-32 A rainbow from a tumbler of water.

the ray. The light falling on the screen at the end of the box is white. Now hold a sheet of red glass or cellophane in the path of the ray. The light falling on the screen is now red. The red glass or cellophane transmitted the red part of the light and absorbed all the other colors of the white light. Repeat, using different colored glass or cellophane. Point out that in the theatre, colored spotlights are thrown on the stage in this way.

If the smoke box is not available, use a focusing flashlight in a darkened room. Cover the glass of the flashlight with black masking tape and make a tiny slit in the tape to produce a single ray of light.

A colored opaque substance will reflect only light of the same color as the colored substance. All the other colors in white light are absorbed. A piece of red cloth looks red because it has absorbed all the colors of the spectrum except red, which it reflects. White cloth looks white because all the light is reflected. Black cloth, on the other hand, looks black because all the light has been absorbed, none being reflected.

Place a piece of red cellophane over the glass of a flashlight. Shine the red light beam upon blue paper. The paper will appear black because it cannot reflect red.

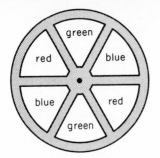

Fig. 16-33 A color wheel produces white. (From A. Joseph et al., *A Sourcebook for the Physical Sciences*, Harcourt, Brace & World, 1961.)

Now shine the red light on red paper. It will be seen as red because it can reflect red. Shine the red light on different colored objects. Make a chart of the results. Repeat, using different colored sheets of cellophane.

PUTTING COLOR TOGETHER

Recall the experiment where you used a magnifying glass to put the colors of the spectrum back together to form white light (described earlier in this chapter).

Have a pupil who owns a metal construction set bring in the toy electric motor that comes with it. Hobby shops also sell tiny electric motors which you can use. Make a cardboard circle 3″ in diameter. Divide the circle into pie-shaped sections (Fig. 16-33). With crayons, color each section. Attach this color wheel to the motor shaft, holding it in place by wrapping cellophane tape around the motor axle. Turn on the motor. All the colors will seem to blend and produce a creamy white color. If one color predominates, scrape some of it off.

Make a similar color wheel, but smaller so that it will just cover the flat surface of a top. Fasten the wheel to the top with a thumbtack. Then spin the top. (Many toy shops sell tops of all sizes with color wheels painted on them.)

Obtain three flashlights of the same size which give the same amount of light. Cover one with layers of red cellophane, one with dark blue cellophane, and one with green cellophane. Experiment with the number of layers needed for each flashlight until all three give colored light of equal intensity. Now shine all three flashlights at one spot in a piece of white cardboard (Fig. 16-34). The spot will appear white. These three colors (red, green, and blue) are called the primary colors. By combining these three primary colors, white is produced. Combining red and green light will produce yellow light. Blue and green will produce blue-green, and red and blue will produce purple. These are the colors of color TV.

When primary colored lights are combined, they add to each other. However, when pigments are combined, they subtract from each other. Mix yellow and blue paint, and you will get a green color. Yellow pigment has some green in it. Blue also has some green in it. If blue and yellow pigments are combined, the yellow and blue are absorbed. This leaves only the green to be reflected. Red and yellow

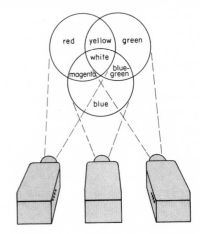

Fig. 16-34 Combining primary color. (From A. Joseph et al., *A Sourcebook for the Physical Sciences*, Harcourt, Brace & World, 1961.)

paint produce orange. Blue and yellow produce green. Red and blue produce violet. The three primary colors of opaque objects are crimson-red, yellow, and peacock-blue. Mix these three paints together, and you get—not white—but black. This combination absorbs all colors and reflects none.

LIGHT CHANGES CERTAIN SUBSTANCES

Fold a piece of dark construction paper in two. Cut a design in the upper half. Put the construction paper on the window sill and let the sun shine on it for a few days. The design will now appear on the lower half of the paper. The sunlight made the construction paper lighter in color.

Place one piece of dark construction paper on the sill for a few days. Put another piece of construction paper in a drawer for the same length of time. Then compare the colors of the two pieces.

Look at a dark blue jacket that has been worn for at least a year. Lift one lapel and compare the color underneath the lapel with the color of that part of the jacket that has been constantly exposed to light.

Obtain a few crystals of silver nitrate (*Caution: This chemical is caustic.*) from your high school chemistry teacher or pharmacist. Dissolve the silver nitrate in a saucer containing about 2 tablespoons of water. With a brush, paint the surface of a smooth sheet of writing paper. Do this in a fairly dark corner of the room. Use caution with the solution as it will stain your fingers and clothes. Now place a coin or button on the paper. Bring the paper over to the window and lay it on the window sill in bright sunlight. After a few minutes remove the coin and examine the sheet. The paper will have turned brown, except where the coin has covered it. Point out that camera film is coated with silver

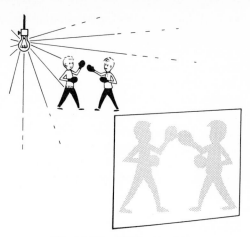

Fig. 16-35 Shadow boxing.

salts. Light affects the salts to produce an image on the film. Repeat, using a negative over the paper. A positive image or picture of the negative will appear. The light splits the silver nitrate, releasing silver which forms the black part of the image.

Place a leaf on fresh blueprint paper. Weigh the leaf down with a sheet of clear glass. Now expose the paper with the leaf on it to the sunlight for several seconds. Remove the leaf and wash the paper with cold water. The blueprint paper is covered with chemicals that are sensitive to light. The chemicals dissolve in water. When light strikes these chemicals, a new chemical is formed that is bright blue. The new chemical does not dissolve in water. The blueprint paper under the leaf was not exposed to the light. The cold water washes away the chemicals that were not changed by the sunlight. This leaves a white leaf on a background of bright blue.

FUN WITH SHADOWS

If an opaque body is placed in the path of a beam of light, a shadow will be formed. Some of the light rays are halted.

Those light rays which pass around the object create an outline for the shadow. To show this, stretch a white bed sheet across the classroom. Darken the classroom. Place a bright lamp about 5′ behind the sheet. Have two boys stand between the sheet and the lamp (Fig. 16-35). The boys can make believe they are boxing, or play dentist, surgeon, or any other pantomime action they wish. Have them watch their shadows and then bring their fists up until their shadows seem to be hitting each other. Thus, although the boys are far apart, their shadows are contacting each other. If you wish to make the boys seem much different in size, have one boy stand near the sheet. His shadow will be about his real size. Have the other boy stand farther away from the sheet and nearer the lamp. He will look like a giant. To show what really happens, remove the sheet and have the boys repeat the action.

CAPSULE LESSONS

16-1 Discuss the difference between direct and indirect lighting. List the advantages and disadvantages of each. Which is best for reading? What is the best position for reading?

16-2 Bring in an expert to show how the school is lighted. Have him demonstrate a light meter and show the pupils how to check the amount of light in different parts of the room, the auditorium, cafeteria, etc.

16-3 Using two mirrors, show how a person can see the back of his head. Attach a pocket mirror to a ruler, using Scotch tape or paper clips. Let the children take turns standing at one side of the door and holding the mirror outside the door. They will not be able to see around corners. Lead into the study of the reflection of light and mirrors.

16-4 Borrow an eye chart and have some pupils demonstrate its use. Lead into the study of near-sightedness and far-sightedness. Discuss the care of the eyes.

16-5 Find a pupil who develops his own pictures. Have him demonstrate the process to the rest of the class. If possible, arrange for the high school photography club, a professional photographer, or a competent amateur to show how enlarging is done.

16-6 Have the children examine the construction and operation of a slide projector or film strip projector. Continue with a study of lenses. Have a student explain why the slides or film are inserted upside down.

16-7 Discuss how motion pictures are made and projected. Let a pupil who has a movie camera and projector at home bring them in for demonstration. Show how persistence of vision creates the illusion of motion.

16-8 Borrow a microscope from the high school biology teacher. Have the class study its operation and the part which lenses play in producing magnification.

16-9 Bring in a book on interior decoration. Have the class find out which colors produce the most pleasing combinations for walls, draperies, and slip covers.

16-10 Let the class study how objects were camouflaged during the war. Have the class investigate which animals are protectively colored to blend in with their surroundings.

BIBLIOGRAPHY

Adler, Irving, *The Secret of Light,* International, 1952. Presents simple concepts on light and color, together with theories about light and its properties. Includes sections on relationship between light and atomic energy and on man's use of light to conquer nature.

Beeler, Nelson, and Franklyn Branley, *Experiments with Light,* Crowell, 1958. Discusses the nature of light and its properties. Includes lenses and their use in microscopes, telescopes, etc.

Bragdon, Lillian J., *Let There Be Light,* Lippincott, 1959. Describes man's use of fire, coal, gas, oil, and electricity to produce light. Also explores future potentialities in lighting.

Meyer, Jerome S., *Prisms and Lenses,* World, 1959. Explains the principles of light as they apply to prisms and lenses.

Paschel, Herbert P., *The First Book of Color,* Watts, 1959. Explanation of light and color and how they are formed.

Perry, John, *Our Wonderful Eyes,* McGraw-Hill, 1955. Describes structure, function, and proper care of our eyes.

17

Fire

Fire is a constant fascination for young and old. Eyes are drawn to the glowing candles on a birthday cake. The changing colors and shapes of the flames in a fireplace or a campfire weave a magic spell of enchantment. The flare and glare of rockets and fireworks at a July 4th celebration stimulate and excite the imagination. The raging flames of a burning building or forest fire invite awe and terror. Fire is a constant part of the child's environment. A natural interest exists in learning the source of fire, its uses, and its control.

STARTING A FIRE

How does fire come into being? What conditions must be present before a fire can start? First, we need a material that will "burn."

What we burn—fuels

Natural fuels include wood, coal, crude petroleum oil, and natural gas. Derived or manufactured fuels include paper, candle wax, coke, charcoal, fuel oil, gasoline, kerosene, fuel gas, and propane or bottled gas.

To show how one fuel—coke—is made, use a metal can with a tight-fitting cover, such as a coffee can. Punch a small hole in the center of the cover. Fill the can about one fourth full of soft coal which has been crushed or broken into small pieces. Heat the can and its contents on a hot plate or electric stove. A smoky gas will soon come through the nail hole. Wait a short while until all air has been driven from the can; then light the coal gas. Heat the can until all the gas has burned. After the can has cooled, let the children examine the contents. The solid black material is coke; the emitted gas was coal gas.

Repeat the experiment, using short pieces of wood. This time charcoal is formed. You may want to try it once more, this time using a crumpled sheet of newspaper or paper towel.

If the children would like to see what happens when the materials are heated in the absence of air, repeat the experiment using a test tube instead of a tin can. Use a Pyrex glass test tube fitted with a one-hole cork stopper containing a short glass tube (Fig. 17-1). Place some crushed soft coal in the test tube, stopper tightly, and heat strongly over a Bunsen burner flame. Keep the burner moving to vary the point of heating. Light the gas that is given off and continue heating until no more gas is formed. Let the test tube cool; then break it and examine the coke that has been formed. Repeat the experiment, using short pieces of wood. You may want to collect the gas in a storage tank as in Fig. 17-1. This experiment illustrates on a small scale some of the methods of gas production and storage.

Have the children compile a list of

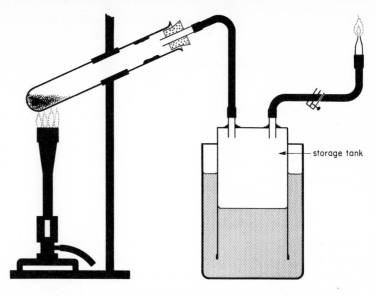

Fig. 17-1 Heating fuels in the absence of air. (From A. Joseph et al., *A Sourcebook for the Physical Sciences*, Harcourt, Brace & World, 1961.)

storage tank

fuels. Classify the fuels as natural or manufactured, and note whether they are solid, liquid, or gas. The children may want to assemble a sample collection of fuels obtained from home or their fuel dealers. Illustrate the burning of a liquid fuel by igniting kerosene or alcohol in a small bottle cap. Use a Bunsen burner to show gas combustion.

Kindling temperature

Some fuels burn more easily than you would expect; others, less so. Usually fuels do not catch fire by themselves, no matter how easily they burn. Fuels must be heated until they are hot enough to burst into flame.

Obtain a candle, celluloid film negative, twist of paper, twist of cotton cloth, thin stick of wood, and piece of coal. Light a Bunsen burner or alcohol lamp. Bring each object to the flame and see how long each takes to start burning. Do not hold the object in your hand, but use either kitchen forceps, pliers, a long-handled spoon, or a long fork with a wooden handle. Have a pan or pail of water handy for safety.

Try out several other substances and

have the children list them in order of ease of burning. Develop the concept that the temperature at which the substance bursts into flame is called its *kindling temperature,* and that each substance has a different kindling temperature.

To compare kindling temperatures, place a sheet of iron or copper 6″ square on a ring stand, on a tripod, or on bricks. A four-armed cross of metal cut from a tin can may be substituted for the sheet (Fig. 17-2). Put the head of a match, a piece of sulfur, wood, and coal on the sheet or on each end of the arm. The materials must be approximately the same size and must be placed at equal distances from the center of the sheet or cross. Place a Bunsen burner beneath the center of the sheet or cross, and light it. Note the order in which each material reaches its kindling temperature and bursts into flame. Do not be surprised if the coal does not burn. Help the children understand that one of the conditions necessary for fire is that the fuel must be heated until it reaches its kindling temperature. Actually a fuel begins to burn only when enough of the fuel has vaporized. The kindling temperature involves vaporizing the material to the tem-

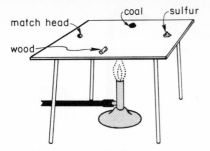

Fig. 17-2 Comparing kindling temperatures of various substances.

perature at which the vapor bursts into flame. A candle burns vaporized wax or paraffin. The wax must melt and then vaporize. This can be shown by inserting a long thin glass tube into the blue part of the candle flame and then burning the gas or vapor in the candle flame at the end of the glass tube (Fig. 17-3).

Air for fire

Halloween time provides an excellent opportunity to show the children that air is necessary to keep a fire going. When preparing the class jack-o-lantern, first cut off the top of the pumpkin and scoop out the flesh and seeds. Place a candle inside the pumpkin, light it, and replace the top of the pumpkin. After a short while, lift up the pumpkin top and note that the flame has gone out. Now cut out the eyes, nose, and mouth. Light the candle again and put back the pumpkin top. The candle continues to burn brightly because it now has a constant supply of air. To show what happens, repeat, using an inverted milk bottle over a candle.

Prepare a series of cardboard squares (metal can covers are better) upon which candles can be rested. Or 5″ × 8″ index cards can be used. Obtain at least six candles no more than 2″ or 3″ long. If necessary, cut new or used candles into the desired lengths and cut the paraffin away from one end until you have a wick at least ¼″ long. Try to get all the candles uniform in diameter and height. To fasten these candles to the cardboard squares, first light one candle. Tilt the candle sideways and allow 3 or 4 drops of the hot wax to drop on the center of the cardboard square. While the wax is still soft, hold the base of the candle against the wax until the wax hardens.

Light a candle attached to a cardboard square. Set a glass jar or drinking glass over the candle. The flame will gradually go out.

Set up five burning candles in a row. Obtain four sizes of glass jars—preferably a half-pint, pint, quart, and gallon jar. This will help the children understand that there is twice as much air in the pint jar as there is in the half-pint jar, and so on. Place each of the four jars over a burning candle at the same time. The fifth candle, uncovered, is the control. Using an electric clock or wrist watch with a sweep-second hand, have the children note how long it takes for each covered candle to go out. The more air there is in the jar, the longer the candle will burn. The candle under the pint jar will burn about twice as long as the candle in the half-pint jar. Have the children find out the relationship between the air in the jars and the length of time the candles will burn.

Place two burning candles side by side. Obtain two glass chimneys (usually from a hardware store) or make your own by using two #2 tin cans with their tops re-

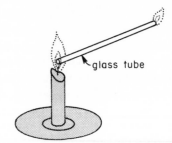

Fig. 17-3 A flame is a mass of burning gas.

moved. With a can opener cut a smaller opening in the bottom of each can. Now set both chimneys over the lighted candles, and slip flat sticks of wood or pencils under one chimney. The candle under the chimney that is resting on sticks or pencils will continue to burn because it has a ready supply of air coming in from the bottom. The other candle goes out.

Air consists primarily of two gases, oxygen and nitrogen. Air contains approximately 21% oxygen, 78% nitrogen, and 1% other gases. Light a birthday-cake candle and fasten it to the bottom of a small pan in the same way as you fastened the candle to the cardboard square. Pour about an inch of water carefully into the pan. Now put a tall clear drinking glass over the candle. The candle will soon go out. Notice how the water rises up in the drinking glass. Help the children understand that a special part of the air (oxygen) is necessary for burning. When this part is used up, the flame goes out. The water rises to take the place of the air that was used up by combustion and pushed out by expansion. Measure the height of the glass; then measure how high the water rose in the glass.

For upper-grade children to measure accurately the amount of oxygen, set some red phosphorus on a flat cork or piece of plywood as a float. Red phosphorus can be obtained from your high school chemistry teacher or from a science supply house.[1] Place the cork on water in a basin and hold a large olive jar over the float. Touch the red phosphorus with a hot wire that has been heated in a candle flame. Then cover the float with the jar. At first a cloud of white smoke forms. This is phosphorus pentoxide (P_2O_5). It will soon dissolve in the water. As it dissolves, water rises up in the jar. Lift the jar to just below

[1] Never use yellow (or white) phosphorus. More active than the red, it bursts into flame on contact with air.

the water surface and measure the amount of water that rose. This should be one fifth the height of the jar.

A comparison of these two measurements will show that the water rose to a height which is about one fifth or 20% of the height of the glass. This roughly corresponds to the per cent of oxygen in the air. Help the children understand that fire needs oxygen in order to burn. Actually a candle (unlike the phosphorus) goes out before all oxygen is removed, or at about the 10% level.

Wrap a piece of soft thin wire around a candle. Bend up the rest of the wire to serve as a handle. Light the candle, lower it into a pint jar, then cover the jar with a sheet of glass or metal. The flame will soon go out. Remove the candle, keep the jar covered, relight the candle, and replace it quickly into the jar. The flame will go out almost at once because so much of the oxygen in the jar has been used up that the air can no longer support combustion.

The children may now be in a position to summarize the three things that are needed to create fire: (1) fuel—a material that will burn, (2) air containing oxygen, and (3) heating of the fuel until it reaches its kindling temperature.

BUILDING A FIRE

Every Boy Scout should know how to start a fire. He arranges the materials so that he will have either a tepee or a crisscross (log cabin) campfire. This arrangement makes plenty of air available to keep the fire burning.

He piles up first dry leaves, then small twigs, and finally heavier wood allowing plenty of air space. He uses a lighted match to heat the thin, quickly heated leaves to their kindling temperature. The heat of the leaves, in turn, heats the twigs to their kindling temperature. As the twigs burn, more air is able to reach up through the pile.

In a fireplace the wood rests upon the andirons. This permits a steady supply of fresh air underneath the fire. Paper, thin pieces of wood, and logs arranged in the same way as in the campfire, progressively reach their kindling points. Coal takes a long time to reach kindling temperature.

The surface area of a fuel plays an important part in getting the fuel to burn. The greater the surface, the easier it will burn. Burn a sheet of paper crumpled into a tight ball and burn a similar sheet spread out. Compare rates of burning. Take two small pieces of absorbent cotton about the same size. Roll one into a tight little ball, hold it with forceps or tongs, and try to burn it. It will burn slowly and quietly for some time. Now spread out the other piece of cotton as much as you can. Holding it in the tongs as far away from yourself as possible, set fire to the cotton. It will flare up quickly and burn completely in a second or two.

Help the children understand that with greater surface area, a greater amount of oxygen can reach the fuel, and thereby the rate of burning is increased. This is why powdered fuel burns so quickly. Try setting fire to a lump of coal. Now powder the coal and place it in a long-handled spoon. Holding the spoon as far away from yourself as possible, sprinkle some of the powdered coal into the flame of a Bunsen burner. The powder will burn quickly, giving off much heat.

Obtain lycopodium powder at the drugstore. Very fine, dry cornstarch will serve just as well. The starch may be dried by placing it in an open dish on top of a hot radiator for a few hours. Loosely fill a soda straw about one fourth full of the lycopodium powder or starch. Blow the powder or starch directly across the top of the flame of a Bunsen burner, alcohol lamp, or Sterno. (Be sure to blow away from children.) A quick long flame results as the powder burns all at one time.

Also try to burn a solid piece of aluminum. Then sprinkle aluminum powder onto a metal tray and put a gas flame to the powder. It will burst into flame. Try burning an iron nail. Of course, it will not burn. Carefully sprinkle iron filings into a gas flame; the iron particles will catch fire. If a Bunsen burner is unavailable, you can use a portable gas tank torch sold in hardware stores, such as the Benzomatic. Torches of this type are available from scientific supply houses and in chain stores such as Sears Roebuck.

STORY OF A FLAME

Set a candle on a cardboard square. Light a match and lower it to the wick. It will be necessary actually to touch the wick in order to light it. Now let the candle burn for 2 or 3 minutes. Notice the pool of melted paraffin around the wick. Blow out the candle flame and immediately begin lowering a lighted match to the smoking wick. The wick will now light up before the match touches it. Sometimes it is possible to light the candle this way when the match is an inch or more above the wick.

When the wick of a candle is first lighted, the heat of the burning wick melts the paraffin. This melted paraffin climbs up the wick, where the flame vaporizes the liquid paraffin into gases. It is these gases which burn. As long as the candle burns, paraffin will melt, rise up the wick, and then change to a gas which burns. When the candle flame is blown out, the warm wick still continues to form gas for a short time. This explains why the wick lit up again before the lighted match actually touched it. Have the children observe how alcohol and kerosene rise up their lamp wicks.

To show that flame is a mass of burning gas, take a glass tube about 6″ long and insert it in a candle flame just above the wick (Fig. 17-3). If the tube is unavailable, hold the wide end of a glass medicine dropper into the flame, using pliers or tongs. Now put a lighted match to the other end of the tube. A flame will appear at this end.

Regions and colors of flame

Have the children examine a candle flame carefully and then draw what they see on the board. Call attention to the two regions of the flame. The region next to the wick is dark, while the outside region is bright yellow. The dark inside region cannot get as much air as the yellow outside region. Therefore, the gas in the dark region is not burning as completely as the gas in the yellow region, and is not as hot. This can be shown by lowering a round stick about 6″ long into a candle flame until it almost touches the wick. Hold it there for a few seconds; then lift it straight out of the flame. Notice the dark ring which is formed, with the center uncharred. The uncharred part was in contact with the cooler inside region. The same effect can be shown by using a filing card. Hold it horizontally in the flame just above the wick. Remove the card as soon as it begins to scorch. A ring with an unscorched center will result.

Recall your previous experiments in making fuel gas. In each case the heated fuels formed gases which burned. Develop the understanding that, regardless of the fuel used, the flame produced is made up of burning gas.

The Bunsen burner offers an excellent opportunity to observe how the supply of oxygen affects a flame.

Adjust the opening at the base of the Bunsen burner so that the flame of the Bunsen burner is blue. Air (which contains oxygen) is able to come in through the opening and mix with the gas. The blue flame shows that the gas is being completely burned. Now put your fingers over the opening. This shuts off the supply of air. The flame changes from blue to yellow. The yellow color comes from hot but not completely burned particles of carbon in the gas.

Hold a white china dish first against the yellow flame, then against the blue flame. The yellow flame will make the dish quite sooty, owing to the presence of the incompletely burned particles of carbon. The blue flame will form little or no soot, because the fuel is burning completely.

The yellow flame is not as hot as the blue flame. Boil equal quantities of water with each flame, and note which flame causes boiling first.

Just as in the candle, the inner portion of the Bunsen flame is cooler than the outer portion because it does not get as much oxygen. Cut the stick of a wooden match to a length of about 2″. Push a pin through the match just below the head until the pin extends about the same distance from each side of the match. Place the match, head up, into the barrel of an unlit burner. The pin rests on the burner and supports the match (Fig. 17-4). Move the match until the head is in the center of the tube. Adjust the opening at the base of the burner to allow as much air as possible to enter. Now turn the gas on full and light the burner, igniting the gas from one side of the top of the barrel. Usually the gas will burn without setting the match on fire. Evidently the temperature of the inner portion of the flame is below the kindling temperature of the match head. Sometimes the match will burst into flame after the gas has been burning a while. If the school does not have a gas supply, use a simple portable gas burner and tank.

Have the children examine a gas stove and compare it with a Bunsen burner.

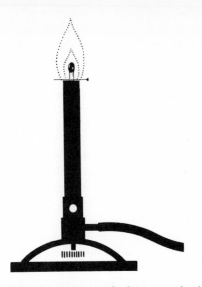

Fig. 17-4 The inner part of a flame is cooler than the outer part. (From A. Joseph et al., *A Sourcebook for the Physical Sciences*, Harcourt, Brace & World, 1961.)

PUTTING OUT FIRE

You have already shown that there are three conditions necessary to have fire. If any one of these is missing, the fire will go out.

If the fuel is removed, the fire cannot continue. A campfire can be put out by scattering the burning wood. When forest fires occur, the fire fighters clear a broad path around the burning area. When the fire reaches the path, it has no more fuel and the fire goes out. When a fire breaks out near an oil tank, the oil is quickly pumped out of the other tanks. If a building is on fire, the gas supply is turned off.

If the burning material is cooled below its kindling temperature, the fire will go out. Try this experiment. Turn on the gas full force in a Bunsen burner. Hold a sheet of iron, copper, or aluminum gauze about 2″ above the barrel. Apply a lighted match to the gas above the gauze. A flame will appear above the gauze but not below it. The heat of the flame is conducted away from the gas by the gauze. This keeps the temperature of the gas un-derneath the gauze below the kindling temperature.

The children may want to make a model of a miner's safety lamp. Take two large flat corks about 2″ in diameter. Set a lighted candle upright on one of the corks. Obtain fine copper or aluminum gauze about 2–8″ wide. Wrap the gauze around both corks and fasten it securely to both the corks with thumbtacks (Fig. 17-5). If the mesh isn't fine enough, wrap the gauze around two or three times. The heat from the candle flame is conducted away by the gauze. If an inflammable gas were brought near the gauze, the temperature would not be high enough to reach the kindling temperature of the gas. If the model of the miner's safety lamp is set inside a jar, the inflammable gas can be allowed to flow into the jar.

Water is most often used to put out ordinary fires. Water does not burn and also is able to absorb much heat. This cools the burning material below its kindling temperature, and the fire goes out. Water also wets the fuel so that it is less combustible.

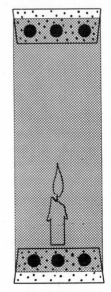

Fig. 17-5 A miner's safety lamp. (From A. Joseph et al., *A Sourcebook for the Physical Sciences*, Harcourt, Brace & World, 1961.)

Dip most of a wooden match in water until it is quite wet. See how long it takes to light the moist head of the match in a candle flame. Compare the time it takes with that required for a dry match.

Soak a handkerchief in a liquid made up of 2 parts alcohol and 1 part water. Squeeze out any excess liquid. Hold the handkerchief with tongs over a metal basin and, keeping it away from inflammable materials, apply a lighted match to the handkerchief. The alcohol will burn but not the handkerchief. The water keeps the temperature of the cloth below its kindling temperature.

Try putting out a candle flame, using a perfume atomizer filled with water.

Fill a very small, thin flat cardboard box half full of water. Place the box on a metal screen supported on a tripod, iron ring, or two piles of bricks. Heat the box with a Bunsen burner. The water will boil, but the cardboard will not burn.

Keeping air away from a fire will make it go out. That is why sand is sprinkled on campfires. The best thing to do when clothing catches on fire is to smother it with a blanket, rug, or woolen coat. Do not run, because the breeze will fan the flames. If there is a fire in a room, opening the windows will only let in more air.

The most commonly used method of keeping air away from a fire is to replace the air with a heavy noninflammable gas such as carbon dioxide.

Dry ice is solid carbon dioxide. Put dry ice in a metal pitcher. Handle the dry ice with a pair of gloves because the dry ice is very cold and can cause frostbite. Let the pitcher stand while the dry ice evaporates to carbon dioxide gas. You can hasten this process by placing the bottom of the pitcher in a pot of hot water. Wrap a thin wire around a lighted candle and lower the candle into the pitcher. The flame will go out. Or pour the carbon dioxide gas over the candle flame. The

flame will go out. This effect is even more spectacular if you pour the carbon dioxide down a trough containing many candles. Set five candles on a narrow piece of wood. Prepare a trough by tacking heavy paper or cardboard to the sides and ends of the wood. Tilt one end of the trough and light the candles. Pour the carbon dioxide gas down the trough. The candle flames will go out in succession.

Carbon dioxide gas can be chemically prepared in the classroom. For details, see Chapter 12. Carbon dioxide gas made in the classroom can be poured over a candle flame in the same way as when it is released from dry ice.

Obtain a carbon dioxide cartridge, the kind that is used to make carbonated water. Puncture the cartridge with a carbon dioxide cartridge gun and aim the escaping gas at a candle flame. Wrap the cartridge in cloth first because the cartridge becomes very cold. The cartridge gun may be obtained at a hobby shop. If the cartridge gun is not available, the cartridge may be punctured with a sharp nail hit by a hammer, but you must work fast before all the carbon dioxide gas escapes.

Another easy way to show the smothering quality of CO_2 is to tip a jar of vinegar

Fig. 17-6 Carbon dioxide gas smothers a flame.

and bicarbonate of soda so that the gas formed flows down a folded paper trough (Fig. 17-6) aimed directly at a candle flame.

Ink-bottle extinguisher

Take an empty ink bottle that has a well on its side. The Skrip ink bottle does quite well. With a hammer and nail punch a hole through the metal screw cap. Insert a straw, glass tube, or straight medicine dropper through the hole. Seal any openings around the hole with chewing gum or sealing wax. You may want to use a plastic medicine dropper. In this case punch a uniform hole slightly smaller than the diameter of the dropper and work the dropper in. This will make the dropper virtually airtight and will thus cut down on the amount, if any, of sealing wax necessary. Fill the side pocket of the ink bottle with powdered sodium bicarbonate. Pour household vinegar into the bottle until it is about one fourth full. While pouring, be careful that the vinegar does not come in contact with the sodium bicarbonate. Screw the cap on the ink bottle securely. Your fire extinguisher is now ready (Fig. 17-7). Crumple some paper in a shallow metal pan and set it on fire. Tip the ink bottle upside down and aim it at the fire.

Not only does the carbon dioxide gas put out the fire, but the water helps as well.

Other soda-acid extinguishers

The same experiment may be repeated on a large scale, using a milk or other widemouthed bottle (Figs. 17-8, 17-9). Insert a glass tube through a cork stopper which fits into the neck of the milk bottle tightly. Put sealing wax or chewing gum around the point where the tube goes through the stopper. Fill the bottle half full of vinegar and water. Fill a small test tube with powdered sodium bicarbonate and wrap some thin wire around the neck. Bend the other end of the wire so that it hangs from the neck of the bottle. Now stopper the bottle very tightly and turn it upside down when ready to use.

Have the children study the commercial fire extinguisher. Call their attention to the fact that the positions of the chemicals are reversed in this case. The small vial contains sulfuric acid, which is a

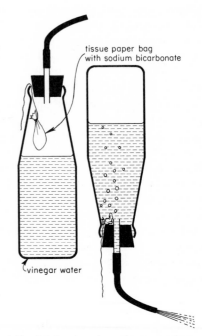

tissue paper bag with sodium bicarbonate

vinegar water

Fig. 17-8 A soda-acid extinguisher.

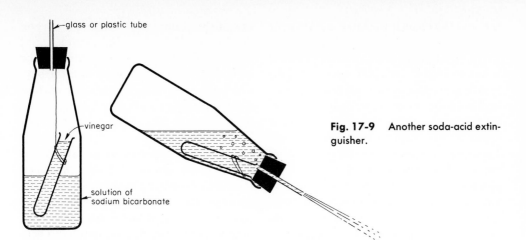

glass or plastic tube

vinegar

solution of
sodium bicarbonate

Fig. 17-9 Another soda-acid extinguisher.

stronger acid than vinegar. The rest of the container is filled with concentrated sodium bicarbonate solution.

Foam extinguisher

Some fires are difficult to put out with water or the usual type of fire extinguisher. Pour ¼ ounce kerosene into a small deep saucer. Light the kerosene and pour water on the burning kerosene. Water is heavier than kerosene and sinks to the bottom, leaving the burning kerosene on top. Repeat this experiment, using the carbon dioxide extinguisher. The rapid stream only stirs up the fire.

To combat kerosene and oil fires, a foam extinguisher must be used. Dissolve as much baking soda as you can in a pint of water. Pour this solution into a large jar. Put the white of an egg, or aluminum sulfate and ground licorice root, into the jar of baking soda solution and stir thoroughly. Now dissolve as much powdered alum as you can in another pint of water. Pour the alum solution quickly into the large jar which contains the baking soda solution. A large quantity of white foamy bubbles of carbon dioxide gas are formed. These bubbles are slow to break up because of the egg white and alum. The foamy bubbles cover kerosene and oil fires effectively, smothering them.

PRODUCTS OF BURNING

Water

Chill a glass or beaker and hold it over a candle flame for a few seconds. Notice the film of moisture that forms on the glass. Repeat the experiment, using a chilled spoon. The spoon fogs up, and even water droplets may form. One of the products of burning, then, is water. Test other flames in this way to see if water is one of the products of burning.

Carbon dioxide

Now take a narrow-necked half-pint or pint bottle. Select a tight-fitting stopper which contains a glass tube through it. If the stopper and tube are not available, use a bottle with a metal screw cap. Puncture a hole through the cap and insert a plastic medicine dropper. The hole should be uniform and slightly smaller than the dropper. Connect a long piece of rubber tubing to the end of the glass tube or dropper. Have the other end of the rubber tubing extend to the bottom of a glass one fourth full of limewater. Put 2 teaspoons of baking soda in the bottle. Add vinegar; then stopper the bottle tightly. The limewater soon becomes milky. This is a test for carbon dioxide gas. The baking soda and vinegar form carbon dioxide gas. The gas flows through the rubber tubing into the clear limewater, making the limewater turn milky.

Apply a lighted match to the bottom of a candle until the paraffin softens. Set the candle immediately in a tall drinking glass and hold the candle firmly until the paraffin hardens. Carefully pour limewater into the glass until it is one fourth full. Light the candle. Cover the glass with a saucer. When the candle goes out, shake the glass, keeping the glass well-covered with the saucer. The limewater turns milky, showing the presence of carbon dioxide. Another product of burning is carbon dioxide gas.

Wrap a piece of copper wire around a candle. Light the candle and lower the candle into a tall bottle. After a while the flame goes out. When this happens, remove the candle. Add some limewater to the jar, hold your hand over the mouth of the jar, and shake it. The limewater turns milky. Pour some limewater into another jar of just air and shake. The limewater remains clear. This shows that the carbon dioxide came from the burning candle.

WHAT IS IN FUELS?

Carbon

Lower a white china dish into a candle flame. A black sooty spot soon appears on the dish. Repeat this experiment, using flames from other fuels. This soot is unburned carbon. Evidently the flame contains carbon which is burning. When the flame touches the dish, the porcelain cools the flame and the unburned carbon deposits on the dish.

Recall your experiments in making gas from soft coal and wood. The remaining products were coke and charcoal, respectively. Both are forms of carbon. This leads to the conclusion that fuels contain carbon.

Recall the experiments showing that one of the products of burning is carbon dioxide gas. Help the children understand that carbon dioxide is formed when the carbon of the fuel combines with the oxygen in the air. The formula for carbon dioxide is CO_2.

Hydrogen

Recall the experiment where chilled objects held against a flame produced mist, fog, or water droplets. Develop the concept that water is composed of 2 parts of hydrogen and 1 part of oxygen (H_2O). Fuels evidently contain hydrogen. In the process of burning, the hydrogen of the fuel combines with the oxygen of the air to form water.

Thus, fuels usually contain carbon and hydrogen in complex forms. Benzene is C_6H_6. Good gasoline is C_8H_{18}. When fuels are burned, the heat breaks up these complex substances into simpler substances which are gaseous. It is these gases which produce the flame.

MAKING COLORED FLAMES

Rainbow pine cones

Obtain a supply of dry pine cones. If cones are not available, small chips or blocks of dry wood will do. Take a large wooden bucket or earthenware jar. In it dissolve copper sulfate (obtained from a science supply house or through the local drugstore) in water, using the ratio of 1 pound of copper sulfate to 1 gallon of water. Stir thoroughly. Place the cones in a mesh bag, like an onion or potato sack, and immerse them in the solution.

Remove the cones after they have soaked overnight. Let them drain over the container for a few minutes. Then spread the cones out on a newspaper to dry overnight. When dry, they can be added to the logs in a fireplace and will produce a beautiful emerald-green color.

Other chemicals can be used. Barium

nitrate produces an apple-green flame; strontium nitrate, red; copper chloride, bluish green; potassium chloride, purple. Of these, potassium chloride and copper chloride are the least expensive.

Do not re-use the bucket or jar for any other purpose unless it is thoroughly cleaned. Also use caution in disposing of any remaining chemical solutions. Do not pour down plumbing fixtures unless the pipes are made of lead. Even then the water should be allowed to run for some time after the chemical solution has been poured down the pipes. An alternate procedure would be to pour the solution down a sewer or into the ground in a waste plot or dump.

Yule logs

Fold newspapers in half and roll them into logs about 3″ thick and 16″ long. Do not make them too thick because they swell on soaking. Tie the paper logs with twine.

Dissolve 5 pounds of copper sulfate (blue stone), 4 pounds of iron sulfate (green vitriol), and 3 pounds of rock salt in about 8 gallons of water. Nurseries usually have these three chemicals. This quantity should make about eight logs. Soak the rolled newspapers in this solution for 3 weeks. Keep the container covered, and frequently turn the paper logs end over during this period of time. Now take the

logs out and let them dry thoroughly, preferably in the sun. One log will burn in a fireplace for several hours, producing rainbow colors.

FIRE HAZARDS

Fire is useful and essential for daily living. However, fire out of control is a dangerous and expensive hazard. There are many ways in which fire can be created accidentally, often with disastrous results.

Tiny particles create a hazard because they burn with such explosive speed. The tiny particles offer a great deal of surface per unit of fuel. Being tiny and surrounded on all sides by oxygen, they burn quickly. Recall the experiment where the soda straw was partially filled with lycopodium powder or fine dry cornstarch. When the powder was blown across a flame, a quick flash resulted.

Cut or punch a round hole at one end of a large metal can that has a tight-fitting cover. Put a funnel into the hole from the inside. Attach a rubber tube to the end of the funnel where it comes out of the can. Set a candle at the other side of the can. Tilt the funnel so that it is aimed at the candle wick. Place a small wad of cotton in the bottom of the funnel and then add a teaspoon of lycopodium powder. Now attach the other end of the rubber tube

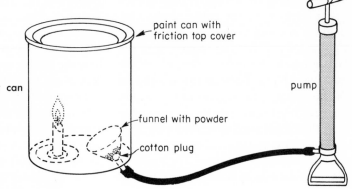

Fig. 17-10 Fine powder can produce an explosion.

paint can with friction top cover

pump

funnel with powder

cotton plug

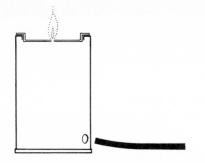

Fig. 17-11 Gas can produce an explosion. (From A. Joseph et al., *A Sourcebook for the Physical Sciences*, Harcourt, Brace & World, 1961.)

to a bicycle pump or use your breath (Fig. 17-10). Light the candle and put the can cover on securely. With the pump blow a blast of air sharply into the can. The powder, now a cloud of dust, is kindled by the candle flame, burning explosively. The resultant sudden heating of the air and production of gases blow the cover up into the air. (*Caution: When doing this experiment, be sure to have children stand back.*) The tin cover flies straight up, and it is therefore wise not to perform the demonstration under a light fixture.

Put some kerosene in an atomizer and spray the kerosene across a candle flame. (*Exercise caution.*) The atomizer breaks the kerosene into many tiny particles which burn with an explosive flash. Keep children back.

Punch a hole in the lower side of a coffee can which has a tight-fitting cover. The hole should be large enough for a rubber tube to fit in snugly. Now punch a smaller hole in the cover of the can. Connect one end of the rubber tubing to a gas supply. Place the other end of the tubing inside the hole at the side of the can (Fig. 17-11). Turn on the gas and let the gas come into the can until you are sure gas has displaced the air inside the can; then light the gas escaping through the hole in the can cover. Now turn off the gas and remove the tubing. The escaping gas burns quietly at first while fresh air is

coming in the hole at the side of the can. Soon the combination of gas and air reaches the proportions of an explosive mixture. At this point there is an explosion and the cover blows off. (*Caution: This experiment should be shielded with fish net, screening, or wire gauze, and the children should stand well away.*)

Help the children understand that the same effect takes place with gasoline. Gasoline evaporates quickly to form a gas. When mixed with air in the correct proportion (about 16 to 1), it forms an explosive mixture.

Show that a lighted cigarette is hot enough to produce a fire. Ask any Boy Scout to bring in some tinder. This tinder is very much like the decayed leaves and brush lying in the forest. You can make tinder by shredding dead bark and heating it in an oven. Place the tinder in a metal pan and put the lighted cigarette on it. Blow gently on the glowing tinder until the tinder bursts into flame. A flipped cigarette and a breeze make ideal conditions for a forest fire.

The sun's rays, when focused properly, can cause fire. Place a match in a metal pan. Use a magnifying glass to focus sunlight on the match head. The head will burst into flame. Focus the sunlight on your hand for a few seconds and notice the heat produced.

Place a round goldfish bowl in the sunlight. Find where the sun's rays come together at a point, just as with the magnifying glass. Place a thermometer near the bowl so that the point where the rays focus strikes the bulb of the thermometer. Note how the temperature rises. Discarded pop bottles can cause forest fires this way.

Have the children rub a pencil eraser briskly on their desks and then place the eraser to their upper lips. The eraser has become quite warm. The heat is due to friction. A knife placed against a grindstone produces enough heat to make sparks. The sparks are caused by the heated particles of stone and iron. Notice how warm a saw or drill becomes when it is used. Persons working in flour mills wear rubber soles to avoid creating sparks caused by leather soles with nails. Such sparks could set fire to the flour dust, and the whole mill would explode into fire. Refer to the experiment with exploding lycopodium powder. Flour dust explodes the same way.

In the home, electrical wiring can be a hazard. Electricity produces heat. Sometimes the insulation surrounding the wires is worn away until the wires are exposed and touch. The heat of the wires when they short circuit may set materials in the walls on fire.

Dismantle the electric cord from an old flatiron. The wire is wrapped in asbestos or mica rather than in the rubber usually found on ordinary electric wire. Hold the asbestos or mica in a candle flame to show that it does not burn. Place a piece of rubber from ordinary electric wire in a candle flame and show that it chars. This proves that ordinary rubber wire would soon scorch and melt if used in a flatiron. Point out the necessity for special asbestos-insulated cords for electric irons, toasters, heaters, and stoves.

Another electrical fire hazard is the burning of paper and fabric lamp shades when they rest too near an electric light bulb. Wrap a piece of paper around a 100-watt electric bulb and place the bulb into a socket. Turn on the current. After a few minutes the paper will scorch.

Christmas trees are very inflammable. Remove a small branch from a pine tree and let it dry in a warm room for several days. Place the branch in a large pan or basin and see how easily it can be set on fire. Take another freshly cut branch and allow it to stand in water for a few days. Try igniting it. It will not burn. Recommend that the bases of Christmas trees be placed in a bucket of water.

Oil or paint rags are a hazard because they can burst into flame by spontaneous combustion. When placed in a closet, the oil or paint in the rag combines slowly with oxygen in the air. In so doing, it gradually becomes warm enough to burn.

FIREPROOFING

Mix equal parts of borax, alum, and ammonium phosphate. Dissolve as much of the mixture as possible in a bowl two thirds full of warm water. When no more can dissolve, there will be a slight excess in the bottom of the bowl. Dip pieces of cloth in this solution and allow to dry. Try to burn these pieces of cloth in a candle flame. Compare the result by burning untreated pieces of cloth.

Another fireproofing solution for cloth may be made by using equal parts of borax and boric acid in enough warm water for both chemicals to dissolve completely. Treat the cloths, and test the same way as stated in the experiment above.

Fireproof paints owe their fireproofing quality to the presence of water-glass (sodium silicate). Paint a strip of wood with at least three coats of water-glass solution. Allow each coat to dry before applying the next coat. When the last coat has been applied and is dry, hold the stick over the flame of a Bunsen burner or gas range. The coating swells and a froth is formed, but the wood does not burn.

Paper may be fireproofed by dissolving 2 ounces of ammonium sulfate, ½ ounce of borax, and ½ ounce of boric acid in enough warm water to dissolve all three chemicals completely. Immerse the paper and allow it to dry. Apply a candle flame first to untreated paper and then to the treated paper.

CAPSULE LESSONS

17-1 Make lists of fuels used in your community. Discuss the advantages and disadvantages of each kind of fuel for various uses. Collect and exhibit different types of fuels. Look into their composition.

17-2 Examine your school heating system. Now discuss what conditions are necessary to create fire and what products are formed by fire.

17-3 If your locality uses coal gas, investigate what it is, where it comes from, and how it is obtained. Do the same for natural gas and bottled gas.

17-4 Investigate the manufacture of the match. Have students report on the history of the match. Demonstrate the differences between friction matches and safety matches. Demonstrate the proper way to strike a match—away from you, not toward you. Discuss the reasons for closing the cover of book matches before striking a match. Discuss other safety rules.

17-5 Make candles, using paraffin, candle wax, and odd pieces of candles. Heat them on a hot plate in the top of a double boiler. Add pieces of colored wax crayons to give the desired color. After the wax is melted, pour the wax into frozen juice cans or tin Jello molds. Put braided wicks in place and allow the wax to harden. The candles may be removed by soaking the cans or molds in hot water. Light the candles and study flames and the process of burning.

17-6 Study the construction and operation of cigarette lighters. Lead into a discussion of the conditions necessary for supporting fire and for extinguishing it.

17-7 Show why certain foods are called "fuel" foods. Heat small amounts of butter or olive oil until they burn. Burn bread and nuts. Sugar first dipped in ashes will burn. By burning these foods, you will show that they are fuels.

17-8 Find out how the fire extinguishers in your school work. Discuss the different methods for extinguishing fires.

17-9 Talk about fire safety in your home. Discuss fire hazards. Make up safety rules for the home.

17-10 Make two costumes of light net fabric. Treat one with fireproofing solution. Hang these costumes from a fence in the school yard. While the class watches, allow a pupil to light a candle and touch it to each costume. Now bring up the topic of reducing and eliminating all kinds of fire hazards.

BIBLIOGRAPHY

Adler, Irving, *Fire in Your Life,* Day, 1955. Historical and mythological background of fire, including the "phlogiston" theory. Explains what fire is and how it is used in industry.

Baer, Marian, *Experiments with Fire,* Holt, Rinehart and Winston, 1947. Discusses factors necessary to produce and to put out fire.

Brandwein, P., et al., *You and Science,* Harcourt, Brace & World, 1960. A junior high school survey of science with many simple demonstrations suggested.

———, *You and Your Resources,* Harcourt, Brace & World, 1960. A junior high school survey of science with many simple demonstrations suggested.

———, *You and Your World,* Harcourt, Brace & World, 1960. A junior high school survey of science with many simple demonstrations suggested.

Bruce, G., *Fuels and Fire,* National Science Teachers Association, Publication Sales Section of N.E.A., 1951. A discussion of fire and fuels, accompanied by experiments.

General Science Handbook, Part 1, Bureau of Curriculum Development, Division of Secondary Education, New York State Education Department, 1951. Many excellent experiments for the classroom.

Parker, Bertha M., *Fire,* Row, Peterson, 1941. Discusses what fire is, how to produce it, and how to put it out.

———, *Fire, Friend and Foe,* Row, Peterson, 1948. Story of fire, including section on fire prevention.

Heat

HEAT MAKES SOLIDS EXPAND

Obtain about 4' of bell wire (#18) from the hardware store. Remove all the insulation. Place two chairs back-to-back about 3' apart on a table. Attach the wire to the back of each chair so that it is stretched tight. Borrow a boy scout knife from one of your pupils. Using cotton thread or string, suspend the knife from the center of the wire. Have the large blade out, and adjust the length of the thread so that the blade point just clears the table top. Now heat the wire by moving a lighted candle or Bunsen burner flame under it. The blade point will now touch the table top. Point out that the wire, when heated, expands and becomes longer. This causes the wire to sag until the blade touches the table. Watch the knife after the flame is removed and the wire allowed to cool. The wire contracts and the blade point clears the table top again.

Obtain two rectangular pieces of wood or round wooden dowels. At your hardware store get a large screw and a screw eye. The head of the screw should be barely able to pass through the screw eye. Now screw each one into the end of the piece of wood, leaving at least 1" of the metal exposed (Fig. 18-1). Heat the screw in a flame for a short while; then try to pass the screw through the screw eye. Because the screw expanded when it was heated, it will not be able to pass through. Now keep the screw hot in one flame and heat the screw eye in another flame. This time the screw will pass through the screw eye because both have expanded. Plunge the screw eye in cold water. The heated screw will not be able to pass through because the screw eye contracted when it was cooled. Cool the screw in cold water. It will contract and be able once again to pass through the screw eye.

The children may ask why the wire, screw, or screw eye expand when heated and contract when cooled. Help them understand that all substances are made up of molecules which are in motion. Heat causes the molecules to move more rapidly. When the molecules move faster, they spread apart. This makes the sub-

Fig. 18-1 Heat expands a screw so that it will not pass through a screw eye. (From G. Blough and M. Campbell, *Making and Using Classroom Science Materials in the Elementary School*, Holt, Rinehart and Winston, 1954.)

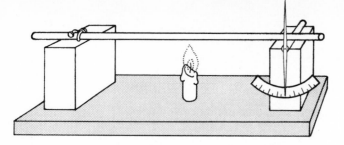

Fig. 18-2 Measuring how much a metal expands.

stance expand. When the substance is cooled, the molecules move more slowly and are closer together. This makes the substance contract.

Measuring metal expansion

There is another way of showing that solids expand when heated. Obtain a piece of wood 3′ × 6″ × ½″; two 6″ lengths of 2″ × 4″ lumber; and a strip of metal about 3′ long. Aluminum or copper is best, but brass or iron will also work well. A flat strip is preferable, but a cylindrical rod (such as a solid brass curtain rod) will also be satisfactory.

Attach a 2 × 4 block firmly at each end of the wooden board, using wood glue or nails hammered in from the underside of the board. Fasten the metal strip securely to one wood block with bent nails (Fig. 18-2). Obtain a small wooden dowel or glass rod about ¼″ in diameter and place it on the second wooden block. Rest the other end of the metal strip on the dowel or glass rod.

Cut out a cardboard arrow, and with a tack attach the arrow at its mid-point to the center of the wooden dowel. If you use a glass rod, glue the arrow to the rod. Cut out a piece of cardboard and draw lines to make a dial. Tack the dial to the wooden block so that it is directly in back of the arrow.

Now heat the center of the metal strip with a candle. As the strip is heated, it will expand. As it expands, it rubs against the dowel or glass rod and causes it to turn.

This turns the arrow, which moves along the dial. Heat the metal strip by moving the candle back and forth under it. Using three candles at one time, see how far you can make the arrow move. The farther it moves, the greater the expansion of the metal strip.

Examples of expansion

Call the children's attention to the space between the slabs of concrete sidewalks. This allows the concrete to expand in hot weather without buckling the pavement. Also call attention to the spaces for expansion between the ends of railroad tracks. Bridge construction also allows for expansion and contraction. In the winter the concrete can contract without forming cracks. For the same reason small spaces are left between sections of steel rail.

Note that telephone wires hang loosely in the summer when it is warm, and become tighter in the winter when it is cold. Sometimes in deep cold, they become so tight they hum or "sing." Iron rims are fitted on wagon wheels while the rims are red-hot. When the rims cool, they contract and fit tightly on the wagon wheel. Steel rivets that hold steel girders together in steel buildings and bridges are put in red-hot. They contract when cold and hold the steel together.

When a metal cover on a glass jar is stuck tight, pouring hot water on the metal cover will cause it to expand, and the cover can then be unscrewed easily.

Rubber seems to be an exception to the

rule that solids will expand when heated. Place a wooden board over two chairs placed back-to-back. Screw a cup hook into the underside of the board. Cut a rubber band in two. Tie one end of the rubber band to the cup hook. Attach a teacup to the other end. Now pass a candle flame rapidly up and down the rubber band many times. Do not hold the flame at any one spot too long, or the rubber will burn. The teacup will be jerked upward as the rubber band contracts.

HEAT MAKES LIQUIDS EXPAND

Fill a soda bottle to the top with water colored with red ink or vegetable dye. Insert a one-hole rubber stopper containing a glass or plastic tube about 12" long into the neck of the bottle. Use a twisting, rotary motion when you put the tube into the stopper. Hold the tube against the stopper as you work it in. When the stopper is pressed into the bottle, the liquid will rise a short way up the tube. Place a rubber band around the tube at the level of the liquid in the tube. Now set the bottle in a jar or pan of hot water. The level of the liquid in the tube will rise. Then place the bottle in a jar or pan of very cold water. The level of the liquid in the tube will fall below the mark set by the rubber band.

The children should now realize that water will expand when heated, and will contract when cooled. If you repeat the experiment with other liquids, such as alcohol or mercury, the same effect will be produced.

Fill the soda bottle full of very hot water. Stopper the bottle or cover the top and sides with Saran Wrap to prevent the water from evaporating. When the water has cooled to room temperature, remove the stopper or covering. The soda bottle will now no longer be filled with water to the top. When the water cooled, it con-

tracted and therefore became smaller in volume.

Point out that when heat is applied to liquids, the molecules move faster. This causes the molecules to move farther apart, and the liquid expands. However, you might also point out that when the molecules spread out, this increases the space between the molecules. Consequently, there are fewer molecules in the same amount of space. This means that, when warm, liquids will weigh less per unit of volume. On the same basis, liquids weigh more when they are cold because the molecules are packed more closely together in the same amount of space.

To prove this, obtain two empty quart milk bottles. Fill one bottle full of hot water that has been colored with red ink or vegetable dye. Fill the other bottle full of very cold clear water. Hold a piece of cardboard firmly over the mouth of the bottle containing the cold water. Holding the cardboard firmly in place, turn the bottle upside down and place it on top of the bottle of hot water. Make sure the mouths of both bottles are exactly in line with each other. Now slowly pull out the cardboard. Immediately the colored hot water will spurt up into the cold clear water. Help the children understand that the clear cold water weighs more than the colored hot water, even though both bottles have the same volume of water. The heavier cold water immediately falls down and pushes up the warmer colored water.

Repeat the experiment but reverse the procedure this time. Fill one bottle with cold water that has been colored red. Fill the other bottle with clear hot water. Place the piece of cardboard over the mouth of the bottle containing the hot water. Turn the bottle upside down and place it on top of the bottle of cold colored water. When the card is removed, little happens because the colder heavier colored water stays in the bottom bottle except for some minor diffusion.

You may also want to call the children's attention to the peculiar behavior of water when it approaches the freezing point. At ordinary temperatures water expands when heated and contracts when cooled, just like other liquids. If you should cool water, it would contract until it reached a temperature of 39° F (4° C). However, if water is cooled still more, it now begins to expand and continues to expand until it freezes at 32° F (0°C). When it freezes and forms ice, it expands even more. This makes ice lighter than water, which explains why ice floats in water.

Since water at 39° F has contracted more than water at 32° F (the freezing point), the water at 39° F is heavier and sinks to the bottom. This keeps the coldest water at the top and it freezes first. This is why rivers, ponds, lakes, and oceans freeze first at the top.

If water did not behave in this unusual manner, but kept on getting heavier as it got colder, then the coldest water would always be at the bottom. Water would then freeze from the bottom up. Ponds and lakes might be frozen solid, and all things living in them would be killed.

HEAT MAKES GASES EXPAND

When gases are heated, they expand; when they are cooled, they contract. Obtain a soda bottle and a one-hole rubber stopper to fit the bottle. Using a twisting motion, insert a glass or plastic tube 12" long into the stopper, and then put the stopper in the neck of the bottle. Fill a bowl or jar with water colored with red ink or vegetable dye. Place the tube into the bowl of colored water.

Now heat the bottle by clasping it tightly with the palms of your hands. If you wish, you may wrap a rag soaked in hot water around the bottle. Bubbles of air will come out of the end of the tube. The air in the bottle is heated and expands, and some of it is pushed out.

Now remove your hands and hold the bottle upright by the neck with your fingers. After a while the colored water will rise up into the tube. Point out that the heated air now cools and contracts. The colored water which enters the tube replaces the air that was driven out. Heat the bottle again and watch the water in the tube go down.

Snap a small balloon over the neck of a soda bottle. It is wise to stretch the balloon first to make sure it will inflate easily. Place the bottle on a hot radiator or in a bowl of very hot water. The balloon will inflate because the air inside the bottle is heated and expands. Now place the bottle in a bowl of ice or very cold water. The heated air cools and contracts, and the balloon deflates.

Gases also weigh less when heated. Two containers, cut from milk cartons, are hung from a ruler or stick in an upside-down position, with a string running to the four corners (Fig. 18-3). The containers should be as equal in size as possible. Adjust the center loop and (if necessary) the end loops until the two containers are balanced. Now hold an electric lamp under the open bottom of one container. As warmed air fills the container, the other container of cold air moves downward, showing that it is heavier. The molecules of air in the warmed container move faster and expand, and some of them leave the container. The cold air contains more molecules because they are closer together than those in warm air. Thus, the container of cold air holds more molecules, and is heavier.

RATE OF EXPANSION

Different solids expand and contract at different rates when heated or cooled. Ob-

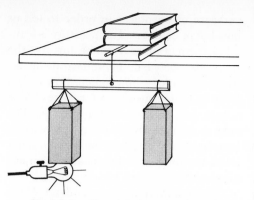

Fig. 18-3 Air weighs less when heated.

tain thin strips of copper and of iron at the hardware store. The strips should be about 12″ long and 2″ wide. If the iron strip is unavailable, you can cut your own strip from a tin can, using tin snips. Brass can be used instead of copper. Trim the edges carefully so that they will not cut you. Place the two strips together and punch holes in them at 2″ intervals with a large nail. Then tightly bind the strips together with small bolts and nuts. Two pieces of wood will provide a handle for the metal strips. Place the pieces of wood together and bore a hole in them the size of a bolt. Place the two strips between the pieces of wood so that an end hole through the metal strips is in line with the hole through the pieces of wood. Insert the bolt through the holes and tighten the wood and metal strips together with the nut. Your compound bar (bimetallic strip) is now ready to operate. You can also purchase a compound bar from a scientific supply company.

Place the compound bar in the flame of a Bunsen burner or container of canned heat. Small cylinders of propane gas are now available at Sears Roebuck, Montgomery Ward, and hardware stores. The cylinder, supported on a stand, has a valve which controls the amount of gas released. It is an excellent substitute for a Bunsen burner. When the bar is heated, the copper expands more than the iron, so that

the strip bends upward with the copper on the outside of the bend. When the bar is cooled, the strip will now bend in the other direction.

Homemade thermostat

The compound bar can be used as a homemade thermostat to show how the thermostat controls the heat in a room. Obtain two dry cells, bell wire, a bell, and a miniature porcelain socket containing a one-cell electric bulb (1½ volts). Make a U-shaped block of wood, as shown in Fig. 18-4. Punch nails in the top and bottom of the block of wood. Connect a dry cell and the bell to one nail and the compound bar. Connect a dry cell and the bulb to the other nail and the compound bar. Support the compound bar between two books, with the copper strip on top. The height of the nails should be adjusted so that they are very close but not touching the compound bar.

Now heat the compound bar. The bar

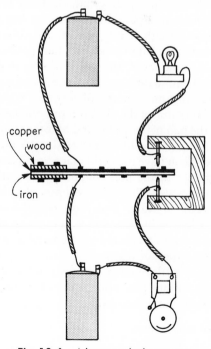

copper
wood
iron

Fig. 18-4 A homemade thermostat.

will curve upward, touch the nail to complete the circuit, and the bulb will light up. This means that there is too much heat. In a real thermostat, the furnace would shut off and heat would now be prevented from coming into the room.

Remove the flame and let the bar cool down. Place small pieces of ice on the compound bar.. The bar will now curl down, touch the other nail, and the bell will ring. This shows that there is not enough heat. In a real thermostat, heat would now be sent up into the room.

HOW HOT? HOW COLD?

The measurement of temperature is something that fascinates children. They know from experience that some things are warmer or colder than other things. Usually they distinguish between hot and cold by using their sense of touch. Point out that our sense of touch may not be accurate, and sometimes it deceives us.

Obtain three pans or jars the same size. Into one pan pour hot water—as hot as the children's hands can stand without discomfort. Into the second pan pour an equal amount of lukewarm water (about room temperature). Into the third pan pour an equal amount of very cold water.

Have one of the children put one hand in the pan of hot water and his other hand in the pan of cold water for about a minute. Then have the child place both hands together in the pan containing the lukewarm water. The child will note that the lukewarm water feels hot to the hand which was in the cold water, while the same water feels cold to the hand which was in the hot water.

The children should now realize that they cannot rely upon sense of touch to measure temperatures.

The thermometer

Thermometers are used to take the tem-
perature of an object in order to tell us how hot or cold it is. Temperature is actually a form of measurement, just like the inch, foot, or yard. These last are measures of distance—how long or how wide a body is; temperature is a measure of heat —how hot or how cold a body is. The ruler is the instrument we use to measure length (distance), while the thermometer is the instrument used to measure temperature.

Obtain a mercury thermometer. Have the children examine it and the markings on it. Note the bulb at the bottom which contains the mercury and the glass tube inside the thermometer where the mercury travels. Place the thermometer in a glass of warm water and see the column of mercury rise up the tube. Then place the thermometer in a glass of cold water and see the mercury column fall.

Point out that the principle upon which the thermometer operates is very simple. When the thermometer comes in contact with warm objects, the mercury becomes warm, expands, and rises up the tube. The amount it will rise depends upon how warm the mercury becomes. When the mercury comes in contact with cold objects, the mercury cools and contracts, and the level of mercury in the tube falls.

Help the children understand that the markings on the thermometer are man-made. Show them how these markings are derived. Place the thermometer in a glass jar containing a mixture of ice and water. Let the thermometer stand in this mixture for 20 minutes. This is called the freezing point of water. On the Fahrenheit scale of temperature measurement the freezing point is 32°.

Now boil water in a small pot and place the thermometer in it for 5 minutes. This is called the boiling point of water. On the Fahrenheit scale the boiling point is 212°. If you live at a high altitude, the boiling point may not register 212° because of

.the reduced air pressure. In this case simply call the children's attention to how close the level of the mercury comes to 212°.

Point out that for the Fahrenheit scale the difference between the boiling point (212°) and the freezing point (32°) is 212 minus 32, or 180°. Thus, the distance between the zero point and the boiling point is divided into 180 equal spaces. Each space is called a degree (Fahrenheit).

On the centigrade (metric or scientific) system, freezing point is 0° and boiling point is 100°. The space between these two points on the thermometer is divided into 100 equal divisions. Each division, or space, is also called a degree (centigrade).

Thus, we see that 32° Fahrenheit, or freezing point, equals 0° centigrade; 212° Fahrenheit, or boiling point, equals 100° centigrade.

It is not necessary to explain the centigrade scale in the lower grades unless children raise the question. Point out that in the United States the Fahrenheit scale is used for everyday nonscientific temperature measurements. The centigrade scale is used in the laboratory for scientific measurements.

A water thermometer

The oldest of the temperature-measuring devices is the water thermometer. To make a water thermometer, obtain a milk bottle, a milk-bottle cap, a plastic "pea shooter" tube, and some red or green ink or vegetable dye. Fill the milk bottle full of water colored with the red or green ink or vegetable dye. Make a hole in the center of the milk-bottle cap to fit the clear plastic "pea shooter" tube. Insert the tube through the hole in the cap and fit the cap on the bottle.

With a medicine dropper add more colored water through the open end of the tube until the water is halfway up the tube (Fig. 18-5). Seal the tube to the cap with candle wax or sealing wax. Also seal the edge of the cap to the top edge of the bottle. Put a few drops of oil on top of the colored water in the plastic tube to prevent the water from evaporating. Finally, fasten a white index card behind the tube with strips of Scotch tape.

Place the thermometer on the window sill. Have the children make a mark on the card behind the level of the liquid. You should also read the actual temperature on a standard commercial thermometer so that the children can mark the temperature on the index card each day. In about a month the water thermometer will be calibrated, and the children can read the temperature directly from the index card.

If the water thermometer is used on the outdoors window sill in winter, add 25% rubbing alcohol to prevent freezing.

If space is available, each pupil can make his own thermometer. Half-pint cream or milk bottles can be used to conserve space.

A gas thermometer

A gas thermometer is the simplest of all thermometers. Yet, strangely enough, it makes the most sensitive and accurate thermometer. Scientists use a gas thermometer that usually contains hydrogen. For elementary school use, ordinary air

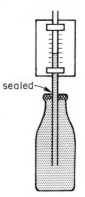
sealed

Fig. 18-5 A water thermometer.

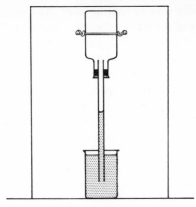

Fig. 18-6 An air thermometer.

will serve well. Obtain a thin-walled, flat-sided medicine bottle that has a metal screw cap. If the screw cap is not available, a cork will serve. Also obtain a thin, clear plastic drinking straw. Make a hole in the center of the cap or cork to fit the straw. Insert the straw through the hole in the cap and put the cap on the bottle. Seal the straw in the hole with candle wax or sealing wax.

Attach the bottle to a thick flat board in an inverted position (Fig. 18-6). Wire or string, fastened with nails, will hold the bottle in place. Place the end of the straw in a small glass or bottle of colored ink or vegetable dye.

Warm the bottle (air thermometer) with your hands until many air bubbles move out of the end of the straw into the liquid below. Then remove your hands and wait at least 15 minutes. A small column of colored liquid will rise in the tube to take the place of the air bubbles that were forced out.

The gas thermometer is now ready for use. Place your hand against the bottle. The bottle acts as if it were a giant thermometer bulb. The air inside expands and forces the liquid in the straw to go down. Now place a sponge soaked in very cold water on the bottle. The air inside the bottle contracts, and the liquid rises up the straw quite rapidly. On this ther-

mometer, one degree difference may produce a difference of one or more inches on the thermometer.

A metal thermometer

When temperatures are very high, a liquid thermometer cannot be used because the liquid would boil and break the bulb. Consequently, a solid is used.

Recall or repeat the experiment in the section on "Heat Makes Solids Expand," which involves the use of a flat metal rod resting on two blocks of wood. Point out again that, as the rod is heated, it expands and rubs against the wooden dowel, causing the dowel to turn. This turns the cardboard arrow, which indicates on the dial the increase in temperature.

Obtain a discarded oven thermometer or purchase an inexpensive one at the dime store. Take the thermometer apart and remove the coiled spiral spring. This spring is actually a compound bar made up of brass and iron welded together. When the coil is heated, the metals expand and cause the coil to turn. This moves a pointer along a dial, indicating an increase in temperature.

Straighten out the coil and punch a hole in each end. Then rewind the coil into a loose spiral about 2″ in diameter, making sure that the brass side is on the outside. Obtain a piece of wood 6″ × 3″ × ½″, and fasten it to a larger piece of wood (Fig. 18-7). A nail or screw from the bottom of the larger piece of wood to the smaller will hold both pieces firmly together. Draw a dial face on a white index card and glue or tack it to the side of the

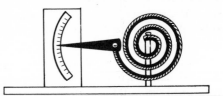

Fig. 18-7 A metal thermometer.

erect piece of wood. Nail a wooden dowel or narrow piece of wood to the base, a few inches away from the dial. The dowel should be about 3″ high.

Bend the inside end of the spring with pliers and tack it to the top of the dowel. Then cut a thin pointer from a tin can, using tin snips. Punch a hole with a nail into the broad end of the pointer and attach the pointer to the outer end of the spiral with a tack or screw. Now bend the outer end of the spring until the pointer is at the mid-point of the dial.

Pass a lighted candle across the spring and notice how the pointer rises. An electric bulb brought near will produce the same effect. Place the thermometer in the refrigerator or outside on a cold day, and note how the pointer falls. Then put it on or near a radiator, and the pointer will rise again.

The clinical thermometer

Bring a clinical thermometer to class or borrow one from the school nurse. Take the temperature of several of the children. Always sterilize the thermometer after each reading by dipping it into alcohol or an antiseptic solution and then rinsing in cold water. Be sure to let the children see you shake the thermometer down after each reading.

Point out that the body temperature of most people is $98\frac{6}{10}$ (98.6)° F. If you have a fever, your temperature will be much higher. Because body temperature is so important in detecting illness, the clinical thermometer is constructed so as to be very sensitive to any changes in temperature. It is marked off in tenths of a degree, rather than in degrees like room thermometers.

Call the children's attention to the fact that you had to shake the thermometer down after each reading. Point out that in an ordinary thermometer the level of the mercury would begin to fall as soon

as the thermometer was taken out of the child's mouth. This would make it impossible to obtain an accurate reading of a person's temperature. To prevent this, there is a narrow constriction in the tube just above the mercury-filled bulb. When the thermometer is placed in the mouth, the mercury expands and forces its way past this constriction. In a clinical thermometer the mercury cannot fall through the constriction back into the bulb. Therefore, the level of the mercury remains at the same place in the tube as when it was in the person's mouth. Shaking down the thermometer will force the mercury past the constriction and into the bulb, so that the thermometer can then be used again.

Maximum-minimum thermometer

While engaged in a unit on weather, the class may want to keep a record of the temperature during a 24-hour period. From the dime store obtain an inexpensive metal dial thermometer, like the one shown in Fig. 18-8. First remove the glass front. Then bend the pointer end of the needle down toward the dial so that it barely misses the dial. Smoke up the dial with a candle flame so that all the temperature numbers are covered with soot.

Fig. 18-8 A maximum-minimum temperature thermometer. (From A. Joseph et al., *A Sourcebook for the Physical Sciences,* Harcourt, Brace & World, 1961.)

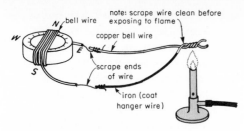

Fig. 18-9 A thermometer that detects the presence of an electric current.

The bent pointer of the needle will move through the soot and leave a white track.

The left end of the track will indicate the lowest, or minimum, temperature. The right end will indicate the highest, or maximum, temperature for the same period of time. The period can be 24 hours or a week end. By rubbing away the soot at each end of the white needle track, the children can read the maximum and minimum temperature during any desired period of time.

If the maximum-minimum thermometer is used to record outdoor temperatures, it should be placed under a shelter to protect it from rain or snow. After a reading is taken, the dial can be resmoked with soot from a candle flame. Commercial maximum- and minimum-temperature thermometers are U-shaped. The liquid pushes two little iron cylinders, called riders. The position of these little cylinders is read in degrees. They are set by means of a small magnet to bring the rider in contact with the mercury in the U-shaped thermometer.

An electrical thermometer

Extremely sensitive, electric thermometers are used to measure the temperature inside engines and other inaccessible places. The operation of such thermometers is based on the fact that under special circumstances heat may produce electricity. When two wires of different materials are twisted together and heated at their point of contact, a faint electric current is produced. The hotter the metals become, the more electric current is produced.

Obtain a piece of #18 copper (bell) wire and a piece of iron wire the same thickness. Both wires should be about 15″ long. Clean both wires with steel wool; then twist the wires together at one end. If you wish, you may use a piece of wire cut from a thin metal coat hanger. Scrape all the paint off with sandpaper. Remove all the insulation from the length of copper bell wire. If necessary, use pliers to twist the wires together at one end.

Make a compass galvanometer by wrapping at least 50 turns of #26 or 28 copper wire around a compass over its north-south axis (Fig. 18-9). Connect the free ends of the copper and iron wires to the wires of the compass galvanometer. Now heat the twisted ends of the wires in a candle or Bunsen burner flame. The compass needle will deflect, showing the presence of an electric current.

Point out that if a dial face were placed underneath the compass needle, the needle would register changes in temperature. The hotter the twisted ends, the more the needle would deflect.

Colder than the North Pole

The children may be interested to know what happens to things in extremely cold temperatures. Obtain some dry ice, acetone, and a #2 fruit or vegetable can. Any local store that sells ice cream can order dry ice for you, or the man who delivers the ice cream to the school lunch room can get it for you. Local colleges and universities may also have dry ice available. Acetone can be purchased at your pharmacy or obtained from your high school chemistry teacher.

First wrap the dry ice in a towel or cloth and, by hitting it with a mallet, break it into small pieces. The temperature of dry ice is approximately 103° below 0° F. Be very careful, therefore, in handling it. Wear gloves and use tongs or a spoon to pick it up.

Place about 2″ of acetone in the tin can. Now add dry ice to it a little at a time. There will be a violent bubbling at first, and a fog will form. This will settle down as the acetone is cooled. When the bubbling stops, add more dry ice until no more dissolves in the acetone and some pieces remain at the bottom of the can. (*Warning: Do not place fingers in the mixture.*)

Take a frankfurter. Show that it is soft and pliable. Place it in the acetone-dry ice combination. After a while remove it and tap the chalk board with the now rock-hard frankfurter.

Place a flower in the mixture. The flower will freeze immediately. Upon removal it will be beautiful but very brittle. If you squeeze it lightly, it will disintegrate into tiny pieces.

Put a celery stalk in the solution. When you take it out, it will be as hard as brick. It will snap into pieces if you try to bend it. Rubber bands will become brittle and break. Connect a length of wire to a grape or a segment of an orange and lower it into the mixture. Wear gloves when holding the wire. The grape or orange, when removed, will be brittle and can be shattered into small pieces.

Place liquid mercury in a Pyrex test tube and put the test tube in the mixture. The mercury will become a solid because it freezes at about 38° below 0° F, while the acetone-dry ice mixture is close to 103° below 0° F. If you lower a small can containing water into the mixture, the water will freeze solid in several minutes.

On the outside of the can containing the mixture, the children will notice a layer of frost forming. Moisture in the form of water vapor in the air condenses in the extreme cold surrounding the tin can to form ice crystals on the sides of the can.

The experiment with the mercury will show the class that mercury thermometers are useless in very cold parts of the Arctic and Antarctic. Now place a Pyrex test tube of rubbing alcohol or a small tin can of alcohol in the mixture. It will not freeze, showing that alcohol is useful for low-temperature thermometers. However, the alcohol is useless for high temperatures, because it boils away at about 178° F. This is even lower than the boiling point of water (212° F). Mercury, however, is good for higher temperatures, because it boils at about 480° F.

If you want to keep the mixture for a few hours, pour it into a widemouthed thermos bottle. Use gloves while handling and be very careful when pouring. When you are through with the mixture, let it stand in the tin can overnight. The surrounding air in the room will gradually bring the mixture up to room temperature. Then you can discard it.

CHANGE OF STATE

Obtain six small empty tin cans. Also obtain an ice cube, a lump of butter, lard or animal fat, a piece of solder, copper wire, and iron or steel wire. Roll the solder, copper, and iron into separate balls. All six solids should be approximately the same size. Place a different solid in each of the tin cans; then heat each can over an electric hot plate. Note which solids melt and, if possible, the time it takes for each solid to melt. The ice, butter, and fat melt very easily. The solder takes longer to melt. However, the heat of the hot plate is not great enough to melt the copper and iron. Point out that the copper and iron will melt if heated to a high enough temperature. The experiment is more graphic when conducted with Pyrex test tubes and Bunsen burners, and when all six are heated at the same time.

Let the cans cool and observe the melted substances become solids again. When we convert solids to liquids, we say that they melt. When liquids are converted to solids, we say that they solidify. Most substances melt and solidify at the same temperature. Butter is one of the exceptions, since it melts at one temperature and solidifies at a slightly lower temperature.

Molecules in motion in solids, liquids, and gases

The children may wonder how heat causes a solid to change into a liquid. Help them understand that all substances are made up of tiny particles called molecules. These molecules are always moving, and there are spaces between the molecules. When heat is applied to a substance, the molecules move faster and are farther apart. When the substance is cooled, the molecules move more slowly and come closer together. In the solid state the molecules are very close together. In fact, scientists believe that in solids each molecule is fixed to a spot and is vibrating. When the solid is heated, the molecules vibrate faster and faster. At a certain temperature, which we call the melting point, the molecules break loose and move around freely. This may account for the fact that solids have a definite size and shape, while liquids have a definite volume but no shape. As the molecules vibrate more rapidly (in the solid state) or move farther apart (in the liquid state), the substance expands. When a liquid is cooled, the molecules come closer together. At a certain temperature, called the freezing point, the molecules stop moving freely and now only vibrate. The liquid has now become a solid again. As the molecules come closer together, the substance contracts.

When your hands are rubbed together briskly, the heat produced is evidence of increased molecular motion. Bending a wire back and forth several times will make it get hot because the molecules have been made to move faster. Recall or repeat the experiments on expansion in order to show that, when heated, molecules of a substance move faster and spread farther apart.

Pour some cold water into a Pyrex pot and heat the pot over a hot plate. Observe the water as it is heated to boiling. At first small bubbles of gas form, some of which cling to the walls of the container. This is dissolved air, which is being driven out of the water. After a while large bubbles of gas form, but they quickly collapse as they rise to meet the colder water above them. The hot water now begins to "hum" and "sing." When the water is heated hot enough, bubbles of gas will form continuously and rise to the surface. This is called the boiling point, and there is a steady conversion of liquid to gas or vapor.

Help the children understand that when heat is applied to a liquid, the molecules move faster and spread farther apart. This continues until the boiling point, when the molecules are moving very rapidly, spread very far apart, and move very freely in space. This explains why gases have neither definite volume nor definite shape.

Hold a cold glass tumbler over the steam escaping from a vigorously boiling teakettle. The water vapor condenses. When the vapor strikes the cold glass, the molecules are cooled, move more slowly, and then condense back into a liquid.

Have the children trace the process of heating ice to water to water vapor (steam), and explain the process in terms of increasing the motion of the molecules and having them spread farther apart. Then reverse the procedure, going from water vapor (steam) to water to ice.

Water expands when freezing

Water is unusual in that it expands

when freezing. Obtain a large tin can. Crack ice into small pieces by wrapping it in an old towel or cloth and hitting it with the broad side of a hammer. Obtain a small bottle with a screw cap. Fill the bottle to the very top with water, so that there is no air space; then screw the cap back on. Wrap the bottle in a piece of cloth. Place the bottle in the tin can and pack the cracked ice all around it. Add salt to the cracked ice in layers so that you have a layer of ice, then salt, then ice. Pack the ice and salt compactly. After a half hour remove the ice and salt until the bottle wrapped in cloth is exposed. Unwrap the cloth carefully. Point out that, when the water began to freeze, it expanded and caused the bottle to burst.

Repeat the experiment, using a small metal can with a screw top. The can may not burst, but it will swell because the water expands when it freezes, stretching the metal.

If the children wonder why a mixture of ice and salt was used, point out that salt lowers the freezing point of water. Place some finely cracked ice in a glass jar or tin can. Add a little cold water. Then add salt, more ice, then more salt, etc. Place a thermometer in the mixture and let stand for 5 minutes. The temperature of the mixture will read well below 32° F (freezing point). Compare with a mixture of ice and water.

Pressure on ice

There are other interesting phenomena associated with water. The children may be interested to know that pressure causes ice to melt, by raising the temperature above the freezing point at the focus of pressure. Place the broad end of an ice cube on top of a soda bottle. Wrap the ends of a piece of thin copper wire (#24 or 26) around the middles of two wooden dowels or pencils. Place the middle portion of the wire across the ice cube and push down hard on the dowels. The wire will slowly cut its way through the ice cube. However, when you are finished, the ice cube will still be in one piece. Help the children understand that, as the wire presses on the ice cube, the ice directly underneath the wire melts. This melting requires heat, which is taken from the rest of the ice. After the wire passes on, the colder ice refreezes the water.

You can accomplish the same effect by pressing two ice cubes together with a great deal of force for about half a minute. The pressure melts the two ends of the ice cubes, which then refreeze when the pressure is released. The making of snowballs depends upon this same principle. Point out that, in skating, the pressure of the blade melts the ice and forms a thin film of water over which the skater moves. This also explains why we slip on ice or why automobiles skid on ice. If the ice is very cold, then the pressure is not great enough to melt the ice, and the skater's blade tends to stick.

Pressure and boiling point

Obtain a Pyrex baby bottle or a Pyrex flask and a tight-fitting cork stopper. Pour about an inch of water into the bottle and heat the bottle on a hot plate until the water boils vigorously. Put a cloth around the bottle, remove it from the hot plate, and place it on a cake tin or baking pan. Stopper the bottle tightly with the cork. Now turn the bottle upside down and pour cold water, a little at a time, over the bottle. The water will boil vigorously each time the cold water is poured over the bottle, even though the water inside becomes cooler and cooler. Point out that, when the cold water is poured over the bottle, some of the steam inside cools and condenses. This lowers the pressure on the water, and enables the water to boil at a lower temperature. The boiling point of water depends upon the air pressure on its surface.

When the pressure is reduced, the boiling point is reduced. If the pressure is increased, as with a pressure cooker, the boiling point is raised. This explains why we can obtain temperatures higher than the boiling point of water inside the pressure cooker and thus cook more quickly.

Evaporation is a cooling process

Review with children the phenomenon of evaporation. Evaporation is a change from the liquid state to the vapor state. Spilled water, rain on the sidewalk, puddles, even ponds in hot weather—all "dry up" because the water evaporates. Wet clothes placed on the clothesline dry because the water evaporates. Point out that the word "evaporate" means to convert into vapor (gas).

Temperature affects the rate of evaporation. Place an equal number of drops of water into each of two dishes. Place one dish on the radiator or in the sun, and the other dish in a cool spot. The water in the dish on the radiator will evaporate more quickly.

Obtain two pie tins the same size. Heat one tin on a hot plate or a heated radiator for a few minutes. Now add an equal number of drops of water to each tin. The water in the heated tin will evaporate first.

The amount of surface, or area, of liquid exposed to the air also affects the rate of evaporation. Obtain a measuring graduate. Pour equal amounts of water into a narrow-necked bottle and a widemouthed bottle. Let the bottles stand open overnight. The next day pour the water from each bottle back into the graduate, and each time measure the amount of water. There will be less water remaining in the widemouthed jar.

Moving air, or a breeze, affects the rate of evaporation. With a wet sponge or cloth make two wet spots of equal size on the chalk board at some distance apart. Fan one spot with a piece of cardboard or an electric fan. The fanned spot will evaporate first. You can repeat the experiment, using two pieces of wet cloth the same size that are suspended from a string by clothespins.

Moisture in the air, or humidity, affects the rate of evaporation. Obtain an embroidery hoop and fasten some cloth over it. Wet the cloth thoroughly. Then make two wet spots of equal size with a wet sponge or cloth on the chalk board at some distance apart. Cover one spot with the embroidery hoop covered with the wet cloth. Leave the other spot open. The open spot will evaporate first. The wet cloth on the embroidery frame also evaporates, and moist air accumulates under the hoop. This makes it difficult for the wet spot on the chalk board to turn into water vapor and go off, or evaporate, into the air. Have the children recall how difficult it is for perspiration to evaporate on a warm, muggy day when the humidity is high and the air is already full of water vapor.

Different liquids will evaporate at different speeds. Place two wet spots of equal size on the chalk board, one wet spot made by water, the other by duplicator fluid or rubbing alcohol. Notice how quickly the duplicator fluid or alcohol dries. Place a drop of water on the back of one hand and a drop of duplicator fluid on the back of the other hand. The duplicator fluid evaporates long before the water does.

Some solids evaporate without melting. Dry ice is converted directly into a vapor without melting. Moth balls and paradichlorobenzene are used to keep moths away from clothes. Icicles and even snow will evaporate in weather too cold for melting.

When liquids evaporate, they create a cooling effect because liquids require heat to evaporate. The liquid takes this heat wherever it can find it, usually from its immediate surroundings. Have the children blow on the index finger. Then have the children dip the index finger into water and blow again. The finger will feel cool. Help the children understand that as the water evaporates it needs heat, and takes up heat from its immediate surroundings, namely, their index fingers.

Incidentally, the quicker the liquid evaporates, the more quickly it takes up heat, and the cooler the finger becomes. Blowing on the finger increases the rate of evaporation.

Thus, liquids which evaporate very quickly have a greater cooling effect because they take up heat more rapidly. Recall or repeat the experiment above, where drops of water and duplicator fluid were placed on the back of your hand. The duplicator fluid evaporated more quickly, and the hand upon which the fluid was placed felt cooler.

Obtain three thermometers and three pieces of cotton gauze. Soak one piece of gauze in water, the second in rubbing alcohol, and the third in duplicator fluid. Wrap the bulb of each thermometer quite well with one piece of the wet gauze. Fan the pieces of gauze with a cardboard or an electric fan. Which thermometer will read the lowest?

Study the section, "Keeping Comfortable with Clothing," in Chapter 19. Review the advisability of wearing garments with loose open weaves in the summer. This permits free circulation of air and better evaporation of perspiration. Point out that evaporation of perspiration keeps our bodies cool. The more rapidly the perspiration evaporates, the quicker it takes the heat from your body and the cooler you feel. Have the children recall how pleasantly cool their faces felt on a hot day when a breeze came up and caused rapid evaporation of the perspiration. Fanning creates the same effect. Water evaporating rapidly from a wet bathing suit can cool you enough to produce a chill.

Point out that in hot dry climates water is kept cool by evaporation. The water is contained in porous earthen jars or pots. Some of the water seeps through the jar so that there is always a small amount of moisture present on the outside of the vessel. As this moisture evaporates, it absorbs heat from the jar and its contents, thereby making them cooler. On a picnic a mother often keeps her baby's milk bottles cool by wrapping a wet towel around the bottle. The evaporation of the water in the towel absorbs heat from the glass bottle.

This effect can best be produced when the climate is dry and there is little water vapor in the air. In moist climates or when the humidity is high, there is so much water vapor in the air that the rate of evaporation is slow. Thus the amount of heat absorbed is quite small, and not much cooling effect is obtained.

Cooling causes condensation

Condensation is a change from the vapor state to the liquid state. Place a teakettle containing water on an electric hot plate. When the water is boiling vigorously, hold a cold square of glass or a glass tumbler near the spout. Droplets of water condense on the glass. Point out that the water vapor leaving the spout is cooled by the glass and condenses back into a liquid again.

This phenomenon of condensation does not take place only when water is boiling. The air contains water vapor in varying amounts. The term humidity refers to the water vapor that is present in the air. Absolute humidity refers to the actual amount of water vapor present in a given quantity of air (such as a cubic foot). Relative humidity is a numerical figure, usually expressed in per cent. This figure gives the ratio between the actual amount of water vapor in the air and the total amount of water vapor the air could hold at a given temperature. During a heavy rain the relative humidity is almost 100%.

When air containing water vapor is cooled, the air contracts. Since it now has a smaller volume, the air cannot hold as much water vapor as it did before. There is a limit to the amount of water vapor a volume of air can hold. If the air has much water vapor in it (a high humidity) and is cooled, it will contract to the point where it can no longer hold all the water vapor contained in it. Consequently, some of the water vapor will condense out as droplets of water. To see this, obtain a small tin can. If the sides are dull, polish them with steel wool. Put some ice and water in the can and let it stand. If the humidity is not too low, droplets of moisture will condense on the sides of the can. If the children believe that the water may have seeped through the can, color the water inside the can with ink or vegetable dye. The colorless clear droplets of water on the outside will convince the children that the water condensed from the air.

On a very dry day, the humidity may be very low and there may be too little water vapor in the air for any to condense out on the sides of the can. If this happens, place the can of ice and water in a wide-mouthed jar containing a wet blotter on the bottom. Cover the jar with a cardboard or pane of glass.

Have the children recall how their mouths exhale "steam" on a very cold day. Point out that this "steam" is actually droplets of water condensing out. Let the children breathe on mirrors and notice the film of moisture that condenses. Cold bottles, pitchers of ice water, and glasses of soda or lemonade will also have droplets of water condense out on their sides. The children who wear glasses will recall all too well how the cold eyeglasses will cloud up when the children enter a warm, humid kitchen. Their mothers are also familiar with clouded window panes in the kitchen when the weather is cold outside and much cooking and boiling has been going on inside.

Recall the experiment with the mixture of ice and water in the can described earlier. Point out that if the temperature of the can's contents were taken at the moment the droplets of water first began to form, this would be the dew point. If the air outside were cooled down to this temperature, dew would form on the ground or rain would fall from clouds.

When the humidity is fairly low, add cracked ice to the tin can with about one third its volume of salt. Both dew and frost will form on the sides of the can. To form frost, place dry ice alone in the can. Point out that when the humidity is low, the air must be cooled quite a bit before the water vapor will condense out. If the temperature at which the water vapor condenses out is below the freezing point, the water vapor condenses out as frost instead of dew.

Children often understand dew point when it is presented as follows. The temperature at which water vapor will condense from the air is called the dew point. This temperature will vary, depending upon many conditions. If there is much water vapor in the air to begin with (that is, the humidity is high), then the air has to be cooled only a little before the air contracts and can now no longer hold all the water vapor in it. So, the water vapor condenses out at a relatively high temperature, and the dew point is relatively high. The ideal conditions for formation of dew are in the spring and the fall when the days are warm and the nights cool. At this time the days are warm, and water evaporates, filling the air with water vapor. The nights are cool, and the air contracts until the water vapor condenses out. On very warm summer nights there is very little dew the next day. The nights are not cool enough for the air to cool and contract and for the water vapor to condense out. When the humidity is low (very little water vapor in the air), dew will not form. The air cannot be cooled low enough for the water vapor to be able to condense out.

Create your own rainstorm

Place a glassful of water in a Pyrex pot, and heat the pot on an electric hot plate until the water is quite hot but not boiling. Remove the pot from the hot plate. Place a plate or saucer on top of the pot and add ice cubes to the plate. The hot water evaporates inside the pot. When this hot moist vapor strikes the cold plate, the vapor cools and contracts, and droplets of water condense on the plate. The droplets of condensed water fall back into the pot, forming a "rain." This process of evaporation, condensation, and precipitation repeats itself just as it does in our own world. Keeping the pot hot will keep this process going for quite some time.

Place about a half pint of hot water into a milk bottle. Then place a large ice cube in the mouth of the bottle. The warm moist air rising from the hot water meets the cold air from the ice cube. The warm moist air cools and contracts, and the water vapor condenses out to form a fog. This is how clouds are formed. Warm moist air rises from the earth and meets cooler air at higher levels, the temperature being 1 F° cooler for each 300′ rise in altitude. A fog is really a cloud at ground level.

In winter, when the humidity is low, the air may be cooled to the point where condensation (or precipitation) takes place below the freezing point. Then snow instead of rain is formed. Sometimes in the winter raindrops fall through layers of air colder than 32° F as they approach the earth's surface. The raindrops then freeze and fall as sleet.

Hail is also frozen rain. Hail is usually formed in the summer when there are thunderstorms. Very often during thunderstorms rain will fall through areas of air where the temperature is below freezing (32° F). The raindrops freeze into tiny pellets of ice. However, during thunderstorms there are strong upward currents of heated air. Sometimes these upward currents will carry the tiny ice pellets up again into the warmer air, where the rain is forming. Water condenses on the surfaces of the pellets of ice, but when the pellets fall back again into the layer of freezing air, the condensed water also freezes, forming a layer of ice over the original pellets. The more condensations and freezings there are, the larger the hailstones become. During a hailstorm try to collect some of the hail. Quickly cut through the stone with a sharp knife. You will see the layers of ice, like rings in an onion, showing just how many times the original raindrop fell into freezing air and was then forced upward again by currents of air. Each layer represents one condensation and freezing.

Distillation

Obtain a flask, a one-hole rubber stopper, three pieces of glass tubing, two small pieces of rubber tubing, a test tube, and a glass tumbler (Fig. 18-10). Connect the

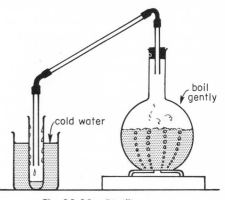

boil gently

cold water

Fig. 18-10 Distilling water.

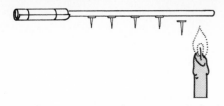

Fig. 18-11 Tacks attached to a bar with wax fall off as heat travels through the bar by conduction.

test tube and flask in the setup as shown. Fill the flask half full of water and add some ink or vegetable coloring to the water. Place the flask on the hot plate and heat the water until it boils. Note the drops of clear water which collect in the test tube immersed in cold water. This process is known as distillation and is a means of purifying water. The boiling water is converted to vapor. The vapor passes through the glass tubing and is cooled when it reaches the cold test tube. It then condenses back to water. The impurities are left behind in the flask. In an emergency, salt water can be converted to drinking water in this way.

HEAT TRAVELS BY CONDUCTION

Fill a glass full of very hot water; then place a silver spoon into the glass. Wait a few minutes; then touch the handle of the spoon. You will find it very hot. Point out that the metal of the spoon carries the heat of the water to your hand, which is touching the spoon.

Help the children understand that the heat traveled through the spoon by the method known as *conduction*. The heat of the hot water causes the molecules in the bowl of the spoon to move faster. These faster-moving molecules collide with their slower-moving neighbors. The neighboring molecules, receiving these harder collisions, begin to move faster also. They, in turn, collide with nearby molecules. In this way all the molecules in the spoon are soon moving faster. When molecules in a

substance are moving faster, the substance becomes warmer. Thus, the heat has been conducted molecule by molecule.

Obtain a round brass curtain rod about 12–15″ long. Roll a strip of paper about 12″ long and 3″ wide around one end of the rod to make a handle. Keep the paper wrapped tightly by slipping two rubber bands over it. Now obtain some long tacks or small nails. Attach the tacks with the paraffin from a burning candle to the brass rod at distances of 1″ (Fig. 18-11). Hold the free end of the rod in the flame of a Bunsen burner, alcohol lamp, or candle. Call the children's attention to the fact that as the heat travels along the rod by conduction, the paraffin melts and the tacks fall off one by one.

A simple way of illustrating conduction is to set upright a row of dominoes so that, when the first is pushed over, they all fall down in turn. Each domino transmits its motion to its neighbor, just as each molecule in a heated body transmits its faster movement to its neighbor.

Rates of conduction by different materials

Solids differ in the rate at which they transmit heat by conduction. Obtain a narrow wood box and four 12″ rods of different materials. Copper, brass, iron,

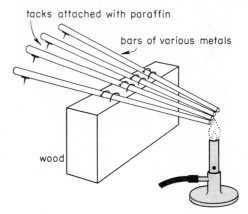

Fig. 18-12 Some metals conduct heat better than others.

and glass rods will do. Punch holes through the sides of the box and attach the rods at an angle so that the four ends meet (Fig. 18-12). At the outer end of each rod attach long tacks or small nails with paraffin. At the point where the four ends meet, apply the flame of a Bunsen burner, alcohol lamp, or candle. Note the order in which the tacks fall off. The better the conductor, the sooner the heat reaches the paraffin and melts it.

Metals are good conductors of heat even though they differ somewhat in the rate at which they conduct heat. Nonmetals, such as wood, glass, paper, and cloth, are poor conductors of heat. Their molecules do not transmit motion very well to neighboring molecules.

Metals are good heat conductors

There are many experiments you can do to show that metals are good conductors of heat. Cut a piece of bare bell wire the length of a wooden match. Light the match and hold it in one hand while you place one end of the wire into the match flame with the other hand. Be prepared to drop the wire quickly because it heats up quite rapidly.

Place a handkerchief or piece of cloth over a silver quarter. Wrap the handkerchief very firmly around the coin so that the cloth is stretched tightly across the coin. Now place the lighted end of a cigarette against the handkerchief. The handkerchief will not char or burn because silver is an excellent conductor of heat. (There will be a slight tobacco stain.) It conducts the heat away before the heat can damage the cloth. If the coin is removed, the handkerchief or cloth will scorch immediately.

Wrap a piece of white paper tightly around a wooden pencil that has a metal band to hold the eraser. Make sure the paper covers both the metal band and the wood. Now heat the pencil over a candle flame at the point where the metal band is located. When the paper begins to char, remove the pencil and unroll the paper. The part of the paper covering the wood will be charred. The part of the paper covering the metal band will be untouched or only slightly charred, because the metal band conducted the heat away.

Pour hot water into an aluminum or other metal tumbler and a plastic tumbler. The metal tumbler will feel warmer because it is a good heat conductor. If cold water is used, the metal tumbler will feel colder because it conducts the heat away from your hands more quickly. A moistened finger applied to a metal rod on a very cold day will often freeze to the rod because the metal carried the heat away from your finger so quickly.

Obtain a piece of aluminum or copper window screening about 6″ square from the hardware store. Light a candle and hold the screen halfway in the candle flame. The flame will burn below the screen, but not above it. This happens because the heat is conducted away from the flame by the wires in the screen, lowering the temperature below its kindling point.

If you have a Bunsen burner and tripod, place the screen on the tripod and turn on the gas. Light the gas above the screen. The gas will now burn only above the screen because the heat is conducted away by the screen and thereby prevents the gas below the screen from reaching its kindling temperature.

Recall or repeat the project of making a model of a miner's safety lamp, as discussed in the section on "Putting Out Fire" in Chapter 17. Point out that the principle of the lamp is based on the experiment with the screen and Bunsen burner just described. The wire mesh conducts the heat of the miner's lamp away, thereby preventing any inflammable gas that might be in the air from reaching kindling temperature.

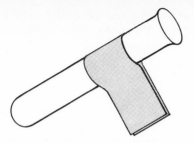

Fig. 18-13 Paper is a poor conductor of heat.

Poor heat conductors

Glass is a poor conductor of heat. Point out to the children that they should not pour hot water into a thick cold glass, or cold water into the glass when it is hot. When hot water is placed inside the thick cold glass, the inner surface expands. Because glass is a poor heat conductor, the outer surface does not expand. The strain produced may crack the glass. Similarly, when cold water is placed in a thick hot glass, the inner surface contracts, but not the outer surface. The shrinking of the inner surface also sets up a strain which may crack the glass.

This does not usually happen with thin-walled glasses, because the heat is transmitted to the outer surface more quickly. Boron has been added to Pyrex glass in order to cut down the amount of expansion and contraction of the glass, and thereby to eliminate most strain.

Obtain a strip of paper 5″ long and 4″ wide. Fold the paper in half, then in quarters, so that you have a folded strip 5″ long and 1″ wide. Wrap this strip around the upper end of a test tube one third full of water. Hold the strip tightly together so that it holds the test tube firmly (Fig. 18-13). Now heat the test tube in the flame of a Bunsen burner or alcohol lamp until the water boils. The paper is a poor conductor of heat and allows you to hold the heated test tube without any discomfort.

There are, of course, variations in the rate of heat conduction among various nonconductors. The tiled bathroom floor feels colder to your bare feet than does the wooden floor. Both floors are probably at the same temperature, but tile is a better conductor of heat than wood. Therefore, the tile carries body heat away quicker, and so feels colder. A carpet is a very poor conductor of heat, and so the carpet feels warmer than the wooden floor. A traffic officer will often keep his feet warmer on a cold day by standing on newspaper or wood, because these carry heat away more slowly than pavement.

Liquids are poor conductors of heat. Fill a test tube three quarters full of water. Place a piece of ice in the test tube and keep the ice at the bottom of the test tube by means of a spring or small weight. Apply the flame of a Bunsen burner or alcohol lamp to the upper part of the test tube. The water will boil away after a few minutes, but the ice remains almost intact. The heat is not carried down to the ice.

Gases are extremely poor conductors of heat. Recall or repeat the experiment with the tin cans and insulating materials in the section, "How Much Heat or Cold Gets Through—Insulation," Chapter 20. Point out that air or gases are just about the poorest heat conductors there are. One reason why asbestos, rock wool, hair, fur, wool, and feathers are such poor conductors of heat is that they are porous or fibrous in structure. Because of this they contain many dead air spaces. The term "dead" is used because the air in such spaces cannot circulate. Such materials make good insulating materials because they are not only poor conductors but are full of dead air spaces which can neither circulate nor conduct heat.

HEAT TRAVELS BY CONVECTION

Recall or repeat the experiments in the section on "Heat Makes Liquids Expand" at the beginning of the chapter. Remind the children again that warm water is lighter and weighs less per unit of volume than cold water.

Obtain a large widemouthed jar. An empty aquarium will be even better. Fit an ink bottle or other small bottle with a two-hole rubber stopper. Obtain a small piece of glass tubing and a medicine dropper. Fit the glass tubing and the glass portion of the medicine dropper into the two-hole stopper (Fig. 18-14). The glass tubing should be level with the stopper and extend almost to the bottom of the bottle.

Fill the ink bottle with very hot water that has been deeply colored with blue or red ink or vegetable dye. Then fill the jar or aquarium with very cold water. Fit the stopper into the ink bottle and wipe off any excess. Now lower the ink bottle into the jar of very cold water. Do this quickly, but carefully, so as to keep the amount of disturbance to a minimum. Notice the way the colored water leaves the medicine dropper, like smoke from a chimney, and rises to the top. Also point out that the ink bottle constantly remains full. Help the children understand that the hot water is lighter than the cold water, and therefore rises to the top. The cold water is heavier and takes the place of the colored hot water as it leaves the ink bottle. Observe the color of the water in the bottom of the small bottle.

Convection currents in water

Obtain a Pyrex coffee pot and fill it with cold water. Put some shredded blotting paper or sawdust into the water. You can shred the blotting paper by rubbing its surface against the fine part of a food grater. Stir the shreds in the water until they become thoroughly soaked and settle to the bottom of the pot. Set the pot on an electric hot plate and heat the water. Notice the behavior of the particles of blotting paper as the water gets hot. The particles move upward at the center and

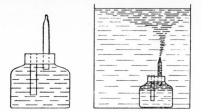

Fig. 18-14 Hot water is lighter than cold water. (From *UNESCO Source Book for Science Teachers,* UNESCO, 1956.)

downward at the sides of the pot. Point out that the particles serve to show the movement of the water as it is heated. The hotter water rises to the top while the less hot water falls to the bottom. In this way the heat is carried from one place to another by currents in the water. This method of heat travel is called convection.

Repeat the experiment, but with this variation. Place the pot to one side of the hot plate so that only one side will be heated. Do not add the shredded blotting paper or sawdust until the water is boiling vigorously. The particles of blotting paper will go around and around the pot. Point out that these particles show the convection currents of the water. The water is going up on the side of the pot away from the heat.

Convection currents in air

Heat can also travel in gases by convection currents. Set a lighted candle in a spot where it will be protected from stray air currents. Hold a lighted cigarette or a piece of smoking rope a short distance above the flame. The smoke will travel straight up into the air. Repeat the experiment over a radiator or electric hot plate. The rising air current will also cause a paper pinwheel to turn.

Wrap a piece of wire around a candle. Light the candle and lower it into a milk bottle. The candle will go out very quickly because the heated air rises and prevents fresh air containing oxygen from entering the bottle in time to keep the candle

upward current
of heated air

downward current
of cool air

Fig. 18-15 Convection currents keep a candle lighted. (From *UNESCO Source Book for Science Teachers*, UNESCO, 1956.)

lighted. Cut a piece of cardboard in the shape of the letter T. The stem of the T should just fit the neck of the bottle. Hold the milk bottle upside down and swish it in the air a few times to fill it with fresh air. Now lower the lighted candle into the bottle again by means of the wire. Place the cardboard T immediately into the neck of the bottle (Fig. 18-15). This time the candle will remain lighted.

Point out that the cardboard separates the warm and cold air currents. Place a lighted cigarette or piece of smoking rope on each side of the cardboard. On one side the smoke will go down into the bottle, showing the presence of a current of cool air. On the other side the smoke will rise, showing the presence of a current of heated air.

Obtain a shoe box and two small mailing tubes or a cardboard paper towel tube cut into two equal lengths. In the bottom of the shoe box cut two holes slightly smaller than the openings of the cardboard tubes. Light a candle and secure the bottom firmly to the table with melted paraffin. Place the shoe box over the can-

dle so that the candle is directly under one of the holes. Then set the two tubes over the holes (Fig. 18-16). Hold a smoking rope or paper over the tube without the candle under it. The smoke will go into the tube, showing that cool air is entering. Smoke will be seen leaving the tube with the candle under it, showing that the heated and therefore lighter air is leaving. Have the children trace the convection currents formed.

The children might like to make a serpent that responds to hot air currents. Draw a spiral on a sheet of heavy white paper. Finish the end of the spiral by drawing the head of a snake (Fig. 18-17). Cut out the spiral, starting from the outside working in toward the center. Pass a knotted thread through the center of the spiral. Now lift the spiral by the thread. If it does not spread out evenly, it means that the lines are either too close together or too far apart. Hold the serpent over a candle flame, hot plate, or radiator. The rising heated air will make the serpent spin around and around.

Recall or repeat the experiments with the ventilation box in the section, "Fresh Air Indoors," in Chapter 20. The children

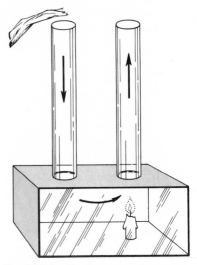

Fig. 18-16 Tracing convection currents.

should remember that the rooms in our homes are heated by air convection currents. Go over again the proper method of keeping windows open to allow proper ventilation and circulation of air in a room. Long, narrow strips of very thin tissue paper attached to a stick or ruler can be used to detect the directions of convection currents in various parts of the room. Smoke can also be used to detect convection currents in the room and near windows opened at the top and bottom.

Have the children look at a heated radiator or hot plate that is in the sunlight. The heated air appears to waver and dance about as it rises. The same effect can be noticed outdoors on hot pavements and roads. Actually it is the bending of the light by the changing density of the rising air that makes us think we see waves.

Point out that in refrigerators the cooling unit is always located at the top. The food at the bottom warms the air which becomes lighter. The heavier cold air from the cooling unit falls to the bottom. The lighter warmer air rises to the top where it is cooled again by the cooling unit. In this way a convection current is set up which helps keep all the food cold.

Winds are air convection currents on a large scale. They are caused for the most part by the unequal heating of the earth's surface at certain points. The air over some heated area becomes warm, expands, and rises. Colder air rushes in to take its place, and soon a convection current is started. In land areas near the equator there is a continuous rise of heated air. There is a corresponding fall of cold air near the North Pole and South Pole. The rotation of the earth helps swerve the direction of these large air currents.

HEAT TRAVELS BY RADIATION

Have one of the children hold his hand palm upward under an unlighted electric

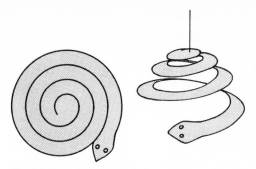

Fig. 18-17   A serpent that is sensitive to hot-air currents.

light bulb that is hanging downward. A bent goose neck lamp with the shade removed will serve the purpose. Now turn on the electricity. The child's palm will feel the heat almost immediately. Point out that the heat could not reach his hand so quickly by conduction because air is a very poor conductor of heat. Nor could the heat reach his hand by a rising convection current because his hand was below the bulb. Help the children understand that the glowing filament in a bulb gives off a radiant energy which is absorbed by the hand and converted to heat. In the lower grades it is sufficient to say that the bulb sends out heat rays that make the hand hot.

Place a pane of glass between the bulb and the child's palm. The child will still feel the heat. Have another child touch the glass, and he will find that it is cool. The children should realize that this radiant heat energy does not heat transparent objects. The rays pass right through the transparent object. However, when the rays are stopped and absorbed by an object, like the child's hand, they are converted to heat and the hand becomes warm.

Let the children stand near the window and have the sunlight fall on their faces. Their faces will feel warm, but the window panes will be cool. Thus, the sun also gives off heat rays.

Focusing heat

Radiant heat rays can be focused. Obtain a magnifying or reading glass and hold it in the sun. Focus the sun's rays to a point on your hand or on a crumpled wad of tissue paper. Your hand will soon feel uncomfortably hot, and the paper will catch on fire because of the focused heat rays.

Note the distance between the lens and the spot where the sun's rays come to a point. Have a child place a tilted mirror halfway between the lens and this point of focus. Let another child feel around with his hand until he finds the new point where the heat rays are focused. The children should now realize that radiant heat can also be reflected.

Recall or repeat the experiments in the sections, "How Much Heat or Cold Gets Through," and "Colors, Heat, and Comfort," in Chapter 20. Remind the children that bright, shiny, or smooth objects reflect heat rays, while dark, rough objects absorb heat rays. Recall the experiment on the effect of the sun's rays on light and dark clothing in the section on "Keeping Comfortable with Clothing" in Chapter 19.

Absorption of heat

Obtain two narrow-necked bottles of the same size. Paint one bottle black with water color or tempera paint. Snap a balloon over the neck of each bottle and place them both in the sun. First stretch out the balloons and test to see that they inflate easily. The black bottle will absorb the sun's rays more quickly, and its balloon will inflate first. Point out that on a hot day the black fender of an auto is hotter than the silvery shiny chromium parts.

Obtain two tin cans of the same size. Cut out two circles of cardboard to cover the cans. In the center of each cardboard punch a hole large enough to admit a thermometer. Paint the outside of one can with flat black paint. Place the cardboard covers on the cans and insert the thermometers. Do all this in the shade and keep the cans in the shade until both thermometers read the same. Now place both cans in direct sunlight. Read the temperature of each thermometer after 20 minutes or so. The black can will show a greater heat rise.

Repeat the experiment, using equal amounts of cold water, but wait a half hour this time. The black can will again show a greater heat rise. Now repeat the experiment, using equal amounts of hot water. This time place the cans in a cool spot out of the sun. The thermometer in the black can will now read lower than the thermometer in the shiny can. Point out that the black can radiated heat faster than the shiny can. As a result, the water in the black can became cooler than the water in the shiny can.

Help the children see that any one of three things may happen to radiant energy (heat rays) when they strike a substance. If the substance is transparent, the heat waves will pass through it, and the substance will remain cool. If the substance is smooth and shiny, the heat waves will be reflected and the substance will again remain cool. If the substance is dark and rough, the heat rays will be absorbed and the substance will become warm.

The vacuum bottle

Bring a Thermos or other vacuum bottle to class. Unscrew the upper part of the metal case and show the children the silvered glass bottle. Draw a diagram of the bottle on the chalk board, showing the double walls in the bottle. Point out that most of the air has been removed from the space between the two glass walls in order to form a vacuum. Also point out that with the air removed, there are very few molecules to conduct the heat away from the hot contents of the bottle. By the same token there are very few molecules to conduct heat into the cold contents of the bottle. Whatever molecules of air are present in the space are very poor conductors anyway.

Call the children's attention to the fact that both inner walls are silvered. If hot liquid is put in the vacuum bottle, the silvered walls will reflect any radiated heat and prevent the heat from escaping. If cold liquid is put in the vacuum bottle, the silvered walls help keep radiant heat from entering the thermos and warming the liquid. Thus, the double walls (with the vacuum) and the silvery coating give double protection in keeping the liquid in a vacuum bottle at the desired temperature.

Land and sea breezes

Obtain two glass tumblers of the same size. Place some dry soil in one tumbler and fill the other tumbler to the same level with water. Place a thermometer in each tumbler and keep the tumblers in a shaded spot until their temperatures are the same. Now set both tumblers in direct sunlight. Read their temperatures every 15 minutes. The soil will become warmer than the water.

Have the children relate this to the formation of land and sea breezes. In the afternoon and early evening the land has heated up more than the neighboring ocean or lake. The air above the land becomes warmer than the air above the water, and a cool breeze blows in from the water. At night and in the morning, the land has cooled down more than the water. The air above the water is now warmer than the air above the land, and therefore a cool breeze blows from the land out toward the water.

HOW YOUR HOME IS HEATED

Ask the children to name the kinds of

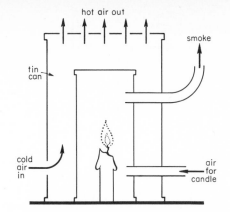

Fig. 18-18 How a hot-air heating system works. (From A. Joseph et al., *A Sourcebook for the Physical Sciences,* Harcourt, Brace & World, 1961.)

heating systems in their homes. Do not confuse the type of heating system with the kind of fuel used. With your help, if necessary, the children should conclude that the three most commonly used heating systems are hot-air, hot-water, and steam. Radiant heating in the floor is circulating hot water. Some wall radiant heaters are electric.

Hot-air heating

Make a model of a hot-air heating unit. Obtain two tin cans, one very much larger than the other. Cut the top and bottom off the larger can. Punch three holes in the large can and two holes in the small can at the locations shown in the diagram (Fig. 18-18). The holes should be large enough to allow glass tubing to pass through.

Pass the tubing through the two adjacent holes in both the large and small cans. The tube through the lower holes supplies fresh air for the burning fuel (candle). The tube through the upper holes acts as a chimney to permit the waste gases from the burning fuel to escape. The hole on the other side of the large can supplies the air which will be heated and go to the rooms upstairs.

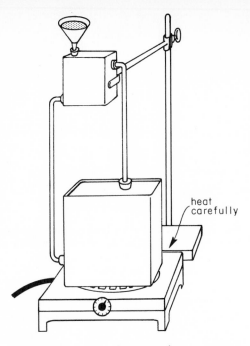

heat
carefully

Fig. 18-19 How a hot-water heating system works.

Fasten a lighted candle firmly to the table with melted paraffin. Invert the small can over the candle, and the unit begins to make hot air. You can show the presence of hot air rising at the top of the larger can with a pinwheel, smoke, or narrow strips of very thin tissue paper attached to a stick or ruler.

Point out that in hot-air heating systems, the heated air rises by convection currents and travels to the rooms by means of large pipes called ducts. The air enters the rooms through iron grillwork called registers, which may be located in the floor, baseboard, or wall. The hot air heats the room by convection currents. When the air cools, it returns through grillwork at the floor and then by ducts back to the furnace. In modern hot-air systems a blower helps move the hot air.

Hot-water heating

To show how a hot-water heating system works, obtain two rectangular metal cans, one quart-size and the other pint-size. Discard the metal screw caps and replace them with one-hole rubber stoppers. In the lower end of one side of the large can punch a hole just large enough to admit a one-hole rubber stopper. Punch similar holes in the upper end of one side and the lower end of the opposite side of the small can (Fig. 18-19).

Obtain lengths of plastic tubing and insert them into the stoppers. If plastic tubing is not available, use glass with rubber tubing to turn corners. Seal any crevices around the stoppers with plumber's sealing compound or sealing wax. Insert a large glass or plastic funnel in the stopper at the top of the smaller can. Use a ring stand and clamps to hold the small can in place.

Remove the stopper and funnel and add water until both cans are full. Then replace the funnel and add more water until the funnel is half full. Now heat the large can on an electric hot plate.

Point out that the large can acts as the boiler. When the furnace heats the water in the boiler, the water expands and rises. Cold water flows down to take its place. As the heating continues, the warm water reaches the small can, which acts as the radiator. Soon a convection current is established, and the water becomes warmer and warmer with continued passage through the boiler. When the water in the radiator is hot, the radiator heats the air in the room. The heated air sets up an air convection current and makes the room warm. The radiator also radiates some of its heat to the various objects in the room.

The funnel represents an expansion tank. Such a tank is necessary because the water expands when heated. Space must be allowed for this, or else the boiler, pipes, or radiator would burst.

Steam heating

To show how a steam heating system

works, obtain a large flask and a one-hole stopper to fit. Also obtain a pint-size rectangular metal can and a one-hole stopper to fit. In the lower end of one side of the tin can punch a hole just large enough for a piece of plastic or glass tubing to pass through. Obtain an 8" length and a 3" length of plastic or glass tubing.

Assemble the apparatus as shown in Fig. 18-20. A ring stand and clamps will help hold the can in place. Fill the flask one third full of water, and then heat it on an electric hot plate.

The flask acts as the boiler. The furnace heats the water in the boiler until it boils. The steam that is formed rises and enters the metal can, which acts as the radiator. The radiator becomes hot and heats the air in the room. The heated air sets up an air convection current and makes the room warm. The radiator also radiates some of its heat to the various objects in the room.

When the steam in the radiator gives up its heat to the air in the room, the steam cools and condenses back to water. This condensed water drains back to the boiler through the same pipe it used for going up as steam. The furnace then reheats the condensed water until it becomes steam again.

The radiator air valve serves to eliminate air that may be trapped in the radiator or pipe line. The hole in the can is for this purpose. It opens to let air out, but closes upon contact with the steam. It also acts as a safety valve, opening when the pressure goes beyond the safety point.

If the class is interested, it can study the advantages and disadvantages of these three major heating systems. Many factors will have to be taken into consideration. These factors include, among others, the type of house, the climate, the supply and cost of fuel, the cost of installing and of maintaining the system, and the cleanliness of the system. Manufacturers of heat-

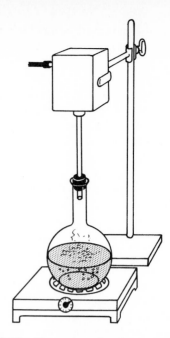

Fig. 18-20 How a steam heating system works.

ing systems will supply you with information. For example, the Minneapolis-Honeywell Regulator Company (2753 Fourth Avenue South, Minneapolis 8, Minn.) puts out a good booklet entitled *Ten Ways To Heat Your Home*.

Radiant heating

A number of new methods of heating have been recently developed. One such method is radiant heating. A network of pipes is built into the floors, ceiling, or even walls. Hot water circulates through the pipes, heating them by conduction, and the pipes, in turn, radiate heat into the room. Because of the large surfaces involved, there is good radiation to all parts of the room. The advantages of such a system are obvious: there are no space-consuming radiators or registers visible; the air does not have to be kept so warm for comfort; all the rooms are heated evenly; drafts are eliminated and dirt is reduced. However, there are also the problems of costly repair of the imbedded heating coils and of maintaining efficient circulation of the hot water or air.

Solar heating

Solar heating uses the sun as its direct source of heat. The sun's heat is gathered by means of special heat collectors which are exposed to the sun. The collector usually consists of a black metal plate or panel behind a double panel of glass. The collectors are situated so that they face the sun. The heat rays of the sun pass through the double panel of glass and are absorbed by the black metal panels, which become hot. Water or air is used to transfer the heat from the collectors to the storage area, which contains chemicals that can store heat. When the heat is needed, it is released from the storage area and passes through the house. Usually the stored heat is converted into warm air and then circulated through the rooms by one or more fans.

Solar heat is also used to supplement the more conventional heating systems. In this case the walls of the building on the sides toward the south consist mostly of large windows. Radiant energy from the sun passes directly into the rooms, where the energy is absorbed and converted into heat. An extended roof provides for shading the solar windows in the summer, when the sun moves more directly overhead.

The heat pump

The heat pump gets its heat from the earth. A network of pipes is buried within the earth. A pump run by an electric motor causes water to flow through the pipes. The circulating water takes heat from the earth. The heat is then taken from the water and concentrated for heating the home. Either a hot-water or hot-air heating system can be used to distribute the heat. The chilled water is returned to the earth. In the summer the entire process can be reversed and the unit can be used to cool the home. Once the heat pump is installed, the only major cost is for the electricity needed to operate the motor that runs the pump.

AIR CONDITIONING IN THE HOME

Discuss the functions of air conditioners in the home during the summer. Point out that the air conditioner does four things. First, it cools the air by means of a cooling system very much like that used in refrigerators. Second, it lowers the humidity by cooling the air until some of the water vapor condenses out as a liquid. Third, it cleans the air of dust by forcing the air through filters. Finally, it circulates the air so that the stale air is removed and fresh air is supplied.

Call the children's attention to the need for good insulation (especially in the summer) so that the air conditioner will work successfully. Poor insulation means that hot air keeps coming into the house in large amounts, and a tremendous load is put on the air conditioner. With air conditioning, the windows must be kept closed.

Point out that air conditioning can also be used successfully in the winter. In this case the air is warmed by passing it over heated coils. The humidity is increased by forcing it through a stream of water. This also helps "wash" the air free of dust. Another method of increasing the humidity is by allowing water to evaporate into the warm air.

CAPSULE LESSONS

18-1 Obtain a glass jar with a metal cover that is stuck tight. You can create such a condition by placing the cover in hot water and then screwing the cover on tightly while it is still hot. When the cover cools, it should be stuck. Pour hot water again on the metal cover. It will unscrew quite easily now. Lead into the study of expansion and contraction.

18-2 If your room has a thermostat to control the temperature, have the children examine it. If not, perhaps the school custodian will show the class where the master thermostat is located and explain how it operates. Lead into the study of expansion and contraction and also of the unequal expansion of metals.

18-3 Bring a Fahrenheit thermometer into class. Observe how it is constructed and note the markings on it. Find the temperature of the air in the room and outdoors. Lead into the study of thermometers and the measurement of temperature. (*Note:* You can also bring in a centigrade thermometer and compare it with the Fahrenheit thermometer. This will lead into the study of how systems of temperature measurement are devised. Some thermometers have both scales on them.)

18-4 Bring in a medical (clinical) thermometer. See how it differs from other thermometers in construction and operation.

18-5 Have the children make their own water thermometers, using small milk or cream bottles, plastic tubing, and colored water. Lead into the study of the thermometer and the measuring of temperature.

18-6 Have the class list the various uses of thermometers. Lead into a study of expansion and contraction, thermometers, and temperature measurement.

18-7 Soak a piece of cloth in water; then suspend it from a string. Ask the class for suggestions regarding how to dry the cloth as quickly as possible. Lead into the study of evaporation and the various factors affecting the rate of evaporation.

18-8 Bring a pitcher of water and ice cubes that has been standing in the refrigerator for some time. Observe the droplets of water that form on the outside of the pitcher. Lead into the study of condensation.

18-9 Fill a glass with very hot water; then put a silver spoon in the glass. Fill an aluminum tumbler with hot water. Note how hot the metal becomes in each case. Lead into the study of heat travel by conduction.

18-10 Devise an experiment to find out whether certain substances are good or poor conductors of heat. Lead into the study of conduction and the molecular theory of heat.

18-11 Cut very thin tissue paper into narrow strips about 6″ long. Attach the strips with tacks or Scotch tape to a ruler or stick. Use this device to find out the directions of air currents in various parts of the room. Lead into the study of heat travel by convection currents.

18-12 Have the children put the palms of their hands near a lighted electric bulb or a heated radiator. Lead into the study of radiation.

18-13 Have the class collect information about the various types of heating systems. They can contact community dealers of heating systems or can write away to manufacturers. Discuss the different methods of heat travel used in these systems. Compare their method of operation. List the advantages and disadvantages of each heating system.

18-14 Have the class visit an air-conditioned store, restaurant, or theatre. Arrange for an expert to show the different parts of the air conditioner and how each functions.

BIBLIOGRAPHY

Adler, Irving, *Hot and Cold,* Day, 1959. Explains heat and how to measure it, convection currents, how electricity produces heat, and how man uses heat to help him do work.

Parker, Bertha M., and Clifford Holley, *Thermometers, Heat and Cold,* Row, Peterson, 1942. Good discussion of temperature and different ways of measuring it.

Clothing

It is easy for the children to understand that clothing is necessary for modern living. Clothing helps our bodies adjust to changes in the weather and climate. Clothing also protects us in inclement weather. The kind and amount of clothing we wear to a large extent depend upon the seasons and also upon the climate in which we live. Clothes also help us in our personal appearance and attractiveness.

KINDS OF FIBERS

Let children help you collect a wide variety of fabrics to bring to class. If possible, include swatches and thread. You can obtain individual threads for comparison by separating them from the various swatches.

Let children classify the fabrics into three main categories: fabrics made from plant fibers, fabrics made from animal fibers, and fabrics made from synthetic fibers. You may want to have the class learn where the fibers come from and how they are woven into cloth.

Plant fibers

Cotton. Let children conclude that the most widely used plant fiber is cotton. Cotton fibers are the hairs found on the seeds of the cotton plant. If possible, obtain a cotton boll on its stem. Obtain some absorbent cotton and place one or two fibers under the high-powered lens of a mi-

croscope. The high school biology teacher will lend you a microscope and show you how to use it. One of the children may have an adequate microscope at home. Another possible source is your physician or an industrial concern in your city or town. Under the microscope the cotton fiber will look like a flattened, irregular, twisted ribbon (Fig. 19-1). If a microscope is not available, many of the newer high school chemistry and physical science textbooks have excellent pictures of fibers under a microscope. There are also books on identifying textiles.

Collect samples of materials made from cotton. Some of these cotton materials are cheesecloth, organdy, chintz, gingham, crinoline, muslin, percale, calico, velveteen, seersucker, cotton poplin, sailcloth, and canvas. Most cotton thread has been treated to make it smoother and give it luster. This is done by stretching the cotton and immersing it in vats containing a strong (concentrated) cold sodium hydroxide (lye) solution. Cotton treated in this manner is said to be mercerized.

Linen. Another common plant fiber is linen, which comes from the flax plant. This fiber is long, lustrous, and smooth. Under the microscope the fibers look like bamboo canes, with jointed cells and split tapered ends (see Fig. 19-1). Point out that linen is used to make handkerchiefs, tablecloths, napkins, and summer dresses and blouses.

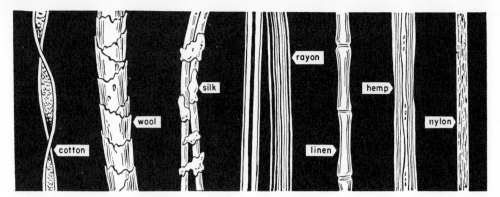

Fig. 19-1 How fibers look under the microscope. (From P. Brandwein et al., *Science for Better Living,* Harcourt, Brace & World, 1952.)

Jute and hemp. Other plant fibers are jute and hemp (see Fig. 19-1). These fibers are not as fine as cotton and linen, and are used to make carpet backing, rope, twine, and sacks.

Animal fibers

Wool. Wool fibers are the most commonly used animal fibers today. These fibers are obtained from the soft, hairy covering of sheep and sometimes goats. Under the microscope the wool fiber looks like a long cylinder with scales on it. (Fig. 19-1). The fiber is very curly and springy.

Samples of material made from wool include cashmere, camel's hair, alpaca, covert cloth, flannel, gabardine, mohair, serge, tweed, and worsted.

Silk. Silk is another common animal fiber. Silk was once quite popular, but now it has been replaced to a great extent by such synthetic fibers as Nylon, Orlon, and Dacron. Silk is made by the mulberry silkworm when spinning its cocoon. Under the microscope the silk fiber appears as a thin, long, smooth, and lustrous cylinder (Fig. 19-1). Materials made from silk include, among others, brocade, brocatelle, chiffon, crepe, velvet, crepe de Chine, foulard, lamé, moire, satin, taffeta, tulle, and faille.

Synthetic fibers

Rayon. Rayon is one of man's first successfully made artificial fibers. It is made from cellulose. When manufactured, the rayon fibers resemble silk. Under the microscope the rayon fiber looks like a smooth, lustrous cylinder (Fig. 19-1). Rayon textiles can be made into materials that are hard to distinguish from silk, cotton, linen, or wool. Celanese is one form of rayon.

Other chemical fibers. Today there are a wide variety of synthetic fibers, all made from chemicals. They all have trade names, such as Nylon, Orlon, Dacron, Vinyon, Aralac, Acrilan, Velon, Dynel, and Saran. Like rayon, these fibers resemble silk, and under the microscope they look like smooth, lustrous cylinders. Synthetic fibers are easily identified because of their uniform thickness. The thickness of natural fibers varies. Synthetic fibers are made into fabrics which have special properties. These will be taken up later in the chapter.

Glass and asbestos. It is interesting to note that glass and asbestos can also be spun into thread and woven into fabrics. Glass fibers are made by stretching melted glass into fine filaments. These filaments are spun into thread for weaving into cloth. Lightweight glass fibers are used to make long-lasting window curtains, drapes, and lamp shades. Heavier glass fabrics are used to make fireproof theater and school curtains.

Asbestos rock, which is fibrous in structure, is shredded to make asbestos fibers. These fibers can then be spun and woven to make asbestos cloth. Asbestos cloth is used in fireproof theater curtains and suits for fire fighters.

IDENTIFYING FIBERS

Not so long ago most fabrics were made of wool, cotton, linen, or silk. It was easy to identify them just by feeling and looking. Today a wide variety of synthetic fibers has appeared on the market, and manufacturers have learned how to combine many fibers in making just a single fabric. Consequently, it is not easy now to analyze completely or identify all fabrics.

However, if the fibers of a fabric can be separated, there are some simple tests which help greatly in distinguishing fabrics. The most common of these are the burning tests and chemical tests.

The burning test

Obtain samples of a wide variety of fabrics. For the burning tests use both a strip of the fabric and individual threads. The strip should be about 2″ wide, and long enough so that you can touch one end to a match flame and still be able to hold it comfortably without burning yourself. Obtain individual threads by pulling them both from the warp (the lengthwise threads) and from the filling (or woof) of the fabric.

When performing the flame test with each sample of fabric, first apply a match flame to the end of the sample; then note carefully the appearance of the burning, the odor given off, and the size and nature of the ash. It might be a good idea to test the thread first and then confirm the test with the strip of cloth. The individual threads may give you some idea of the mixtures of fibers used.

Cotton and linen. Pure, untreated cotton or linen burns with a large flame and leaves almost no ash. The odor, if any, is quite similar to that of burning "rags" or paper. After the flame goes out, a glowing spark may continue to travel through the unburnt material.

Cottons treated to give them a special finish will burn with a much smaller flame. The cloth seems to char rather than burn completely. The ash retains the shape of the original material.

Wool. Wool will either smoulder or burn with a very tiny flame. However, the odor of burnt hair or feathers is unmistakable. A gummy, beady, coke-like ash accumulates and forms balls along the edge of the burning portion. Wool leaves much more ash than cotton or linen.

Silk. Pure, untreated silk also burns slowly and with a tiny flame. The characteristic odor of burnt hair or feathers will appear. The ash is black and shiny and forms into tiny brittle balls along the edge of the fabric. The balls crush easily when pressed between the thumb and forefinger.

Often silk is weighted (stiffened) by soaking the silk in a solution of mineral (metallic) salt, usually a tin compound. Weighting the silk gives the pure silk more "body" and also makes it easier to dye the silk. With the burning test the weighted silk will not burn, but just char. It leaves a black ash which has the same shape as the original cloth.

Rayon. All types of rayon, being made from cellulose like cotton and linen, will burn with a large flame. However, the ash will vary, depending upon the kind of rayon. Viscose rayon and cuprammonium rayon, if unweighted, will burn, like cotton, with a large flame and leave little or no ash. Acetate rayon burns with a large flame and gives off an odor of burning punk. [Acetate rayon dissolves in acetone (nail polish remover).] However, the material melts as it burns and leaves an ash very much like silk. The ash is black and shiny and, like silk, also forms tiny balls. However, these balls of ash become quite hard when cool and cannot be crushed easily between the thumb and forefinger.

Other synthetics. Nylon and the other synthetic fibers do not burn at all. However, combustible dyes and finishes may produce burning. Usually the fibers melt, leaving a brown mass at the edge of the material. In some cases a characteristic odor is given off. Since all the synthetic fibers react the same way to a flame, the burning test can only serve to identify the synthetic fibers as a group, and not individually.

Chemical tests

When identifying fibers by chemical tests, use very small pieces of fabric. Your high school chemistry teacher can help you with the chemicals. He can either make up the solutions and give them to you or advise you in ordering the chemicals and then help you make the proper solutions. When working with chemicals, especially acids and bases, take care not to spill them on your person or clothes. If this should happen, quickly wash with plenty of water.

With sodium hydroxide. Obtain a Pyrex glass container, such as is used in the kitchen for boiling water. Make a dilute solution of sodium hydroxide by dissolving 2 teaspoons of lye in a pint of water. (*Caution: Use care in adding lye to water.*) Boil the solution *gently,* using a gas stove, electric stove, or a hot plate. With forceps drop the sample of cloth in the boiling solution and boil gently for about 10 minutes. Animal fibers, such as wool

and silk, will dissolve. All the other fibers will not.

If you have a sample of cloth which is a mixture of wool and cotton, the wool will dissolve, leaving the undissolved cotton behind. This is also a test to determine whether material is pure wool or not. If you wish you may weigh the cloth sample carefully before putting it in the lye solution. After 10 minutes remove what is left, using a forceps. Wash the remnant in running water. Then put it on blotter or other absorbent material and let the remnant dry completely. Weigh the dried material carefully. From the two weights you will now be able to calculate the percentage of wool and other material in the fabric.

With hydrochloric acid. Pour cold concentrated hydrochloric acid (*Use caution.*) in a small beaker or glass tumbler. *Never, never pour water into acid.* Always pour the acid into water. Put very small pieces of fabric, or even just fiber threads, into the acid. Use a glass rod or swizzle stick to stir the fabric or fibers in the acid. Silk will dissolve in the hydrochloric acid. Rayon will also dissolve, but very, very slowly. Wool fibers will swell, but will not be destroyed. Cotton and linen are unaffected by the acid. Nylon is weakened and becomes brittle, but Orlon is not affected.

When you are finished with the acid, pour it slowly into a large container of water. Then pour the mixture down the sink or drain, letting the water faucet run for some time. This will protect the plumbing from the corrosive action of the acid.

With sulfuric acid. Secure from a druggist a 2% solution of sulfuric acid. Pour some of the sulfuric acid solution in a small beaker or glass tumbler. Stir the solution with a glass rod or swizzle stick. Now put a drop or two of the solution on the pieces of fabric to be tested. Animal fibers will be unaffected. Vegetable fibers will char. Nylon becomes slightly brittle, but Orlon is unaffected.

To test if a sample of fabric is a mixture of wool and cotton, add 2 drops of the sulfuric acid solution to the sample. Allow the acid to penetrate through the fabric. Then place the sample between two sheets of paper and press with a hot iron. If the material contains cotton, a charred spot will appear where the acid was dropped. Rub the charred spot gently between your thumb and forefinger. It will fall away, leaving the unaffected wool behind.

With indicator paper. Place a small piece of the same fabric in each of the two test tubes. Push the fabric down to the bottom of the test tube with a glass rod, swizzle stick, or pencil. Across the top of one test tube place a piece of moistened red litmus paper. Across the top of the second test tube place a piece of moistened lead acetate paper. (*Caution: Dry lead acetate is highly inflammable by spontaneous combustion. It must always be kept in a water solution.*) If prepared lead acetate paper is not available, cut narrow strips of filter paper and dip them in lead acetate solution. Heat both test tubes. Cotton, linen, rayon, and synthetic fibers do not give off fumes which affect these papers. Wool and silk both give off ammonia vapor, which turns the red litmus paper blue. In addition, wool gives off sulfide vapors which turn the colorless lead acetate paper black or brownish black.

With ink. Linen is hard to distinguish from cotton, especially if the cotton has been treated. The best test for identifying linen is by looking at it under the microscope. There are also some effective chemical tests. Wash and dry thoroughly a piece of linen and a piece of cotton. Then place a drop of ink on each sample. In the linen sample the ink will be absorbed quickly in an even circle. In the cotton the ink will be absorbed irregularly and not so quickly.

With oil. Obtain two fresh, dry, clean samples of linen and cotton. Add a drop of olive oil or glycerin to each sample. In linen the spot becomes translucent. In cotton the spot remains opaque.

With solvents. Acetate rayon will dissolve in acetone, chloroform, and to some extent in alcohol. No other rayons or other fibers will dissolve in these reagents.

With chlorine bleaches. Chlorine bleaches will destroy animal fibers but will not affect plant fibers. Bleaches which do not contain chlorine, such as hydrogen peroxide, must be used for animal fibers. Chlorine bleaches weaken Nylon, but do not affect Orlon.

PROPERTIES OF FIBERS

Wear resistance

Here is one demonstration that will test the wear resistance of fabrics. Obtain a small electric motor. Toy stores and fun shops sell all kinds and sizes of inexpensive motors. One of your pupils may have a small motor at home that he might bring in. Then get a piece of wood dowel about 1″ long. A short length of broomstick will also do. Drill a hole in the dowel longitudinally through the axis. The diameter of the hole should be slightly smaller than the diameter of the shaft on the motor. Force the motor shaft firmly into the hole in the dowel (Fig. 19-2). Now cement fine sandpaper around the dowel, with the sandy side up. The sandpaper is the abrasive which will test cloth for its wearing quality. If you can obtain it at the hardware store, use crocus cloth (#400 or 600) instead of sandpaper. The crocus cloth contains very finely powdered emery, which is an excellent abrasive.

Obtain samples of different fabrics 6–8″ long and 2–3″ wide. The thickness of the samples should be about the same.

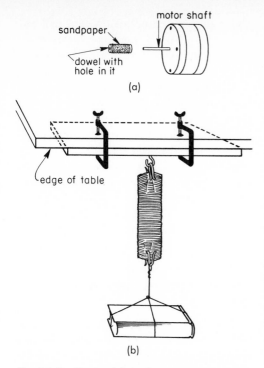

motor shaft

sandpaper

dowel with
hole in it

(a)

edge of table

(b)

Fig. 19-2 Testing fabrics for resistance to wear: (a) equipment for applying abrasion; (b) cloth holder.

Sew a very small hem at the top and bottom of each length of cloth. This will prevent the cloth from ripping when stretched. Then get a piece of pine board about 4′ × 6″ × ¾″. Clamp the board to the edge of a table, or rest the board upon the backs of two chairs placed back-to-back a few feet apart. You may want to place the chairs on a table for better vision. Screw a cup hook into the underside of the board. Obtain two large drapery hooks, the kind you use to hang heavy drapes from traverse or kitchen rods. Slide one hook in at the top of one length of fabric and suspend it from the cup hook attached to the pine board. Slide the other hook in at the bottom of the same length of fabric. Tie a string around one or two books and attach the string to the drapery hook at the bottom (Fig. 19-2). This will keep the cloth taut while you test the cloth for wear.

Now set the motor running and hold the rotating shaft and sandpaper against the taut piece of cloth. Note how long it takes to wear a hole in the cloth. Repeat the experiment with the other cloth samples and note how long it takes to wear out the cloth in each case. Make a list of the fabrics in the order of the time required to wear each out.

Dry and wet strength

Obtain samples of different fabrics 6–8″ long, 2–3″ wide, and of about the same thickness. Sew small hems at the top and bottom of each length of cloth to prevent ripping. Obtain a piece of pine board about 4′ × 6″ × ¾″. Clamp the board to the edge of a table, or rest the board upon the backs of two chairs placed back-to-back a few feet apart. Attach the cloth top to the board by means of a row of tacks. Attach a small board to the other end (bottom) of the cloth with tacks, also. Hang a drapery hook over the bottom board. Attach a strong cord to the handle of a small bucket or pail and connect the cord to the drapery hook (Fig. 19-3).

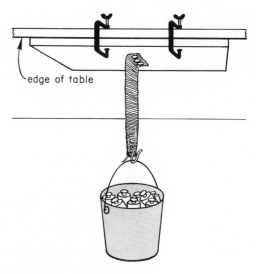

edge of table

Fig. 19-3 Testing fabrics for wet and dry strength.

Now add weights to the bucket until the fabric rips. If standard weights are not available, cloth bags filled with sand will serve just as well. Add quarter-pound, half-pound, and pound quantities of sand to cloth bags; then sew the bags tightly at the top. The weight of the bucket plus the sum of the weights inside the bucket will give you the strength of the dry fabric. Repeat the experiment with the other cloth samples.

You will find that the synthetic fabrics like Nylon, Orlon, and Dacron are the strongest. Cotton and silk are next in line, followed by the rayons and finally wool.

Once the dry strength of the fabrics is known, repeat the experiment, using the same materials when wet. Cotton is the only material which becomes stronger when wet. Saran loses no strength at all. Silk, wool, Nylon, Orlon, and Dacron lose strength slightly. All the rayons become much weaker when wet.

Water-absorbing property

Obtain cloth samples of different kinds of fabric. Cut the samples of equal size (about 6″ square) and try to have them all the same thickness. Iron each sample flat before you begin the experiment. Stretch a cord or clothesline across one end of the room and obtain a number of spring-type clothespins. Obtain a number of glass tumblers, all the same size and shape, and pour water into all the tumblers to the same level.

With forceps or tweezers dip each cloth into a tumbler of water for at least a minute. Then lift the cloth from the glass and let any excess water drip back into the tumbler. Hang each cloth up to dry on the clothesline. Note how much water each cloth sample soaked up and how long each sample took to dry.

Wool will absorb the most moisture, followed by pure rayon, then silk, and then acetate rayon, linen, and cotton (all about the same amount). Nylon will absorb only a little water, and Orlon even less. Dacron will absorb almost no water at all.

You will recall that the cloth samples were ironed flat before you wet them. Now note the smoothness of each sample after it has dried. Have any of the materials shrunk? Also, wet them again and try stretching them this time while they are wet. Which materials can be stretched, and how much?

Have the children discuss the effects of water on different fabrics and the implications for use in protecting against rain.

KEEPING COMFORTABLE WITH CLOTHING

There are many factors which must be taken into consideration when selecting the proper clothing to keep you comfortable during the winter or summer.

Nature of the fabric

The nature of the fabric is one important factor. Wool is one of the warmest fibers. Examine some wool fibers again under the microscope. Also examine closely a woolen sweater. Notice the air spaces between the wool fibers. These are "dead" air spaces because the air cannot circulate. This lack of circulation gives good heat protection by preventing the heat of your body from escaping.

Recall the section, "How Much Heat or Cold Gets Through—Insulation," in Chapter 20. Rock wool is cited as an excellent insulating material because it is fluffy and traps many air spaces.

Examine the fur lining of a glove. Notice again the air spaces between the hairs. These are also dead spaces and protect against the loss of heat in your body.

Nature of the weave

The nature of the weave of the fabric

is another important factor in keeping comfortable. For the summer, loose open weaves are desirable since your comfort depends upon air circulating freely through the garment. This allows the perspiration to evaporate faster. The quicker the perspiration evaporates, the cooler you feel.

Obtain a small amount of denatured alcohol and place it in a small bottle. Also obtain two medicine droppers. Pour some water in a second bottle, and let the bottles of alcohol and water stand overnight so that they both reach the same temperature. Now have a child place one hand out, palm down. Fill one medicine dropper with water and put a drop of water on the back of the child's hand. The drop will evaporate and the hand will feel cooler. Now have the child place both hands out, palms down. Fill one medicine dropper with water and the other with alcohol. Simultaneously put one drop of water on the back of one hand and one drop of alcohol on the back of the other hand. The alcohol will evaporate more quickly than the water, and the hand with alcohol will feel cooler.

Point out that when a liquid evaporates, it requires heat. It takes this heat from the surface from which it is evaporating. That is why the child's hands felt cooler. Help the children understand that because alcohol evaporates faster, it takes heat away from the surface faster, thereby producing a greater cooling effect. Thus the faster a liquid evaporates, the greater the cooling effect.

Have the children recall what happens when they go swimming. Whenever they come out of the water, they feel cool or even cold, especially on a windy day. The evaporation of the droplets of water on the skin results in rapid cooling.

Therefore, the more open the weave, the better the circulation and the better the opportunity for faster evaporation of the perspiration. The closer the weave, the poorer the circulation and the less opportunity for fast circulation.

Call the children's attention to the warmth of leather jackets, coats, and gloves. Leather has tiny pores, but they are so tiny that the spaces even between very tightly woven material seem like huge holes by comparison. The air cannot penetrate the leather even in cold windy weather. A combination of leather on the outside and wool or fur on the inside is just about the warmest combination possible. The Eskimos are well aware of that. Incidentally, you might want to point out that we use leather for our shoes because it protects us from injury and moisture as well as from the cold and heat.

Fit

Fit is still another factor in keeping us comfortable. In the summer, loose clothes allow free air circulation to evaporate perspiration. In the winter, a tighter fit is more desirable (but not too tight). Actually the tightest fit should be around the neck to prevent heat from escaping. A small layer of trapped, still air helps conserve body heat.

Weight

Another factor is the weight of the fabric. The heavier the fabric, the more layers of fiber there are. This increases the amount of dead air spaces and prevents the body heat from escaping. This is why we wear heavy clothes in the winter and light clothes in the summer or during warm weather.

Color

Finally, the color of the cloth makes a difference too. Review the section, "Colors, Heat, and Comfort," in Chapter 20. Perform the experiments showing that the darker the material, the more radiated or radiant heat it absorbs, and the hotter the material becomes. Point out that the sun radiates heat, too. Obtain two thermometers. Wrap the bulb of one thermometer in black cloth, and the other bulb in white cloth. Both pieces of cloth should be of the same material. Place both thermometers in the direct sunlight and read the thermometers at 10-minute intervals for a half hour. The thermometer under the black cloth will show a greater rise in temperature. Thus, light clothes are preferred in the summer because they are cooler than darker clothes.

REMOVING STAINS

Removing spots and stains has become a common practice in the home. However, there are certain safety precautions which should be called to the children's attention. Spot removers are sold under many trade names, but most of them consist of benzene, gasoline, naphtha, or carbon tetrachloride. All but carbon tetrachloride are highly inflammable, and their vapors can be explosive. (*Caution: The fumes of carbon tetrachloride are toxic and should not be inhaled.*) A tiny spark created by the friction of rubbing is enough to cause the vapors of all but carbon tetrachloride to ignite. The heat of an electric iron or other appliance, or the spark produced when a plug is removed from the wall outlet, can also cause fire or explosion. Although carbon tetrachloride is noninflammable, its vapors are poisonous. Consequently, when using all spot removers, be sure to work in a well-ventilated room or outdoors, and to avoid excessive heat, flame, or electric sparks.

The children may be interested in removing some common stains. Before doing so, point out that there are a few basic rules which should be observed. Stains should be treated promptly while they are fresh. If not, they will harden and set, damaging the fabric and becoming more difficult to remove. Try to determine the nature of the fabric. What is it made of? Can it be washed? Is it affected by acids or alkalies?

Before trying to remove a stain, try to determine exactly what it is. The wrong treatment may set a stain so that it is impossible to remove. Or you may remove not only the stain but the color of the cloth as well, so that what was once a stain becomes a faded spot. Always test any commercial spot remover first on a sample of the cloth or on a hidden part of the garment, such as the hem, to make sure it will not change color or damage the fabric. This applies also to water.

Always try sponging with cold water first, providing the fabric is not affected by water. Hot water sets many stains and makes it hard to remove them. Test a sample of the fabric to see if water spots it.

The standard procedure in removing stains is to place the stained fabric on a pad of clean, absorbent cloth, with the stain face down on the cloth. Use clean soft cloth to sponge the fabric. Dampen the cloth with water or dip it into the spot remover. Then sponge the stain with light, brushing motions, working from the outside of the stain in toward the center. Spread the solvent unevenly into the fabric around the stain, to prevent a ring from forming. Work rapidly and use the solvent sparingly. It is better to apply the water or spot remover many times for short intervals than to apply a large amount at once and then leave it on for a long time. Change the pad or the face of the pad every time you apply fresh water or spot remover.

If a ring does form, try removing it by sponging the material with fresh water or by shaking it in the steam of a vigorously boiling teakettle. Sometimes the ring can be removed by scratching it with your fingernail or with a stiff brush or by rubbing the cloth between your hands. Blowing on the stain while applying the water or spot remover will help the spot dry quickly and will prevent a ring from forming. Patting the treated stain with a dry cloth will also help.

If the stain does not come out easily, do not rub. Rubbing may cause the fabric to look lighter or wear out. Stop treating the stain yourself and send it to a professional cleaner.

The following are a few of the methods used to treat some common stains. If the pupils become interested in stain removal, have them read the comprehensive yet simple booklet *Stain Removal from Fabrics, Home Methods,* Farmers' Bulletin No. 1474, 1942, U. S. Department of Agriculture. The booklet costs five cents and can be obtained by writing to the Superintendent of Documents, Washington, D.C.

ADHESIVE TAPE: Sponge with carbon tetrachloride.

BLOOD: Blood stains will usually come out if soaked or rubbed in cold or lukewarm water. Never use hot water because it sets the stain. For silk or wool simply sponge the stain with cold or lukewarm water. For washable materials soak or rub the blood stain in cold water until it turns light brown in color. Then wash in warm soapy water. If the stain is old and dried, add 2 tablespoons of household ammonia for each gallon of water used for soaking. Salt water (about 2 cups of salt for each gallon of water) will also help loosen old, dried stains.

CHEWING GUM: If the material is not affected by water, apply an ice cube to the gum. This will harden the gum, which can then be scraped or rubbed off with a dull knife. For hardened gum inside the fabric, soften the gum with egg white, and then wash. Another method is to sponge with carbon tetrachloride, then water.

CHOCOLATE AND COCOA: More than one method is often necessary to remove chocolate and cocoa stains because they usually contain other substances, such as milk, sugar, starch, and fat. First scrape off as much as you can with a dull knife. If the material is washable, wash with warm soapy water. Stubborn stains may be removed from white cotton or linen by using a commercial chlorine bleach (you can smell the chlorine in it). If the fabric is not washable, sponge it with carbon tetrachloride to dissolve the fatty contents of the chocolate. The remainder can be removed with hydrogen peroxide.

COFFEE AND TEA: Fresh stains as well as most old ones can be removed from washable materials by ordinary laundering. If a slight trace of stain remains, dry in the sun; if the material is white, bleach with a commercial bleach or hydrogen peroxide. If the stains are on wool or silk, sponge immediately with cold or lukewarm water. If a grease spot remains, treat it with carbon tetrachloride.

FRUITS AND BERRIES: If the stain is on washable material, stretch the stained material over a bowl or other vessel and pour boiling water on it from a teakettle at a height of 3'. This will permit the water to strike with some force and wash away the stain. If the material is white and a trace of stain remains, treat the fabric with commercial bleach.

GRASS: If the material is washable, use hot water and soap, rubbing the stain vigorously. Remaining traces in white cotton or linen can be bleached out with commercial bleach. If the material is not washable, sponge with warm alcohol (either wood or denatured). (*Caution: Alcohol is inflammable.* Warm by standing an open bottle in a dish of hot water.)

GREASE AND OILS: First scrape or wipe off as much of the grease as possible. If the material is washable, use warm water and soap, rubbing the spot thoroughly. The standard, and most effective, method is to use such grease solvents as carbon tetrachloride, benzene, naphtha, or gasoline.

ICE CREAM, MILK, OR CREAM: If the material is washable, rinse in cold or lukewarm water; then wash with soap and hot water. For nonwashable material, first sponge with carbon tetrachloride or benzene to remove the greasy part of the stain. Let it dry. Then sponge carefully with cold water to remove the other materials.

INK: If the ink stain is still wet, apply corn meal, cornstarch, talcum powder, or salt to remove any ink not yet absorbed by the material and to keep the stain from spreading. Work the powder into the stain. Shake off the powder as it becomes soiled and repeat the process. When the dry absorbing material fails to take up more ink, make it into a paste with warm water and apply again. If the fabric is washable, some types of ink may be removed with soap and water. Another method is to add some milk and then blot the milk and ink with an absorbent cloth or blotter. Then use carbon tetrachloride or benzene to remove the milk.

IODINE: If the material is washable, use soap and water on a fresh stain. If the material is nonwashable, sponge with denatured alcohol. The most effective method is to sponge with sodium thiosulfate solution (1 tablespoon of sodium thiosulfate solution to 1 pint of water). Sodium thiosulfate, known as "hypo" to most amateur photographers, can be obtained at any camera shop.

LIPSTICK: Sponge with benzene or carbon tetrachloride. If a trace of color remains, sponge with denatured alcohol.

MERCUROCHROME: Mercurochrome stains are very hard to remove and must be treated promptly. First sponge with a solution made of equal parts of denatured alcohol and water. Next work glycerin into the cloth to help loosen the stain. Then wash well in soapsuds and rinse with water containing a few drops of household ammonia. If this treatment does not completely remove the stain, use a bleach.

PAINTS: Scrape off as much paint as possible. Then sponge the stain with turpentine or paint remover. If the paint has hardened, first loosen the paint by rubbing Vaseline, oil, or even butter into it. Then treat with turpentine or paint remover.

RUST: Sprinkle the stain with salt; then squeeze lemon juice on it and spread in the sun to dry. If the stain still shows, add more lemon juice and repeat the process. Rinse well afterward. A most effective rust remover is oxalic acid solution (3 tablespoons of oxalic acid crystals to 1 pint of water). Oxalic acid is a poison and must be handled with care.

TAR: First scrape off as much tar as possible. Then rub in Vaseline to soften the stain. Now sponge with benzene, carbon tetrachloride, naphtha, or gasoline. Repeat the treatment until the stain is removed. Tar is extremely difficult to remove from cotton.

WATER SPOTS: Some wools, silks, and rayons are spotted by water. Dampen the entire material evenly. Either sponge with clean water or shake in the steam of a vigorously boiling teakettle. Then press while the fabric is still damp. Scratching with the fingernail or with a stiff brush, or just rubbing the cloth between the hands, is often enough to remove the spot.

CAPSULE LESSONS

19-1 Bring in different samples of cloth and have the children try to identify the material. Let them also try to identify the material in their garments. Lead into the study of the different kinds of fibers.

19-2 Have the children make a list of articles in the home which are made from synthetic fibers. Lead into the study of the various fibers, natural and synthetic, and their different properties.

19-3 Discuss the kinds of clothing worn in different seasons of the year. Compare the value of different materials for keeping comfortable in warm and cold weather.

19-4 Make a list of clothing worn in the summer and winter. Include such things as open-toed shoes in the winter and furs in the summer. Discuss whether the selection is based upon fashion or common sense. Go into the study of keeping comfortable with clothing.

19-5 Make a list of rules for taking care of clothing. Lead into the study of different fabrics and their care.

19-6 Bring in some different samples of cloth. Stain or spot them in various ways; then call for suggestions on how to remove the stains. Lead into the study of fibers and fabrics and how to keep them clean.

BIBLIOGRAPHY

Ahrens, M. R., N. K. Bush, and R. K. Easley, *Living Chemistry,* Ginn, 1957. Contains excellent chapter for teacher reference on fibers and clothing. Includes tests for identification of fibers.

Allen, Agnes, *The Story of Clothes,* Roy, 1958.

Nighbert, Esther, *The True Book of Cloth,* Childrens Press, 1955.

Housing

WHERE PEOPLE LIVE

Begin with a study of the different kinds of homes used today. Flash back to earlier and cruder dwellings such as caves, tents made of animal skins, and buildings made of mud, sod, clay, logs, stone, and brick. Discuss the different types of roofing used for the various dwellings.

Lead into a study of the types of houses used all over the world and point out the relationship between shelter and climate. Classify the types of houses according to areas of climate. Discuss the conveniences and inconveniences of each type of home.

In hot, dry climates

Start off with the types of houses used in hot, dry lands. The desert nomads who must carry their homes with them use lightweight tents made of cloth or material woven from goat and camel hair. Tents provide not only shelter from the hot sun but also from sandstorms. Because of the stifling heat of the desert, one side of the tent is kept open to provide circulation of air; there may also be a top opening. In other arid lands (such as Mexico) adobe houses are used. Adobe consists of blocks of clay, mixed with straw to hold the clay together, baked dry in the sun. The thick adobe walls help keep out the sun's heat. In the Congo, grass huts are used. These huts look like bowls placed upside down. They are covered from top to bottom with long grass or fibers obtained from bamboo, cocoanut palms, etc. A grass hut is the coolest kind of home that people can have, providing good protection from the sun's rays and excellent circulation of air.

Help the children realize that the type of house depends upon the climate and the kind of materials and tools that are available.

In hot, wet climates

In hot, wet lands grass huts are also used. They are placed on long poles and stilts or are built in trees to protect the inhabitants from the damp or muddy ground. This type of home not only provides a suitable and cool shelter but also protects the people from floods and animals.

In cold climates

Two types of homes are used in cold lands. In the very far north, the Eskimos build snow houses, called igloos, for shelter during the winter. The igloo consists of a round hut and a tunnel, both made of blocks of snow. The tunnel prevents the cold wind from coming into the igloo. In the summer when the snow is gone, the Eskimos use tents made of animal skins. Farther south, Eskimos and Indians live in houses made of earth. These houses are half under and half above the ground level. The people find that their house is warmer if part of it is under the ground.

In temperate climates

Houses in U. S. farm lands are usually one- and two-story wood frame houses, with brick or stone chimneys. A wood barn, much larger than the house, stands nearby.

In the cities and suburbs, there are many kinds of houses. They may be single buildings containing one and two stories, or they may be apartment buildings containing many stories. The houses may be made of stone, brick, wood, or combinations of these three. Many different materials are used in building these homes. They include concrete, stucco, tile, marble, glass, metal, plastics, etc.

Discuss the many different styles of homes. Some of these are the Cape Cod, Ranch, Bungalow, Cottage, Georgian, Tudor, Colonial, Spanish, Italian, French Provincial, and Southern. In many cases more than one style is incorporated in the construction.

WHAT MATERIALS WE USE TO BUILD A HOUSE

If it should happen that a house or apartment building is being built in the vicinity of the school, take advantage of this opportunity to have the class learn how a house is built and also what materials are used in its construction. Make periodic visits with the class at each important phase of construction. If such an experience is not available, your local building contractor can be quite helpful. Ask him to visit the class and tell about building a house. He may also be able to bring samples of material, pictures, and booklets showing how a house is built. Furthermore, various children may be able to report to the class about new houses going up in their neighborhoods.

The foundation

The children should be able to tell you that a building begins with the foundation.

A firm foundation is necessary to support the heavy load of a house and its contents. A deep hole may be dug to serve as a future basement. The floor and walls of this basement are lined with any one of many materials. Concrete is most commonly used because it is very sturdy and economical. Concrete is made by mixing cement, sand, gravel, and water. The cement serves to bind the ingredients together. Cement itself is a mixture of limestone and clay, baked until it forms a hard mass. This mass is then ground into a fine powder. Have the children observe how the workmen mix the concrete and then pour it into wooden forms where the concrete is allowed to harden. After it has hardened, the wooden forms are removed.

A heavy wood sill usually completes the foundation. This sill is placed in soft mortar on top of the concrete and then bolted so that it cannot slide. It must be set absolutely level because it is the basis for the entire framework of the house.

Another material used for foundations is concrete blocks. These blocks usually have open spaces that reduce the weight and the amount of concrete needed. These spaces reduce somewhat the supporting strength of the concrete blocks, but not enough to make a difference. Other types of materials for basement are natural stone, hollow tile blocks, and bricks. Bricks and tile are both made from clay which is baked. Where the foundation must support a very large framework, steel beams are used for additional support. These beams are usually called I-beams because of the shape of their cross sections.

When the basement of the house is to be used as a playroom or "den," asphalt, vinyl, or rubber tile is usually laid over the concrete base. Your local hardware or department store or your contractor might give you samples of all kinds of tile used for this purpose.

Today many houses are being built without basements. The upper surface of the earth is removed; then a big slab of concrete is poured directly on the ground. Such items as the furnace, hot-water heater, and laundry equipment are then put into a utility room, usually located next to the kitchen. Have the class discuss the advantages and disadvantages of homes with and with basements.

Framework and walls

Once the foundation is in, a wall framework is put up. This consists of long pieces of wood called "two by fours" because they measure roughly 2″ thick by 4″ wide. For large apartment houses steel beams or girders are used as framework.

When the framework is up, the house is covered with an outer wall and an inner wall. If the house is to be a wooden one, first a layer of boards is nailed to the two by fours. This layer is called the sheathing. Sometimes the sheathing is made of synthetic materials. Then a layer of heavy building paper goes over the sheathing. Its purpose is to prevent the air from seeping out between the cracks where the sheathing boards meet, and also from any knot holes that may be present. The third layer is the one you see when you look at the house. This outer layer is called the siding. It usually consists of long narrow boards which are laid so they overlap. This overlapping helps make the house weathertight. Sometimes wood shingles or asbestos shingles are used as an outer layer. An aluminum siding which looks like wood is also used.

Other materials are used for outside walls. Brick is quite popular. The bricks are held together by mortar, a mixture of lime, cement, sand, and water. The mortar also helps make the brick wall weathertight and water-resistant. The brick is usually colored red, but many other colors are available. Natural and artificial stone is often used instead of brick. In many cities, especially in warm climates, stucco is used as an outside wall. Some stucco is made of cement and sand, while other kinds are made of lime and sand. The stucco is made up into a thick paste with water and then daubed onto a wire mesh fastened to the framework of the house. This material hardens and forms a thick layer over the outside of the house. Stucco can be colored any shade and seldom needs refinishing. Terra cotta is an ornamental building material made of clay which is baked.

A recent development in wall-building is the use of translucent-glass bricks. Each brick or block is made from two glass boxes sealed together to form a hollow block. Air is partially withdrawn during its manufacture to insure better insulating qualities.

The most common type of inside wall is made of plaster. First stiff sheets of wire mesh are nailed to the two by fours. Then a first coat of rough plaster is put on. This rough plaster has the same ingredients as mortar, namely, lime, sand, a little cement, and water. After this first coat has dried, a second final coat which is quite smooth is added. This coat is composed chiefly of plaster of Paris and water, with a little lime. The finished plaster is then either painted or wall-papered.

Plasterboard, a sandwich of cardboard with a plaster filling, is often used for interior walls. Plywood, used for both floors and walls, is made by binding together with resins thin sheets of wood under heavy pressure and high heat. The layers of wood are called plies. Collect samples of plywood and have the children count the number of plies. The most common number is three, but plywood with five and seven plies is readily available.

In some homes, panels and veneers of costlier wood (mahogany) are used as inside walls. Also glass blocks serve as both an inside and an outside wall.

Floors

The best floors are doubled. First a poorer grade of lumber is laid down. Then a top-grade hardwood lumber is placed over the first layer. This lumber has a tongue and groove so that it can fit very tightly together. Usually long lengths of oak are used, but less costly pine is also popular. In some homes the top layer consists of small pieces of wood set in a mosaic pattern. Such floors are called parquet floors. Some of the larger, more ornate homes indulge in the luxury and expense of marble floors.

Quite common in the kitchen and bathroom are floors covered with asphalt, rubber, composition, or ceramic tile. Often the bathroom floor consists of brick tile.

The roof

The framework construction for the roof is usually two by sixes. On top of these go a sheathing similar to that used for the outside walls of the house. Then the water-resistant part of the roof goes over the sheathing. Various materials are used for the roof depending upon their cost. High-cost materials include slate, clay tile, and such metals as aluminum, copper, and lead. These materials last indefinitely and need little or no repair. Medium-cost materials include asbestos shingles, cement tile, and metal tile. These need occasional repairs. Low-priced materials include wood shingles, asphalt shingles, galvanized iron (iron coated with zinc), and sometimes just tar paper. These need frequent replacement, repairs, and painting.

Fixtures

Steel is used in making nails, bolts, hinges, screws, and locks. Gutters and rain spouts are made of aluminum, copper, or galvanized iron. Bronze, an alloy of copper and tin, is often used for special door knobs, locks, and hinges. Cast iron, lead, copper, and brass are used in plumbing pipes and traps. The heating system is usually made of cast iron, steel, or sheet metal. Plumbing fixtures may be chromium-plated, nickel-plated, or iron.

PROTECTING A HOUSE FROM THE ELEMENTS

How much heat or cold gets through—insulation

Obtain four large tin cans of equal size and four smaller tin cans of equal size. The smaller cans should be able to fit inside the larger cans and leave at least 1″ of space at the bottom and around the sides. Obtain rock wool and sawdust from the hardware store or lumberyard, and ground cork from the supermarket or grocery store (grapes and other fragile fruit usually come packed in ground cork).

Now place the four smaller cans inside the larger cans (Fig. 20-1). Pack the rock wool so that there is at least 1″ of this insulating material around and under one small can. In the same manner imbed the second small can in ground cork, and the third small can in sawdust. For the fourth small can obtain two corks about 1″ high. If the corks are too high, cut them down to size. Place the two corks on the bottom of the larger can and rest the smaller can on the corks. This will provide an air space around and under the small can.

Cut four squares of heavy cardboard, each square large enough to cover the larger tin cans. In the center of each cardboard make a small hole just large enough for a thermometer to slip through snugly. Now heat water until it just begins to boil. Fill each inner can almost full, making sure you fill all the cans to the same height. Cover each can with a cardboard cover

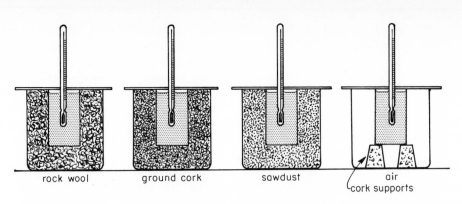

rock wool   ground cork   sawdust   air

cork supports

Fig. 20-1 Testing insulating materials.

containing a thermometer. Have the children take the temperature of the water in each can every few minutes. Note which can of water cooled the slowest and which the quickest. List the cans according to their rate of cooling, putting the slowest on top and the quickest at the bottom. Distinguish the cans by the material in which they were packed. The children should now realize that the material which made the water cool the slowest is the best insulator, a substance that is a poor conductor of heat. Look at the sections of different insulating material through a magnifying glass.

Help the children understand that, for home comfort and economy, it is quite important to prevent heat from escaping, especially in the winter. The opposite is true in the summer, for then heat should be kept out. The chief heat passage is through the walls and roof. Therefore, it is both wise and economical to insulate a newly built house. Rock wool is an excellent insulator. Being fluffy, it traps many small air spaces in which the air cannot move ("dead air") and therefore cannot conduct heat.

Fluffy rock wool is made up into large and thick flat mats or batts which are laid over the attic floor and fastened into the side walls when the house is being built. For older houses already built without insulation, this rock wool can be blown into hollow spaces between the outer and inner walls. Other materials used for insulation are mica, cork pellets, and rock wool pellets. Sometimes wallboard or mortarboard is used as an insulator.

Point out to the children that good insulation will not only prevent the heat from escaping in the winter, but will also keep out the heat during the summer.

However, it should also be pointed out that insulation has one major disadvantage. Moist air, that is, air containing water vapor, gets into the insulating material. When temperature changes occur, the water vapor condenses into water. This water inside the walls and ceilings helps cause decay, and spoils plaster, wall paper, and paint.

Recently, thin sheets of bright metal (foil) such as aluminum have been used as insulation. This thin sheet of metal is put on the surface of some fiberboard or wallboard material, or even on paper. The bright metal surface reflects the radiant heat waves and thus prevents them from passing through the walls, ceilings, or roof.

A simple experiment will demonstrate this graphically. Obtain a heavy rectangular cardboard box. The box should be large enough to accommodate a 60-watt bulb and leave about 2″ to spare on each side of the box. Have one end of the box

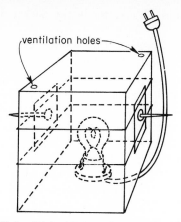

Fig. 20-2 Bright shiny metal is a good insulator.

open. Cut two small holes at diagonally opposite corners of the top of the box to let the heated air escape and thus prevent the cardboard from burning (Fig. 20-2).

Obtain two small panes of glass, slightly narrower than the side of the box. Cut a window in two opposite sides of the box. Each window should be smaller than the pane of glass. Cut out a piece of aluminum foil the same size as a glass pane and glue it to one pane at the edges. Make sure the aluminum is pressed closely to the pane and is quite smooth. Now attach both panes of glass to the windows, using glue, Scotch tape, or rubber bands. The pane covered with the aluminum should have the aluminum on the outside, away from the bulb.

Using the hot paraffin from a burning candle, attach a long tack to the outside surface of each pane. Insert the 60-watt bulb into the box, turn on the current, and note which tack falls off first. Also touch each outside surface to see which one is hotter. The pane with the aluminum foil reflects the radiated heat of the bulb and is therefore cooler. As a variation you can use two panes of glass. On the surface of one attach aluminum foil and to this a tack with paraffin. Stick a tack to the other glass pane and arrange

the panes of glass equidistant on either side of a candle or light bulb. The tacks should be pointing away from the heat source. The panes of glass can be held upright by insertion between books lying flat on a table.

There is also heat loss around doors and windows of homes. The children can feel cold air coming in by placing their hands near the bottoms of outside doors. This loss can be overcome by filling cracks around the frames of windows and doors with a putty-like material such as calking compound. Cracks between the frames and door or window sashes can be closed by using weather stripping made of felt or thin springy metal. In cold climates storm windows help reduce the loss of heat because the air space between them and the regular windows is a poor heat conductor, that is, a good insulator. Storm doors work the same way.

Colors, heat, and comfort

Color can play a part in the comfort of your home. Obtain a tin can. With flat, black paint blacken one half of the tin can inside and out. Leave the other half shiny. With the paraffin from a burning candle fasten two long tacks to the outside of the can. One tack should be in the center of the blackened portion. The other tack should be directly opposite in the center of the shiny portion (Fig. 20-3). Now put a lighted candle inside the can at the exact center of the base of the can.

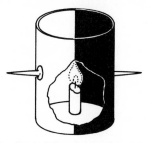

Fig. 20-3 Dark dull surfaces absorb heat better than shiny smooth surfaces.

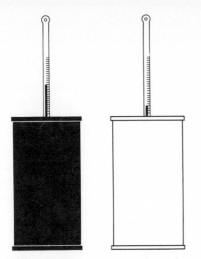

Fig. 20-4 Water in a darkened can becomes warmer in the sunlight than that in a light, shiny can.

Note which tack falls off first. Also test which surface—the shiny or the black—becomes hotter by touching them with your finger tips.

Obtain the tops of two tin cans of equal size. Blacken both sides of one of the tops with flat black paint. Leave the other top shiny. Using spring-type clothespins as holders or forceps, hold both tops equally close to a 100-watt lighted bulb or directly in the bright sun's rays. After a while note which top heats up more quickly. Do this by touching the tops with your finger tips and by holding the palm of your hand close to but not touching the tops themselves.

Obtain two large tin cans and a thermometer. Darken the outside of one can by smoking it thoroughly with a candle flame. Now fill a glass or beaker with cold water from the faucet. Place both cans side by side on a table and pour the same amount of cold water in each one. Take the temperature of the water in each can and record the readings. Stand the cans in bright sunshine for at least a half hour (Fig. 20-4). Then take the temperature of the water in each one again and record the readings. The water in the darkened tin can will be warmer.

The children should now realize that objects with dull, dark surfaces absorb and radiate radiant heat better than objects with smooth, shiny surfaces. Objects with smooth, shiny surfaces reflect radiant heat very well but are not good absorbers or radiators of radiant heat.

Help the children understand that black or dark-colored roofs will absorb the sun's rays in the summer and make houses warmer. On the other hand, light-colored roofs will reflect the sun's rays and thus help keep houses cooler. Some children will suggest that dark-colored roofs are a help in the winter. While this is true, remind them that insulation already helps keep houses warm in the winter, and the additional heat from a dark-colored roof in the winter is more than offset by the discomfort produced in the summer.

Point out also that dark-colored radiators in the home would give out more radiant heat than radiators that are silvered or painted white. However, most people forego this advantage because light-colored radiators seem more attrac-

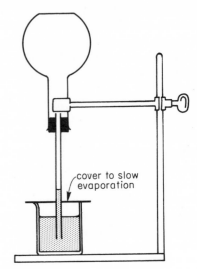

cover to slow evaporation

Fig. 20-5 The effect of radiant heat on different colors.

tive to them than the dark-colored ones.

You may want to show the effect of radiant heat on different colors. Borrow from a high school science teacher four Florence flasks, four one-hole rubber stoppers to fit the flasks, four 12″ lengths of glass tubing to fit the holes in the stoppers, four beakers, four ring stands, and four burette clamps. Paint the bottom and round portion of three flasks with different colored tempera (washable) paints. Paint the fourth flask silver or aluminum. Insert a piece of glass tubing in each one-hole rubber stopper. Use a twisting motion when inserting the glass tubing so that the tubing will not break in your hands. Insert the tubing so that the end of the tubing is flush with the bottom of the stopper.

Now put a stopper in each flask and support the flask upside down by a burette clamp attached to the ring stand (Fig. 20-5). Fill each beaker almost full of cold water colored with red or blue ink. Then either raise or lower the burette clamp so that the glass tubing is well into the beaker.

Have four children warm the flasks with both hands until the bubbles stop coming out of the glass tubing in the colored water. Then have the children take their hands away. In a short while the colored water will rise in each tube. Mark the level of the water in each tube with a wax crayon or by twisting a small piece of wire around the tubing.

Now move all four flasks and ring stands to bright sunlight. After at least a half hour note which colored water level went down the most. The children will realize that the darker the paint, the more heat is absorbed. The hotter the flask becomes, the hotter the air is inside the flask, and the farther down this hot air pushes the colored water in the glass tubing.

Fresh air indoors

The circulation of air in a room is a very important problem in ventilation. A ventilation box will show this quite clearly. Obtain a wooden or heavy cardboard box about 20″ long, 15″ wide, and not more than 4–6″ deep. Bore three holes about 1″ in diameter as follows: two holes in one end of the box and one hole in the top of the box at one side (Fig. 20-6A). Insert three cork stoppers into the holes. Paint the inside of the box a dull black. Obtain a pane of glass the same size as the open end of the box. Your local hardware dealer or glazier will supply the glass and cut it to proper dimensions. Hammer long thin nails part way into each end of the box (top and bottom); then bend them sideways to the front of the box. These bent nails will serve as grooves to keep the pane in place. Scotch tape the pane at its ends to the box so that the pane will fit snugly.

Now place a small burning candle in the center of the box. Remove the bottom end cork for a moment and allow some smoke to enter the ventilation box. You can create smoke with a cigarette, punk or joss stick, a smoking facial tissue, or paper towel. If the tissue or paper towel is used, roll up a piece tightly and light it with a flame. After it has burned for a few seconds, blow out the flame. As soon as some smoke has entered the ventilation box, replace the cork stopper and observe the pattern in which the smoke moves. Two currents will be noticed, in which the smoke rises and then falls. These are called convection currents. Point out to the class that the air next to the flame is heated and thus expands, thereby becoming lighter. This lighter air floats to the top and is replaced by colder air which flows down to take its place. This colder air soon becomes heated, expands, and rises; then it, too, is replaced by colder air flowing down to take its place. In this way, a convection current is set up, and the smoke traces the path and direction of this current. Convec-

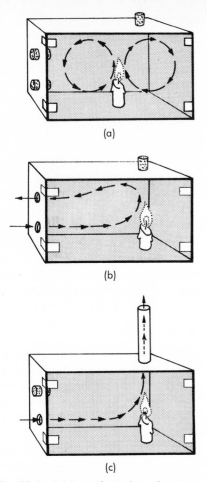

(a)

(b)

(c)

Fig. 20-6 (a) A ventilation box, showing convection currents; (b) the effect of opening a window at the top and bottom in a heated room; (c) the action of a draft in a fireplace or furnace with a chimney.

tion currents are taken up in greater detail in Chapter 18.

Now move the candle over to the end of the box opposite the holes. Allow smoke to enter from the bottom end hole for a few moments; then replace the cork. Observe the convection current set up now. Compare the action of this current with that set up by a radiator in a room.

Now blow quite a bit of smoke in at the bottom end hole. When the box is thoroughly filled with smoke, remove both end corks (Fig. 20-6B). This will give you

the same effect as opening a window at the top and bottom in a heated room. A convection current of air is set up which covers every part of the room. Thus, a proper circulation of air is provided. Provide a continuous supply of smoke at the bottom end hole.

Call the children's attention to the fact that, wherever possible, radiators are placed under windows. In this way the cold air which drops down from windows passes immediately over the hot radiator. The radiator then heats this air and sets up a convection current. Thus, the room is thoroughly heated; yet there is a constant supply of fresh air.

The children may wish to detect and trace convection currents in the room. Attach long narrow strips of very thin paper to a stick or yardstick. Thumb tacks will serve to hold the strips of paper in place. Now place the paper strips over a hot radiator and notice the direction that the strips assume. Repeat the process in different parts of the room and at different heights. Use a chair, table, or step ladder to reach near the ceiling.

Study the action of a draft in a fireplace or in a stove or furnace with a chimney. Fill the ventilation box thoroughly with smoke. Then remove the corks at the bottom end hole and at the hole in the top of the box (Fig. 20-6C). Place a glass chimney over the hole at the top of the box. If a chimney is not available, use pieces of mailing tube or the hollow tube from a paper towel roll, about 6″ long. Continue supplying more smoke at the bottom end hole. Note the direction of the draft or convection current in this case. The cold air flows in at the bottom while the hot air and/or waste gases go up the chimney.

Proper window ventilation is also illustrated by a convection box made from a cigar box. Cut holes in the side to fit small chimneys or glass cylinders. Replace the cover with a pane of glass hinged with adhesive. Use Sterno (small size) for the heat source. Trace convection currents by introducing smoke first at the upper hole and then at the lower hole. Proper ventilation is attainable only by opening windows (sash) at both top and bottom. This, of course, does not apply to casement windows.

Keeping water out

How to keep water from the outside from coming through basement walls is often a difficult problem. Cement blocks, tile, and mortar are all porous. The best way to make basements waterproof is to apply heavy coatings of asphalt to the outside walls.

Silicones and other plastic resins are also good, but they are more expensive than asphalt. When these protective materials are applied to the outside walls, the water runs off the walls smoothly and quickly. But when these materials are applied to the inside walls, apparently the water pushes these materials right out of the concrete.

Sometimes house walls are waterproofed on the outside. The materials used in this case are wax or fatty oil dissolved in naphtha, kerosene, or benzene. The waterproofing material is then applied as paint.

Ordinary house paints are used to protect the wood from the elements. This includes water as well. The paint not only prevents the water from rotting the wood, but helps keep the water out.

The children may like to test some waterproofing materials. Obtain wood shingles from the lumber yard and asphalt paint or other waterproof paint from the paint shop or a painter. Coat some shingles with the waterproof materials. Compare the effects of water on waterproofed and nonwaterproofed shingles. Obtain paraffin wax (clear candles will serve the purpose). Use about a quarter of a pound of paraffin. Melt the paraffin in an old

pan over a hot plate on low heat only until paraffin turns liquid. (*Caution: It is inflammable.*) In another pan heat a pint of water nearly to boiling. Then, stirring vigorously, add the melted paraffin slowly to the hot water. Remove the pan containing the mixture from the hot plate and continue stirring while the mixture is cooling.

With a brush, coat a piece of paper, cardboard, or fiberboard on the side which is to be in contact with water. Place this paper in the oven set at a temperature of 125° (the melting point of paraffin). Keep the paper in the oven for a very short time, just long enough for the wax to coalesce into a continuous film. No matter how long you expose this surface to water, the material will be waterproof.

Protecting against fire

Fire is a constant hazard, especially with homes. You might like to collect various building and roofing materials and test them with a flame for their ability to burn. Let children decide which are fireproof, or inflammable. Point out how fireproof materials are made of stone, brick, tile, slate, clay, plaster, and metal. Note the fire-resistant qualities of asphalt, mica, rock wool, and porcelain.

Fireproof paints usually contain water glass (sodium silicate). This chemical may be obtained from your hardware store, paint store, or chemical supply house. Paint a strip of wood with at least three coats of water-glass solution. Allow each coat to dry before the next one is applied. When the last coat has been applied and is dry, hold the stick over the flame of a Bunsen burner or a gas range. The coating will swell, and a froth will form, but the wood does not burn.

Methods of fireproofing paper and cloth have already been described in Chapter 17.

CAPSULE LESSONS

20-1 Have the children make a list of the materials used to build a house. Lead into a study of different kinds of houses and the materials used to build them.

20-2 Make a list of the different provisions made when building a house to prevent heat loss. Lead into the study of insulation and insulating materials.

20-3 Have the children describe those conditions which they think make for ideal weather. They should include a temperature a little over 70° F, air that is neither too moist or dry, a good circulation of air, and air that is free from dust. Point out how we try to duplicate these conditions in the home. Have the pupils name and study the different parts of the home that help maintain comfortable weather conditions indoors.

20-4 With long strips of thin paper attached to a stick, explore the air currents rising above a radiator. Also investigate air currents at the top and bottom of an open window, and at different levels and parts of the room. Lead into the study of convection currents, proper ventilation, and good circulation of air in a heated room.

20-5 Discuss the problem of water in the basement, and study ways and means of preventing water from entering a house.

20-6 Have a member of the Fire Department speak to the class on home fire hazards and how to prevent them. Lead into a discussion of fireproofing materials for the home.

BIBLIOGRAPHY

Ahrens, M. R., N. K. Bush, and R. K. Easley, *Living Chemistry,* Ginn, 1957. Contains a chapter on housing material and kinds of homes. Good for teacher reference.

Carter, Katherine, *The True Book of Houses,* Childrens Press, 1957. Very simple treatment of homes and building materials.

Case, Bernard, *The Story of Houses,* Sterling, 1957. Describes different kinds of building materials used in houses, and their functions.

Godspeed, J. M., *Let's Take a Trip to Watch a Building Go Up,* Putnam, 1956. Simple description of how a house is built and the materials used in building it.

Magnets and magnetism

NATURAL MAGNETS

Natural magnets, found in many parts of the world, may be purchased at any scientific supply house. Your high school physics teacher can help you order one. The natural magnet resembles a dark-colored rock and contains magnetic iron ore. It is usually called "lodestone" or "magnetite," said to have been named by shepherds in a part of Asia Minor called Magnesia.

Iron filings, excellent for investigating the properties of magnets, may also be purchased from the scientific supply house in a convenient shaker-type container. However, you may want to make your own iron filings. Obtain a piece of soft iron (not steel) from a machine shop or scrap metal dealer. Clamp the iron firmly in a vise and file it with a medium-coarse file. The finer the filings, the better they behave in the presence of magnets. A power-grinding wheel produces the best filings and does the job very quickly. If you know a person who works in a machine shop, he can get you as many filings as you need. (Aluminum filings, of course, are useless.) Make sure the filings are free of oil and grease; wash them in detergent and dry in a pan on a stove. Put the filings in a salt shaker whose cap has good-sized holes.

Pour some iron filings on a sheet of paper. Try picking up the filings with the natural magnet. Repeat the experiment, using finely cut pieces of steel wool, iron tacks, and paper clips.

ARTIFICIAL MAGNETS

Artificial magnets, usually made of hard steel, come in different shapes. Bar magnets can be rectangular bars or round rods. Other magnets are horseshoe- and U-shaped. The most powerful magnets, alnico, contain not only steel but also quantities of aluminum, nickel, and cobalt as well. (The word "alnico" contains the first two letters of the three metals other than steel.) These metals are made not only in all the forms described above but also as circular disks.

You can obtain magnets from old radio and hi-fi speakers, from old telephone receivers, and from old automobile speedometers. Your ten-cent store sells them as horseshoe magnets or as tiny bar magnets in magnetic trays, etc.

Using artificial magnets, try picking up iron filings, contents of children's pockets or desks, cut steel wool, iron or steel tacks, and paper clips. Let the children note the force which holds the objects to the magnet, and how hard they have to pull to take the objects off the magnet. The force which holds objects to the magnet is called *magnetic attraction*. To show that magnetic force is a *mutual* attraction, use an iron nail to pick up a magnet.

Fig. 21-1 Suspending a paper clip in mid-air.

WHAT WILL MAGNETS ATTRACT?

Collect a wide variety of materials. A likely group would include thumbtacks, needles, pins, paper clips, toothpicks, a penny, a dime, a gold ring, brass paper fasteners, rubber bands, sand, and bits of glass, leather, cloth, paper, aluminum, and tin foil. Now test each object with a horseshoe magnet and see which ones the magnet will attract or pick up. Make a chart of two columns, one column of those objects which the magnet picked up and one of those objects the magnet did not pick up. Such a list motivates reading with young children. Point out to the children that all the objects that were picked up by the magnet were made of metal. Yet the magnet did not pick up the copper penny, the silver dime, the gold ring, and the brass paper fasteners. If any of the other objects were made of brass, the magnet also did not pick them up.

Now have the children examine the list of objects which the magnet did pick up. They should begin to see that all these objects have one thing in common. They all contain iron or steel. The children may then arrive at such conclusions as (1) magnets will not pick up nonmetals, and (2) magnets will pick up only certain metals,

such as iron or steel. Magnets will also pick up nickel or cobalt. A Canadian nickel will be picked up by a magnet because it is nearly pure nickel. American nickels contain too much copper.

See if the object will attract a "tin" can. A tin can is really made of sheet steel with a coating of tin.

Magnets attract through nonmagnetic materials

Bring a magnet gradually closer to iron filings or thumbtacks. Notice how the filings or tacks do not wait until the magnet touches them before they are attracted or picked up. They jump through the air and cling to the magnet.

You may find it convenient to make a wooden magnet stand. Obtain a piece of soft wood or plywood about 12″ square and ¾″ thick. Also secure three sticks of soft wood or plywood. Cut two sticks 6–8″ long, 2″ wide, and ½″ thick. The third stick should be 12–15″ long, 2″ wide, and ½″ thick. Using screws, make the sticks into a U-shape (Fig. 21-1). Now attach one side of the U to the wooden square with screws. You can make a temporary stand by hanging the magnet from a ruler held in place by a stack of books above and below it.

Suspend a horseshoe magnet by cotton thread from the top of the magnet stand. Loop a piece of thread around the point of a thumbtack and press it into the base of the magnet stand directly underneath

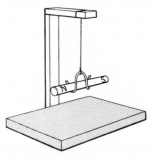

Fig. 21-2 A magnet stand.

the magnet. Tie a paper clip to the other end of the thread. Bring the clip up to the magnet so that it is about ¼″ away from the magnet (Fig. 21-2). The paper clip will be suspended in air and seem to defy gravity. The magnetic attraction passes through air and is able to overcome the force of gravity. This can also be done without a stand.

On a pane of glass supported by two piles of books place some iron filings or thumbtacks. Move a magnet about against the underside of the glass. The filings or tacks will move around with the magnet. Repeat the experiment, using thin sheets of cardboard, wood, cloth, and aluminum foil.

Attach an iron nail with adhesive tape to the underside of a very small plastic auto with wheels that turn. Place the auto on the sheet of glass or cardboard. Hold the magnet underneath the glass and make the auto move. A drop of oil between the wheels and axle will help the auto move more easily.

Into an aluminum pan or Pyrex dish pour just enough water to permit a cork stopper to float freely. Attach a thumbtack to the underside of the cork stopper to counterbalance or stabilize. Now hold the magnet underneath the pan or dish and make the cork move.

Place a thin sheet of iron on the books. Put some iron filings or thumbtacks on the sheet of iron. Move the magnet underneath the iron sheet. This time the filings or tacks will not move. The sheet of iron prevents the magnetic force of the magnet from attracting the filings or tacks. Because iron is easily affected by magnetic force, the sheet tends to short-circuit the magnet. Thus the magnetic force of the magnet travels into the sheet of iron and directly back into the magnet. For this reason, the filings or tacks are not affected by the magnet. The children should conclude that magnetic force will pass through nonmagnetic materials but not through (magnetic) materials, like iron, which attract magnets.

HOW DO MAGNETS BEHAVE?

The strength of a magnet is located at its poles

Sprinkle some iron filings or thumbtacks evenly on a cardboard or glass pane. Now lay a bar magnet on the filings or tacks and then lift the magnet.

The filings or tacks will be clustered at the ends of the magnet. These ends are called the poles of the magnet, one end being the north and the other the south pole. (To identify the poles, suspend the magnet by a thread from a stand. The end pointing north is the north pole.) Repeat the experiment, using a horseshoe or a U-shaped magnet. In the case of a lodestone, you will find it has many poles.

Attraction and repulsion of poles

Suspend a bar magnet with a strong thread from the top bar of a magnet stand. You may also hang it from a ruler inserted into a pile of books. A double loop of copper attached to a thread, as in Fig.21-2, is one effective way to suspend a magnet. When the magnet comes to rest, bring the south pole of another bar magnet close to the north pole of the suspended magnet. Do the reverse.

The class should soon be able to discover the basic law of magnetic attraction —namely, that unlike poles attract each other while like poles repel each other.

Obtain two strong alnico bar magnets and lay them on the table. Have the children take turns pushing unlike poles together and then like poles together. Note the way the unlike poles seem to rush to each other. Also note the way the like poles push and resist or repel each other. With strong magnets it is very difficult for the children to push two like poles to-

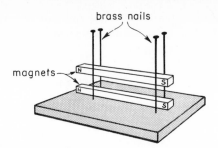

brass nails

magnets

Fig. 21-3 Making one magnet "float" above another magnet.

gether. The experiment can also be done with ordinary steel bar magnets, but the effects are not so pronounced.

Place one strong magnet upon another so that the north pole of one is on top of the north pole of the other. This also brings both south poles together. Hold the magnets firmly in place with your fingers. Now release the fingers suddenly. Watch how the top magnet will spring high into the air because of the repulsion between the like poles of the magnets.

If you can obtain circular rod magnets you can make one rod move quickly toward or away from you. The direction will depend upon whether the like or unlike poles of the magnets are facing each other.

Obtain a rectangular piece of plywood about 12″ × 6″ × ½″. Drive four long brass nails into the board, two on each side so that the nails will hold a bar or cylindrical magnet in place (Fig. 21-3). If long brass nails are unavailable, punch four holes in the plywood with a nail. Make the holes about the same diameter as a match stick. Insert match sticks into the holes, first smearing the ends with some glue.

Now place one magnet between the nails or match sticks. Then place a second magnet on top of the first, with the like poles facing each other. The top magnet will be repelled and will "float" on air.

Repeat the experiment so that the unlike poles of both magnets face each other.

The experiment works best with short strong magnets, either bar or cylindrical. The brass or wooden pegs help prevent the repelled magnets from turning around so that they will attract each other. Iron nails will spoil the effects of the experiment because of their response to the magnetic force of the magnets.

Pictures of a magnetic field

Place a sheet of white cardboard or a pane of glass over a bar magnet. Sprinkle iron filings from a salt shaker on the cardboard or glass. The filings should be sprinkled from a height of about 8–12″. Now tap the cardboard or glass gently, or jar it by pounding the table top with your fist. The filings will arrange themselves in a definite pattern.

Call the children's attention to the magnetic lines that are formed. The lines are thick at the poles where the magnetic force is greatest. The lines are thin near the center of the magnet where the magnetic force is weakest. These lines which the iron filings follow are called lines of force. Lines of force themselves are actually invisible. We are able to identify and locate these lines only when magnetized metal is brought in their midst. They represent the strength and direction of the magnet's force.

Repeat the experiment, using a horseshoe or U-shaped magnet. Note the heavy concentration of filings about the north and south poles.

Put two bar magnets on the table with the north pole of one about 1½″ away from the south pole of the other. Cover the magnets with white cardboard or a pane of window glass. Sprinkle iron filings on the cardboard or glass where the unlike poles are facing each other. Tap the cardboard or glass gently to set the filings in a

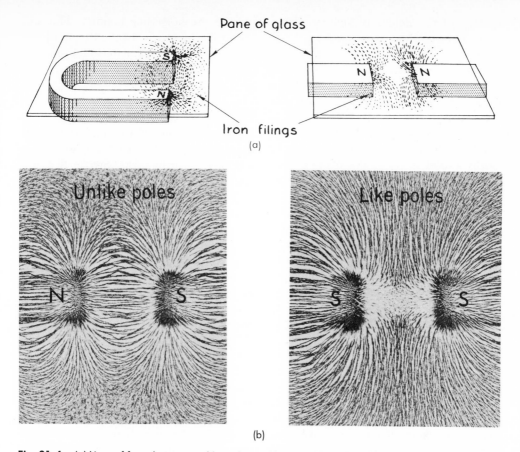

Pane of glass

Iron filings

(a)

Unlike poles

N   S

Like poles

S   S

(b)

Fig. 21-4 (a) Lines of force between unlike poles and between like poles, demonstrated with iron filings on glass panes. (From *General Science Handbook, Part II,* New York State Education Department, 1952.) (b) Detail of patterns of filings at the poles. (Bell Telephone Laboratories.)

definite pattern. Note the pattern of the lines of force showing the attraction between the unlike poles.

Repeat the experiment with two like poles about 1½″ from each other. Note the pattern of the lines of force showing the repulsion between the like poles (Fig. 21-4).

You may want to make a permanent picture of these magnetic fields. Obtain a piece of blueprint paper. Lay it on a square of cardboard or a pane of glass. Place this combination over one or two bar magnets. Decide which patterns you want; then sprinkle iron filings on the

blueprint paper. Place the blueprint paper and cardboard in direct sunlight and let it stand for 10 minutes or more (or use two 100-watt bulbs for a longer period). Be careful not to jar the pattern of the iron filings. Remove the filings and wash the blueprint paper in water. The pattern created by the filings will appear white. Ozalid paper will produce a brown and white pattern. If photographic contact paper is used, expose for 1 minute and then develop (see Chapter 12). If the magnetic field is made on stiff paper, it can be sprayed with clear lacquer from a spray pressure can to give a permanent pattern of the field outlined by filings.

Another method of making a permanent picture of magnetic fields is to melt candle wax or paraffin in a cookie tin. Heat slowly. While the wax or paraffin is liquid, dip sheets of paper in it. Then take the paper sheets out and allow them to cool until the wax or paraffin on them hardens. Or ordinary kitchen wax paper works almost as well. Place the coated paper on cardboard. Underneath the cardboard place a magnet or magnets to obtain the pattern you want. Pour iron filings on the coated paper and tap the cardboard gently. Carry the cardboard and waxed paper carefully to a heated radiator or electric hot plate turned on low. As the coated paper warms, the paraffin will soften, allowing the iron filings to sink into it. Cool the paper, and a permanent picture of the magnetic field is produced.

MAKING TEMPORARY MAGNETS

Place some tacks (or paper clips, pins, nails, etc.) on a table. Touch one of the tacks with a horseshoe magnet and bring this tack to a second tack. The second tack will be attracted to the first tack. See how long a string of tacks you can make. Remove the horseshoe magnet. All the tacks fall off and separate. The tacks become magnets only when the horseshoe magnet holds the first tack. As soon as the magnet is removed, the tacks lose their magnetism. The tacks are said to be magnetized by induction and are called temporary magnets.

From a hardware store obtain a large soft iron nail. Hold this nail about ½″ away from the bottom of one leg of a strong U-shaped magnet. While holding the nail in this position, let the tip of the nail touch a pile of tacks on the table. Some of the tacks will cling to the tip of the nail. The nail, temporarily magnetized by induction, picks up the tacks. Now

remove the horseshoe magnet. The nail loses its temporary magnetism, and the tacks will fall off. (Some steel nails may remain slightly magnetized.)

MAKING PERMANENT MAGNETS

Obtain a large soft iron nail and a steel knitting needle. Test each one to see if it will pick up iron tacks. Stroke first the nail and then the knitting needle with one end of a bar magnet. Stroke each one 40 times, being careful to stroke in only one direction and to lift your hand between strokes. Now test each one again to see if it will pick up the tacks. Both will behave as magnets. See how many tacks each one will pick up. Put the nail and the needle away for a day; then test them again for magnetism. See how many tacks each one will pick up now. Although iron is easily magnetized, it loses its magnetism just as easily. Steel is more difficult to magnetize, but its magnetism is permanent. Try magnetizing the blade of a pocket knife, a file, or a pair of scissors in this way.

Obtain a hacksaw blade or a steel knitting needle. Stroke the blade or needle with one end of a bar magnet. However, this time slightly change the stroking procedure. Let the north pole end of the magnet stroke from the center of the blade or needle to one end of the blade or needle. Be careful to stroke from the center to the end only, lifting your hand between strokes. Stroke this way for 40 times. Make a chalk mark on the end of the blade or needle denoting that this end was stroked by the north pole of the magnet. Now with the south pole end of the magnet, stroke from the center to the other end of the blade or needle. Do this for 40 strokes. Make a chalk mark on the end of the blade or needle showing that this end was stroked with the south pole of the magnet.

Now suspend the blade or needle from

a magnet stand. Bring the north pole of a magnet first to one end of the blade or needle, then to the other end. The end of the blade or needle which is attracted to the north pole of the magnet is the south pole of a newly formed magnet. However, be sure the children see that the end of the blade or needle that was stroked by the north pole of the magnet has become a south pole. Similarly, the end that was stroked by the south pole of the magnet has become a north pole. Test the hacksaw blade or knitting needle with tacks or paper clips for magnetism.

Magnetize three steel sewing needles in the same way so that you produce in each needle point a north pole and in each eye a south pole. Now slice thin disks of equal size from a cork stopper. Push the needles through the cork disks. Place them in a large glass or plastic dish of water (Fig. 21-5). The dish should have sloping sides. Float all three with the points up. The corks will all repel each other. Now reverse one needle so that it floats with its point down. It will be attracted to the other needles because of the relationship of like and unlike poles.

Making permanent magnets with electricity

Children are usually interested in watching a steel object such as a nail file or knife blade become permanently magnetized. Wind insulated copper wire of any kind about a narrow cardboard tube. A mailing tube or the tube inside a roll of paper towels will do.

Wind about 100 closely wound turns of the wire around the cardboard tube. Have the ends of the wire lead to the terminals of a dry cell, but do not connect the wires. Place the steel object to be magnetized inside the tube. Try to keep the object inside the area covered by the turns of wire. Now touch the two end wires to the terminals of the dry cell for only 1 or 2 seconds

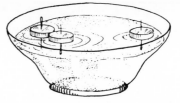

Fig. 21-5 Like poles repel each other; unlike poles attract each other. (From *General Science Handbook, Part II,* New York State Education Department, 1952.)

(no more). Test the (magnetized) object for magnetic attraction on some iron or steel tacks.

If the magnetized object is made of hard steel, it will remain a (permanent) magnet. However, if the object is made of soft iron, it will gradually lose its magnetism.

DEMAGNETIZING

Magnetize a steel knitting needle and note how many tacks it will pick up. Now hold the needle with a pair of pliers in a flame until it is red hot. Heat the needle for quite some time. Now let the needle cool and test it again to see how many tacks it will pick up. Some of the magnetism has been lost because of the heating. If you could get the needle hot enough and heat it long enough, it would lose all its magnetism.

Magnetize another knitting needle and note again how many tacks it will pick up. Now pound the needle with a hammer or strike the needle repeatedly against a solid object. Test the needle again to see how many tacks it will pick up. Jarring the needle caused it to lose some of its magnetism.

Caring for magnets

Unless properly cared for, magnets will gradually lose their magnetizing power. To keep a horseshoe or U-shaped magnet strong, a small flat piece of iron

Unmagnetized

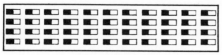

Partially magnetized

```
■□ ■□ ■□ ■□ ■□ ■□ ■□
■□ ■□ ■□ ■□ ■□ ■□ ■□
■□ ■□ ■□ ■□ ■□ ■□ ■□
■□ ■□ ■□ ■□ ■□ ■□ ■□
```

Magnetized

Fig. 21-6 Molecules in unmagnetized and magnetized materials. (From R. Brinckerhoff et al., *Exploring Physics*, Harcourt, Brace & World, 1959.)

is placed across the poles of a magnet. This piece of iron is called a keeper. If you do not have a keeper, an iron nail will serve as a substitute. Usually bar magnets come in pairs. When you put bar magnets away, place them side by side with the north pole of one magnet next to the south pole of the other.

Be careful not to jar your magnets by pounding or dropping them. Never put your magnets into a fire or keep them in a hot place such as next to a radiator.

WHY MAGNETS BEHAVE AS THEY DO

The children are bound to wonder why magnets behave the way they do. Scientists believe that each atom (or related groups of atoms called *domains*) which makes up magnetic materials acts like a magnet. Every atom (or domain) is a tiny magnet with north and south poles. Ordinarily, these magnetized particles are arranged every which way, that is, in no definite order. Consequently, the north and south poles of these particles, being randomly oriented, neutralize each other's force.

However, when a piece of iron is mag-

netized, many of the particles (in reality, millions of tiny magnets) shift so that a large number of the north poles point in one direction and the south poles in the opposite. The more particles which do this, the stronger the magnetism (Fig. 21-6). Make a rough sketch or diagram on the blackboard. Let children observe the diagram carefully and observe why one end of the magnet is a north pole and the other end a south pole. The free north and south poles at each end of the magnet also explain why the magnet's force is strongest at its poles. This realignment of the particles in a piece of iron can be brought about by stroking the iron with a magnet, inserting the iron inside a coil of wire carrying an electric current, or tapping or stroking the iron when it is placed in a magnetic field and the iron is lined up with that field's north and south poles.

Fill a small vial, test tube, or even glass toothbrush tube about three fourths full of hard steel filings. Stopper the vial and hold at an angle of 45°. Stroke the vial 20–30 times with the pole of a strong magnet. Be sure to stroke the vial always in the same direction, and be most careful not to jar the filings in the vial. Now bring a compass near each end of the vial and test it for polarity. The filings have arranged themselves in a definite order, and the entire vial behaves like a magnet.

Now shake the vial vigorously and then bring the compass near each end again. The filings are rearranged in all directions, and the vial has lost its magnetism and polarity.

Secure a narrow strip of heavy cardboard or wood at least 18″ long. Magnetize six sewing needles by stroking them with the pole of a strong magnet. Tie a piece of thread about 12″ long around the middle of each needle. Suspend the needles from the cardboard about 3″ apart so that the needles swing freely and horizontally in space. The needles will thus be arranged in random order and point in all directions. Now move one pole of a strong bar magnet underneath the needles. Always move the bar magnet in one direction. The needles will line up in a definite order and all point in one direction.

Magnetize a knitting needle at least 10″ long by stroking it repeatedly with a pole of a strong bar magnet in the same direction. A hacksaw blade or a piece of steel clock or watch spring will do just as well. Bring a compass needle near each end of the needle and test the needle for polarity. Mark the poles with chalk. At the same time test the middle of the needle with tacks for magnetism. Now cut the needle at its center with cutting pliers. Test each end of the two pieces for magnetism and polarity. Cut these two pieces at their center with cutting pliers. Again test each end of all four pieces for magnetism and for polarity. Each time the needle is cut, two new magnets are formed.

These experiments seem to substantiate the scientists' theory of magnetism. This theory also serves to explain why heating or jarring magnets will make them lose their magnetism. The jarring and heating serve to break up the definite order in which some of the basic particles have been arranged.

USING A COMPASS

Obtain a compass from a local Army surplus or variety store. Or borrow one from a Boy Scout or high school physics teacher. Examine the compass carefully. The case is usually made of brass. Why? The card has printed letters on it standing for the directions, N, E, W, S (which spells NEWS). The compass needle is usually diamond-shaped. The half of the needle that points toward the north is usually colored so that it can be identified easily and quickly.

To use the compass, hold it flat in the palm of your hand, keeping the compass as level as possible. The colored end of the needle will point north. In order to locate the other directions easily, turn the case of the compass around until the letter N is directly under the colored end of the needle. Now you know approximately where north, south, east, west, and their intermediate points are located. To know exactly, you must know the compass deflection for your area. Magnetic north and true north are rarely the same.

A compass needle is magnetized. You can prove this by bringing a bar magnet near the compass (do not touch the compass case with the magnet). The north pole of the magnet will repel the north pole of the compass needle and attract the south pole of the compass needle. The north pole of the compass needle is usually called the north-seeking pole.

Lay a bar magnet on the table. Move a compass around the magnet. Notice how the direction of the compass needle changes as you move it around the bar. As long as the needle is in the magnetic field of the bar magnet, the needle always points toward the nearer pole of the magnet. Have the children compare the positions of the compass needle as it moves around the magnet with the positions the iron filings assumed around a magnet. The children should soon realize that a compass needle in a magnetic field points in the same direction as the lines of force in the magnetic field.

A compass needle enables you to determine the unmarked poles of a magnet. Magnetize a steel knitting needle or hacksaw blade. Let the children bring the knitting needle or hacksaw blade near the compass and find out what the poles are.

Fig. 21-7 A model earth magnetic globe.

THE EARTH AS A MAGNET

Why does a compass needle always point to magnetic north? (The north magnetic pole is above Hudson's Bay in Northern Canada, approximately 73° 35′ N. lat., 92° 20′ W. long.) Scientists say that the earth itself is a magnet, behaving just as if there were a huge magnet inside it running north and south. (The south magnetic pole is at approximately 70° S. lat., 148° E. long.) As a result, the earth is able to magnetize objects. Secure a steel rod about 2′ long. A solid iron curtain rod will do. Take a small magnet with you to test to see that it is steel when you buy it. With a compass find out which direction is north. Now hold the iron rod in a magnetic north-south position, i.e., parallel to the direction of a compass needle. Tilt the rod at the angle of magnetic dip for your area. (To learn how to determine this, see below, "Making a Dipping Needle.") A tilt of 65° is a rough approximation which will serve for many areas in the United States. Strike the end of the rod sharply a few times with a hammer. The rod will be magnetized slightly. Test the rod with a compass. The upper end of the rod will be a south pole and attract the north-seeking end of the compass needle. The lower end of the rod will be a north pole and attract the south-seeking end of the compass needle.

If you would like to reverse the poles of the iron rod, just turn the rod around and tap it again. To demagnetize the rod, simply hold it in an east-west position and strike it sharply a few times with the hammer.

Many iron and steel objects which stand vertically may be magnetized by the earth's magnetism. Have the children bring a compass near steel pipes, steel lamp stands, steel fence posts or rails, steel bridges, to see if they are magnetized. Test them at both ends to check their magnetic poles.

Recall the experiment where you showed that magnetic force would not pass through magnetic materials like iron and steel. The children should then be able to explain why a compass case is usually made of a nonmagnetic material like brass. The earth's magnetic force would never reach the compass needle if the case were made of iron or steel.

To make a model earth magnetic globe take a small (6″ diameter) cardboard or plastic globe and insert a bar magnet with the south pole up (Fig. 21-7). Orient so that the top (south pole of the magnet) emerges near the upper end of Hudson's Bay, and the bottom (north pole of the magnet) emerges near the Antarctic at 70° S. lat., 148° E. long. Then place compasses at different positions on the globe and notice how the compass needles line up with the lines of force. It may be necessary to tilt the globe at times.

The poles—magnetic and true

At some time you will want to point out that magnetic north and true north differ. The magnetic north pole is located in northern Canada above Hudson's Bay, at approximately 73° 35′ N. latitude, 92° 20′ W. longitude. The magnetic south pole is located near Antarctica, at approximately 70° S. latitude, 148° E. longitude.

Since a compass needle points to the magnetic north pole, it does not really tell you exactly where true north is. Thus, the compass needle is in error. The angle between true north and the direction in which a compass needle points is known as magnetic declination. This angle varies at different parts of the earth.

Locate the north magnetic pole on a globe and then estimate the angle of declination for your area. The angle may be determined by drawing two lines: one from your area to the true North Pole, and one from your area to the magnetic north pole.

Why the compass north pole points north

The children, having learned that like poles repel each other, will wonder why the north pole of a suspended bar magnet points to the north magnetic pole. This also holds true for a compass needle, where the north pole of the needle points to the north magnetic pole.

Point out that when men first learned about magnets and their poles, they called the pole that pointed to the north the North Pole. This was before they learned that the earth behaved as a huge magnet. This later created a problem. If the earth behaves as a magnet, then it is logical to assume that the earth's north magnetic pole is in the north, and its south magnetic pole is in the south.

Therefore, if the north pole of a suspended bar magnet or a compass needle points to the north magnetic pole, it must really be a south pole. But we have become accustomed to calling a pole that points to the north a north pole. And it would create much confusion now to change the names of the poles of our magnets. We compromise by calling a north pole of a magnet a north-seeking pole, and the south pole of a magnet a south-seeking pole.

MAKING A COMPASS

Children usually like to make their own compasses. Magnetize a steel knitting needle or hacksaw blade by stroking with a bar magnet. Remember to stroke one half of the needle or blade with the north end of the magnet at least 40 times. Then stroke the other half of the needle or blade with the south end of the magnet 40 times. Always stroke from the middle to the end of the needle or blade. You can also magnetize with an electromagnetic coil, as described earlier in this chapter. With a thread suspend the magnetized needle or blade from the magnet stand. Suspend it so that it is free to move about. The magnetized needle or blade will soon come to rest in a north-south position. Have the children check this position with a compass. Be sure not to bring the compass too near the magnetized needle or blade.

A horseshoe or U-shaped magnet can also be made to act as a compass. Make a stand from a piece of wood 4″ square and ½–1″ thick. Hammer a long thin nail through the center of the block and file a point on the nail. A well-sharpened pencil glued upright in a hole makes an even better support since the graphite of the pencil lead acts as a lubricant. Place the horseshoe or U-shaped magnet on the point of the nail or pencil so that it balances (Fig. 21-8). The mag-

Fig. 21-8   Making a horseshoe magnet act like a compass.

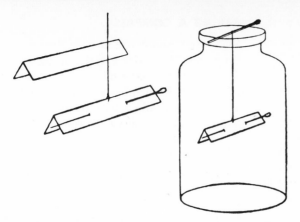

Fig. 21-9 A cardboard compass. (From *UNESCO Source Book for Science Teachers*, UNESCO, 1956.)

net will slowly turn until it is in a north-south position. It should now be quite clear to the children that a compass is no more than a small magnet.

Columbus used a simple floating compass when he discovered America. Magnetize a large sewing needle as described above. Cut a flat circular disk from a cork stopper. Push the needle through the cork so that it is perfectly horizontal (see Fig. 21-10). Place the cork on the surface of some water in a paper nut cup with sloping sides. Be sure to keep the cork and needle away from the sides of the dish. The needle will point north and south. As a variation you can float the needle inside a milk straw.

If you like, you may accomplish the same effect without using the stopper or straw. Simply grease the magnetized sewing needle slightly with shortening, Vaseline, etc. Then, holding the needle horizontally 2–3″ above the surface of the water, lower the needle carefully and gently onto the water. The surface tension of water will keep the needle afloat. The needle will assume a north-south position.

You can have the children make a compass without using water. Take a milk bottle with its milk cap. Fold a piece of very thin cardboard into an inverted V shape (Fig. 21-9). Now magnetize a sewing needle and pass it through the folded cardboard. Suspend the cardboard from a fine thread that is attached to the milk bottle cap. The magnetized needle will turn until it points north and south. Any tall glass jar will do for a milk bottle.

How magnets make electric motors spin

Make a floating compass needle by pushing a magnetized sewing needle through a small flat circular piece of cork stopper. Float the stopper and needle on water contained in a dish with sloping sides. Attach a thin string to the U-portion of a horseshoe or U-shaped magnet.

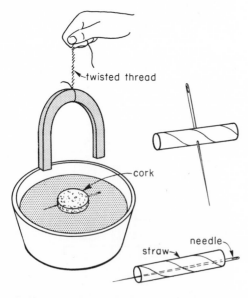

Fig 21-10 How magnets make electric motors spin.

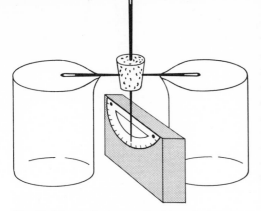

Fig. 21-11 A dipping needle. (From A. Joseph et al., *A Sourcebook for the Physical Sciences*, Harcourt, Brace & World, 1961.)

Hold the magnet over the floating compass needle (Fig. 21-10). Twist the string by rotating the magnet many times. Now release the magnet and let the string untwist. As the magnet spins, the compass needle below it will also spin. This phenomenon is usually employed in alternating-current (a.c.) motors. If you like, you may use a regular pocket compass in place of the homemade floating compass. For more details on motors, including how to build models, see Chapter 22.

Making a dipping needle

If a compass needle were allowed to swing freely, it would be completely horizontal at the equator. The closer it approached the north magnetic pole, the more it would dip down. At the pole the compass needle would be absolutely vertical, with the north-seeking pole of the compass downward. This happens because the compass needle takes a direction which is parallel to the direction of the lines of magnetic force.

Have the children find out how much a compass needle will dip in their latitude and longtitude. Secure a steel knitting needle, a large sewing needle, two glass tumblers, and a large cork stopper (Fig. 21-11). Push the knitting needle through the center of the cork stopper. Now push the sewing needle also through the center of the cork, but crosswise to the knitting needle. Set the ends of the sewing needle on the glasses and adjust the knitting needle until it balances evenly. Next, using a compass, point the knitting needle toward the north magnetic pole. Now magnetize the knitting needle strongly and return it to the glasses. The knitting needle will dip. This is called the angle of dip and is exactly parallel to the lines of force of the earth's magnetic field in your location. The amount it dips can be measured with a protractor. This angle varies from locality to locality. A compass needle merely indicates the horizontal direction of the lines of force.

CURRENT PRODUCES A MAGNETIC FIELD

Secure a ½-pound coil of insulated bell wire from the hardware or ten-cent store. Remove 1″ of the insulation from each end of the wire and about 4″ of insulation from the middle of the wire. Connect one end of the wire to a binding post of a dry cell. Sprinkle a small pile of iron filings on a piece of white cardboard. Now bring the bare middle part of the wire near the pile

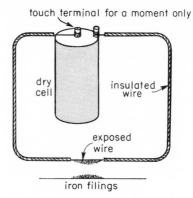

Fig. 21-12 A wire carrying an electric current acts like a magnet.

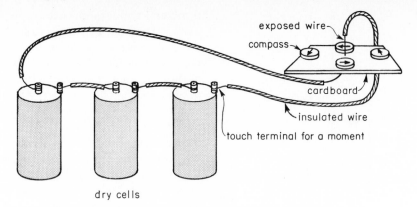

Fig. 21-13   Lines of force about a wire carrying an electric current.

of filings and touch the other end of the wire to the second binding post of the dry cell for a few moments (Fig. 21-12). The filings will be attracted to the wire. A wire carrying an electric current acts like a magnet. (*Caution: This experiment and all following experiments draw a very large amount of current from the dry cell. If you run the current for any length of time, the dry cell will be used up very quickly, and the wire will get too hot to hold. Consequently, it is wise to do the experiment quickly, taking just enough time to produce the desired effect.*) Repeat the experiment, without filings, with a compass needle parallel to the wire when the current is off. When the battery is connected to the wire, the compass needle will turn at right angle to the wire. This was how electromagnetism was discovered early in the nineteenth century.

Lines of force around a wire

Make a small hole about ¼″ in diameter in a square of white cardboard. Draw a circle about 4″ in diameter around this hole. Place the cardboard on two piles of books. Connect one end of the bell wire to three dry cells that are connected in series, as in Fig. 21-13. Run the wire through the hole in the cardboard, and shape it so it forms a vertical line (Fig. 21-13). Adjust so that the bare middle of the wire is located

just at the hole. Place four small compasses on the circle drawn on the cardboard. Arrange the compasses in a north, east, south, and west position around the cardboard. Now touch the dry cell terminal to complete the circuit for 2 or 3 sec-

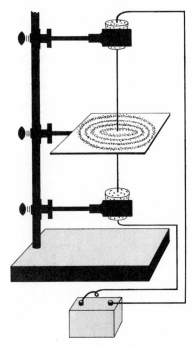

Fig. 21-14   Concentric lines of force about a wire carrying an electric current. (From A. Joseph et al., *A Sourcebook for the Physical Sciences*, Harcourt, Brace & World, 1961.)

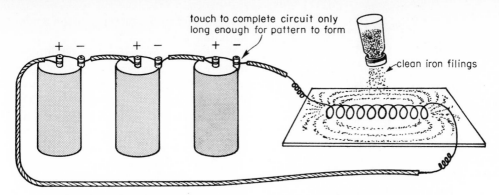

Fig. 21-15 A coil of wire carrying an electric current acts like a magnet.

onds only. While the current is flowing, have the children note the new positions of the four compass needles. They form the outline of a circle.

Remove the compasses and sprinkle some iron filings on the cardboard. Connect the dry cells for 2–3 seconds and tap the cardboard gently (Fig. 21-14). The iron filings form a circular pattern around the wire. Let the children find out that a wire carrying an electric current creates magnetic lines of force around it.

A coil as a magnet

Wind about 2′ of the bell wire around a pencil to make a coil. Remove the pencil. Attach one end of the wire to a dry cell. Touch the other end of the wire to the dry cell. Bring a compass near one end of the coil. Note that the coil has become a magnet. Bring the compass near both ends of the coil and determine which are the north and south poles of the coil. Try picking up filings or tacks with one end of the coil. The children should soon come to the conclusion that a coil of wire carrying an electric current acts as a magnet with north and south poles. Reverse the connections of the wires to the terminals of the dry cell. With a compass check the poles of the coil again. By reversing the direction in which the current flows, the poles in the coil change as well.

Place the coil upon a piece of white cardboard. Sprinkle iron filings about the coil. Connect the ends of the wire to the dry cells and tap the cardboard gently (Fig. 21-15). The filings will arrange themselves in the same pattern as that produced with the bar magnet. The coil of wire forms a magnetic field when an electric current is flowing through it.

A diving nail. The children might like to see how you can make a nail dive into the wire. Wind bell wire into a coil around a wide test tube (or olive bottle) containing water (Fig. 21-16). Use many more turns than are shown in the illustration. Push an iron nail into a small cork as far as it will go. Place the cork and nail into

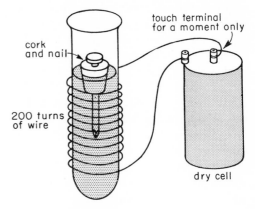

Fig. 21-16 A diving nail.

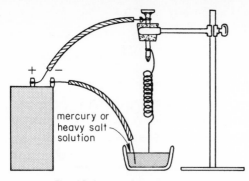

Fig. 21-17 A dancing spring.

the test tube. Connect one end of the wire to one terminal of the dry cell. Touch the other end of the wire to the dry cell for a few seconds. The cork and nail will dive into the water because the coil of wire acts as a magnet.

A dancing spring. Making a "dancing spring" is a spectacular method of showing that a coil of wire acts like a magnet when it is carrying an electric current. Drive a copper nail through a cork stopper. Hold the cork stopper firmly in place by means of a clamp attached to a ring stand (or stand made of wood). Make a copper coil by wrapping some thin copper wire many times around a pencil. Have the bottom of the coil end in a straight wire (Fig. 21-17). Pour some mercury into a small beaker or shallow dish. If mercury is not available, a concentrated solution of salt in water will do. Now wrap the top of the coil firmly around the pointed end of the copper nail. Then adjust the straight wire at the bottom end of the coil so that the wire is slightly below the surface of the mercury or salt water. Let the copper wire from one terminal of a dry cell be attached to the head of the copper nail. The copper wire from the other terminal of the cell is then placed into the beaker of mercury or salt water. The coil will now dance up and down, and sparks will form at the surface of the mercury. You may have to adjust the depth of the straight wire in the mercury to get a constant dancing up and down.

When the electric current passes through the copper coil, the coil becomes a magnet with a north and south pole. Since north and south poles attract each other, the turns of the coil are pulled together. This pulls the end of the straight wire at the bottom of the coil out of the mercury or salt water. However, when this happens, the circuit is broken. The coil now no longer acts as a magnet and returns to its original position. The straight end of the coil touches the mercury or salt water again, and the whole process is repeated.

An electromagnet

Wind a number of turns of bell wire around a large iron nail. Remove the iron nail. Connect the ends of the wire to a dry cell and see how many tacks or paper clips you can pick up with the coil. Now put the iron nail back into the coil and repeat the the experiment (Fig. 21-18). Note how many more tacks or clips have been picked up. By inserting an iron core (the iron nail) into the coil, its magnetic strength was increased. When a coil of wire carrying an electric current contains an iron core, it is called an electromagnet.

Check the poles of this electromagnet with a compass. Now swap the connec-

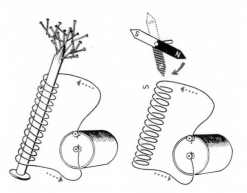

Fig. 21-18 An electromagnet. (From R. Brincker-hoff et al., *Exploring Physics,* Harcourt, Brace & World, 1959.)

tions of the ends of the wire to the binding posts of the dry cell. Check the poles of the electromagnet again with a compass. Also try to pick up tacks or clips with both the coil and the electromagnet when they are not connected to the dry cell. The children will soon realize that this type of magnetism is temporary, existing only when an electric current is flowing through the wire.

A paper-clip buzzer.[1] See. Fig. 22-24 for details on constructing this simple buzzer. Wrap a piece of Scotch tape around the nail before wrapping it with 20–30 turns of #26 enamel-covered wire. Make the spacing at B as close as possible without touching; adjust A for great upward tension.

Making electromagnets stronger

Wrap 25 turns of bell wire around a large iron nail. Connect the ends of the wire to the terminals of a dry cell. Count the number of iron or steel tacks you can pick up with this electromagnet. Next attach two dry cells in series to the electromagnet. Again count the number of tacks you can pick up with the electromagnet.

Now wrap 50 turns of bell wire around the iron nail and connect the ends of the wire to the terminals of one dry cell. Count the number of tacks you can pick up. Finally, attach this nail with 50 turns to two dry cells in series and again count the number of tacks picked up.

In each case be sure to keep the current on for as little time as possible. This will prevent the dry cells from weakening rapidly or being used up.

By noting the number of tacks picked up in each case, the children should readily come to the conclusion that electromagnets can be made stronger by increasing (1) the number of turns of wire, and (2) the strength of the current.

[1] Created by Mr. Katashi Nose, Kauai High School, Lihue, Hawaii.

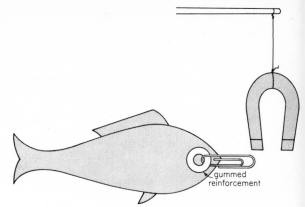

Fig. 21-19 A magnetic fishing game.

FUN WITH MAGNETS

Younger children might like to play a magnetic fishing game. Have the children trace and cut out 24 paper fish, each about 3–4" long. The children can look for pictures of different kinds of fish and use them as patterns. Draw a circle on one side of each fish and give the fish a numerical value from 1 to 5. Paste a circular gummed reinforcement at the mouth of each fish. Now attach a paper clip to each fish, making sure the paper clip goes through the gummed reinforcement (Fig. 21-19). Have the children color

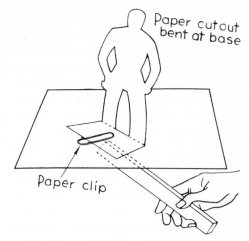

Fig. 21-20 A magnetic acting game. (From *General Science Handbook, Part II*, New York State Education Department, 1952.)

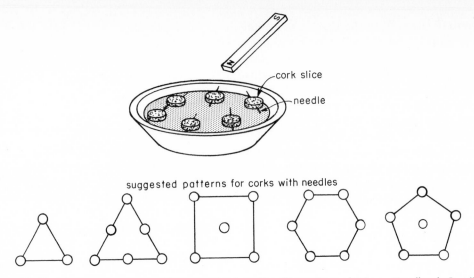

suggested patterns for corks with needles

Fig. 21-21 Geometric patterns with magnetized needles. (From *General Science Handbook, Part II,* New York State Education Department, 1952.)

each fish to make it look as real as possible. Remind them not to color in the circle containing the numerical value of the fish.

Now place the fish in a large fish bowl or aquarium. Obtain four long narrow sticks. Tie 12–18″ of string to each of four horseshoe magnets and attach each string to one of the four sticks. You now have four fishing poles available. Select four children as fishermen and let them all fish at one time. When the fish are all caught, add up the numbers on each fish. The fisherman with the highest score wins.

A simpler variation of this game is to use iron objects instead of fish. For example, you could use nails, screws, nuts, bolts, and tacks. Assign each kind of iron object a numerical value from 1 to 5. Place the objects in a glass bowl and have the children fish for them as described above.

A test of skill uses iron nails with broad heads. Stand the nails upright on their heads on a piece of glass with each one about ½″ apart from the other. Now have the children take turns with a horseshoe magnet to remove one nail at a time, with-

out picking up or knocking over any of the adjacent nails. The child who can remove the most nails this way is the winner.

You can attach a nail or thumbtack to the underside of very small wooden boats. Place the boats in an aluminum pan supported by two piles of books. Move a magnet underneath the pan and make the ships move.

Some pupils might be interested in making a stage with moving actors. Obtain a cardboard box, the top of which will serve as a stage. Wings and backdrops can be added. Make your actors by cutting out very small paper men and women (Fig. 21-20). Fold over some of the paper below the feet to act as a stand. Insert a small paper clip on the fold. Stand the "actors" on the cardboard stage and move a magnet underneath each "actor." The "actor" will follow the magnet.

Magnetize six sewing needles so that their eyes all have north poles. Cut six circular disks, all the same size, from cork stoppers. Push the needles through the cork disks and place them in a dish of water so that all the eyes of the needles are pointing up (Fig. 21-21). The dish should have sloping sides. Now bring the south pole of a bar magnet near the corks; they will all cluster around the magnet. Reverse the magnet so that the north pole is near the corks; the corks will all be repelled violently. Arrange these floating magnets into different geometric patterns.

CAPSULE LESSONS

21-1 Bring in some toys (or parts of a machine) that utilize magnets. Discuss the properties of magnets and how two magnets behave when brought close to each other.

21-2 Before the class enters, suspend a horseshoe magnet from a magnet stand or other support. Then attach a thin black thread to a paper clip. Adjust the length of the thread so that the clip is just short of the magnet. Fasten the free end of the thread to the magnet stand with a thumbtack or with a piece of Scotch tape. Adjust the height of the magnet so that the clip remains suspended in mid-air under the magnet. Create this effect against a wet blackboard as a background; the thread will not be visible. Use this demonstration to create an interest in magnets, magnetic materials, and magnetic attraction. Place sheets of paper, wood, aluminum, cloth between the clip and the magnet to show that magnets attract through nonmagnetic materials. Repeat, using a thin sheet of iron, and see what happens.

21-3 Mix brass pins and sewing needles together. You can also use copper and iron tacks. Have the children separate them with a magnet. Lead to a discussion of magnets, magnetic attraction, and what materials magnets will attract.

21-4 Obtain a Canadian nickel. Test both American and Canadian nickels with a horseshoe magnet. Have the children find out which is mainly nickel. Discuss which metals are attracted by magnets.

21-5 Use a magnet to find out how many things in your school and classroom are attracted. Make a list of the materials and determine which metals can be magnetized.

21-6 Before class begins, magnetize the head of a small hammer by stroking it with one end of a bar magnet. Stroke it many times but always in the same direction. Now show the children how you can pick up a tack with the head of the hammer and hold the tack in position while you drive it in. Lead into a discussion of how to make temporary and permanent magnets.

21-7 Place a bar magnet under a piece of white cardboard. Sprinkle iron filings on the cardboard and tap the cardboard gently to bring the filings into line. Use this effect to study the magnetic field and lines of force about a magnet.

21-8 Bring a compass to class. Locate the directions of familiar landmarks near the school. Bring a magnet near the compass. Initiate a discussion of magnets and how the earth behaves as a magnet. Paint cardinal points on floor or playground.

21-9 Suspend a bar magnet by a piece of thread or light string. When the magnet comes to rest, check its position with a compass. Use this to discuss how the earth behaves as a magnet and also the earth's magnetic field.

21-10 Make an electromagnet by wrapping bell wire around a large iron nail and connecting the wire to a dry cell. Compare the strength of an electromagnet with that of a bar magnet or horseshoe magnet. Do this by counting the number of thumbtacks or paper clips each will pick up. Discuss electromagnets, how they are made, how they can be made stronger, and their commercial uses.

BIBLIOGRAPHY

Branley, F. M., and E. K. Vaughan, *Mickey's Magnet,* Crowell, 1956. Simple experiments with magnets, showing what objects a magnet will attract and how to make a magnet from another one.

Parker, Bertha M., *Magnets,* Row, Peterson, 1944. Simple, comprehensive treatment of magnets, their properties, and uses.

Pine, Tillie S., and Joseph Levine, *Magnets and How to Use Them,* McGraw-Hill, 1958. Properties of magnets, together with the various kinds of magnets and their uses.

Reuben, Gabriel H., and Gloria Archer, *What Is a Magnet?,* Benefic, 1959. Simply described material covering the basic principles of magnets.

Yates, Raymond F., *The Boy's Book of Magnetism,* Harper, 1941. Includes many games and tricks with magnets.

Electricity

When planning experiences in electricity, the teacher must always keep one important fact in mind. Humidity plays an important part in experiments with electric charges. These experiments work best during cold and dry winter weather or in a steam-heated room. The colder and drier, the better the experiments work.

On warm, humid days in the fall and spring, the experiments often do not function. An invisible coat of moisture on the materials permits the electric charges to run off into the ground. Furthermore, the warm, moist air will conduct electric charges away as soon as they are formed.

ELECTROSTATICS

Sparks from rubbing

Have the pupils recall what happens when they walk across a deep rug on a cold, dry day and then touch a wall switch plate or other grounded metal object. A spark is formed, and they feel an electric shock. If the school has a deep rug, let one child scuff his shoes the length of the carpet and then touch a friend's finger or the metal radiator. Use rubber-soled shoes because they work better than leather ones. Rubber soles prevent the accumulated static (electrons) from being grounded and build up a stronger charge.

Blow up a rubber balloon; first stretch the balloon in all directions to make it easier to inflate. Then tie it with a string so that it won't deflate. Rub the balloon briskly with a piece of nylon, wool, or fur. Darken the room and have one of the children bring his finger near the balloon. An electric spark will jump from the balloon to the finger.

Find out how many children produced a spark or experienced a shock when, on a dry winter day, they slid across the plastic seatcover of a car and then touched the door handle.

Have the children do the following experiments at night in a dark room. Obtain a roll of the black, sticky bicycle tape. Pull a piece of tape away from the roll. A glow will appear at the place where the piece of tape pulls away from the roll.

If a member of the family has been wearing a nylon slipover sweater all day, have the person remove the sweater at night in a dark room. Long, crackling sparks will be produced.

To understand why rubbing produces electric sparks, it is necessary to understand the structure of matter and of the atom. All matter is made up of tiny particles called atoms. Atoms contain three basic particles: electrons, protons, and neutrons.

Electrons are negative (−) particles of electricity. Protons are positive (+) particles of electricity. Neutrons have no electrical charge. Electrons move about freely in many substances, whereas protons and neutrons are generally stationary. Under normal circumstances, a substance will have the same number of electrons ($-$) and protons ($+$). Ordinarily, therefore, the electrons and protons will neutralize or cancel out each other, and no electrical charge is apparent.

However, when an object is rubbed, things begin to happen. Since electrons move about freely, friction will rub electrons off one object and onto another. Now you can explain what happened when the child scuffed his feet on the rug. He rubbed electrons off the rug and onto his shoes. In this way, his body accumulated additional electrons (negative particles). When he brought his finger near the wall switchplate or another child's finger, the additional electrons left his body in the form of an electric spark.

When the balloon was rubbed with nylon, wool, or fur, electrons were rubbed off the fabric and onto the balloon. The balloon now had an extra number of electrons. These electrons jumped from the balloon to the child's finger in the form of an electric spark.

Have the children explain the other experiments (described above) in terms of rubbing electrons onto an object and thereby producing an electric spark.

This effect may now be shown again in a more dramatic manner. In total darkness (after eyes have been given time to adjust) rub the glass tube of a fluorescent lamp with a piece of nylon or silk. In a few seconds the lamp will glow faintly. The rubbing will strip some electrons off the glass, and these electrons make the white (phosphor) coating glow. This works only on very dry days.

This same effect may also be produced by rubbing an inflated balloon with a piece of nylon, wool, or fur. Then touch the end of the fluorescent tube to the balloon in a darkened room. Sparks from the balloon will light up the fluorescent tube.

The word "static" means "at rest" or "stationary." When the balloon was rubbed with nylon, wool, or fur, a surplus of electrons was rubbed onto the balloon. These electrons remained on the balloon and did not run off. We say that the balloon became "electrically charged." The term "static electricity" refers to electric charges that remain on materials without running off. When a spark is formed, the moving electric charges are now called "current electricity" or an "electric current."

Positive and negative charges

In the previous section it was pointed out that, under normal circumstances, an object will have the same number of electrons ($-$) and protons ($+$), and therefore the electrons and protons will neutralize or cancel out each other. It was also pointed out that electrons move about freely, while protons are stationary. When an object is rubbed, the friction will rub electrons off one object and onto another. This upsets the balance of electrons and protons.

The object that gains electrons (negative particles) now has more electrons than protons (positive particles). This object is said to be negatively charged. On the other hand, the object that loses electrons ends up with more protons ($+$) than electrons ($-$). This object is said to be positively charged.

Electrically charged objects have properties of attraction and repulsion. These properties follow a basic law, namely, that like charges repel and unlike charges attract. Consequently, two negatively charged bodies will repel each other. However, a negatively charged body and a positively charged body will attract each other.

Inflate two balloons. Tie a long thread around the neck of each inflated balloon. Then stretch a string across the room well above the pupils' heads. Suspend the two balloons by the threads to the same point on the string stretched across the room. Now rub each balloon with nylon, wool, or fur. The two balloons will move away from (repel) each other. Both balloons picked up electrons from the nylon, wool, or fur and became negatively charged. (Fig. 22-1).

Now take a comb that is made of hard rubber. Rub the comb with nylon, wool, or fur and bring it near the charged balloons. The comb will repel both balloons. It, too, has picked up electrons from the nylon, wool, or fur and become negatively charged. Consequently, it will repel other negatively charged objects.

Cut two strips of nylon about 1' long and 3" wide from a nylon stocking. Place both strips on white paper or cardboard and rub them briskly with your hand. Now lift up the two pieces of nylon and hold them between your fingers. The two loose ends will repel each other. In this case, electrons have been rubbed off the nylon strips, leaving them both positively charged. Being alike, these charged nylon strips repel each other. Now bring a charged strip of nylon near one of the charged balloons. The positively charged nylon will attract the negatively charged rubber balloon.

Take a glass rod and rub it with nylon or silk. The rod from a glass towel rack will do. If this is not available, the glass handle of a Silex coffee-maker, or a long, thin glass jar or vase, or a glass drinking tube will serve. The friction causes the glass rod to give up its electrons to the nylon, and the glass becomes positively charged. Bring the glass near the suspended, negatively charged balloons. The balloons, being oppositely charged from the glass, will promptly move toward the glass.

The children can now experiment with different materials rubbed with nylon, silk, wool, or fur to see what kind of charge is produced.

When two objects are rubbed together, both are affected because electrons are rubbed off one object and onto another. Thus the one that gains electrons becomes negatively charged, while the one that loses electrons becomes positively charged. In the list given below, when any two of the substances are rubbed together the substance higher on the list will become positively charged, while the lower one will become negatively charged. The farther apart the two substances are on the list, the greater will be the charge produced.

> glass
> fur
> wool
> nylon
> cotton
> silk
> Lucite
> sealing wax
> hard rubber
> Vinylite

Uncharged bodies are attracted

Charge a hard rubber or plastic comb or a plastic coat hanger by rubbing it with nylon, wool, or fur. Bring it near some tiny pieces of thin paper and notice how the paper is attracted to the comb. The children will wonder why the paper is attracted since it is not charged (neutral).

Point out that the comb is negatively charged. As it nears the neutral paper, it repels the negatively charged electrons on the near side of the paper and pushes them to the far side of the paper. This makes the near side positively charged, and the paper is attracted to the comb.

The children might like to make a "kissing balloon." Inflate a balloon and tie a thread around its neck. With a soft brush and ink, paint a face on the balloon.

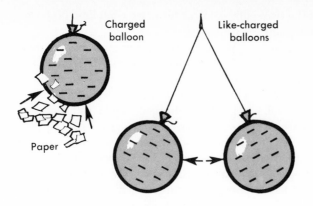

Charged balloon

Like-charged balloons

Paper

Fig. 22-1 Like charges repel each other; unlike charges attract. (From R. Brinckerhoff et al., *The Physical World*, Harcourt, Brace & World, 1958.)

When the ink is dry, suspend the balloon from a string stretched across the room. Now rub the balloon with nylon, wool, or fur. The balloon will try to "kiss" the hand or face of any pupil that comes near it. Help the children understand that the negatively charged balloon repels the electrons in the hand and pushes them as far as possible to the other side of the hand. Thus the negative charge on the balloon creates a positive charge on the side of the hand nearest the balloon. There is now an attraction between the negatively charged balloon and the positively charged side of the hand. The balloon, being lighter, is pulled toward the hand.

There are many more interesting experiments which demonstrate this phenomenon. Rub an inflated balloon with a piece of nylon, wool, or fur. Place the charged balloon against the wall, and it will stay there. The demonstration is even more spectacular to the children if you just rub the balloon against your sleeve.

Using nylon, wool, or fur, rub a plastic pen or pencil, a stick of sealing wax, or any nonmetallic object. In each case the object will become charged enough to pick up bits of cork or paper. These same charged objects will make hair stand on end. Or they will attract a ping-pong ball and make it move toward you. They will make long cotton or nylon threads stand up and weave to and fro like snakes.

Adjust the water flow from a faucet so that you get a thin steady stream of water. Charge a comb by rubbing it with nylon, wool, or fur. Now bring the comb near the stream of water. The stream of water will be attracted by the comb and bend toward it.

Hold a newspaper flat against the wall or blackboard and rub the entire surface briskly with a piece of cloth or fur. The paper will stay on the wall for hours. Pull one of the corners loose; then let go. The paper will be attracted back to the wall. Listen for crackling noises when you pull the paper loose. If it were dark, you would see the many sparks that are produced.

Obtain a nylon stocking and a dry polyethylene fruit or vegetable bag. You can make sure it is polyethylene because it stretches quite a bit when you try to tear it.

Now hold the stocking by the toe against the wall and rub it briskly with the polyethylene bag (shirts and many other articles of clothing come in such bags). Take the stocking away from the wall and let it hang freely. The stocking will blow up just as if it were filled with air. This happens because both sides of the stocking have lost electrons and become positively charged, and thus repel each other. Notice how the stocking will stick to the wall or your body.

Call the children's attention to Saran

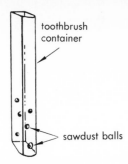

toothbrush container

sawdust balls

Fig. 22-2 Making objects jump up and down. (From *General Science Handbook, Part II*, New York State Education Department, 1952.)

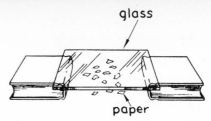

glass

paper

Fig. 22-3 Dancing paper dolls. (From *General Science Handbook, Part II*, New York State Education Department, 1952.)

Wrap. The friction of separating it from the roll is enough to charge it. It becomes very highly charged and will stick to most objects.

Jumping objects. Charge a hard rubber or plastic comb by rubbing it with nylon, wool, or fur. Dip the comb into a box of puffed rice or wheat. When you withdraw the comb, it will be covered with the kernels of rice. Hold the comb in the air. After a while the kernels will start popping off. This is a case of first attraction, then repulsion. The comb has been negatively charged. It first attracts the neutral kernels of puffed rice. However, the negative electrons in the comb slowly pass into the kernels which are touching the comb. After a while the kernels receive enough electrons so that they, too, become negatively charged. Now the comb and the kernels, both negatively charged, repel each other and the kernels drop off.

The same experiment may be repeated using bits of cork, paper, sawdust, or other kinds of cereal. Or you can place them in a plastic toothbrush container and then rub the container with nylon, wool, or fur. The small particles will stick to the sides of the container at first. Then, as they too become charged, they will be repelled by the container and also by the other bits of material. The bits of material will jump up and down (Fig. 22-2).

Place a pane of glass upon two books resting several inches apart on the table. Cut out several tiny paper men no larger than ½" tall and ½" wide. (Or you may use small pieces of paper.) Onionskin paper will serve well. Place the paper men underneath the glass pane. Now rub the glass briskly with a piece of nylon or silk (Fig. 22-3). The little men will jump up and stick to the glass. After a while they will drop down, and then jump up again. The children should be able by now to explain this phenomenon. The glass pane becomes positively charged and the paper men are attracted to the glass. The men soon become charged positively also, then are repelled by the glass, and jump back to the table. After a while they lose this charge and are attracted by the glass again. This process is repeated again and again. An inverted Pyrex pie dish or bowl can be used instead of the glass pane and the books.

The same effect can be produced by using a plastic cheese container and any small, light objects. Place the paper men inside the container, put the cover back on, and then charge the container by rubbing with nylon, wool, or fur.

You may want to show this effect by making an "electrostatic airplane." Cut a small piece of aluminum foil into the shape of an airplane. Charge a hard rubber or plastic comb by rubbing it with nylon, wool, or fur. Hold the comb up in the air and bring the airplane near it. The comb attracts the airplane at first. However, the plane soon receives the same charge as the comb and jumps away from

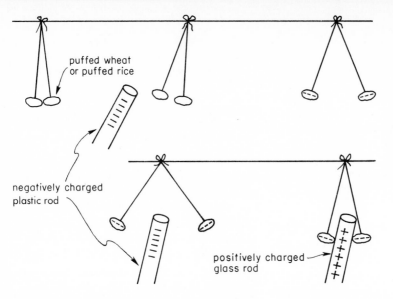

puffed wheat or puffed rice

negatively charged plastic rod

positively charged glass rod

Fig. 22-4 Detecting charged objects. (From *General Science Handbook, Part II*, New York State Education Department, 1952.)

the comb. The comb now repels the plane and you can keep the plane in the air as long as you wish and make it fly wherever you want it to.

Electron detectors

Paint two kernels of puffed rice or wheat with a very thin coating of aluminum paint. Then pass a needle and silk thread through each grain. Hang the two threads from the same point to a string stretched across the room (Fig. 22-4). Now charge a rubber or plastic comb or rod by rubbing with nylon, wool, or fur. Bring the charged comb near the uncharged neutral kernels and note how they are attracted to the comb. Now touch both kernels at the same time with the comb. The kernels become negatively charged also and now repel each other. If the comb is placed between the charged kernels, the kernels will be repelled even farther away. Charge a glass rod or narrow glass tube positively by rubbing it with nylon or silk. Bring the positive glass rod between the negatively charged kernels. The kernels will be attracted to the oppositely charged glass.

This device can be used to identify charged objects. If the object is negatively charged, it will repel the negatively charged kernels. And if the object is positively charged, it will attract the oppositely charged kernels. See what happens when you bring a neutral object to this electron detector. Can you explain it?

Small balloons, ping-pong balls coated with aluminum paint, and other light objects can also be used as electron detectors. You can even make one by rubbing a long strip of paper (about 15″ long and 1½″ wide) with a piece of wool until it is charged and then laying it over a ruler.

The scientific term for an electron detector is an electroscope. Most electroscopes use metal "leaves" to detect the electric charges. Obtain a bottle, cork stopper, long copper nail, and thin aluminum or tin foil. Chewing gum wrappers are coated with thin aluminum foil. To remove the foil, soak the wrapper in rubbing alcohol; then work the foil loose with your fingers. (Very fine electroscope foil is available from scientific supply houses for a very modest sum.) Push the copper nail through the cork until the head of the nail is about 1″ above the stopper. Cut two strips of aluminum foil about 2–3″ long and ½″ wide. Sew their upper ends together and tie the foil to the lower end of the nail with the remaining thread (Fig. 22-5). Now insert the cork firmly into the bottle. To operate the electroscope, touch the head of the nail with a negatively charged comb. Electrons from the comb will flow into the nail and down into the aluminum leaves. The leaves will become negatively charged and will separate because they repel each other. Now if a negatively charged object is brought near the nail head, the leaves will separate even further. If a positively charged rod is brought near the nail head, the leaves will come together.

If you wish to remove the charge from any of the electron detectors and make them neutral, simply "ground" them by touching the kernels, balloons, ping-pong balls, or nail head with your fingers.

Take an empty plastic water bag or plastic air pillow and fold it over itself several times. Then take a small aluminum pie pan to which a wooden or plastic handle has been cemented in the center. Rub the pie pan vigorously against the plastic. Then lift the pie pan and bring a knuckle of the hand near the pan; a large spark will jump out. This may also be done without any shock if heavily insulated wire is used, one end of which is connected to a water pipe.

CURRENT ELECTRICITY

Electrons in motion

Introducing children to the idea of invisible yet very real particles flowing through a wire can well be done by first pointing to the effects produced, i.e., a glowing bulb, a ringing bell, a running motor, a hot toaster, etc. Then you develop the concept of the existence of moving electrons which are carriers of energy.

This chapter will have occasion to refer many times to the direction an electric current takes through an electric circuit.

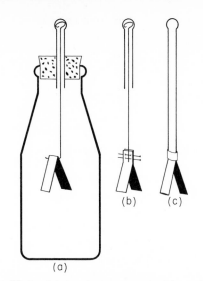

Fig. 22-5 (a) An electroscope. In this model a strip of folded foil hangs from a bent wire, the top of which is inserted in the ball end of a hollow curtain rod. (b) Two strips of foil are attached to the wire with pins. (c) Two strips of foil are Scotch-taped to the ball end of a hollow curtain rod. (From A. Joseph et al., A Sourcebook for the Physical Sciences, Harcourt, Brace & World, 1961.)

In every case the description will be given in terms of the direction in which the electrons actually flow through the wire. This direction is opposite to the conventionally assumed direction of electric current flow, which is really a fiction.

A little background may be of help here. Most physics texts and engineering manuals discuss circuits in terms of the electric current flowing from the positive to the negative electrode (or terminal) of a dry cell or battery. This assumes that there is a positive charge flowing through the wires because a positively charged body will be attracted to a negatively charged body. All of this started with an honest mistake of Benjamin Franklin. On the basis of his experiments in electricity nearly 200 years ago, he speculated that the carrier of electrical energy through a wire was positive in nature. He did not know then of the existence of electrons.

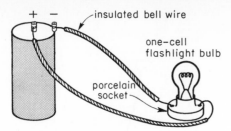

+ − insulated bell wire

one-cell
flashlight bulb

porcelain
socket

Fig. 22-6   A simple electric circuit.

As a result the convention became firmly entrenched that electric current flowed from the positive terminal (or electrode) of a dry cell or battery to the negative terminal. Later evidence was found proving that the actual carriers of this energy were negative "free electrons" that therefore really moved in the opposite direction through the wire, i.e., from the negative terminal to the positive.

It seems logical to start with the truth when teaching electricity to children. It is a real challenge to inculcate the idea of moving electrons, so tiny that no one can see them, and to teach the actual direction in which these electrons flow. Later on they can learn about the "conventional" flow of current and realize that it is just a convention.

Simple electric circuit

There are at least three parts to a complete electrical circuit: (1) a source of electric current, such as a cell or generator, (2) a path for the current to travel, such as wires, and (3) an article to use the current, such as a light bulb, electric iron, toaster, bell, or motor.

From a hardware store obtain #6 dry cells, bell wire, 1.1- or 1.2-volt flashlight bulbs, and miniature porcelain sockets into which the bulbs may be screwed. (*Caution: Get small sockets of the size that will take the flashlight bulbs.*)

Note that the dry cell has two binding posts to which wire may be attached. The center post or terminal is called the positive terminal, while the end (side) post or terminal is called the negative terminal. Look for this information which is usually printed at the top of the cardboard jacket which covers the dry cell. To connect wire to the binding posts, first partially unscrew the knob of the binding post, then wrap the wire from which the insulation has been stripped around the screw, and finally screw the movable knob down firmly.

There is no need to worry about electric shocks when using a dry cell. The electrical pressure or voltage of a dry cell is 1½ volts, just the same as that of a flashlight cell. Ordinary house current usually has about 110–120 volts. It is well worth pointing out to the pupils that although the wire connected to a dry cell is safe to handle, wire carrying 110 volts or more (house current) is very dangerous.

For working with dry cells, #18 insulated copper wire is best. This wire is called bell or annunciator wire. Usually the wire is wrapped in a cotton covering (often waxed), but the newer bell wire is plastic-covered. If #18 wire is unavailable, #20 or 22 wire will serve as well.

The porcelain socket will be a miniature of the larger sockets used for ordinary electric light bulbs. At the base of the socket are two screws which can be loosened with a screwdriver to serve as binding posts around which the wire can be wrapped. Tightening the screws serves to hold the wire in place.

In making a simple electrical circuit, first cut two pieces of bell wire about 15″ long. Then remove about 2″ of the insulation from the ends of each piece of wire. This can be done by cutting the insulation with a knife, using a sawing motion. The cotton covering can be unwrapped. Start at a point about 2″ from the end of the wire; then cut the insulation all around the wire. When the insulation has been cut through and separated, it can be pulled off the end of the wire. Alligator clips connected to each end of a wire can save much time in connecting apparatus.

Now screw a flashlight bulb into the porcelain socket. Connect the end of one wire to a binding post of the dry cell. In setting up a simple electrical circuit, it makes no difference to which post you attach the wires. Connect the other end of the wire to either screw of the porcelain socket. Then connect one end of the second wire to the remaining binding post of the dry cell and the other end of the wire to the second screw of the porcelain socket. The bulb will light up, and you will have a simple electrical circuit (Fig. 22-6).

Let the children examine the circuit carefully. Have them look closely at the wires. Ask them to trace the path of the electric current. Follow the current as it flows from one binding post through the wire to the socket, into the bulb, back into the socket again, through the second wire, back to the other binding post. The electric current then travels through the cell back to the first binding post. If the children are confused about how the electricity passes through the socket, let them see that there are wires leading from each screw to the base of the socket where the bulb is screwed in. Let them take apart an old socket and make a large-scale drawing of the socket for the bulletin board. (Let the children examine the bulb closely so that they can see the wire leading in and out of the bulb.)

Point out to the children that the path which the current follows is called a circuit. Now disconnect one end of a wire leading to the bulb. It makes no difference whether you disconnect the end which is connected to the dry cell or the one connected to the socket. The light will go out. Connect the wires again, but this time unscrew the bulb. The light will go out again. Help the children understand that the electric current will flow only if it can travel all the way around the circuit. Whenever a wire is disconnected or the bulb is unscrewed, the electric current is unable to flow. When this happens, we say the circuit is broken. Cutting one of the wires in two is a good example of showing how a circuit may be broken.

When the current can flow all the way from the cell to the socket to the bulb and back again to the cell, we call this a closed circuit. When the current is unable to flow because the circuit is broken, we call this an open circuit.

Reverse the connection of the wires to the binding posts of the dry cell. Then do the same thing with wires at the screws of the porcelain socket. The children will realize that in each case the circuit remained closed, and thus the bulb remained lit.

Point out to the children that scientists have learned the direction of electron flow in the dry cell or battery. It is from the positive to negative *inside* the dry cell, then out the negative terminal through the outside circuit and back to the positive terminal.

Switches

In the simple electric circuit described above, the only way to stop the flow of electricity is either by disconnecting a wire or by unscrewing the bulb. This is inconvenient, not only for a simple circuit but also for electrical appliances in the home. Usually a device is inserted in the circuit which can open or close the circuit easily. This device is called a switch.

From a dime store or hardware store obtain a small inexpensive knife switch and a pushbutton switch. Both these switches have screws, just like those in the porcelain socket, to which wire can be connected. Now cut a piece of bell wire about 6–8″ long and remove about 2″ of the insulation from each end of the wire. Use this wire to connect the knife switch

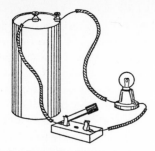

Fig. 22-7 A simple electric circuit containing a switch. (From *UNESCO Source Book for Science Teachers*, UNESCO, 1956.)

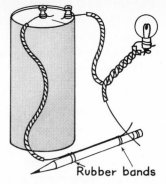

Rubber bands

Fig. 22-8 A simple electric circuit containing a homemade switch. (From *UNESCO Source Book for Science Teachers*, UNESCO, 1956.)

into a simple circuit containing a dry cell and one-cell flashlight bulb, as shown in the diagram (Fig. 22-7). Let the children turn the light off and on by manipulating the switch. Point out that the knife edge, when closed, acts as a bridge and permits the electric current to flow in an unbroken path through the circuit. When the knife edge is open, the circuit is broken.

Repeat this demonstration, using a pushbutton switch. The children should now be able to see how pushing the button will close the circuit.

Homemade switch. A simple switch may be made with a wooden pencil and rubber bands. Let one wire run from a dry cell binding post along the length of the pencil. Two rubber bands will serve to hold the wire fast to the pencil, leaving the end of the wire free. Now let one wire from the circuit to be closed be connected to one end of the pencil quite close to the free end of the wire from the binding post. Use another rubber band to hold the second wire firmly to the pencil. The loose end of the first wire can now act as a switch by latching under the second wire (Fig. 22-8). Another switch can be made by using paper clips that slide into one another.

Tap-key switch. A tap-key switch is useful when you want to turn electricity on and off quickly. Obtain a piece of smooth wood about 5″ × 3″ × ¾″. From

the hardware store obtain thin sheet copper about 5″ long and 1″ wide; or use linoleum metal stripping. The metal can be cut with ordinary scissors. If you are adept with tin snips and can trim ragged edges, you may want to use tin from a tin can instead of the copper. Cut the copper into two pieces, one 3″ long and the other 2″ long. Attach a small piece of a wooden dowel to one end of the 3″ copper strip by means of a brass screw. Place the copper strips on the wood as shown in the diagram (Fig. 22-9). Tack each strip to the wood as follows: Drive one tack into each copper strip as far as it will go. This will hold both strips firmly in place. Then, right next to each tack, drive another tack into each strip. Do not drive the second tack all the way in; leave just enough room to wedge in the bell wire. Thus, the second tack will serve as a binding post in each case. Now bend the 3″ strip of cop-

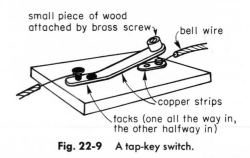

small piece of wood attached by brass screw

bell wire

copper strips

tacks (one all the way in, the other halfway in)

Fig. 22-9 A tap-key switch.

per up so that it will not touch the other strip. Using the wooden dowel key, you can push the copper strip down to close the circuit.

You might want to make a similar switch, but one that will stay down as long as you want it to. Obtain another piece of wood 5″ × 3″ × ¾″. Also obtain a strip of thin copper 4″ long and 1″ wide. Attach a piece of wooden dowel to one end of the copper by means of a brass screw. Now tack the copper strip into the wood. Drive the tack almost all the way in, leaving just enough room so that bell wire can be connected to it. The copper strip is now free to move sideways. At the opposite end of the wood, drive a roofing nail (with a wide head) halfway into the wood. The roofing nail serves as a binding post and also holds the copper strip, which is hooked under the head of the nail (Fig. 22-10). Be sure to bend the copper strip up. Be careful in estimating the position where you drive in the roofing nail so that the copper strip will be able to hook under the nail head.

A spring-type clothespin makes a simple "on and off" contact switch. Wrap bare wire around each handle and press one against the other to make contact.

How a flashlight works. Now that the children have had the opportunity to trace the path of the electric current in a simple electrical circuit, you may want to challenge their imagination by tracing the path of the current in a flashlight.

It might be wise to first set the stage by comparing the #6 dry cell and the flashlight cell. Point out that for both cells the center terminal is the positive terminal, and the zinc covering around each cell is the negative terminal. The dry cell has binding posts while the flashlight cell has none. The flashlight cell has an electrical voltage (electrical pressure) of 1½ volts, the same as the dry cell.

Wrap the free end of a piece of bell wire

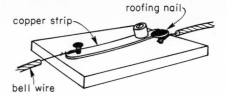

Fig. 22-10 A homemade switch that will stay down.

firmly around a one-cell flashlight bulb (1½ volts). Use tape to hold the other end of the wire against the base of the flashlight cell; then bring the silvery button on the base of the light bulb in contact with the center terminal of the flashlight cell. The bulb will light up. Have the children trace the path of the electric current through the circuit.

Continue by making a two-cell flashlight. Cut a piece of paper so that it is the same length as two flashlight cells placed end to end. Place the cells on the paper so that the positive terminal of one is touching the base of the other (Fig. 22-11). Take a piece of bell wire and wrap one free end around a flashlight bulb. Use a bulb made for a two-cell flashlight (about 3 volts). Put the wire on the paper alongside the two flashlight cells. The wire should be long enough so that both the ends extend beyond the paper. Now roll the cells and wire up neatly with the paper. Place rubber bands horizontally around the roll so that the paper will not become loose. Also wrap a thick rubber band vertically around the roll so that both cells will be touching all the time. It is important that both cells be in contact at all times. Otherwise, the circuit will be broken. Now hold the loose end of the wire against the bottom of the lower cell. Then bring the base of the flashlight bulb against the center terminal of the top cell. The bulb will light up. The children should have little difficulty in tracing the path of the current. The electrons flow from the bottom or lower cell (negative terminal)

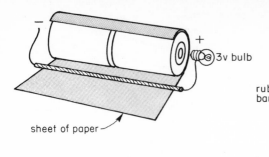

3v bulb

sheet of paper

rubber bands

Fig. 22-11 A homemade two-cell flashlight.

through wire into the bulb, back to the center (positive) terminal of the top cell and then through both cells back to the bottom of the lower cell.

You have just made a flashlight; yet the pupils will be quick to point out that this flashlight is different from the commercial model. The big difference is that the commercial flashlight has no wires, and yet the current flows in an unbroken path when the switch is pressed or pushed. Let the children examine a commercial flashlight closely. A large diagram (Fig. 22-12) on the blackboard will further help to explain its operation. Point out to the children that the bulb is at the center of a small metal bowl. The switch at the side of the case consists of a piece of metal which can be pushed back and forth. When the switch is closed, it has been pushed forward so that the metal piece touches the metal bowl. The spring at the bottom of the case makes sure that both flashlight cells are touching at all times.

Now trace the path of the current when the switch is closed. The electrons flow

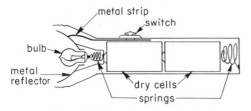

metal strip
switch
bulb
metal reflector
dry cells
springs

Fig. 22-12 How a commercial flashlight works.

from the bottom or lower cell into the spring, along the metal case, through the switch, into the bulb, back to the center terminal of the top cell, and then through both cells back to the bottom cell again.

Flashlights are not all alike in that their switches may vary. But if you are successful in tracing the path of the current through the type of flashlight described above, you will have little trouble in explaining how any other type operates.

Ringing a doorbell. Ringing an electric doorbell or buzzer is another example of closing a simple electrical circuit. Obtain an electric doorbell from the hardware store. You will note it has two binding posts, very much like those in the #6 dry cell. Wire up a dry cell, a pushbutton or knife switch, and the doorbell so that they form a complete circuit. Whenever the switch is closed, the bell will ring. Have the pupils trace the path of the current through the circuit. The switch opens and closes almost too fast to see, as the bell rings. See Chapter 21 for the principle of buzzer operation.

Series and parallel circuits

The pupils may have wondered why, in making a two-cell flashlight, the positive terminal of one cell was pressed against the bottom side of the other cell. You were also cautioned to use a flashlight bulb specifically made for a two-cell

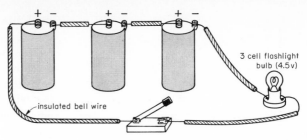

Fig. 22-13 Connecting cells in series.

3 cell flashlight bulb (4.5 v)

insulated bell wire

flashlight. The cells of this homemade flashlight are said to be connected in series. That is, the negative pole of the top cell is in contact with the positive pole of the bottom cell.

Connecting cells in series. Show the pupils how to connect cells in series and what effect this connection has. Obtain three #6 dry cells, bell wire, a knife switch, a miniature porcelain socket, and a flashlight bulb designed for a three-cell flashlight (about 4½ volts). Set up the three cells side by side. Wire the cells, switch, and socket as shown in the diagram (Fig. 22-13). Note that when the cells are connected together, the center (positive) binding post of one cell is always connected to the outside (negative) binding post of the adjoining cell. In this way a wire always leads from a positive terminal to a negative terminal. Even the outside connection to the switch and lamp is connected by wires which run from a positive to a negative terminal (or vice versa).

When cells are connected in series, the electric current flows through each cell. This makes the voltage cumulative. Thus, if the voltage of one cell is 1½ volts, the combined voltage of the three cells is three times that of a single cell, or 4½ volts. This is why two-cell and three-cell flashlights need special bulbs. If a one-cell bulb were used in a three-cell flashlight, it would quickly burn out because of the increased voltage. Automobile storage batteries have 2-volt cells. New cars have 12-volt batteries of six 2-volt cells; older cars have 6-volt batteries with three 2-volt cells in series.

To show this cumulative voltage, first connect the three cells in series and attach the combination to a switch and a three-cell flashlight bulb (about 4½ volts) in a porcelain socket. Close the switch and observe the brightness of the bulb. Now connect only two cells in series and observe how the light of the bulb is dimmed. Finally use only one cell and note how dim the light from the bulb has become.

Connecting cells in parallel. There is a second way in which cells may be connected, namely, in parallel. Wire the cells as shown in the diagram (Fig. 22-14). This time use a flashlight bulb designed for a one-cell flashlight (about 1½ volts). Note that in this setup, the center (positive) binding post is always connected to an-

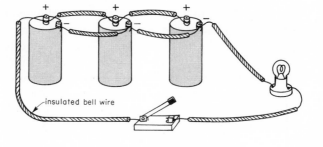

Fig. 22-14 Connecting cells in parallel.

insulated bell wire

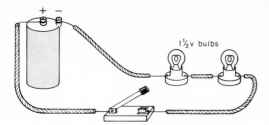

Fig. 22-15 Connecting light bulbs in series.

other center (positive) binding post, and the outside (negative) binding post is always connected to another outside (negative) binding post.

When cells are connected in parallel, the electric current also flows across each cell, like a branch current. In this case, therefore, the voltage is not cumulative at all, and the total voltage of all the cells is just the same as the voltage of one cell (1½ volts).

To show the effect of cells connected in parallel, connect the three cells in parallel and wire this combination to a switch and a one-cell flashlight bulb in a porcelain socket. Close the switch and observe the brightness of the bulb. Now connect only two cells in parallel and close the switch again. The brightness will not change at all, since no matter how many cells are connected in parallel the total amount of voltage delivered is equal to the amount delivered by just one cell.

In actual practice, cells are connected in series in order to take advantage of increased voltage and are connected in parallel to increase current. It is good to know both methods of connection in order to explain more easily how lamps are connected in series and in parallel.

Connecting light bulbs in series. Just as cells, light bulbs can be connected in series or in parallel.

Obtain a #6 dry cell, bell wire, a knife switch, two miniature porcelain sockets, and two flashlight bulbs designed for one-cell flashlights (1½ volts each). Screw

the bulbs in the sockets and arrange the sockets in a row so that the screws are side by side. Wire the cell, switch, and sockets as shown in the diagram (Fig. 22-15). Note that the wires lead from a screw on the left to a screw on the right. Thus, when tracing the path of the current, the pupils should be led to understand that the current flows through the cell and through each socket.

Now close the switch and observe how both bulbs light up. Have the pupils trace the path of the current through the entire circuit. Unscrew one of the bulbs and note that the other bulb also goes out because the circuit is now broken. Some pupils may recall they have Christmas tree bulb sets which are arranged in series. They will be able to describe the difficulty they had in finding out which bulb burned out, since all the other bulbs also went out.

Connecting light bulbs in parallel. To connect bulbs in parallel, wire the cell, switch, and sockets as shown in the diagram (Fig. 22-16). Point out that the wires lead from left screw to left screw on the sockets, and from right screw to right screw. Thus, when tracing the path of the current, help the children understand that the current flows both *through* and *across* the sockets. This means that we have created branch circuits for each lamp. When the current from the cell reaches the first socket, part of the current flows through the socket and part of the current branches off toward the second socket. At the second socket the current branches again, part of it going through the second socket and the other part going toward the third socket.

Let us see what effect parallel wiring has on the lighting of the bulbs. Closing the switch lights up all the bulbs. Unscrew one of the bulbs and note that the other two remain lit. Repeat, unscrewing any one of the bulbs, and then any two.

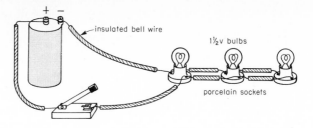

Fig. 22-16 Connecting light bulbs in parallel.

Help the pupils understand that, when one bulb is unscrewed, the entire circuit is not broken. Only one particular branch is affected, permitting the current to flow through the other two branches. Therefore, the other two bulbs remain lighted.

Household wiring is connected in parallel. It should now be apparent to the pupils that, although they cost more, strings of Christmas bulbs connected in parallel are more convenient to use. When one bulb goes out, it can be spotted and changed immediately, while the other bulbs remain lighted.

DETECTING ELECTRIC CURRENTS

After having worked with cells and electrical circuits, the pupils should take to the suggestion of making their own cells and producing electric current. However, they will find that the electric current they produce most likely will not have the electrical pressure (voltage) comparable to that of the dry cell or the flashlight cell. It is easy to detect the electricity from a commercial cell, since all you have to do is wire up a light bulb, bell, or buzzer. If the bulb lights up or the bell or

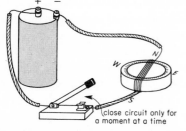

Fig. 22-17 A compass galvanometer.

buzzer creates a sound, you know that you have an electric current.

However, when the flow of electricity is so slight that it will not make a bulb light up or bell ring, a more sensitive device is needed to detect the presence of an electric current. Such instruments are called galvanometers.

Homemade galvanometers

Compass galvanometer. To make a homemade galvanometer you will need a compass, copper wire, a switch, and a dry cell. The compass may be obtained at a ten-cent store or an Army surplus store. The other materials can be found at the hardware store. The thinner the wire, the better the galvanometer works. Ordinary bell wire is #18 copper wire. The higher the number, the thinner the wire; #28 or 30 insulated copper wire is best for a galvanometer, but if it is unavailable, bell wire will serve the purpose.

Wrap some wire many times around the compass and connect the wire to a switch and dry cell (Fig. 22-17). Set the compass so that the needle points north and south, and wrap the wire so that it runs parallel to the compass needle. Make as many windings as you can and yet be able to see both ends of the compass needle. When the switch is closed, the electric current passing through the coil of wire will cause the compass needle to swerve sharply from its north-south position.

The children will wonder why this deflection occurs. Remind them that the compass needle is magnetized. They should remember that, when an electric

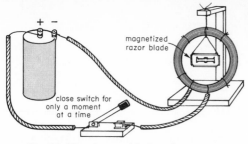

+ −

magnetized
razor blade

close switch for
only a moment
at a time

Fig. 22-18   A razor-blade galvanometer.

current passes through a coil of wire, the coil becomes magnetized. The magnetic field of the coil causes the magnetic needle of the compass to deflect from its usual position. The deflection is usually at right angles to the customary north-south position. This happens because the magnetic field produced in the coil is at right angles to the direction of the coil, and the compass needle therefore tries to line up with the coil's magnetic field.

Reverse the connections of the wires to the binding posts of the cell. The needle will now swerve in the opposite direction. Evidently, reversing the connections will reverse the deflection as well.

Razor-blade galvanometer.   A more sensitive galvanometer can be made using a double-edged razor blade. Magnetize the razor blade by stroking it with a strong permanent magnet at least 50 times. Always stroke the blade with one pole of the magnet and in the same direction. Or, if you like, you may magnetize the blade by wrapping a coil of bell wire around it and attaching the ends of the wire to a dry cell for a few moments.

Now obtain #28 cotton-covered copper wire and wrap about 50 turns of the wire neatly and compactly around the side of a glass bottle about 3″ in diameter. The purpose of this is to make a loop of wire wide enough to contain the magnetized double-edged razor blade. Slip the wire off the bottle and bind it at a few points with thread, wire, or tape so that

it will not become undone. Leave about a 12″ length of wire on each end of the coil. Then tie some thread over the top of the coil and connect the thread to the top of a wooden stand so that the coil hangs freely. Using thread, suspend the razor blade within the coil so that it can move freely (Fig. 22-18).

Now connect the loose ends of the coil of wire to a switch and dry cell. When the switch is closed, the blade will move. The distance the blade will move will depend upon the strength of the current flowing through the coil of wire. This is a rough means of indicating the strength of an electric current.

Needle galvanometer.   Another kind of galvanometer makes use of two magnetized needles instead of the razor blade. Magnetize the needles, holding the points in the same direction, in exactly the same manner you magnetized the razor blade. Cut a strip of cardboard about 3″ long and ⅛″ wide. Thread one end of the cardboard and suspend it from the top of the wooden stand (Fig. 22-19). Turn the coil upright on its side and split it so that the cardboard can slide through it. Make the split wide enough so that the cardboard can turn freely. Anchor the coil upright on its side with bent-over nails. Put both needles through the cardboard so that one needle is just above the top of the coil and one is within the oval made by the coil. Insert the needles so that their poles are opposite, as shown in the diagram. When the current flows through the coil, the needles will turn.

The pupils may wonder why the needles were inserted with their poles opposite. Recall what happened to the deflection of the compass needle when the connections to the dry cell were reversed. This same thing happens when the compass is placed above and below wire carrying the electric current. By reversing the poles of the needles, we are able to

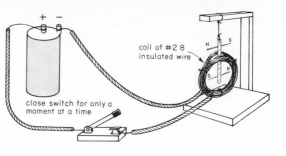

Fig. 22-19 A needle galvanometer, a model of the earliest Faraday galvanometer.

coil of #28 insulated wire

close switch for only a moment at a time

get them both to swing in the same direction at the same time.

Potato tester. A novel but effective method of detecting an electric current involves the use of a dry cell, bell wire, and a potato. Slice the potato in half. Attach two wires to the binding posts of a dry cell and stick the bare ends of the wires into the potato. Keep the wires fairly close together, but do not let them touch inside the potato. After a minute or two, pull out the wires. The hole made by the wire connected to the positive terminal of the dry cell will now have a greenish blue rim around it. Since this only happens with the wire connected to the positive terminal of a cell, it becomes a method for detecting the positive terminal as well.

A similar test involves the use of one third a glassful of vinegar. Dip the wires into the vinegar, holding them close to each other but not touching. In a short time many bubbles of gas (hydrogen) appear at the wire connected to the negative terminal of the dry cell. None or just a few bubbles appear at the wire connected to the positive terminal. Examine the wires after a minute or two. The negative wire is still shiny, while the positive wire has become dull and rough.

PRODUCING ELECTRIC CURRENT BY CHEMICAL REACTION

Now that they have a device for detecting electric currents, the pupils may be in-

terested in preparing their own electric cells and producing their own electric current. They can do so by preparing a voltaic cell, also known as a "wet" cell.

Voltaic or "wet" cell

Obtain a strip of copper sheeting and a strip of zinc sheeting from the hardware store. The strips should be about 4-5" long and about ¾" wide. Then get 1 pound of ammonium chloride salt from the drugstore and dissolve in 1 pint of water.

Pour the ammonium chloride solution into a glass jar or beaker. Obtain a narrow strip of wood about ¾" thick and long enough to rest on top of the jar. Tack the copper and zinc strips to the wood. Punch a hole at the top of each strip, just large enough for a piece of bell wire to pass through. Now fasten the bare end of a piece of bell wire to the hole in each strip and connect the other ends of the wires to a galvanometer. Then place the strips (not touching each other) in the jar of ammonium chloride. The galvanometer will show the presence of an electric current. The current should be strong enough to light up a one-cell flashlight bulb placed in a miniature porcelain socket. (A carbon rod from an old dry cell may be used instead of the copper strip.)

Rinse the copper and zinc strips in clear water; then wipe dry. Touch the strips together. Replace the copper with a carbon rod. The galvanometer will show no current being produced in each case. Place

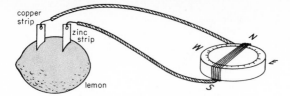

Fig. 22-20   Producing electricity with a lemon.

the strips in a glassful of distilled water and note the effect on a galvanometer. Repeat the procedure, using solutions of vinegar, orange juice, sugar, salt, washing soda, and other common household chemicals. In each case rinse the copper and zinc strips well after each test. Note the effect of each on the galvanometer.

Try using two strips of copper, then two strips of lead, then strips of dissimilar metals such as aluminum and iron, copper and lead, zinc and iron, etc.

The pupils should now be able to name the essential parts of a cell. These include two strips of different metals and a chemical solution to help conduct electricity. For those pupils who are interested, chemicals whose solutions help conduct electric currents are called electrolytes. Only three kinds of chemicals are electrolytes: acids, bases, and salts. Vinegar and fruit juices are examples of acids; ammonia is a base; and salt and baking soda are salts.

An electric current was produced because a chemical reaction took place. Because of the chemical action, the copper strip develops a scarcity of electrons, while the zinc strip accumulates electrons. This differential in charge causes the accumulated electrons to flow through the wire from the zinc strip to the copper strip which lacks electrons. This flow of electrons through wires is what we call electric current or flow of electricity. Electricity flows from areas having excess free electrons to those deficient in electrons.

Let the pupils test the wires from the copper and zinc strips with the potato tester. The wire from the copper strip will produce a hole with a greenish blue rim.

This shows that the copper strip is the positive terminal of the cell.

You can produce electricity by using a lemon voltaic cell. Obtain a lemon, then roll it firmly against the table or squeeze it in order to break up some of the inside tissue and release the juice. Cut two slits in the lemon and insert a copper and a zinc strip (Fig. 22-20). Make sure the metal strips do not touch inside the lemon. Connect the metal strips to a galvanometer so that the current may be detected. Repeat the experiment, using different kinds of fruit.

You can even make a voltaic cell out of coins. Soak a piece of blotting paper thoroughly in salt water and place it between a penny and a dime. Connect two wires to a compass galvanometer and touch the penny with one wire and the dime with the other. A current of electricity will be detected. If the movement of the compass needle is very slight, substitute an iron washer for the dime.

Have your pupils ever "tasted" electricity? Clean the copper and zinc strips thoroughly with soap and hot water. Now let a pupil place both strips in his mouth, one on each side of his tongue. The tingly feeling indicates the existence of an electric current. In this case the saliva is the electrolyte. The pupils might like to repeat the experiment, using a clean penny and dime.

What is in a dry cell?

Did you know that a dry cell is not really dry? Save one of your worn-out dry cells to prove this and also to show how a dry cell is constructed. With a hacksaw, cut the dry cell down the center lengthwise, so that you will get a good cross section of the cell (Fig. 22-21). Now examine the contents carefully. The dull metal can is made of zinc, which is the negative terminal. Note how it has been eaten away on the inside. The rod in the center is made of carbon, which is the positive terminal. Carbon is used instead of copper because it is cheaper and also works better. The pasty material between the carbon rod and the zinc can contains three chemicals: ammonium chloride (white), fine carbon particles, and manganese dioxide (black).

The ammonium chloride is the chemical which, when moistened, acts as the electrolyte which permits the chemical reaction to take place between the carbon rod and zinc can. When the cell is being used, a chemical reaction takes place and hydrogen bubbles accumulate on the carbon rod. When a layer of bubbles forms, it interferes with the flow of electrons (electric current). This is where the black manganese dioxide is put to use. The manganese dioxide reacts with the hydrogen bubbles, removing them as they are formed. In the process, water is formed.

When the cell is new, the paste is quite moist. When the cell is dead, the paste has become dry. Every precaution is made to keep the paste moist as long as possible. Note the layer of absorbent paper next to the zinc can. This paper was originally soaked in ammonium chloride solution. Recall the ammonium chloride wet cell. In order to keep the cell as waterproof as possible, the top of the cell has been sealed with hot pitch or sealing wax.

An almost worn-out dry cell may be revived for a short while. Punch a few holes with a nail into the bottom of such a cell. Place the cell in a jar. Add ammonium chloride solution until it is one third the way up the dry cell. Let the cell stand in the ammonium chloride-water solution

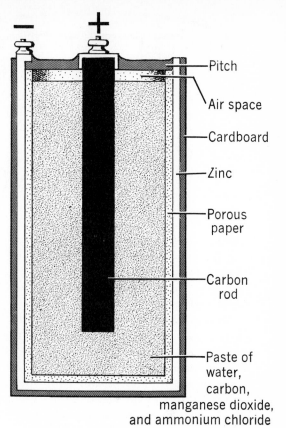

Fig. 22-21 Cross section of a dry cell. (From R. Brinckerhoff et al., *Exploring Physics*, Harcourt, Brace & World, 1959.)

for at least a half hour, preferably longer. Now try to light a flashlight bulb with the cell. If the pupils try to light the bulb before and after soaking the cell, the result will be quite striking.

A simple storage battery

Certain kinds of cells can be recharged when they seem to be worn out. Many pupils will recall how their parents have the batteries in the family automobile recharged. You can show the charging and discharging process quite effectively in the classroom.

From a plumber obtain two pieces of lead sheeting about 6″ long and 2″ wide. Also obtain some dilute sulfuric acid from

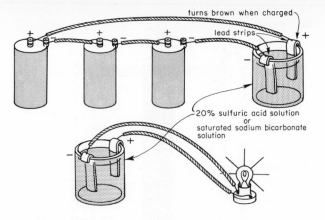

turns brown when charged

lead strips

+ + + +

−

20% sulfuric acid solution
or
saturated sodium bicarbonate
solution

+

Fig. 22-22 Charging a simple storage battery.

an automobile battery store (20% concentration). (*Caution: Be careful with the acid. If any spatters on your skin or clothes, wash it off immediately with lots of water. Do not let children ever handle sulfuric acid solution. Keep corked with* rubber *cork only.*)

Punch a hole at one end of each of the lead strips. Fill a glass about three quarters full of acid. Clean the lead strips well by sandpapering their surfaces. Bend the ends of the lead strips and hang them over the sides of the glass. Attach wires to the holes in the lead strips and connect the wires to a galvanometer. No current is indicated.

Now charge the cell as follows: Connect three dry cells in series and attach the wires to the lead strips by means of the holes in the strips (Fig. 22-22). The three dry cells in series will deliver about 1½ volts each (4½ volts in all) to the lead cell. If a pupil has a d.c. battery substitute or the rectifier used for model H-O gauge trains, it may be used to charge the "storage cell." Let the current from the dry cells flow through the lead strips and acid for several minutes. The pupils can readily see that a chemical reaction is taking place. Bubbles of gas will appear at both lead strips, and the lead strip connected to the positive terminal of a dry cell will become brownish. (This strip is being converted to lead oxide.)

After several minutes disconnect the dry cells. Now connect the wires from the lead strips to a one-cell flashlight bulb in a porcelain socket. The bulb will light up. Each lead cell delivers 2 volts.

Point out that, when the battery is delivering electric current, we say it is discharging. When we put electricity into the battery, we say it is charging.

If you do not wish to use sulfuric acid in your homemade storage cells, use a saturated solution of baking soda (sodium bicarbonate). To make a saturated solution, dissolve as much of the baking soda as you can in water at room temperature. You may also use a saturated solution of sodium sulfate instead of sulfuric acid.

GENERATING ELECTRIC CURRENT IN A MAGNETIC FIELD

The class has seen how to produce an electric current in cells or batteries by means of chemical reaction. However, cells can be used only for a limited time and must be replaced when they are worn out.

For commercial generation of electricity a much simpler and inexpensive method is used. This method requires only coils of wire and magnets.

Wrap some bell wire about 50 times

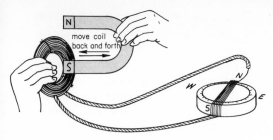

Fig. 22-23 Moving a coil in a magnetic field generates an electric current.

about a narrow olive jar. Slip off the coil and fasten it with thread, wire, or tape at several points so that the coil won't come apart. Connect the ends of the coil to a compass galvanometer (Fig. 22-23). Hold a U-magnet (or bar magnet) motionless in one hand and move the coil over one end of the magnet. Note that the compass needle is deflected, showing the presence of an electric current. Now remove the coil by sliding it back. The compass needle is deflected again, but this time in the opposite direction. Move the coil over the other pole of the magnet. The deflection is opposite to the one produced when the coil was moved over the first pole.

Move the coil over one end of the magnet again; then stop. The compass needle will also stop being deflected. Evidently electricity will be generated only as long as the coil is moving.

Move the magnet in and out of the coil and note what happens. See what moving either the magnet or coil faster will do to the compass needle. Place the like poles of two bar magnets together and see what increasing the strength of the magnets will do to the deflection of the compass needle. Note the difference when a coil of 100 turns of wire is used.

The pupils should realize, then, that a coil of wire moving in a magnetic field generates an electric current. Increasing the strength of the magnet or the number of turns of the coil of wire will increase

the amount of electric current produced. Increasing the speed with which the coils or magnet move will increase the rate of production of the electric current.

MAKING ELECTRICITY DO WORK

Most pupils are well aware that electricity is used to operate appliances in the home. However, they should be led to understand that the heart of many of these appliances is the electric motor.

A simple, inexpensive, and easy-to-understand St. Louis motor can be purchased from any commercial scientific supply house, complete with instructions. Toy stores also offer a variety of electric motors. Usually there is one boy in the class who knows all about motors and is more than willing to bring one in and explain how it operates.

Paper-clip motor[1]

A few paper clips, some enameled wire, and other common items are all you need to make the model of a motor shown in Fig. 22-24. Study the figure for a few moments, and you will see how simply it all goes together. Each model requires about 15' of #26 enamel-covered wire (from a radio store), six large thumbtacks, seven medium-size paper clips, one ungalvanized finishing nail, one baseboard. The motor is operated by two dry cells.

Making model motors

If you like, you may construct a simple motor with corks and pins. You will need three corks, some pins, two bar magnets, two small blocks of wood, a dry cell, and some insulated copper wire (#28 or finer). One cork should be about 2½-3" long. The other two corks should be shorter and wider, both the same size.

[1] Created by Mr. Katashi Nose, teacher in Kauai High School, Lihue, Hawaii.

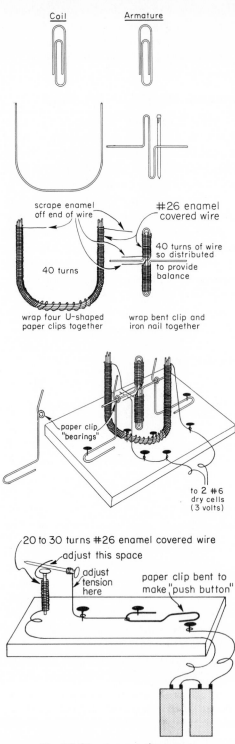

Coil   Armature

scrape enamel
off end of wire

#26 enamel
covered wire

40 turns of wire
so distributed
to provide
balance

40 turns

wrap four U-shaped
paper clips together

wrap bent clip and
iron nail together

paper clip
"bearings"

to 2 #6
dry cells
(3 volts)

20 to 30 turns #26 enamel covered wire

adjust this space

adjust
tension
here

paper clip bent to
make "push button"

Fig. 22-24 A paper-clip motor.

Stick a pin into each end of the large cork. Center the pins as best as you can, so that when the cork rotates using the pins as a shaft or axle, it will wobble as little as possible. Now wind about 10′ of the fine insulated copper wire firmly around the cork. Wind the wire length-wise, making sure that there is an equal number of turns on each side of both pins (Fig. 22-25). Fasten the wire securely with thread, so that the wire will not come loose when the cork is revolving.

When winding the wire around the cork, arrange it so that both free ends of the wire (the starting and finishing ends) are at the narrow end of the cork (see diagram). Bend these ends so that they are at right angles to the coil of wire, thus making the ends parallel to the pin. Cut the ends so that they protrude about ½″. Strip the insulation from both ends and clean them with fine sandpaper. Then adjust the ends again so that they are par-allel to the pin, one on each side.

Drive two pins criss-cross into each of the two short, wide corks. The points where the pins criss-cross should be ap-proximately the same height. This is be-cause the pins from the cork containing the coil of fine wire will rest on the grooves and behave like an axle. However, do not criss-cross the pins at too sharp an angle, because this will increase the friction to the extent that the cork will not rotate.

Now assemble the motor. Set the two corks containing the criss-cross pins in a north-south position. Place the pins of the cork containing the coil of wire on the criss-cross grooves. Lay the magnets on small blocks of wood, and arrange them so that they are as close as possible to the sides of the cork, without touching. Spin the cork by hand a few times to make sure the magnets are not touching the cork. A north pole should be on one side of the cork, and a south pole on the other side.

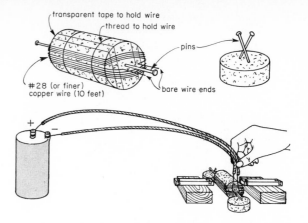

Fig. 22-25 A cork and pin motor.

Connect two pieces of bell wire about 15″ long to a dry cell. The loose ends should be stripped about 2″. Hold the wires between the thumb and forefinger and bring the ends close to the cork with the coil of wire. Bend out the ends of the wires connected to the dry cell, so that when the cork revolves, the ends of these wires will just touch or brush the ends of the two wires on the revolving cork.

Give the cork a push to start it spinning, and hold the long wires in your hand so that they make contact with the two wires on the cork when it revolves. Be sure to use only very light pressure; otherwise, the friction will be too great to permit the cork to revolve. Yet you must use enough pressure to have the wires make good contact with each other.

The cork will revolve in only one direction. Therefore, try pushing it first one way, then the other. If you start it revolving in the right direction and hold the wires with just the right amount of pressure, the motor will keep revolving quite rapidly.

Point out the essential parts of the motor. The revolving cork is called the armature. The two wires projecting from the armature are called the commutator. The wires from the dry cell brush against the rotating commutator, and are therefore called brushes. They lead the electric cur-

rent into the coil. The magnets produce the necessary attraction and repulsion and are called field magnets. The dry cell supplies the electric current.

Help the children understand how the motor operates. When the electric current from the dry cell enters the coil of wire through the brushes, the coil becomes an electromagnet with north and south poles. These poles are attracted to the poles of the permanent magnets, and the cork or armature revolves. However, once the poles of the electromagnet face the permanent poles of the bar magnets, we must change the poles of the electromagnets. Otherwise, the electromagnet would remain fixed due to its attraction to the bar magnets. This is where the "brushes" and "commutator" come in.

You will notice that as the cork revolves, the wires touch the brushes leading to the dry cell. Thus, the current flowing from the dry cell enters first one commutator segment, then the other. This has the effect of reversing the poles of the electromagnet. Now it should be clear why the armature continues to rotate. When the current enters the coil through one wire of the commutator, an electromagnet is formed with north and south poles. These are attracted to the opposite poles of the bar magnets, and the cork or armature rotates. By rotating, the current from the dry

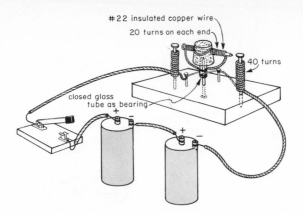

#22 insulated copper wire
20 turns on each end
40 turns
closed glass tube as bearing
+

Fig. 22-26 A motor that uses only electromagnets.

cells enters the coil through the other wire. This reverses the poles of the electromagnet, and they are now repelled by the same poles of the bar magnet which first attracted them.

The commutator serves to reverse regularly the poles of the electromagnet. Consequently, each pole of the electromagnet is first attracted and then repelled by the opposite pole of the permanent magnet. The result is continuous rotation of the cork or armature.

The stationary magnets in a motor are usually called field magnets. Most motors use electromagnets rather than bar magnets as field magnets because greater magnetic attraction and repulsion are produced, and, consequently, a much faster-moving armature results.

With four large nails, a piece of wood, a cork, #22 copper wire, a piece of glass tubing, and two dry cells, you can make a motor which uses only electromagnets. Obtain a piece of wood, preferably pine, about 6″ × 4″ × ¾″. Obtain four nails about 3″ long. Drive one nail up from the center of the board so that its point extends into the air (Fig. 22-26).

Obtain a piece of glass tubing slightly wider in diameter than the nail. Heat one end of the glass tubing in a hot Bunsen burner flame until the end is closed. When the glass is cool, cut the glass tubing at the other end so you have a piece about 1½″

long. It will now fit over the sharp end of the nail which acts as a pivot so that the glass can turn easily. Use half of a large gelatin or soap capsule as a bearing.

Obtain a large cork and make a hole halfway up into the wide end. Ream out the hole with the square end of a rattail file. The hole should be very slightly smaller in diameter than the diameter of the glass tubing. This will enable the glass tubing to fit snugly into the cork.

Now drive a nail through the upper portion of the cork so that an equal length protrudes from each side. Be careful not to drive the nail into the hole you made for the glass tubing. Fit the glass tubing into the cork and let the tubing rest on the point of the nail.

Drive two nails into the wood, pointed ends first. The nails should be spaced so that their heads just clear either end of the nail driven through the cork. The object is to get the nails as close to the horizontal nail as possible, so that the horizontal one can spin without touching. Try also, to keep all three nails on the same level.

Wind about 40 turns of #22 wire around the horizontal nail (20 on each side). If necessary, wind the wires in layers. Have the bared ends of the wire come down to each side of the glass tubing. Fasten the ends to the glass tubing with thread or tape.

Now wind about 40 turns of #22 wire

around each vertical nail, making layers if necessary. *Note:* Wind the wire around each nail in the same direction. Let children decide why this is necessary, e.g., flow of current. Then strip about 3″ of insulation from the ends of each coil of wire. One bare end of wire is wrapped around a small nail driven into the wood, and then is bent so that it just touches one of the wires taped to the glass tubing. Thus, one end of the wire acts as a brush.

The other ends of the wire from the vertical nails are connected to a switch and two dry cells connected in series. The motor should operate quite efficiently now. Close the switch and give the horizontal nail a push so that the motor turns.

Push it in both directions until you get the right one to make the nail rotate.

Make sure your connection with the brushes is not too tight and not too loose. Sometimes a third dry cell (connected in series) is necessary.

A simple electric lamp

Let the pupils examine a clear unfrosted 100-watt bulb. Any size bulb will do as long as the glass is transparent. Call the children's attention to the wire that leads in and out of the bulb. Help them understand that this wire actually goes into the base of the bulb. Screwing the bulb into a socket and turning the switch enables the electricity to flow through the base of the bulb and into the wire inside the bulb. Using a gooseneck lamp, have the children watch how the wire in the bulb glows when the switch is turned on. Point out how thin the wire is. This thin wire in a bulb is called a filament.

Try making your own electric light bulb. Obtain a small widemouthed bottle and a cork that fits the bottle snugly. With an ice pick or awl make two holes in the cork which are wide enough for bell wire to pass through. If the cork is rather long, cut off some of the bottom part of the cork.

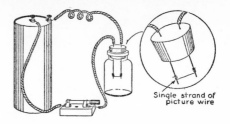

Fig. 22-27 A bottle electric lamp. (From *UNESCO Source Book for Science Teachers*, UNESCO, 1956.)

This will make it easier to punch the two holes in the cork. Strip about 4″ of cotton insulation from one end of each of two pieces of bell wire. Then push the stripped end of the wire through the holes in the cork.

Now obtain a short piece of thin iron wire. One strand untwisted from ordinary iron picture wire will serve the purpose. Wind the piece of iron wire around each end of the bell wire extending through the cork. Then insert the cork into the bottle. Connect the other ends of the bell wire into a circuit containing one or more dry cells and a switch (Fig. 22-27). Your bottle lamp is now ready to operate.

Close the switch. When the fine iron wire begins to glow, open the switch. Do this several times until the wire finally burns out. The oxygen in the air inside the bulb combines with the filament to burn it away.

If you wish to make your filament last longer, replace the iron wire with a piece of Nichrome wire, obtainable at an electric repair shop or a radio and TV repair shop. In this case more than one dry cell (connected in series) may be necessary. Point out the poor light efficiency.

CONDUCTORS AND NONCONDUCTORS

The children by now should realize that bell wire has been used in most of the experiments with electricity. Let them examine the wire itself. The reddish gold metal is copper. Show the children some

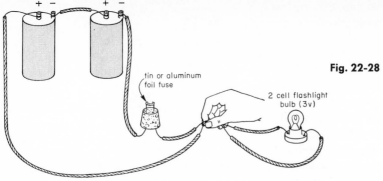

Fig. 22-28   A homemade fuse.

wire used to connect lamps in the home. The wire consists of many thin pieces of copper. Evidently copper conducts electricity quite well.

The children may also recall that in the wet cell, zinc also conducted electricity. So does the wire in a light bulb. The question may arise whether all substances conduct electricity. Wire up a dry cell and a one-cell flashlight bulb (1½ volts) in a porcelain socket. Cut the wire and strip the ends. Bring the ends of the wires together and note that the bulb lights up. Have the pupils trace the path of the electric current through the circuit. Now hold the ends of the bell wires against a dime and see if the bulb will light. Repeat the experiment using other coins, a piece of glass or a marble, a rubber eraser, an iron nail, and pieces of wood, china, porcelain, cloth, friction tape, etc.

Have the pupils make two lists on the blackboard: those materials that let electricity flow through them easily and those that do not. Those that do are called conductors; those that do not are called nonconductors. Nonconductors are also called insulators.

SAFETY WITH ELECTRICITY

The hazards involved in the use of electricity are so many, and the consequences so great, that it is absolutely necessary to teach safety factors and precautions as early as possible in the elementary school. In these days even the youngest children use many electrical appliances and lamps in the home.

The best way to teach the necessary safety uses and precautions in electricity is in actually showing children how the equipment is used and the damage that results because of failure to follow the safety rules.

Obtain two #2 dry cells, some bell wire, some one-cell (1½ volts) and two-cell (3 volts) flashlight bulbs, and miniature porcelain sockets. Remove all the insulation from two pieces of bell wire. Connect the pieces of bell wire to the terminals of a dry cell and a porcelain socket containing a one-cell flashlight bulb. Now touch the two wires together, and the light will go out. You can accomplish the same result by placing a screwdriver blade across both wires. Point out that, by touching the wires together, you made it possible for the current flowing from one wire to flow into the second wire at the point of contact, and then flow back to the cell again. By touching the wires together, a new and shorter circuit was formed. Because this new circuit was shorter than the circuit through the bulb, the current traveled through the shorter path. This short cut is called a short circuit. The children should now realize the importance of covering the wire with insulated or nonconductor material—so that the bare copper wires do not touch.

You may wish to repeat the experiment, using insulated bell wire. However, this time cut the insulation of each wire at one point so that it is frayed and the bare wire is exposed. Touch both wires together at the point where they are bare. A short circuit will form again. Emphasize the importance of replacing electric cords in the home as soon as they begin to fray.

Make a short circuit again, using wires completely stripped of insulation. Keep the short circuit going and feel how the wires forming the short circuit become warm, even hot. Point out that if the short circuit were allowed to continue, the wires would become red hot. In the home these red-hot wires could set the walls on fire.

To prevent wires from becoming red hot, a fuse is inserted in the circuit. Cut a very thin thread-like strip of tin or aluminum foil or use the foil obtainable from gum wrappers; fasten it to two bare ends of bell wire projecting through a cork stopper (Fig. 22-28). This will serve as a fuse. Connect two dry cells in series; then insert into the circuit the fuse and a two-cell flashlight bulb in a porcelain socket. Remove a portion of the insulation of both wires before you make the connection.

Now touch both bare portions of the wires together, causing a short circuit. The fuse will melt, breaking the circuit, and the lamp will go out. If the fuse does not melt, cut a thinner strip of foil. You may have to experiment with different kinds of foil and different widths until you finally get a fuse which will permit the current to flow when connected properly, but will melt when there is a short circuit. Lead foil makes the best fuses because lead melts easily. Lead may be obtained from a plumber's shop. Scientific supply corporations sell lead fuse wire.

Have the children examine good fuses and burned-out fuses. Point out that the strip of metal used in the fuse is made of a metal that melts easily when heated. When a short circuit occurs, the metal becomes heated and melts. This breaks the circuit and acts as a safety device to prevent a possible fire.

When too many appliances are placed in one circuit, the wires carrying the current may become overheated and cause a fire. Too many devices in a circuit "overload" the circuit. Fuses again act as safety devices to prevent fires caused by heated wires in overloaded circuits.

Connect two dry cells in series. Then insert in the circuit a fuse and a two-cell flashlight bulb in a porcelain socket. Now add more two-cell flashlight bulbs in *parallel* until the circuit becomes overloaded and the fuse melts.

Point out the danger in inserting a penny instead of another fuse when the fuse is "blown" or melted. A fuse can melt but the penny can't. This means the wires may get too hot and may cause a fire in the walls.

Show the pupils why they must never hold an appliance, pull-chain, or switch in one hand and touch a radiator, water pipe, or any other metal pipe leading to the ground. This could create an electrical circuit with the child in the middle.

You can show how electrical sparks can cause fires. Connect a pair of wires to a dry cell. Obtain a cigarette lighter. Just above the wick of the lighter touch the wires; then separate them slightly to make a spark. The lighter will ignite. (This experiment should be done by the teacher.)

Point out that an electrical spark can ignite gas which is leaking from a stove, furnace, hot-water heater, etc. This is also true with vapors from gasoline, benzene, inflammable cleaning fluids, paints, lacquers, and alcohol. If gas or these vapors are in the room, a spark from a switch or appliance can cause an explosion.

To show the powerful spark produced

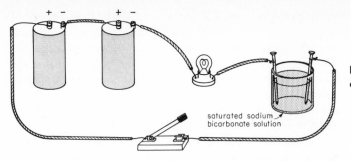

Fig. 22-29 A water solution conducts an electric current.

saturated sodium
bicarbonate solution

when disconnecting appliances, plug an electric iron into the wall. Have the pupils note the spark at the plug when you disconnect it from the wall socket. Discuss what might happen if a woman had just been cleaning dresses or gloves with inflammable cleaning fluid and then began to do some ironing.

Another important safety problem is the effect of moisture on electric wiring. Moisture will cause leakage of electricity, which may lead to dangerous electric shocks.

Show that a water solution can carry an electrical current. Fill a glass tumbler two thirds full of water and add as much sodium bicarbonate as the water can dissolve. Obtain two dry cells, bell wire, a switch, a two-cell flashlight bulb (3 volts), a porcelain socket, and two long nails. Connect them into a circuit with the glass of saturated sodium bicarbonate solution (Fig. 22-29). The current flows through the solution; the bulb lights up, showing a complete circuit.

You may want to tell the children about the work of the Board of Fire Underwriters Laboratories, who set up standards for safe electrical equipment in this country. Show electrical appliances that carry "approved" labels of the laboratory. Also show pieces of electric wire that carry a small yellow paper and metal ring around the wire to show that it meets the laboratory specifications.

Warn the children that radio and television sets all operate at high voltage.

These sets should never be opened or tampered with. Point out that here, too, you should never touch metal parts of the set and a grounded pipe at the same time.

Point out that all electric appliances that produce heat are potential causes of fire if brought too close to or in contact with inflammable materials. Such appliances include electric irons, stoves, heaters, toasters, etc. Even an electric bulb can cause a fire if it comes in contact with a curtain or paper shade. This can be easily shown by placing a piece of paper on a lighted 100-watt bulb. The paper will very shortly scorch. In doing this experiment, conduct it over a sheet of asbestos, on a fire-resistant pad, or on the stone top of a science table.

COPPERPLATING WITH ELECTRICITY

The electricity from a dry cell can be used to copperplate metallic objects. Obtain a strip of copper about 6″ long and 2″ wide from the hardware store. From the drugstore or hardware store purchase some copper sulfate (blue vitriol) crystals.

Dissolve copper sulfate in a glass or jar of water until the solution is a deep blue color. If the copper sulfate crystals are quite large, they will dissolve very slowly. Therefore, it would be a good idea to grind the crystals to a powder in a mortar and pestle, or wrap them in a clean cloth and break them up with a hammer. Also add 5 drops of dilute sulfuric acid. The

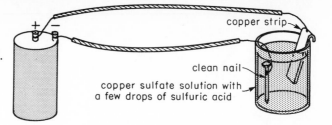

Fig. 22-30 Copperplating a nail.

copper strip

clean nail

copper sulfate solution with a few drops of sulfuric acid

drugstore can make up the solution for you.

Punch a hole at one end of the copper strip, and then bend this end over so that it will hang from one side of the glass. Connect bell wire from the positive terminal of a dry cell to the hole in the copper strip; then put the strip into the copper sulfate solution. Obtain a large iron nail. Sand it so that it is free of rust, and wash it with soap and water to remove any grease. A steel wool pad containing soap will do both operations at one time.

Connect bell wire from the negative terminal of the dry cell to the head of the nail. Place the nail in the solution on the other side of the glass (Fig. 22-30). Do not let the nail and copper strip touch.

In a short while the nail will be plated with copper. Point out that the copper in the copper sulfate solution plates out on the nail. As the copper leaves the solution to plate out on the nail, more copper from the strip dissolves to take the place of the copper that left the solution.

Try plating other metallic objects with copper. Always connect these objects to the wire coming from the negative terminal of the dry cell.

ELECTRICITY FROM HEAT AND LIGHT

Under special circumstances heat and light may produce electricity in small quantities. Cut a piece of wire from a metal coat hanger. Scrape all the paint off with some sandpaper. Cut a similar length of bell wire and remove all the insulation. Now with pliers twist one end of the coat hanger wire together with one end of the copper bell wire. Connect the other ends of the wires to the wires of a compass galvanometer (Fig. 22-31). Now heat the twisted ends of the wires in a candle flame or, preferably, in a hotter Bunsen burner flame. The compass needle will deflect, showing the presence of an electric current.

Bring a photoelectric light meter into class. Point out that the meter contains a cell or tube inside. This cell is coated on the inside with a metal, such as selenium, which is sensitive to light (photosensitive). When light strikes the cell, a flow of electrons (electricity) leaves the selenium. The more intense the light, the greater the flow of electrons. Demonstration photoelectric cell units may be obtained from commercial supply houses. These cells can be used to turn light off or on, open a door, or ring

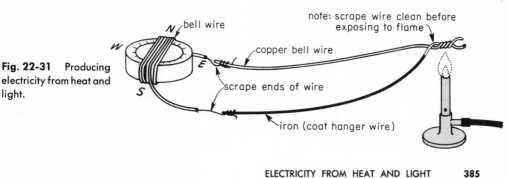

Fig. 22-31 Producing electricity from heat and light.

bell wire

note: scrape wire clean before exposing to flame

copper bell wire

scrape ends of wire

iron (coat hanger wire)

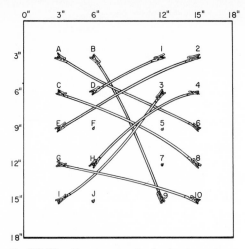

Fig. 22-32 How to wire the back of an electric question-and-answer board.

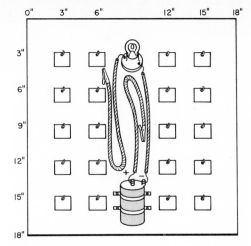

Fig. 22-33 Setting up the front of the electric question-and-answer board.

a bell. One very common use of photoelectric cells is to open the doors in supermarkets, hotels, and railroad stations.

FUN WITH ELECTRICITY

The children may like to make their own model of a street lighting system. The poles are made by nailing rectangular pieces of wood to a square base and then attaching small cross pieces. Two glass pushpins on each cross piece serve as insulators around which the bell wire is fastened. Miniature porcelain sockets containing two-cell flashlight bulbs (3 volts) become street lamps. The lamps are connected in parallel. The bare ends of the wires from the porcelain sockets are connected to exposed portions of the bell wire. Then all the bare portions are wrapped with black adhesive tape. A switch and two dry cells complete the circuit.

Some children may prefer to wire a doll house for electricity. Miniature porcelain sockets can be placed in each room. Wired in parallel, separate switches in each room will light up individual rooms one at a time. Some houses may even have a master switch and also a fuse box.

An electric question-and-answer board can be both instructive and entertaining. Obtain a piece of thin plywood or other wood about 18″ square. Draw four vertical lines at the 3, 6, 12, and 15″ marks. Draw five horizontal lines at the 3, 6, 9, 12, and 15″ marks. At the points where the lines intersect, screw in brass cup hooks. The cup hooks should be large enough so that the ends of their screws protrude beyond the plywood when screwed all the way in. Now turn the board around so that the protruding ends of the cup hooks face you. This is the back of the board. With a black crayon, number the two rows of hook ends on the right from 1 through 10. Letter the two rows of hook ends on the left from A to J. Cut 10 lengths of bell wire, each about 20″ long, and strip the insulation from the ends of each wire.

From the hardware store obtain two dozen small alligator clips. The ends of the bell wires can be connected to the alligator clips, and the clips may then be clamped onto the protruding hook ends. Decide which number-letter combinations you want to use and attach the wires accordingly (Fig. 22-32). For example, you may want to connect hook #2 to hook E. Write down on a card the 10 combinations you have selected.

Now turn the board around so that the hooks face you. This is the front of the board. Use two strips of tin or any other metal to attach a dry cell to the bottom of the board. Attach a porcelain socket and one-cell flashlight bulb (1½ volts) to the top of the board. Connect the bulb to the dry cell, leaving two wires loose as shown in the diagram (Fig. 22-33). To the ends of these loose wires attach alligator clips.

Now take 10 3″ × 5″ cards and cut them in half. Punch a hole in the top of each card. On 10 of these half cards write 10 science questions. On the other 10 write the 10 answers. Referring to your list of number-letter combinations, slip the question cards on the cup hooks in the two left rows and the appropriate answer cards on the cup hooks in the two right rows. The question-answer board is now ready to use.

Have the child clip one cup hook containing a science question. Then let him clip a hook which he thinks carries the answer to the question. If the child has answered the question correctly, the bulb will light up.

You may make up any number of questions and answers. Also, you may want to change the combinations, so that the children will not tend to connect the "right" hooks rather than try to select the right answer.

You may want to substitute a bell or buzzer for the light bulb. Or you may even prefer to cut out an owl's head. Place two bulbs (connected in series) where the eyes should be; if the correct answer is selected, the wise old owl's eyes will light up.

CAPSULE LESSONS

22-1   Have the children recall experiences at home that produced sparks on a dry day. Lead into a discussion of how and why this phenomenon took place.

22-2   Rub a thin piece of Styrofoam with wool, fur, or nylon. Then place the Styrofoam against the wall. The Styrofoam will stick to the wall for a long time. Raise the problem of why this happens.

22-3   Discuss what happens when the children comb their hair on a dry day. Discuss the nature of the crackling sound produced and the reason why the hair won't stay down. Bring a charged balloon over the heads of some pupils. Why does the hair stand up on end?

22-4   Rub a hard-rubber comb with nylon, wool, or fur and bring the charged comb near some lengths of nylon thread. Discuss why the threads can be made to weave to and fro like snakes.

22-5 Discuss what causes lightning and how the charges are formed. Find out the relationship between the lightning flash and the spark produced from a charged object in the room.

22-6   Discuss the different situations where sparks for charged objects can be a safety hazard. Call the children's attention to the chain that usually dangles from the rear of a gasoline truck. Ask the children to explain the purpose of the chain.

22-7   Have the children make a list of all the electrical appliances used in their homes. Plug one such appliance into an electrical circuit and trace the flow of electricity from the outlet into and out of the electrical appliance. Discuss and study electrical circuits.

22-8   Bring an assortment of electrical switches to class. Find out how the switches work. In what ways are they alike? How do they differ? Discuss the reasons for using switches.

22-9   Take a porcelain lamp socket apart. You may have to break the porcelain. Show how wires are built into the socket to conduct the electric current into and out of the socket. Discuss the use of porcelain for the socket and also the need for a completed circuit for the bulb in the socket to light up.

22-10 Take a worn-out flashlight or dry cell apart. Use a hammer and chisel, screwdriver, or hacksaw and separate the cell lengthwise so you can get a good cross section of the cell. Study the composition of the cell and the function of each component and chemical.

22-11 Bring in two sets of Christmas lamps: one arranged in series and the other arranged in parallel. Study the way they are set up. Plug the sets in and observe what happens when one bulb is removed. Lead into a study of series and parallel circuits.

22-12 Bring in a variety of lamp bulbs of different wattages and designed to operate at different voltages. Let the children examine the different parts of the lamps. Break one bulb inside a cloth or bag (Caution.) and observe the characteristics of the filament. Compare new and worn-out bulbs. Study the construction and operation of electric lamp bulbs.

22-13 Discuss the purpose of insulation on wires that carry electricity and the reason why the ends of such wires are stripped bare when connected into a circuit. Lead into the study of electrical conductors and nonconductors.

22-14 Discuss reasons why an electrical device should never be taken apart or adjusted while the electric current is on. Lead the pupils into a study of electrical safety. Make a list of unsafe practices in the use of electricity. List safety rules to observe.

22-15 Arrange for an electrician or other competent person to take small groups of pupils to see the master control panel, fuse boxes, electric meter, etc., in the school. When the pupils return you might bring up either electrical circuits, fuses, or electrical safety.

22-16 Break up or take apart blown-out fuses and new fuses. Find the wires built into the socket. Show how these wires serve to conduct the electric current into and out of the fuse. Examine the metal strip which acts as the fuse. Discuss the essential properties of a fuse.

22-17 Make a list of electrical appliances that produce other forms of energy, such as heat, light, sound, mechanical energy, etc. Study the various uses of electricity.

22-18 Electric trains are excellent for studying electricity. They can be used to study an electric circuit, wiring, insulators, motors, etc.

BIBLIOGRAPHY

Beeler, Nelson, and Franklyn Branley, *Experiments with Electricity,* Crowell, 1956. Excellent experiments illustrating the basic principles of electricity.

Epstein, Sam, and Beryl Epstein, *The First Book of Electricity,* Watts, 1953. Good treatment of the nature and uses of electricity.

Freeman, Ira, *All About Electricity,* Random House, 1957. Gives basic principles of electric currents, electromagnets, and their use in motors and measuring devices. Shows how electricity is used to operate telephone, radio, and television.

Morgan, Alfred, *A First Electrical Book for Boys,* Scribner's, 1954. Discusses what electricity is, where it comes from, and its uses.

———, *Things a Boy Can Do with Electricity,* Scribner's, 1940. Contains experiments on both static and current electricity.

Yates, Raymond F., *A Boy and a Battery,* Harper, 1942. Experiments on electricity using a dry cell and simple materials.

———, *Atomic Experiments for Boys,* Harper, 1952. Information and experiments on electricity.

Communications

TELEGRAPH

A tin-can telegraph

Nothing is more fascinating to children than the operation of a telegraph set. They will spend hours on it, sending and receiving messages in Morse code or in their own secret codes. There are two parts to a telegraph set, the key and the sounder. These can be bought in toy stores. Also both are quite easy to make.

Start with the sounder. Obtain a piece of wood 6″ × 5″ × ½″; obtain a block of wood about 3″ × 2″ × 2″. Nail the smaller block of wood to one end of the larger piece of wood.

Select two iron nails about 2½″ long. Drive them into the other end of the piece of wood, about 1½″ apart. Obtain about 25′ of insulated magnet wire (#22 or 20 bell wire). (It might be a good idea to buy a spool of this wire because you will find many uses for it. It is obtainable from radio and TV repair shops and from hardware stores.) You will also need two dry cells, preferably 1½-volt cells with the threaded binding post terminals at the tops.

Use tin snips or an old pair of scissors to cut a T-shaped strip from an empty tin can. The thinner and more springy the metal, the better it will work. The strip should be about 5″ long, with the body of the T about 1″ wide, and the head of the T about 2½″ wide. Trim, file, or emery-cloth the edges if they are sharp. Wind the wire around each nail as shown in Fig. 23-1A. Note the special way of winding the wire. Wrap the wire around one nail, from top to bottom, in a clockwise direction. Then wrap the wire around the second nail, from bottom to top, in a counterclockwise (or opposite) direction. Wind about 20–25 turns of wire around each nail.

Now punch a hole with a nail at the

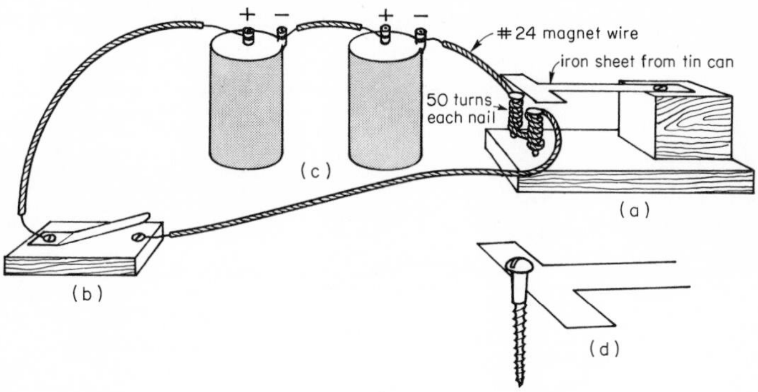

Fig. 23-1 A homemade telegraph.

(labels in figure: + − + −, #24 magnet wire, iron sheet from tin can, 50 turns each nail, (a), (b), (c), (d))

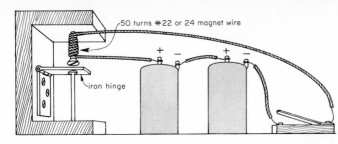

Fig. 23-2 A hinge telegraph.

long end of the T-shaped strip and screw the metal strip to the block of wood. The head of the T should be about ⅛″ above the two nail heads. This distance from the nail heads may have to be adjusted later when you try out the telegraph set.

Now you are ready to make the telegraph key. Obtain a piece of wood about 5″ × 3″ × ½″. From a tin can cut a strip of metal about 5″ long and 1″ wide, and trim the edges if necessary. Punch a hole with a nail in one end of the strip. Fasten the metal strip to the block of wood with a screw driven almost all the way in. Bend the metal strip back so that the strip is at an angle and does not touch the wood (Fig. 23-1B). At the other end of the piece of wood insert a screw. Do not drive the screw all the way in; leave about ¼″ exposed.

Now connect the key and sounder to the dry cells as shown in Fig. 23-1C. Press down on the metal strip in the key. The T-shaped metal strip will hit the two nail heads with a click. Release the key and the metal T will spring back. You may have to adjust the distance between

the T and the nail heads to get a good click; do this by bending.

Point out that the key is just a simple switch, which either opens or closes the electrical circuit. Also note that the wire-covered nails become an electromagnet when electric current flows through them. Have the children trace the flow of electric current when the key is closed.

Help the children understand that, when the key is closed, the wired nails become an electromagnet which attracts the head of the T-shaped strip. When the key is released or open, the electrical circuit is broken. The wired nails no longer become an electromagnet, and the head of the metal T is released. How long you keep the key pressed down will determine the time between clicks. In Morse code with a telegraph sounder a long space between clicks is called a dash, and a short space between clicks is called a dot.

You might like to put a long screw between the two wired nails (Fig. 23-1D). Adjust the height of the screw so that the head of the T just touches the underneath part of the head of the screw. Now when the key is released, there will be an-

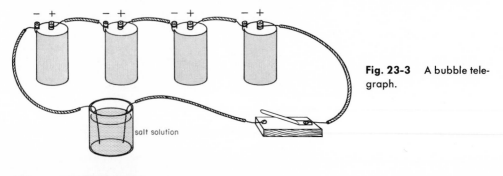

Fig. 23-3 A bubble telegraph.

other click when the metal T springs back and hits and is stopped by the head of the screw. This makes the telegraph set more efficient.

International Morse Code

Following is the code which is most in use today. Added are some short expressions which the children might enjoy learning.

A .—	K —.—	U ..—	5 .....
B —...	L .—..	V ...—	6 —....
C —.—.	M ——	W .——	7 ——...
D —..	N —.	X —..—	8 ———..
E .	O ———	Y —.——	9 ————.
F ..—.	P .——.	Z ——..	0 —————
G ——.	Q ——.—	1 .————	(.) —.—.—
H	R .—.	2 ..———	or .—
I ..	S ...	3 ...——	(,) —..—..—
J .———	T —	4 ....—	(?) ..——..

Short expressions in International Morse Code

code	letters	meaning
—.—	K	End of message, go ahead and answer
.—.	R	Message received and understood
.—.—.	A R	Sign off—no acknowledgement necessary
....	Series of dashes	Error, will resend word
—...—	B T	Beginning of message (U.S. Navy)
.—.—	A A	Unknown person (or ship), Who are you?
...—	V	From
—	Single dash with light	After person has sent a word. Used mostly to mean, "I have received and understood the last word you sent."
—.	N	Negative—no
.—	A	Affirmative—yes
..—..	I M I	Repeat
—...—.—	B T K	End of message, have you received and understood what I sent? (U. S. Navy)

A hinge telegraph

Make a U-shaped frame from three pieces of wood, as shown in Fig. 23-2. From the hardware or ten-cent store obtain an iron or steel hinge. Screw the hinge to the upright piece of wood. The hinge should move up and down easily. If necessary, add a few drops of lubricating oil to the joint.

Drive a nail into the bottom piece of wood until the loose part of the hinge just rests horizontally on the nail head. Insert a long screw into the upper piece of wood so that the head of the screw is just above the loose part of the hinge when it rests upon the nail. There should be about ⅛″ of space between the head of the screw and the hinge.

Now wrap at least 20–25 turns of insulated magnet wire (#24) around the shank of the screw. Connect the ends of the wire to two dry cells (in series) and a key. When the key is closed, an electric current flows through the wire wrapped around the screw and forms an electromagnet. The screw then attracts the hinge and causes a click. When the key is opened or released, the current stops flowing, and the hinge drops back on the nail head, producing a second click. Adjust the distance from the head of the screw to the hinge until you get the best results.

A bubble telegraph

Obtain four 1½-volt dry cells and connect them in series with #18 bell wire. Remove 6–8″ of insulation from each end of the bell wire. Fill a clear glass tumbler about three fourths full of water. Dissolve as much table salt as you can in the water.

Place the stripped copper wires into the salt solution (Fig. 23-3). The ends of the wires should be about 1″ from the bottom of the tumbler. Insert a telegraph key or switch into the electrical circuit, and your bubble telegraph is ready to operate.

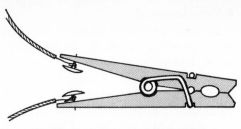

Fig. 23-4   A clothespin telegraph key.

When the key is closed, an electric current flows through the solution. Bubbles of gas will be formed at one of the exposed wires. If the key is closed a long time, a long stream of bubbles or a dash will be produced. If the key is closed a short time, a short stream of bubbles or a dot will be produced.

A clothespin key

Obtain a spring-type clothespin. Push two tacks into the inside portion of the clothespin (Fig. 23-4). Push the tacks almost all the way in. Now wrap wires around each tack and connect the wires to a telegraph sounder and two dry cells (in series). Pressing on the clothespin will complete the electrical circuit, while releasing the pressure will break the circuit.

A two-way telegraph

The children might like to send messages from one end of the room to the other. Or they can even send messages from one room to another. Make two tin-can telegraph sets (sounders and keys) as described in this chapter. Obtain an ample length of magnet wire and set up a two-way system (Fig. 23-5).

Call the children's attention to the fact that the person who is receiving must keep his key down. Otherwise the electrical circuit will be broken, and no clicks will be produced. You can show this by tracing the flow of electric current through the circuit.

Also the electric current becomes weaker when it has to flow through a longer distance. This means that the electromagnet formed will also be weaker. If this happens, increase the strength of the current by connecting more dry cells in series.

Of course, you may wire the sets independently so that the receiver does not have to hold his key down when receiving. This takes as much wire as the circuit shown in Fig. 23-5. The same batteries can be used for both circuits.

A buzzer

Make a tin-can telegraph set (including the screw which touches the T-shaped metal strip) as described earlier. However, connect the wires differently, as shown in Fig. 23-6. Note that a wire is now connected to the long screw which touches the head of the metal T. Another wire is connected to the smaller screw which holds the metal strip to the block of wood. Use a screwdriver to raise this screw a little so that the wire can be wrapped around it. Also make sure the head of the metal T is touching the underneath part of the head of the long screw.

Now when the key or switch is closed, a buzzing sound will be produced. If the buzzer does not operate immediately, ad-

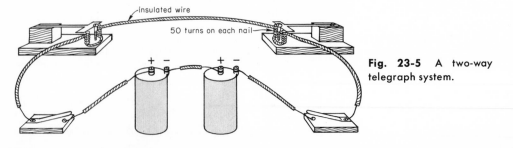

insulated wire

50 turns on each nail

Fig. 23-5 A two-way telegraph system.

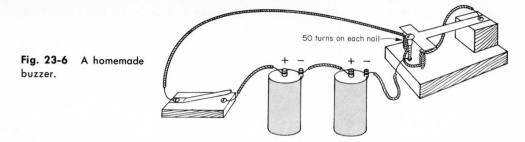

Fig. 23-6   A homemade buzzer.

50 turns on each nail

just the distance between the head of the T and the wrapped nails. Also make sure the head of the T is touching the screw.

Trace the electric current as it flows through the circuit. It goes through the long screw, the metal T-strip, and through both wrapped wires. It also travels through the key and back into the cell again. Call the children's attention to the fact that the wired nails become an electromagnet when the electric current flows through them. The electromagnet then attracts the head of the metal T and pulls it downward. Help the children understand that the metal strip now does not touch the screw any longer. This breaks the electrical circuit. The nails no longer behave as an electromagnet, and the metal strip is released. The strip springs back, touches the screw again, and the circuit is completed once more. The nails become magnetized again, attract the metal strip, and break the circuit again. This process happens again and again, producing a rapid series of clicks, and thus making a buzzing sound.

Electric bells work the same way as an electric buzzer. Obtain an electric bell from the hardware store, remove the cover, and examine it. Connect it to one or two dry cells and a switch. Watch the metal spring move back and forth very rapidly, causing the hammer to strike the bell.

TELEPHONE

A cigar-box telephone

Obtain a cigar box, preferably a wooden one, and two double-edged razor blades. Force both razor blades into the top of the cigar box so that they stay upright (Fig. 23-7). The blades should be about 1½" apart and placed along the grain of the wood so that they will stay more securely in position.

Remove the insulation from the ends of two pieces of bell wire (#18). Wrap one end of each wire securely around a hole of the razor blade. Insert two small screws partially into the cigar box and wrap each wire around a screw. This will

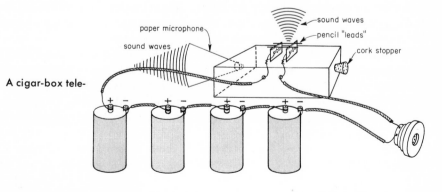

Fig. 23-7   A cigar-box telephone.

paper microphone
sound waves
sound waves
pencil "leads"
cork stopper

prevent tension on the wires from pulling the blades out of their position in the box.

Now split a #2 pencil lengthwise and remove the piece of carbon or "lead." Cut two sections of carbon about 2″ long and place them across the sharp edges of the razor blades.

Obtain a telephone receiver. The telephone company should have a supply of discarded ones. If a receiver is unavailable, get a set of headphones from a radio repair shop. The headphones have the added advantage of eliminating distracting noises.

Connect the wires from the blades in the cigar box to the telephone receiver and also to a source of current, as shown in Fig. 23-7. For your source of current you may use four dry cells connected in series, a 6-volt storage battery, a 4½-volt A battery from a portable radio, or a 9-volt transistor battery.

Your cigar-box telephone is now ready to use. Test it for reception first. Put the receiver to your ear and roll the pieces of carbon gently over the edges of the blades. You should hear noise which is very much like static on the radio. Then place a loud-ticking alarm clock with its face up on the cigar box. Listen in on the receiver while you adjust the position of the pencil carbons on the blade edges. Try to find a sensitive position which enables you to hear the clock ticking very loudly.

Now take the receiver some distance away from the cigar box. Have one child lean over the box and talk very distinctly at the pencil carbons. Another child, with the receiver to his ear, will hear the words quite distinctly. The child with the receiver should put his finger to the other ear if the receiver is fairly near the cigar box. This should not be necessary when the receiver is a long way from the cigar box or when earphones are used.

Place buzzing insects (flies or grasshoppers) inside the cigar box. The sounds they make will be heard quite clearly in the telephone receiver.

Cut a hole about 1½″ in diameter in each end of the cigar box (Fig. 23-7). Make a megaphone or mouthpiece from the cardboard tube of a paper towel roll or from a cone-shaped paper cup with the bottom cut off. Insert the megaphone into one of the holes and attach it firmly with sealing wax, chewing gum, or glue. The children can now speak into the mouthpiece when they transmit messages. If they like, the children can place the cigar box in another room and "eavesdrop" on what is going on there.

How the telephone works

The children will wonder how the cigar-box telephone is able to reproduce the human voice and send it over a wire to the receiver. Let them trace the electric current as it flows from the cells to one of the razor blades, across the pencil carbons to the second blade, then through the wire to the receiver, and back again to the cells.

Help children conclude that the sound waves of the voice make the cigar box vibrate. If a child rests his fingers lightly on the box while you speak, he will be able to feel the vibrations.

Explain that the vibrating of the box causes the pencil carbons to rattle or vibrate also. Show this by rubbing the top of the cigar box with your finger. The vibration affects the amount of contact of the pencil carbons with the edges of the razor blades. This will cause the amount, or strength, of the current flowing through them to vary.

Obtain a small round box, such as a thumbtack box or a pill box. Also obtain two iron washers and carbon particles from an old dry cell. To make carbon particles, remove the carbon rod from a dry cell and break it up into small pieces about ⅛″ in diameter. Fasten the stripped end of some bell wire to one washer and

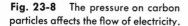
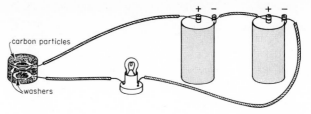

Fig. 23-8 The pressure on carbon particles affects the flow of electricity.

carbon particles

washers

place the washer in the bottom of the pill box. Then cover the washer with a layer of carbon particles. Attach the stripped end of another piece of bell wire to the second washer. Place the second washer on top of the layer of carbon particles. Now attach both wires to a two-cell flashlight bulb and two dry cells (Fig. 23-8). Apply varying degrees of pressure to the second washer and notice the effect it has on the brightness of the bulb.

The children should now realize that the tighter the carbon is pressed together, the better the flow of electric current, and vice versa. Point out that in the cigar-box telephone the vibrations of the pencil carbons affect the strength of the electric current in the very same way.

If you can obtain a telephone transmitter, open it up. Note the tiny particles of granulated carbon present. These particles are in contact with a disk, called a diaphragm, that can move in and out. The sound waves of the voice cause the disk to move in and out. This varying pressure against the carbon particles causes the electric current to change in strength continuously.

Obtain an alarm clock, a dry cell, a set of radio earphones, and a strip of copper about 3″ long and 1½″ wide. You can get the earphones from a radio and TV shop,

and the copper strip from the hardware store. Remove the carbon rod from an old dry cell and break it up into small pieces. Bend the copper strip in half; with a nail, punch a small hole at one end.

Lay the clock face downward on the table. Spread the small pieces of carbon rod on the metal back of the clock. Set the bent copper strip on top of the carbon particles (Fig. 23-9). Connect a length of bell wire from the hole in the copper strip to one of the earphones. Connect a second length of wire from the other earphone to one terminal of the dry cell. Then connect a third length of wire from the frame of the clock to the other terminal of the dry cell. Now adjust the copper strip over the carbon particles until you can hear the clock ticking clearly in the earphones.

Point out to the children that you have just made your own telephone transmitter. Help them understand that the electric current flowing through the circuit is small because the carbon particles offer great resistance. When the clock ticks, it sets up sound vibrations. The vibrations of the metal back cause varying pressure against the carbon particles, which, in turn, varies the strength of the current flowing through the carbon. Thus, the electric current varies whenever the pressure against the carbon particles varies.

Fig. 23-9 How a telephone transmitter works.

copper strip

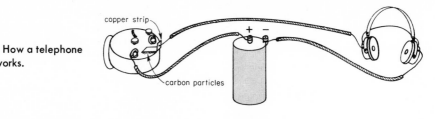

carbon particles

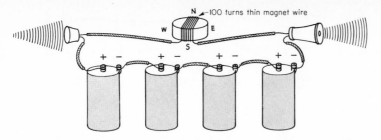

N —100 turns thin magnet wire

Fig. 23-10 A one-way telephone system.

In turn, the pressure on the carbon particles varies whenever the vibrations due to the sound vary. In this way the differences in sound are transmitted to the receivers of the earphones.

Obtain an old telephone receiver. Open it up and examine its parts. Notice the sheet iron disk and the electromagnet in it. Test the electromagnet with some iron objects for permanent magnetism. Point out that in the telephone receiver the electromagnet is made by winding coils of wire around a permanent magnet. In this way, the iron disk is always attracted to the magnet. However, this magnetic attraction will become stronger as the electric current becomes stronger, and weaker as the current becomes weaker. This causes the iron disk to vibrate in accordance with the changes in current. The vibrations of the disk produce sound waves which are identical to those which were originally created.

Connect a telephone transmitter and a receiver to four dry cells set up in series (Fig. 23-10). Use several feet of bell wire between the transmitter and receiver. One child can talk into the transmitter while another child listens.

Insert a compass electric current detector, or a regular galvanometer, into the circuit (Fig. 23-10). The directions for making the compass galvanometer can be found in the section, "Detecting Electric Currents," in Chapter 22. While one child talks into the transmitter, have the class observe the action of the needle in the detector. Notice how the deflection of the needle varies when the child talks loudly, then softly. Remove the diaphragm of the transmitter and push on the button with a pencil. Vary the pressure on the button and notice the effect on the needle deflection in the galvanometer.

The children should now be able to understand clearly that varying pressure on the carbon particles in the transmitter causes the strength of the electric current flowing through the circuit to vary. This affects the strength of the electromagnet in the receiver. As a result, the iron disk or diaphragm vibrates in accordance with the change in strength of the electromagnet.

Obtain a dry cell, telephone receiver, iron file, and bell wire. Attach one length of wire to the receiver and to the dry cell.

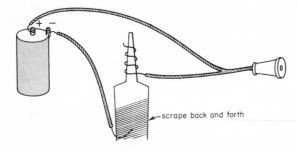

— scrape back and forth

Fig. 23-11 How sound waves are produced in a telephone receiver.

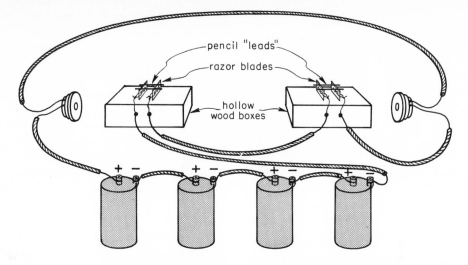

Fig. 23-12 A two-way telephone system.

Attach a second length of wire from the receiver to the handle of the file. Attach a third piece of wire to the other pole of the dry cell and leave the other end free (Fig. 23-11). Now scrape the free end of the wire along the file and note the effect when you listen in the receiver.

The current varies because electrical contact is made only when the wire touches the ridges. As the strength of the current varies, the receiver's electromagnet changes, thus causing the receiver disk to vibrate. This produces the sound waves.

A two-way telephone system

Set up a two-way telephone system as shown in Fig. 23-12. Use two cigar-box telephones and two receivers. The children will enjoy using this system both in the same room and in two different rooms.

RADIO AND TELEVISION

Recall or repeat the experiments in the section, "Current Produces a Magnetic Field," in Chapter 21. Point out again that a wire carrying an electric current creates a magnetic field. Thus, a vibrating or pulsating electric current traveling in a wire will send out electromagnetic impulses or waves.

Also recall or repeat the experiments on generating an electric current from a coil and a magnet. These experiments are found in the section, "Generating Electric Current in a Magnetic Field," in Chapter 22. Point out that this is a way of converting electromagnetic waves back to electricity again.

In radio, the sound waves are converted to a pulsating or vibrating alternating electric current. The electric current causes electromagnetic waves to be sent out from the antenna of the radio station. These electromagnetic waves reach the antenna in the radio set and are then converted back to electricity. The speaker converts the electricity back to sound.

In television, light waves are converted to a pulsating current which sends out electromagnetic waves. These waves travel to the antenna on the roof and enter the television set. Here the electromagnetic waves are converted back to electricity and then to light waves again. The sound is transmitted in the same way as is done for radio.

You may want to show the children

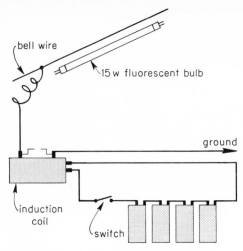

Fig. 23-13 Sending electricity through the air without wires.

that electricity can be sent through the air without wires. Obtain an induction coil from a scientific supply house, a radio or TV repair shop, or the high school physics teacher. A Fordson Model TT tractor coil or Ford Model T ignition coil will also serve; they can be obtained *by mail order only* from Sears Roebuck Company or Montgomery Ward Company. The induction coil is used to develop a high voltage.

Run some bell wire across the whole length of the room. This wire should be connected at each end to a nonconductor such as wood. If the room has no wood, attach the ends of the wire to thick rubber bands. The object is to insulate both ends of wire.

Connect the primary of an induction coil to a source of direct electric current and a switch (Fig. 23-13). Four dry cells connected in series will supply enough current, as will a 6-volt storage battery or 10 volts from an electric toy train transformer. Then connect a length of wire from one terminal of the induction coil secondary to a small bared spot in the wire extending across the room. Attach another length of wire to the other termi-

nal of the induction coil secondary and "ground" the other end of the wire by tying the end, from which the insulation has been removed, to a radiator or pipe.

Now close the switch and hold a 15-watt fluorescent tube near and parallel to the length of wire strung across the room. The tube will light up, showing that electromagnetic waves are being sent out by the wire.

You can also bring in a portable radio, tune it to a silent spot, and bring it near a lighted fluorescent tube. The radio will pick up hiss and static from the tube.

You can show that the picture in a television set is made up of electron impulses which are being converted to light impulses. Bring a strong magnet near the window of the television set. Move the magnet back and forth. This will affect the lines of electron impulses, and the picture will wiggle and move. The magnetism is bending the beam of electrons that are "painting" the picture on the TV screen.

Making a crystal set

Some of the children may be interested in making a crystal set. The materials are not too expensive, the set is easy to make, and the result is well worth the effort.

Obtain a piece of wood about 8″ square and ½″ thick. From the radio store obtain a spool of #27 or 28 insulated copper wire, a pair of earphones, a crystal diode detector, and a variable condenser. Also obtain a piece of cardboard tubing from a paper towel roll. The tubing should be about 6″ long and 1½–2″ in diameter.

Although it is not absolutely necessary, it might be a good idea to shellac or varnish the wood and the cardboard tubing. First dry the tube in a warm (not hot) oven. The shellac will seal the pores and prevent moisture from being absorbed. This treatment will help make the tube a better insulator. Also it will prevent the

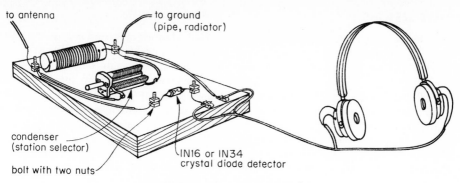

to antenna

to ground
(pipe, radiator)

condenser
(station selector)

bolt with two nuts

IN16 or IN34
crystal diode detector

Fig. 23-14 A homemade crystal set.

tube from shrinking or expanding with changes in temperature and humidity, thus causing the wire wrapped around it to loosen.

First unwind a long piece of wire from the spool. With a sharp thin nail make two holes at each end of the cardboard tube (Fig. 23-14). Push about 8″ of wire into one of the two holes, then up and through the second hole. This will help hold the wire firmly in place. Now hold the tube and the end of the wire in one hand. Wrap about 80–100 turns side by side carefully around the core.

Now cut the wire, leaving about 8″ to spare. Push the end of the wire into one of the two holes, then up and through the second hole. Draw both ends of the wire tight. Place the coil on one end of the piece of wood and fasten it to the board with a thumbtack at each end. Be careful that the thumbtacks do not touch any part of the wire.

At each end of the cardboard tube drill a hole for the insertion of a bolt. Place the variable condenser in front of the tube and then put the crystal detector in front of the condenser (see Fig. 23-14).

Wrap the 8″ lengths of wire at each end of the tube around the bolts. Connect one wire to a binding post of the crystal detector. Attach the second wire to one of the tips of the earphones. Another length of wire is then needed to connect the other tip of the earphone to the second binding post of the crystal detector. Now trace the circuit to make sure it is complete. Radio waves will travel from one bolt to the crystal detector, across the detector into the earphones, then through the earphones, and back to the second bolt.

Now wrap a second short length of wire around each bolt. Attach one wire to the condenser post which is connected to the stationary plates. Attach the other wire to the condenser post which is connected to the plates that turn. By turning the plates of the condenser in and out of each other, you are able to select stations.

For good reception you will need an antenna or aerial. Use at least 100′ of wire. The longer and higher the antenna, the better the reception. Attach one end of the wire to the roof or a tree and connect the other end to one of the bolts. Now "ground" the crystal set by wrapping another piece of wire around the other bolt and then connecting it to a radiator or pipe. The antenna must have insulators at each end.

Your crystal set is now ready to operate. Turn the movable plates of the condenser, while listening carefully with your earphones, until you find a spot which brings you the best reception from a radio station.

CAPSULE LESSONS

23-1 Bring a telegraph set into class and examine its construction and operation. Lead into a study of how we communicate by telegraph.

23-2 Bring a buzzer or bell to class and examine its construction and operation. Lead into the study of how electricity can produce sound.

23-3 Take apart an old telephone transmitter and receiver, and examine their parts. Note the diaphragm and carbon particles in the transmitter. Also note the diaphragm and electromagnet in the receiver. Lead into the study of the telephone.

23-4 Discuss radio and television. Describe in simple terms how sound and light are converted to electricity in the radio and TV station, and then back to sound and light again in our homes. Lead into the study of how sound and light can be converted to electricity, and then back again to sound and light.

23-5 Visit a telegraph office, telephone building, radio station, or television station. Learn about its operation. Lead into the study of how we communicate with electricity.

BIBLIOGRAPHY

Bendick, Jeanne, and Robert Bendick, *Television Works like This,* McGraw-Hill, 1959. Tells the behind-the-scenes story of television. Includes pay television, closed-circuit television, and video tape.

Buchheimer, Naomi, *Let's Go to the Telephone Company,* Putnam, 1958. Simple but exact explanation of the scientific principles involved in the use of the telephone.

———, *Let's Go to a Television Station,* Putnam, 1959. Greater emphasis on how a television program is put on than on how television works.

Buehr, Walter, *Sending the Word; the Story of Communication,* Putnam, 1959. Traces man's development of methods for transmitting words and ideas.

Freeman, Ira M., *All About Electricity,* Random House, 1957. Contains section on the operation of the telephone, radio, and television by means of electrical power.

Hogben, L. T., *The Wonderful World of Communication,* Garden City, 1959.

Irving, Robert, *Sound and Ultrasonics,* Knopf, 1959. Although this book deals primarily with the nature of sound and high-frequency sounds, there is a special section on how sounds are recorded and transmitted.

Morgan, Alfred, *The Boy's Second Book of Radio and Television*, Scribner's, 1957. Advanced but clear treatment of radio and television.

Yates, Raymond F., *Boy's Book of Magnetism,* Harper, 1959. Includes explicit instructions on how to make simple telegraph sets.

Atoms and radioactivity

In almost any grade, pupils are certain to raise questions concerning atoms and the structure of atoms. Since the atom has electrons in the outer portions of its structure, it is necessary to review the work on electrons and their nature and behavior developed in Chapter 22.

BUILDING ATOMIC MODELS

To build a model of the hydrogen atom, get some thin wire (copper is excellent) and modeling clay. Hydrogen has the simplest nucleus of all atoms, consisting of one proton. Take a small ball of clay of one color and mark a plus sign on it. This will represent the single proton nucleus.

Take a short length of wire and pass it through the center of the clay "nucleus." Make a small circle of wire and attach the "nucleus" wire across the wire circle as shown in Fig. 24-1A. The wire circle represents the orbit of the electron that circles the nucleus like a planet around the sun. Next we must add the planetary electron. Take a small ball of clay of another color and attach it to the wire "orbit." Mark a minus sign in the clay. Remember that you have made a model billions of times larger than a hydrogen atom. You could place about 20 billion hydrogen atoms side by side along a line 1″ long.

There is another kind of hydrogen called "heavy" hydrogen, the isotope known as deuterium. About one in every 6000 atoms of hydrogen is heavier than an ordinary hydrogen atom. Let us build a model of a heavy hydrogen atom. Your model of ordinary hydrogen will be the starting point. Take another small ball of clay, the same size and color as your original "proton," and to it add a smaller ball of clay the same size and color as your original electron. Now you have a proton and an electron. Place the two clay balls together. Imagine now that the plus charge of the "proton" has been neutralized by the minus charge of the "electron." What you now have is a neutron. The neutron is only slightly heavier than the proton. Add your neutron to the nucleus. There is only one electron in the orbit just as in ordinary hydrogen. The new atom is twice as heavy because it contains both a proton and a neutron in the nucleus (Fig. 24-1B).

Atoms of the same element that have a different weight are called isotopes. In the case of heavy hydrogen, notice that it differs in weight from ordinary hydrogen because it has an extra neutron.

Heavy hydrogen is not radioactive; that is, it is stable and does not disintegrate or break down. There is also a triple-weight isotope of hydrogen called tritium. To make a model of this, add two clay neutrons to the nucleus in addition to the proton. You can make a model of tritium as shown in Fig. 24-1C. Tritium breaks down and is therefore an unstable or radioactive isotope. Tritium is an essential part of a hydrogen bomb.

Making complex atoms from simple atoms

The sun contains tremendous amounts of hydrogen. The hydrogen combines to form helium, the second simplest atom. In forming helium, a tremendous amount of energy is released. This process, a chain of thermonuclear reactions on a grand scale, is the same as occurs in the hydrogen

bomb "fusion" reaction. Let us set up clay models of the atoms involved in this reaction. First make four models of ordinary hydrogen atoms (Fig. 24-1A). Each of the four hydrogen atoms contains one proton nucleus and one planetary electron. Helium, on the other hand, has two protons and two neutrons in its nucleus and two planetary electrons. Now let us make a model helium atom from the four hydrogen model atoms. First we need two protons. Take these from any two of the hydrogen atoms. Next we need two neutrons. Combine one proton with one electron. Combine a second proton with another electron. You have now used two protons and two electrons to make two neutrons. The two protons combine with the two neutrons to form the nucleus of the helium atom as shown in Fig. 24-1D. The two electrons that remain are planetary electrons.

When four hydrogen atoms actually combine together to form helium, the four original hydrogen atoms weigh more than the helium atom that they form. This is a peculiar kind of arithmetic. The small amount of matter that seems to disappear changes into energy. This nuclear reaction which releases a tremendous amount of energy is the same as occurs on the sun,

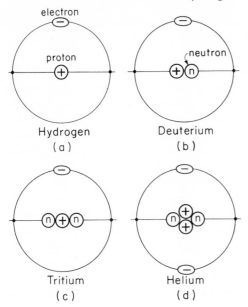

Hydrogen
(a)

Deuterium
(b)

Tritium
(c)

Helium
(d)

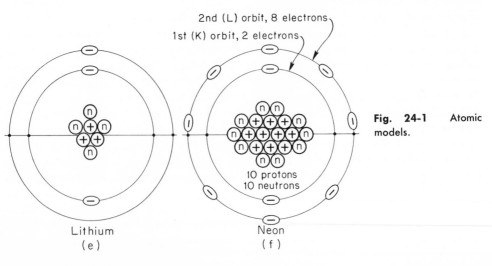

2nd (L) orbit, 8 electrons
1st (K) orbit, 2 electrons

10 protons
10 neutrons

Lithium
(e)

Neon
(f)

Fig. 24-1 Atomic models.

and can only take place if the temperature is over many millions of degrees. Getting atomic energy this way is called fusion—because smaller atoms fuse or combine to form a larger atom. The hydrogen bomb is a fusion bomb; the high temperature needed to start the fusion process comes from an ordinary atomic bomb.

Protons, neutrons, and electrons by element

In Table 24-1, all the currently identified elements are listed in the order of their atomic number. The atomic number of an element and the number of protons it has in its nucleus are one and the same. Therefore, hydrogen with one proton has an atomic number of 1, helium with two protons has an atomic number of 2, and so forth.

To use this table for model building, look up the element whose model you wish to construct, as, for instance, lithium. Lithium has 3 protons, 4 neutrons, and 3 electrons (Fig. 24-1E). Notice that the electrons are in two different orbits, K and L. These letter names for the electron orbits are arbitrary. Table 24-1 tells you the number of electrons by orbit from the inside out. The number of electrons always equals the number of protons. As another example look up neon; it has 10 protons and therefore its atomic number is 10. From Table 24-1 you further learn that neon has 2 electrons in the first (or K) orbit and 8 electrons in the second (or L) orbit (Fig. 24-1F).

You may draw models on a blackboard, using different colors of chalk for the various particles. Children may also make cutouts of the three basic particles—protons, neutrons, and electrons—and arrange these on pieces of paper or cardboard.

Many materials for making atomic models can be suggested. For instance, poker chips of various colors can first be labeled by children with crayon with +,

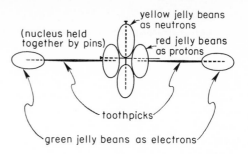

Fig. 24-2 Jelly bean atomic model of helium.

—, and n, and then laid out on the desk. Jelly beans (some teachers find they are best preserved if they are first shellacked) and toothpicks can also be used to make models (Fig. 24-2). Older students can use wire, cardboard, wood, and beads to make standing models. Notice that the number of protons is marked on the center clay ball or wooden shape. You may also add the number of neutrons (12 for sodium, 17 for chlorine).

Take a 3″ circle of heavy cardboard as a base. Take a short stick about 3″ long as a stem. Drill small holes at the points indicated in the figure. Make wire circles for the orbits as needed and slip these through the holes. Instead of a label you can make a nucleus in the center from tiny balls of clay. You might want to use one color for the protons and another for the neutrons. On the orbit wire place small balls of clay as "electrons," using clay of a third color. Another method is to use colored beads, jelly beans, or gum drops. You will think of other materials and combinations of materials for atomic model building. As in many areas of elementary science, you can let your imagination be your guide.

Pupils may want to build large atomic models to hang overhead in the classroom or to put up for display. An ambitious pupil may even want to make an atom as complex as uranium. For this a tennis ball makes a good nucleus, and ping-pong

Table 24-1
Number of protons, neutrons, and electrons by element

name	symbol	protons	neutrons	electrons K	L	M	N	O	P	Q
hydrogen	H	1	0	1	0	0	0	0	0	0
helium	He	2	2	2	0	0	0	0	0	0
lithium	Li	3	4	2	1	0	0	0	0	0
beryllium	Be	4	5	2	2	0	0	0	0	0
boron	B	5	6	2	3	0	0	0	0	0
carbon	C	6	6	2	4	0	0	0	0	0
nitrogen	N	7	7	2	5	0	0	0	0	0
oxygen	O	8	8	2	6	0	0	0	0	0
fluorine	F	9	10	2	7	0	0	0	0	0
neon	Ne	10	10	2	8	0	0	0	0	0
sodium	Na	11	12	2	8	1	0	0	0	0
magnesium	Mg	12	12	2	8	2	0	0	0	0
aluminum	Al	13	14	2	8	3	0	0	0	0
silicon	Si	14	14	2	8	6	0	0	0	0
phosphorus	P	15	16	2	8	5	0	0	0	0
sulfur	S	16	16	2	8	6	0	0	0	0
chlorine	Cl	17	18	2	8	7	0	0	0	0
argon	A	18	22	2	8	8	0	0	0	0
potassium	K	19	20	2	8	1	0	0	0	0
calcium	Ca	20	20	2	8	2	0	0	0	0
scandium	Sc	21	24	2	8	9	2	0	0	0
titanium	Ti	22	26	2	8	10	2	0	0	0
vanadium	V	23	28	2	8	11	2	0	0	0
chromium	Cr	24	28	2	8	13	1	0	0	0
manganese	Mn	25	30	2	8	13	2	0	0	0
iron	Fe	26	30	2	8	14	2	0	0	0
cobalt	Co	27	32	2	8	15	2	0	0	0
nickel	Ni	28	31	2	8	16	2	0	0	0
copper	Cu	29	35	2	8	18	1	0	0	0
zinc	Zn	30	35	2	8	18	2	0	0	0
gallium	Ga	31	38	2	8	18	3	0	0	0
germanium	Ge	32	40	2	8	18	4	0	0	0
arsenic	As	33	42	2	8	18	5	0	0	0
selenium	Se	34	45	2	8	18	6	0	0	0
bromine	Br	35	45	2	8	18	7	0	0	0
krypton	Kr	36	48	2	8	18	8	0	0	0
rubidium	Rb	37	48	2	8	18	8	1	0	0
strontium	Sr	38	50	2	8	18	8	2	0	0
yttrium	Y	39	50	2	8	18	9	2	0	0
zirconium	Zr	40	51	2	8	18	10	2	0	0
niobium	Nb	41	52	2	8	18	12	1	0	0
molybdenum	Mo	42	54	2	8	18	13	1	0	0
technetium	Tc	43	56	2	8	18	14	1	0	0
ruthenium	Ru	44	57	2	8	18	15	1	0	0
rhodium	Rh	45	58	2	8	18	16	1	0	0
palladium	Pd	46	61	2	8	18	18	0	0	0
silver	Ag	47	61	2	8	18	18	1	0	0
cadmium	Cd	48	64	2	8	18	18	2	0	0
indium	In	49	66	2	8	18	18	3	0	0
tin	Sn	50	69	2	8	18	18	4	0	0

name	symbol	protons	neutrons	electrons						
				K	L	M	N	O	P	Q
antimony	Sb	51	70	2	8	18	18	5	0	0
tellurium	Te	52	76	2	8	18	18	6	0	0
iodine	I	53	74	2	8	18	18	7	0	0
xenon	Xe	54	77	2	8	18	18	8	0	0
cesium	Cs	55	78	2	8	18	18	8	1	0
barium	Ba	56	81	2	8	18	18	8	2	0
lanthanum	La	57	82	2	8	18	18	9	2	0
cerium	Ce	58	82	2	8	18	20	8	2	0
praseodymium	Pr	59	82	2	8	18	21	8	2	0
neodymium	Nd	60	84	2	8	18	22	8	2	0
promethium	Pm	61	84	2	8	18	23	8	2	0
samarium	Sm	62	88	2	8	18	24	8	2	0
europium	Eu	63	89	2	8	18	25	8	2	0
gadolinium	Gd	64	93	2	8	18	25	9	2	0
terbium	Tb	65	94	2	8	18	27	8	2	0
dysprosium	Dy	66	96	2	8	18	28	8	2	0
holmium	Ho	67	98	2	8	18	29	8	2	0
erbium	Er	68	99	2	8	18	30	8	2	0
thulium	Tm	69	100	2	8	18	31	8	2	0
ytterbium	Yb	70	103	2	8	18	32	8	2	0
lutetium	Lu	71	104	2	8	18	32	9	2	0
hafnium	Hf	72	107	2	8	18	32	10	2	0
tantalum	Ta	73	108	2	8	18	32	11	2	0
tungsten	W	74	110	2	8	18	32	12	2	0
rhenium	Re	75	111	2	8	18	32	13	2	0
osmium	Os	76	114	2	8	18	32	14	2	0
iridium	Ir	77	116	2	8	18	32	17	0	0
platinum	Pt	78	117	2	8	18	32	17	1	0
gold	Au	79	118	2	8	18	32	18	1	0
mercury	Hg	80	121	2	8	18	32	18	2	0
thallium	Tl	81	123	2	8	18	32	18	3	0
lead	Pb	82	125	2	8	18	32	18	4	0
bismuth	Bi	83	126	2	8	18	32	18	5	0
polonium	Po	84	126	2	8	18	32	18	6	0
astatine	At	85	126	2	8	18	32	18	7	0
radon	Rn	86	136	2	8	18	32	18	8	0
francium	Fr	87	136	2	8	18	32	18	8	1?
radium	Ra	88	138	2	8	18	32	18	8	2
actinium	Ac	89	138	2	8	18	32	18	9	2?
thorium	Th	90	142	2	8	18	32	18	10	2
protactinium	Pa	91	140	2	8	18	32	20	9	2?
uranium	U	92	146	2	8	18	32	21	9	2
neptunium	Np	93	144	2	8	18	32	23	9	2?
plutonium	Pu	94	148	2	8	18	32	24	9	2?
americium	Am	95	148	2	8	18	32	25	9	2?
curium	Cm	96	149	2	8	18	32	25	9	2?
berkelium	Bk	97	152	2	8	18	32	26	9	2?
californium	Cf	98	151	2	8	18	32	28	9	2?
einsteinium	E	99	155	2	8	18	32	29	9	2?
fermium	Fm	100	152	2	8	18	32	30	9	2?
mendelevium	Mv	101	155	2	8	18	32	31	9	2?
nobelium	No	102	?	2	8	18	32	32	9	2?

balls on heavy steel wire "orbits" serve as the electrons.

Commercial kits for building atoms are sold by scientific supply companies.

EXPERIMENTING WITH A GEIGER COUNTER

The first step in experimenting with a Geiger counter of any type is to get the background count. Count the number of clicks per minute. This includes emissions from radioactive deposits in the rocks in your neighborhood plus cosmic rays. Granite, a very common rock, always contains traces of radium and uranium sufficient to give a Geiger counter reading. (The quantity of radium or uranium present is much too small to warrant its use as an ore.) Take several background counts and average them together. If you take five counts and find that you get the following different readings, 36, 40, 42, 44, 38, add them together and get the average by dividing by 5. In this case the average background count is 40 per minute.

Detecting gamma and beta rays

For these experiments you need a piece of uranium ore or a radium watch dial. Gamma rays are natural x-rays given off by radioactive material; beta rays are ejected electrons. Bring the sample of ore or the dial of a radium dial watch near the Geiger tube. You will get a strong count. Different pieces of ore naturally contain different amounts of uranium or radium ore. Different watches contain different amounts of the radium paint. Therefore, you can expect different results. Another good radioactive material is thorium, found as thorium oxide in the gas mantles for gasoline lanterns. These can be purchased at hardware and sporting goods stores. The reading you get will consist of gamma and beta rays.

The alpha particles given off by radium cannot be detected with the ordinary Geiger counter. (Alpha particles are helium nuclei given off by splitting atoms.) Take a radium dial watch and a strong magnifying lens (10 power) into a dark closet. Wait 10 minutes for your eyes to become accommodated to the dark. Then focus on one number of the radium watch dial. You will see individual flashes. Each flash is the breakdown of one radium atom. Commercial devices that do the same thing are sold for a small sum. They are called spinthariscopes.

To separate the gamma from the beta rays, place a sheet of aluminum between the ore or other radioactive source and the counting tube. Without the aluminum plate, you will get a total count of gamma and beta rays. With the aluminum plate between your radioactive source and the Geiger tube, you will get the gamma count. If you subtract the gamma count from the total count without the aluminum plate, you will get the beta count. Always remember to subtract your background count. Now test the total count and the gamma count at 1″, 2″, and 3″.

TAKING PICTURES WITH RADIOACTIVITY

Radioactive atoms and isotopes give off alpha, beta, and gamma rays. These rays can be put to work to help you take pictures of easily obtainable radioactive ores. With the same materials you can take pictures of metallic objects without using any light.

Self-portrait of a radioactive mineral

Most chemistry and mineral sets that children use today contain rock or ground-up samples of uranium or radium ore. Hobby shops that sell minerals also sell samples of these mineral ores. To get a self-portrait, first take a roll of new film of the 120 or 620 size. The next size smaller or larger may also be used. Slowly unroll the red or green paper wrapper until you feel the very beginning of the actual film. Place the sand or mineral against the paper at this point and rewrap the film. Allow the film and mineral to stand in a closed drawer for 2 weeks. Much in this way the first discovery of radioactivity was made by A. H. Becquerel in 1896. He accidentally placed uranium ore (pitchblende) against a lightproof covered photographic plate and found an outline of the ore after developing the plate. This led to the investigation of the cause of this strange picture by his student, Madame Marie Curie. After 2 years of research she isolated radium in the uranium ore as the cause of the photographic image on the plate.

After 2 weeks of exposure to the radiation, rewrap the film after removing the mineral ore. Only have the film developed, as you need no paper copies. The picture you will get will depend upon the amount of radioactive material in the mineral you used.

The ores you can use vary. You will probably find that a yellow sandstone, carnotite, from the Rocky Mountains is the most easily obtainable radioactive mineral. Sands containing radioactive thorium are also obtainable. There are some deserts in the southwestern part of the United States covered with this sand. Pitchblende is difficult to obtain.

If you do not wish to use whole rolls of film, you can buy cut film in the 2¼″ × 3¼″ size and wrap each piece in lightproof paper in a darkroom. Ordinary roll film that is not panchromatic can be cut up under a dim, red darkroom safelight for use in the same way. X-ray film from a dentist can also be used.

Radioactive dishes

If you can procure some orange-colored "Fiesta Ware," its autograph can be taken. These are solid color dishes that are

Fig. 24-3 Radioaurograph. The key shape outlines the area where radiations did not affect the film. (Alexander Joseph.)

very popular. Although they are made in many colors, the color you need is orange. The orange glaze or color is pure uranium oxide. Fiesta Ware can be found among the dishes of many homes in the United States. Even broken dishes are useful for experimenting in the home laboratory.

To use the dish to make a self-portrait by the action of the gamma rays, you need a piece of flat film. Allow the plate to rest on the film for 2 weeks and then develop. If you have a large plate, allow the plate to cover only part of the film. This will give a sharp outline to the edge of the plate in the picture.

The next experiment requires a flat key or any other small metal object. Place on the lightproof covered film; then put the radioactive dish over the objects and allow to stand several weeks. Develop in the usual way (Fig. 24-3). In all of the experiments thus far you will find that dental x-ray film will work better and faster than ordinary film. A dentist can give or sell such film to you. (The pieces cost 10–20¢ each.) Develop them in ordinary developing chemicals.

Radioautograph of a radium watch dial

If you have a radium watch dial that can be read in the dark, you can try another radioautograph experiment. First allow the watch to run down. Remove the rim and the glass that it carries. Lay the watch face down against a piece of dental x-ray film and place inside a lightproof box. Allow the watch and film to stay undisturbed about 10 days.

When the film is developed, you will see a picture of each number of the dial and of the hands. The numbers will appear slightly fuzzy and reversed. If you look through the back of the film, you can read them correctly. If you get a faint image, you have a dial that does not contain much radium chloride. Such a watch may have to remain against the film twice or three times as long. If you do not get any results, your watch does not have a real radium watch dial. A few watches use a compound called a "phosphor" painted on the numbers. It picks up light from other sources and then glows for several hours afterwards if held in the dark. If you leave a watch of this type in the darkness of a drawer for several days and then take it out in the dark, you will see that the dial does not glow. Fortunately for your ex-periment, most watches that have dial faces that glow in the dark contain tiny amounts of real radium chloride.

Testing rocks for radioactive ores

Radium ore and uranium ore occur together. Today the main source on this continent for rich uranium ore is the Great Bear region in Canada, north of the Arctic Circle. Before the days of exploring with Geiger counters, a very simple system was used. When a prospector found rocks that looked as if they might contain uranium, he would drop unopened rolls of film on the ground in the area and return some time later to pick them up. When the film is developed, the telltale tracks of gamma rays will show up on the film if there is any radium and uranium ore in the rocks below.

You can apply the same procedure to rocks you suspect as possible sources of radioactive material. In the darkness of a drawer place the rock against a piece of film for a week or two and then develop.

CAPSULE LESSONS

24-1 As a long-term project, have the children use Table 24-1 to build models of the common elements.

24-2 Have pupils prepare and label bottles containing samples of elements around them, e.g., aluminum, copper, iron, etc.

24-3 Use a Geiger counter or a scintillation counter borrowed from the Civil Defense of your town to measure the natural radioactivity of the rocks in your area.

24-4 Let interested students who have built radio sets make the simple Geiger counter presented in I. D. Jaworski and A. Joseph, *Atomic Energy,* Harcourt, Brace & World, 1961.

24-5 Use a gas mantle from a Coleman gasoline lantern to make a radioautograph on dental film. Develop as usual. The radioactive material in the gas mantle is thorium.

BIBLIOGRAPHY

Hecht, Selig, *Explaining the Atom,* Viking, 1960. Lucid exposition for teacher or upper grade student.

Hughes, Donald J., *The Neutron Story,* Doubleday, 1959. An excellent book for the nontechnical reader. Teacher reference.

Jaworski, I. D., and A. Joseph, *Atomic Energy,* Harcourt, Brace & World, 1961. A sourcebook for the student who wants to experiment safely.

Romer, Alfred, *The Restless Atom,* Doubleday, n.d. A fine reference book for teachers with no science training.

Simple machines and engines

WORK

Most children are all too familiar with the word *work*. The chores they do around the house are often considered work. Usually the children will consider anything requiring physical effort as work. But scientists have their own definition of work. Not only is physical effort involved, but distance is involved as well. According to this definition, work is done only when a body moves. That is, *work* is the result of a *force* moving through a *distance*. And force is defined as a push or a pull.

The children will recall how they may have pushed and pushed against a certain object without making it budge an inch. Even though they were all tired out from the effort, no work was done because the object did not move.

Measuring work

Place a cardboard or wooden box on a bathroom scale. Add sand or stones to the box until the box, cover, and contents weigh just 4 pounds. Now cover the box and tie it firmly with strong string. Insert the hook of a laundry spring balance underneath the string and lift the box into the air. Note that the spring balance also reads 4 pounds. Help the children understand that the force necessary to lift an object and overcome the pull of gravity is equal to the weight of the object. Thus, you need a force of 4 pounds to lift a weight of 4 pounds.

Now lift the box just 1′ off the floor. To find the amount of work accomplished we must multiply the force exerted times the distance the force traveled. In this case a force of 4 pounds moved through a distance of 1′. The amount of work done is 4 × 1, or 4 foot-pounds. Call the pupils' attention to the term "foot-pounds." Point out that this label shows us both force and distance. If you lift the box 2′ into the air, the work done would be 4 × 2, or 8 foot-pounds.

Now place the box on the table. Insert the hook of the spring balance underneath the string at one end of the box. Then pull the spring and box across the table. Make sure you hold the spring balance absolutely horizontal while you are pulling it. Also try to have the box slide across the table as evenly and smoothly as you possibly can (to minimize friction). While the spring balance and box are moving, read the pointer on the spring balance. You may have to take a few readings and obtain an average in order to determine the force necessary to pull the box across the table. Call the children's attention to the fact that it takes less force to slide the box than to lift it. Now calculate the work accomplished in sliding the box 3′. If all you need is a force of 2 pounds to slide the box 3′, then you accomplish 2 × 3, or 6 foot-pounds of work. Point out that, since you did not lift the box off the ground, you did not have to worry about how much it weighed. To calculate the work in this case, all you had to know was how much force it took to push or pull the box across the table. Therefore, for lifting, the force is equal to the weight of the object. For pushing or pulling, the force is just the force necessary to move the object across the surface.

HOW MACHINES HELP US

We all know that machines help make man's work easier. But before learning about the different kinds of machines in use, it might be a good idea to review the different ways we use machines to help us do our work. As a result, we can call the pupils' attention to these ways when we are studying the machines themselves.

All machines help us by *transferring a force*. When you sweep the floor, you transfer a force from your hand to the floor. With a hammer you transfer a force from your hand to the nail. When you ride a bicycle, you transfer a force from your feet to the wheel. Have the class show how a force is transferred when using pliers, scissors, nutcrackers, and other tools.

Most machines help us by *decreasing the degree of force* that must be applied by increasing the distance it is applied. In this way a small force is able to overcome a larger force or resistance. This is easily shown by such tools as can openers, screwdrivers, and bottle openers. Have the class list some other tools or simple machines that help us by decreasing the force applied.

Other machines help us by *changing the direction of a force*. The small grooved wheel, called a pulley, helps us this way. With a pulley you can hoist a flag or use a clothesline. You turn the handle of an egg beater, and the gears turn the blades in opposite directions.

Still other machines help us by *increasing the speed and distance of a force*. As you sweep a broom, the upper handle of the broom moves back and forth a short distance. But the lower part of the broom moves much more quickly and farther. When you swing a tennis racket or a baseball bat, the same thing happens.

While learning about machines, the children may want to know why a machine cannot increase both force and distance at the same time. If a machine could do both, it would save work. But this is impossible. Help the children understand that a machine can make man's work easier, but it cannot save work. While experimenting with the various machines, look for opportunities to show that you cannot increase both force and distance at the same time. Many such opportunities will arise.

All the machines that man uses are composed of one or more of a few simple machines. These are the lever, the wheel and axle, the pulley, and the inclined plane of which the wedge and the screw are special forms. Let us study how each one helps make man's work easier.

Making work easier with the lever

The seesaw or teeter-totter is a classic example of a lever. If you have a teeter-totter in the school playground, use it for a lesson. Call the children's attention to the place in the center where the board turns or pivots. This is known as the fulcrum. Place two children of equal weight at opposite ends of the pivot or fulcrum. Naturally, they will balance. Now place a heavier child on one side. The teeter-totter will go down. Have the heavier child move forward until the balance is restored. Now help the children understand why this happened. Point out that in order for the lighter child to balance the heavier child, the lighter child must be further away from the pivot. In other words, a smaller weight was used to balance a larger weight, but the smaller weight needed a larger distance to do it.

If you have three children of identical weight, you can make one child balance the other two. Place the two children halfway along the teeter-totter while one child is at the opposite end. Point out that one child is able to balance twice his weight. Scientists call the relationship between one force or weight and the other force or weight it can lift or balance *mechanical advantage*. Note also that the distance of the one child from the pivot was twice the distance of the two children from the pivot. This relationship between distances is another way to find the mechanical advantage.

If a teeter-totter is unavailable, you can make your own in the classroom. Place two chairs on top of a table or desk back-to-back about 30″ apart. Rest a yardstick on the backs of the chairs. Obtain a stick of uniform thickness and wrap a string around the center. Then attach the string to the yardstick (Fig. 25-1).

If the stick will not balance, slide the string along the stick until it does balance. Using paper clips as weights, repeat the experiment of the teeter-totter. You can suspend the clips from the stick by tying the clip with one end of a thread and making a loop with the loose end of the thread. Try hanging a weight on just one side, and move the supporting string (which is really the pivot) toward the weight until the stick is level.

Take a pair of pliers. Point out the long handles and the short jaws. Point out the pivot, which, in this case, is round. The long handles and short jaws make it possible for a small force at the long handles to apply a large force at the jaws. This is analogous to the single child balancing twice his weight because his side of the teeter-totter is twice as long. The children should be able to understand readily the mechanical advantage in the pliers.

Scientists have special names for the

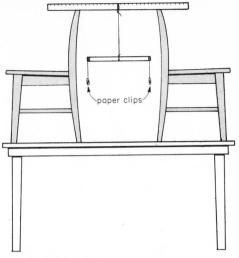

Fig. 25-1 A classroom teeter-totter.

forces or weights and their distances. The force applied at the handles of the pliers is called the *effort* because this is where you apply an effort. The distance from this effort to the pivot is called the *effort-distance*. The large force applied at the jaws is called the *resistance* because this is the point where a resistance is presented to the effort you exert. The distance of this resistance to the pivot is called the *resistance-distance*. Of course, the pivot is called the fulcrum. However, in the lower grades it is not necessary to use these terms. Forces (or weights) and pivot will serve the purpose.

First-class levers.   Levers like the teeter-totter and the pliers are called first-class levers. In all first-class levers the pivot is between the two forces. Scissors are another example of a first-class lever, as is a tack-puller. In the tack-puller the blunt part is the pivot, a force is exerted at the handle, and a larger force is applied at the claws. Measure the distances of both forces from the pivot. If the distance from the handle to the pivot is 12″ and the distance from the tack to the pivot is 3″, the mechanical advantage is 12 divided by 3, or 4 times.

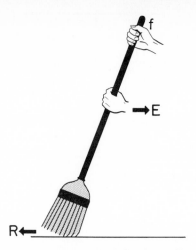

Fig. 25-2 A broom is a third-class lever. (From A. Joseph et al., *A Sourcebook for the Physical Sciences*, Harcourt, Brace & World, 1961.)

Nutcracker—a second-class lever. Bring a nutcracker and some filberts to class. Let some pupils try to crack the filberts between their hands. Even if they are successful, the force required will be great. Now use the nutcracker machine. Call the children's attention to the pivot (or fulcrum), which is located at the end. The filbert, or resistance, is between the pivot and the handles where the force or effort is exerted. Compare the distance between the filbert and the pivot with the distance between the ends of the handle and the pivot. If the filbert distance is 2″ and the handle distance is 6″, the mechanical advantage is 6 divided by 2, or 3 times.

The nutcracker is an example of a second-class lever. In a second-class lever the pivot or fulcrum is at one end, and the resistance is between the fulcrum and the effort. Incidentally, a door is a good example of a second-class lever. The hinges are the pivots, the door itself is the resistance, and the door knob is where the effort is applied. Point out that the door knob is located as far away from the hinges (pivots) as possible in order to give us the best possible mechanical advantage.

Another example of a second-class lever is the school paper-cutter.

Help the children understand that first- and second-class levers enable a small force to apply a larger force. However, in order to do so, the small force must move through a larger distance than the smaller force.

Third-class levers. Sometimes we want a machine to help us increase the speed and distance of a force even if we have to exert a larger effort or force to do so. A broom is an example of this type of machine. By exerting a strong force at the upper end of the broom we are able to make the lower part move farther and more quickly. The pivot in this case is the hand nearest the top of the broom. The broom is also a lever, but it is called a third-class lever. Here the pivot is at one end (the top), the resistance is at the other end (the bottom), and the effort is between them (Fig. 25-2).

The children may be interested to know that their arms are third-class levers. Place an apple in a pupil's outstretched arm; then have the child pull his arm up to his shoulder and back again. The forearm is the lever in this case. The elbow is the pivot and is at one end of the forearm. The apple, the weight or resistance to be raised, is at the other end of the forearm.

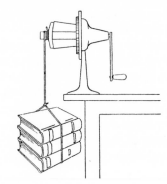

Fig. 25-3 A classroom wheel and axle. (From *UNESCO Source Book for Science Teachers*, UNESCO, 1956.)

The muscle in the forearm is the effort which exerts the force to raise the apple.

Another example of third-class levers is a pair of sugar tongs. All third-class levers have a mechanical advantage which is less than 1. This means exerting a greater force to begin with, but we are willing to do this as long as we can increase the distance and speed. Remind the children that you cannot increase both force and distance at the same time.

**Making work easier
with the wheel and axle**

Remove the cover from a pencil sharpener. Tie two fairly heavy books together with a string. Have the pupils lift the books with the string. Note the force needed to overcome the force of gravity (weight) pulling on the books. Then tie the other end of the string very tightly around the protruding axle of the sharpener (Fig. 25-3). Make sure the string is tied tightly to the shaft or it will slip when the shaft is rotating. Now turn the handle. Call the children's attention to how much less force is now needed to lift the books.

The handle of the sharpener is called the wheel, and the shaft is called the axle. Note that one complete revolution of the wheel produces one complete revolution of the axle. However, the wheel covers more distance during one revolution than the axle. This difference in circular distances is responsible for the mechanical advantage of the wheel and axle. As a matter of fact, the wheel and axle machine is like the lever, except that the wheel and the axle travel in circular distances.

Another good example of a wheel and axle is the door knob. The school custodian will be glad to lend you one. Point out that the round knob is the wheel and the square shaft is the axle. With a screwdriver unscrew the knob on a closet door. Have the pupils try to open the door just by turning the axle. Now put the knob back on again and note how easy it is to open the door. Here again is an example of a small force being used to apply a larger force.

Use string to find the circumference of the knob and of the axle. Then measure the lengths of the strings. If the circumference of the knob is 6″ and that of the axle 1″, the mechanical advantage of the machine is 6 divided by 1, or 6 times. Incidentally, you will get the same value if you measure the diameters of the knob and axle and compare their values.

Other wheel and axles the class can explore are the rotary can opener, the egg beater, and the steering wheel of an auto.

Making work easier with the pulley

Obtain a soft pine board about 4′ × 6″ × ½″. Place two chairs back-to-back about 3′ apart on a table. Have pupils bring in two ordinary clothesline pulleys. If none are available, you may obtain them at your hardware store. Obtain cord and two medium-sized cup hooks. Screw one cup hook into the board and place the board on the backs of the chairs. Suspend one pulley from the cup hook with a piece of cord (Fig. 25-4). Now pass another piece of cord through the groove of the pulley and attach a book of equal weight at each end of the string. The books do not move because they are in balance.

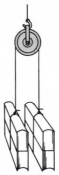

Fig. 25-4 A single fixed pulley.

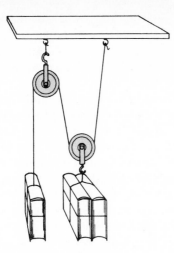

Fig. 25-5 A combination fixed and movable pulley.

Point out that the pulley is like the teeter-totter, or lever. In this case the pivot (or fulcrum) is the pulley axle. Since the length of each cord from the book to the pulley axle is the same, there is no mechanical advantage to a single pulley arranged this way. Why, then, do we use the pulley? Have one of the pupils pull down one of the books. The other book will go up. In this case we use the machine as a convenient way of changing the direction of a force. To make one book go up, we must exert the same force as the weight of the book. The book going up will travel at the same speed and over the same distance as the book going down. There most likely will be some friction in the pulley, and you will therefore have to exert a slightly larger force downward to raise the book. However, since we are interested only in changing direction, it is worth it.

Attach another cup hook about 6″ away from the first one. Now arrange two pulleys as shown in the diagram (Fig. 25-5). Hang one book from the top pulley and two books of equal weight from the bottom pulley. One book will now support two books. If the children wonder why, have them count the number of cords supporting the two books. There are two cords. Each supports one half of the weight. The last cord is balanced by the single book at the end of the cord.

Point out that the top pulley is called a *fixed pulley,* and the bottom one is called a *movable pulley.* Just pull on the single book and you will know why the pulleys were given these names.

You may want to make your own pulleys. Obtain two spools, two nails to fit loosely through the spools, and pieces of wire. You can borrow a wire cutter and use pieces of lightweight clothes hangers as the wires. Then pass the wires through the spool holes and attach them (Fig. 25-6). Repeat the previous experiment, using one and two books.

Now obtain five books of the same size and weight. Arrange the pulleys as shown in Fig. 25-7. Attach four books to the bottom pulley and one book to the free end of the cord. Have the children count the number of cords supported by the bottom pulley. There are four. Each supports one fourth of the total weight. The fourth rope is balanced by the single book at the end of the cord. In this case the mechanical

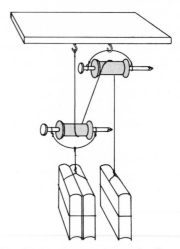

Fig. 25-6 Homemade spool pulleys.

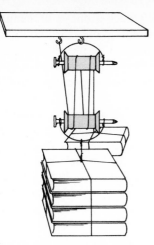

Fig. 25-7 One book can lift four.

advantage is 4 times because one book balances four.

This is the way heavy objects are lifted. You can show this quite dramatically by a scientific tug-of-war. One boy can balance the pull of four boys of the same weight and strength. To do this get two broomsticks or mop handles. A strong rope is tied to the end of one stick, then looped around both sticks two complete times, keeping the loops evenly spaced from stick to stick (Fig. 25-8). The single boy is called the "strong man." He wraps the free end of the rope around the palm of his hand. Now the four boys holding the broomsticks start pulling in opposite directions. The "strong man" pulls also and is able to balance the pull of the four boys. Count the ropes. The children will notice that there are four. But each rope carries the force of only one fourth the "strong man's" pull. The pull on the end rope is balanced by the pull of the "strong man."

If two boys drop out, one for each stick, the "strong man" will not only be able to balance the pull of the remaining two boys, but he will be able to bring the sticks close together.

Have the children bring lists of devices that use pulleys. They can see pulleys on a wrecking truck, a derrick, a steam shovel, on elevators, and on a barn hoist.

Making work easier with the inclined plane

Obtain a board 4′ × 6″ × ½″. Set one end of the board on a stack of books or on a block of wood. Next get a roller skate or toy truck and a laundry spring balance or scale of the type that measures from 0 to 30 pounds. Now tie three books to the skate. Lift the roller skate and books with the balance and mark the weight on the blackboard (Fig. 25-9).

Place the roller skate and books on the inclined board. With a thin wire attach the spring balance to the rear end of the skate. Now pull on the skate with the spring balance so that the skate will move up the incline. Try to hold the balance so that it is horizontal with the board at all times. Have a pupil read the scale while you pull. Write this value on the blackboard.

The children will see that it takes less force to pull the load up the hill than it would to lift it. However, they should also understand that the load travels a longer distance uphill than it would if it is simply lifted straight up to that height. We therefore use less force in this case, but the load must travel a longer distance.

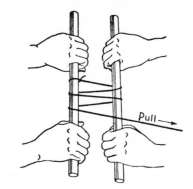

Fig. 25-8 A tug-of-war with broomsticks. (From *UNESCO Source Book for Science Teachers*, UNESCO, 1956.)

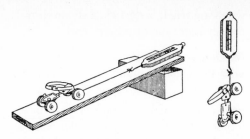

Have the children measure the length of the board, and then the height of the stack of books supporting the end of the board. The load must travel the length of the board in order to reach the height of the books. If we divide the length of the board by the height of the books, our answer will be the mechanical advantage of the inclined plane machine.

Repeat the experiment, using inclines at different angles. Set the board at different angles by simply adding to or subtracting from the stack of books that support the incline. The pupils will find that the steeper the angle, the greater the pull required. On the other hand, the gentler the hill (or angle), the less the force required. For this reason, hills on highways are made as gentle as possible. You can always hear truck engines working harder on steep hills than on gentle hills.

The class may be interested in seeing what happens to the mechanical advantage when the height of the incline is raised or lowered. Simply measure the new height in each case; then divide the length of the inclined plane (board) by the height.

Making work easier with the wedge

Almost all cutting tools and kitchen cutting utensils are inclined planes that are forced into an object. These simple machines are called wedges. A wedge is another form of an inclined plane. The only difference is one of procedure. With the inclined plane, the incline remains stationary and we move the object up the incline. With the wedge, the body remains stationary and we force the wedge into the body.

Borrow a wedge from a carpenter or cut one from wood. Place the narrow end of the wedge under a table leg; then tap the broad end with a hammer. The wedge will lift the table.

Obtain a chisel and show the inclined plane that makes up its edges. Show the inclined plane or wedge of a knife blade. Needles, pins, and nails are also wedges.

A pair of scissors is a combination of two wedges and a lever. The cutting edges make up the wedges. The handles and blades are the arms, like the sides of the teeter-totter. The screw in the scissors is the pivot. If you can borrow a pair of metal-cutting scissors or tin snips, point out the very long handles used to increase the force applied to the blades.

Making work easier with the screw

Another important simple machine is the screw. A screw is nothing but an inclined plane or little hill wrapped in a spiral. You can show this quite easily. Draw a right triangle on a piece of white

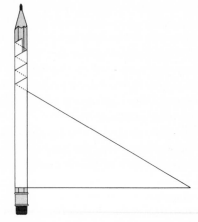

Fig. 25-10 A screw is a spiral inclined plane.

paper. Make the height 10″ and the base 5″. Cut out the triangle and color the edge along the hypotenuse with red crayon. Now roll the paper around a pencil (Fig. 25-10). Begin by wrapping the base of the triangle. The children will see the spiral formed by the colored edge. Now unroll the paper triangle to show its return to an inclined plane. Compare the paper spiral with the spiral in a wood screw.

Next borrow an automobile jack of the screw type. Your garage man probably has one or knows someone who can lend one to you. Have the garage man use it to jack up a car. The children will see how little effort is required to lift a 3000–4000-pound automobile. The screw helps man exert a very small force to lift a very heavy object. However, the garage man has to turn the screw very many times to raise the automobile only a few inches. In this case a small force is used to lift a very large force, but the small force must travel a large distance to raise the large force a small distance.

If the school has a workshop bench, the vise to hold the wood for sawing or planing has a similar screw. This screw is used to apply great force to hold the wood in place.

Changing speed or direction of forces

Obtain a piece of wood about 8″ × 4″ × ½″. Obtain two spools of different sizes and two nails which fit loosely in the spool holes. Put the nails through the spool holes and fasten the spools to the wood about 3″ apart. Now slip a rubber band around both spools (Fig. 25-11). The rubber band should grip both spools rather tightly. With your hand give the larger spool one full turn. Note that the smaller spool makes more than one full turn and thereby moves faster.

Also point out that both spools move in the same direction. Now turn the rubber band so that it makes a cross between the

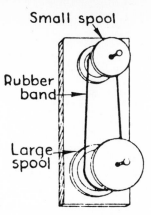

Fig. 25-11 Wheels can change the speed or direction of a force. (From *UNESCO Source Book for Science Teachers*, UNESCO, 1956.)

spools. Turn either one of the spools and note that the other now turns in the opposite direction.

Repeat the experiment with the wheel and axle, using the pencil sharpener (described earlier in this chapter). After you have raised the books, release your hand from the crank handle and pull down on the books. Note how rapidly the handle turns.

Recall or repeat the experiment described earlier in this chapter which uses the spool pulleys with four supporting strings. Note how quickly you lift the four books when you pull on the string holding one book.

Have the children swing baseball bats or tennis rackets. Help the children understand that the longer end of a lever moves farther and faster than the shorter end when the pivot is not in the center. Another such example is sweeping with a broom.

Gears change speed or direction. Gears are most commonly used to change speed or direction. Actually, gears are no more than modified wheels and axles. They are simply wheels with teeth in them. Have a boy bring in a metal construction set. He can set up a large and a small gear wheel so that one can turn the other. If

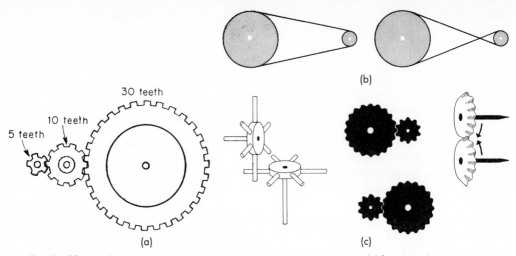

Fig. 25-12 (a) Gears can change the speed or direction of a force; (b), (c) homemade gears. (From A. Joseph et al., *A Sourcebook for the Physical Sciences*, Harcourt, Brace & World, 1961.)

he turns the large wheel, the small one will move many times as fast. Also point out that the gears turn in opposite directions. Have the children count the number of teeth in each gear. If the large gear has 10 teeth and the small gear 5 teeth, then every time the large gear revolves once, the small gear revolves twice. A diagram on the board will help make this clear. Help the children understand that a 1-pound force applied at the 5-tooth gear becomes a 2-pound force at the 10-tooth gear.

Draw a diagram on the board of three different size gears with their teeth enmeshed (Fig. 25-12A). The large gear has 30 teeth, the middle gear 10 teeth, and the small gear 5 teeth. Help the children understand that the speeds, forces, and directions are not the same at all wheels. If the 30-tooth gear revolves once, the 10-tooth gear makes three turns, and the 5-tooth gear makes six turns. A 1-pound force applied at the 5-tooth gear becomes a 2-pound force at the 10-tooth gear. This, in turn, becomes a 6-pound force at the 30-tooth gear. All three wheels turn whether a force is applied to the 30-tooth gear or to the 5-tooth gear. If the large

gear is made to rotate in a clockwise direction, the middle gear will turn counter-clockwise, and the small one clockwise.

This is how gears are used in an automobile to change the speed during shifting. When the driver shifts to "low" or "first" gear, he uses the largest gear. In this case he gets little speed but much force or power.

In "second" gear, now that the car is under way, a smaller gear is used to get less force and more speed. When he shifts to "third" or "high" gear, he uses the smallest gear to give him maximum speed. In an automatic shift, the gears are made to shift automatically.

You can make your own gears. Obtain five bottle caps that have not been twisted out of shape. With a hammer and nail make holes in the exact centers of each cap. Place two caps on a small block of wood so that their toothed projections mesh together (Fig. 25-12B). Holding the caps in place, fasten them down with tacks, making sure that the caps will turn easily. Turn one of the caps and note the direction that the other turns. Point out that since each cap has the same number of projections, both caps revolve at the same speed. All we have done is change direction. Repeat the experiment using three caps and note the direction that each turns.

Place a bicycle upside down. Turn the pedal wheel exactly one turn and note the number of turns made by the rear wheel. Count the number of teeth in the gear attached to the pedals and compare it with the number of teeth in the gear fastened to the rear wheel.

Operate an egg beater or hand drill and note the increase in speed. Compare the number of teeth in the gears involved in the operation. Remove the back of a broken wrist watch or clock. Observe the gears, count the teeth, and have the pupils figure out any changes in speed, direction, and force. Turn the knob that controls the minute hand so that you can locate the gears for the minute hand and hour hand. Note the difference in size and in the number of teeth.

Making an elevator. The children might like to make their own elevator to show change in direction. First take a sheet of plywood or heavy cardboard about 24″ long and 12″ wide to use as a background and support. Now obtain six small wooden spools and place them in the positions shown in Fig. 25-13. Use nails or long spread-type paper fasteners to hold the spools in the proper places. For the elevator car use a small cardboard box.

Pass a string through a hole in the center of the "car" at A. Knot the string so that it cannot slip out. Pass the string down and around spool B, then to spool C, making two turns around spool C. Be sure to make two turns around spool C or the elevator will not operate. Now pass the string over spools D and E. At H in the center top of the "car" insert the end of the string. Add a second string, put it through H, and knot the two strings together. Pass the second string over spools

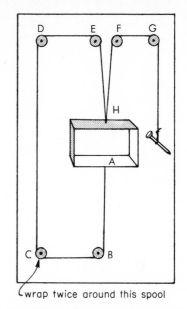

Fig. 25-13   A homemade elevator.

F and G and tie a nail (or other weight) to the end of the string. This weight should counterbalance the weight of the car plus any toy figures placed inside the car. You may have to try lighter or heavier nails to counterbalance properly.

Turning spool C will cause the car to move up or down. Point out that the force of gravity will help the car descend, but will hinder it when the car has to go up. If enough weight is added as a counterweight, the car can descend by itself. In a real elevator, spool C is turned by a motor.

MACHINES IN THE SCHOOL AND HOME

Conclude the study with an inventory of common machines used in the average classroom and school. The children will be surprised to find what a number there are, as, for example, window fasteners, pulleys, faucets, radiator valves, hinges, closet fasteners, pencil sharpeners, etc.

There is a multitude of tools, utensils,

and devices in the home that are either simple machines or combinations of simple machines. This provides a wonderful opportunity to bring in familiar objects and show how they function as machines. Because there are so many machines in the home, it seems well worth while to list and classify some of them and also to show what simple machines are included in combinations.

Examples of first-class levers in the home are: scissors, garden shears, pliers, wire cutter, tin or metal snips, tack-puller, crowbar or pinch bar, forceps, and beer-can opener. Have the children identify the pivot or fulcrum in each case, the point where the small force is applied, and the point where the larger force is exerted or overcome. Compare the distances of both these forces from the fulcrum and note the effects when the distances are large or small. If possible, compute and compare mechanical advantages. Do this as well for the other machines listed below.

Second-class levers include: nutcracker, lemon squeezer, bottle opener, can opener (hand), crowbar, door, and rowboat oars. Examples of third-class levers are: sugar tongs, tweezers, broom, spoon, baseball bat, tennis or badminton racket, golf club, fly swatter, pitchfork, and mouse trap. All the third-class levers aim for more speed and distance rather than more force.

Wheels and axles use a small force to overcome a much larger force. They include: rolling pin, meat grinder, screwdriver, door knob, rotary can opener, egg beater, pencil sharpener, hand drill, bicycle wheel and pedal, auto steering wheel, and all gear combinations. Pulleys are used with flag poles, clotheslines, old-fashioned window sashes, and blocks and tackles.

Inclined planes include the staircase, the escalator, a hill, and a winding mountain road. Wedges include: knife, chisel, saw (has many chisel edges), pin, needle, nail, ax, and the round circular wedge used in delicatessen and grocery stores to cut thin slices of meat. Examples of the screw are: lifting jack, wood screw, bench vise, nut and bolt, mechanical pencil, and piano stool.

Compound machines

When two or more simple machines are combined to make one machine, the combination is called a compound machine. Most of the machines that we use belong in this group. With careful examination, the children should have little difficulty in identifying the various components of compound machines and understanding how each one functions.

For example, the handle of the shovel, hoe, or ax is a lever, while the blade is a wedge. Scissors are a lever with two wedge-shaped blades. Hand-operated hair clippers are a lever and many shearing wedges.

The rotary can opener is a combination wheel and axle and round wedge. The crank handle of the pencil sharpener is part of a wheel and axle; it turns two screw-like or spiral wedges which cut the wood. The lawn mower operates the same way. The meat grinder is a combination wheel and axle, screw, and wedge: the crank handle turns a screw; the meat is caught in the screw and pushed against wedge-shaped threads which grind the meat into little pieces. The hand drill and the water faucet both contain a wheel and axle and a screw. The Stillson (pipe) and the "monkey" wrench use a screw to open and close the jaws, and then act as a wheel and axle.

The egg beater is interesting to observe. The handle turns two gears which then turn two blades. This is a combination of wheel and axle and gears (which are modified wheels and axles).

Have the children observe and identify

the combinations of simple machines in such familiar items as the typewriter, hand vacuum cleaner, sewing machine, alarm clock, toy run by a spring or an electric motor, bicycle, automobile, tractor, plane, and locomotive.

FRICTION DUE TO RUBBING, SLIDING, AND ROLLING

Obtain a block of wood and a wooden board, both with rough surfaces. Have the children try to slide the block of wood over the board. Call the children's attention to the difficulty they have in getting the block to slide easily. Note the resistance which both surfaces offer each other. This resistance caused when one surface is rubbed against another is called friction.

Examine the surfaces of the block and board with a magnifying glass. Point out the uneven places in the wood. The children can see and feel the bumps and hollows, which make it difficult for the block to slide over the wood.

When machines do work, some of their parts also rub against each other. Metals may feel and look much smoother than rough pieces of wood. But if you should examine the pieces of metal under a microscope, you would still see tiny bumps and hollows.

Now obtain another block of wood and board, this time with smooth surfaces. Or, if you like, use sandpaper on the rough pieces until they are smooth. Notice the difference in the amount of effort you have to use in sliding the block over the board.

Obtain fine sandpaper, a rough stone, smooth and rough wood, and a mirror or pane of glass. Feel the roughness of each object with your fingers. Then rub pieces of fluffy cotton over each surface, and note the amount of cotton left behind. The smoother the surface, the less the cotton will catch and tear.

Put a screw eye into one end of a block of wood and attach a string to the screw eye. Obtain a board with a rough surface, a board with a smooth surface, and a large pane of glass. Place three books on the block of wood; then pull the block over the surfaces of both boards and the glass. Notice the difference that smoothness makes in the amount of force required to pull the block of wood. You may measure this force by attaching the string to a laundry spring balance and pulling horizontally on the spring balance.

Repeat the experiment, but this time put six books on the block of wood. It is now much harder to pull the board across all three surfaces. Help the children understand that the greater the pressure between two surfaces rubbing together, the more friction there is.

Lubrication to reduce friction

The children should now realize that one way of reducing friction is to see that the surfaces are smooth. Another way is to put some slippery material like oil or grease between the surfaces.

Obtain two pieces of metal and try to slide one piece over the other. Now add a few drops of oil on the surfaces and slide the pieces again. The friction is reduced, and the pieces of metal slide quite easily.

Lay two mirrors or panes of glass side by side. Place a few drops of oil on one mirror. Have the children rub with their fingers first the dry glass, then the oiled one, and notice the difference. Help the children understand that the oil helps reduce friction because the particles of oil fill in the holes in the surface and also form a film on the surface. This makes the surface smoother.

Rub two pieces of sandpaper together and notice the friction produced. Then put a thick layer of grease between the two pieces of sandpaper and rub again. Shortening for cooking will also serve the purpose. The grease fills up the cavities

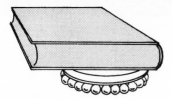

Fig. 25-14 Ball bearings reduce friction.

in the sandpaper and cuts down the amount of rubbing and friction. You can also get the same effect with two pieces of cold toast and a generous supply of butter. Automobiles are greased to cut down costly friction.

Examine tools and other machines for parts that rub together. Look for a rusty hinge, bicycle wheel, or roller skate that either squeaks or does not turn very easily. Apply a few drops of oil and notice the difference. You might like to time how long a bicycle wheel, cart wheel, or roller skate turns before and after oiling.

Oil and grease are not the only lubricants. Soap works quite well with desk drawers or wooden window frames that stick. So does the wax or paraffin from a candle. Powdered graphite will help a door catch that sticks. If powdered graphite is not available, rub the catch with the lead from a soft pencil. The "lead" is really graphite.

Bearings

Try sliding a large book across the table. Now place a few round pencils under the book and notice how much easier it is to move. Call the children's attention to the fact that you have now substituted rolling for sliding. Rolling friction is much less than sliding friction because you make one surface roll over another instead of sliding across it. In this way the bumps are lifted out of the hollows and also away from each other.

Obtain a coffee can lid with a rim and a handful of marbles. First try spinning a book on a table top. The book will not spin easily because the friction between the book and the table top stops it. Now put the marbles on the table and cover them with the lid (Fig. 25-14). Place the book on top of the lid and try spinning the book again. This time the book will spin easily.

Point out that a third method of reducing friction is to use wheels, rollers, or balls. These balls are usually called ball bearings. Roller-skate wheels usually have ball bearings which you can hear when you shake the skate. Ask the children to bring in beginner's skates and ball-bearing skates. The beginner's skate only has a simple bearing. The ball-bearing skate has a ring of balls around the axle. This means that the load on the skate does not press down as much on the ball-bearing skate as it would on a beginner's skate. See which wheel will turn longer.

Friction produces heat and wear

Help the children realize that friction produces heat. Have them rub their hands together very briskly. They can also rub a pencil eraser briskly on the table top, and then quickly put the rubber tip to their upper lips and notice the heat produced. When wood is sawed or a hole is bored through a thick board, the metal tool becomes quite hot. Automobile tires also become quite hot after they have been running for a while.

The children should now realize that friction wears things out. Shoe soles become thin, as do rugs and carpets. Lead pencils become dull, and rubber erasers wear away. Rubber tires become thinner and lose their tread. Tools and machinery wear away and then break. Reducing friction in this case is economical and promotes safety.

However, friction can also be helpful and is often quite necessary. Sand is put on icy spots in the street so that automobile tires will not spin or skid. Chains are also put on tires to help them move through ice and snow. Sandpaper is used to make things smooth. Without friction you could not walk on the ground because your feet would skid. All objects in the room would have to be fastened down to prevent them from sliding all over the room. But what would you do to fasten them down? Nails and screws would pull right out of the wood. Ropes would slide. You could not even unscrew a jar top. Wet your hands with soapy water or rub them with cold cream; then try unscrewing the metal cover from a glass jar. Can you do it?

INERTIA

Rest a coin on a small square of heavy cardboard placed on a drinking glass or empty milk bottle. Now snap the card with your finger. The card will fly out from under the coin so that it drops into the tumbler.

Pile four checkers one on top of the other. Place a fifth checker 2 or 3″ away. Now with your finger flick the fifth checker at the bottom checker in the pile. The bottom checker will fly out while the rest of the pile remains behind.

Bodies at rest

In both experiments the coin and the checker are following Newton's law of inertia, one part of which states that a body at rest tends to stay at rest. This tendency is called inertia. If a body at rest is to be moved, the force of inertia must be overcome by additional forces.

Obtain a toy truck and put some weights in it if it is very light. Attach a rubber band to the truck. Place the truck on the table so that it is at rest. Now carefully stretch the rubber band until the truck begins to move. Note how much the rubber band had to stretch. Once the truck is moving, keep pulling it along at a steady rate of speed. Now the stretch on the band will be considerably less. The children should realize that it took extra force to overcome the tendency of the truck to remain at rest.

Rest a metal or plastic tumbler half full of water upon a sheet of typewriter paper. Place the tumbler about an inch from one end of the paper. Now with one hand grasp the center portion of the other end of the paper and jerk the paper quickly toward you. The paper will come out from under the tumbler while the tumbler will remain where it is. Help the children understand that, when you gave the paper a quick jerk, you overcame the inertia of the paper but not that of the tumbler. In fact, by doing this quickly, you did not give the tumbler much chance for the force of your jerk to act on it. Thus, the tumbler remained where it was. Repeat the experiment, but this time pull slowly and steadily on the paper. By pulling slowly you are able to overcome the inertia of the tumbler as well, and both glass and paper move.

Obtain two medium-sized stones and tie each one with thread so that the stone has a length of thread above and below it. Tie one end of each thread to a door knob (Fig. 25-15). Now pull slowly and steadily downward on the bottom of one thread. The upper thread will break. The force you exerted overcame the inertia of both the lower thread and the rock, and enabled you to break the thread at the top.

Now grasp the bottom of the second thread and pull downward with a quick jerk. The bottom thread will break. You now overcame the inertia of the lower thread but not that of the rock; thus, only the lower thread broke.

Bodies in motion

Newton's law of inertia also states that a body in motion tends to remain in mo-

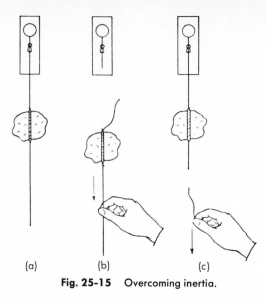

(a)　　　(b)　　　(c)

Fig. 25-15　Overcoming inertia.

tion. Cut away one end of a long card-board box. A shoe box or a milk container will serve. Place a small rubber ball inside the box. Slide the box quickly along the table. The ball will remain at the closed end of the box because it is moving at the same speed as the box. Now bring the box to a sudden stop. The ball will keep going at its original speed and will fly out at the open end. The ball was in motion and continued to stay in motion because there was nothing to stop it.

Have the children recall what happens when they are in an auto which starts up very quickly. They fall backward on the seat. They are at rest when the car starts and they tend to stay at rest. The car moves quickly forward while they are still at rest; thus, they fall back. If the moving car were to stop suddenly, the children would now be thrown forward because they tend to continue in motion. Remind the children that a force was required to put both the car and children in motion, and another force was required to stop them.

The children should now understand that a body at rest tends to stay at rest, and a body in motion tends to continue

in motion. Furthermore, a force is required in both cases to change this condition. That is, a force is needed to put a stationary object in motion, and a force is needed to stop a moving object.

SIMPLE ENGINES

Almost all engines depend upon the same basic principles. All convert chemical into mechanical energy. In all engines it is the mechanical energy of gas molecules that finally moves a piston, drives a turbine, or produces the jet that results in the forward motion. The first engine was probably made in Alexandria more than 2000 years ago by the Greek scientist, Hero.

Commercial Hero engines made of glass or metal are sold by scientific supply houses. These are heated by means of a burner, an electric test tube heater, or several candles. The glass ones are very fragile.

A homemade Hero engine can be made from a thoroughly cleaned can with a friction cover. (Paint comes in a can with a friction cover.) Punch holes on opposite sides of the walls near the top. Into the holes place metal or glass tubes bent at a right angle and each pointing in the same rotational direction, i.e., clockwise or counterclockwise. Solder the metal tubes in place, being certain that the tubes are clear and not clogged. If glass tubes are used, wrap rubber electrician's tape around the tubes and insert the tubes snugly into the holes. Next wrap wire around the can just under the rim at the top. To this attach two thin wires about 18″ long. These meet and are attached to a piece of pull-chain from an old electric socket. This permits freedom of rotation. Next place an ounce of water in the can, suspend it from a support, close the cover, and heat the can. When the water boils and steam forms, the steam will escape from the tubes, causing the can to rotate in a direction away from that of the steam jet.

A simpler variation uses a rectangular spice can. Holes are punched diagonally opposite each other (Fig. 25-16). Hang from a fishing line swivel or pull-chain, as above. This is the oldest type of engine known. Later you will see how this reaction engine was a forerunner of jets and rockets (pp. 429–32). Another way to show reaction or propulsion by reaction is to take a tank-type vacuum cleaner and place it on a well-oiled, ball-bearing roller skate. The skate should rest on a very smooth floor. Simply use the tank cleaner with its electric cord and no additional parts. Before turning the machine on, remove the dirt-collecting sack and reclose. The air rushing out of the back end of the cleaner will act as a jet, and the reaction will cause the vacuum cleaner and the roller skate to move forward.

The cannon, which provided mechanical energy from burning gunpowder, suggested the next idea in the development of the steam engine. The French physicist Papin demonstrated that the principle of the cannon could be used to lift a weight and he thereby devised a means to use steam to raise a piston. From this, instead of firing a projectile, Newcomen developed his engine which depended upon the condensation of steam and atmospheric pressure for one half cycle of the operation. Watt changed this engine into the double-acting steam engine that made its adaptation to transportation possible. Experiments with internal-combustion engines operated on illuminating gas were done in France as early as 1853. By the 1870's, successful gas engines were in use. Aircraft steam-turbine engines showed the way for turbojet engines by requiring lightweight, high-horsepower engines. The advent of jet engines and rockets put old principles back to work.

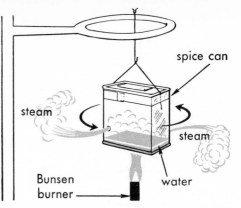

Fig. 25-16 A homemade Hero engine. (From P. Brandwein et al., *You and Science*, Harcourt, Brace & World, 1960.)

How steam engines work

To show the conversion of steam to mechanical energy, place 3 cc of water in a heavy Pyrex test tube set in a clamp attached to a stand. Fit the test tube with a cork. The tube should aim at 45° upward toward a wall. A target may be used if desired. A few trials will show where the cork will hit. Heat the water. A few seconds after the water boils, the cork will be expelled and hit the target. For safety against shattering, wrap the test tube in a layer of ordinary metal window screening made of iron or galvanized iron. The screening can be secured in place with lengths of wire tied about the tube.

Some students will have model steam engines in working order. In most cases they are electrically heated. Point out the fact that fuels such as coal or oil normally heat the boiler to make steam.

If you can remove the electrical heating unit, you can get a more realistic effect by heating the boiler with a Bunsen burner or an alcohol lamp. Some model steam engines use alcohol as a fuel. A can of Sterno (alcohol in solidified paraffin) also makes a good source of heat.

Valves and pistons. To demonstrate the action of the valve, make a large form

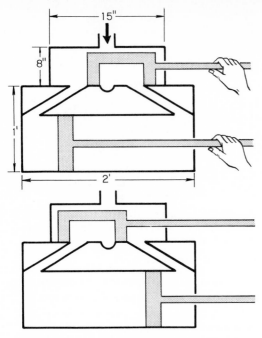

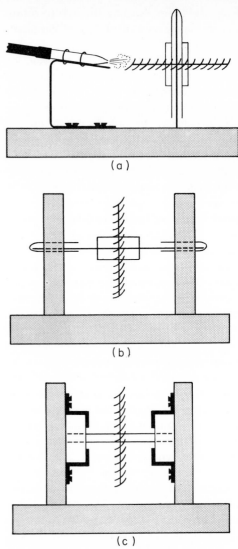

Fig. 25-17 Illustrating the action of a valve and piston. (From A. Joseph et al., *A Sourcebook for the Physical Sciences*, Harcourt, Brace & World, 1961.)

of the valve, as in Fig. 25-17, and a model of the piston with attached connecting rod. Wood stock 1″ × 1″ is excellent for making the valve and piston; heavy cardboard will also serve. On the blackboard draw a cross-section diagram of a steam engine to fit around the wood valve and the piston. Use colored chalk for the cylinder and white chalk for the other parts. Have one child hold the piston and rod in position against the diagram on the blackboard or on a large chart. Another child does the same for the valve rod. As one child simulates the motion of the piston, the other child moves the valve rod to the correct position for the next stroke.

Steam turbines. To show the principle of the turbine, direct a jet of steam from a glass nozzle connected by rubber tubing to a steam generator. Aim the nozzle at an ordinary toy plastic pinwheel or one cut from lightweight aluminum sheet metal.

Fig. 25-18 (a) A steam turbine; (b) alternative turbine wheel mounting with a glass tube as bearing at each end of the turbine axle; (c) alternative turbine wheel mounting with a skate wheel as bearing at each end of the turbine axle. (From A. Joseph et al., *A Sourcebook for the Physical Sciences*, Harcourt, Brace & World, 1961.)

The circle that is removed from the top of a tin can by a mechanical can opener makes a good form for cutting a turbine wheel. Every ¼″ along the circumference draw a line to the center of the circle.

Into each line, cut a ⅜″ line with metal cutting snips (Fig. 25-18). In the center, drill or punch a 1″ hole. Take a ¼″ glass tube and heat one end until it closes. Cut off the sealed end to form a 2″ length. Bore a ¼″ hole in the center of a cork that is just over 1″ in diameter. Place the tubing inside the cork.

Bend the metal between each ⅜″ cut with pliers, twisting each blade to approximately 45°. Then curve each blade slightly. Next place the cork through the center of the turbine wheel. Drive a 3″ finishing nail through the center of a board about 4″ × 4″ × ¾″. Next file the nail to a sharp point. Slip the glass tube and turbine wheel over the nail. The closed glass tube will act like a low-friction bearing.

Now take a medicine dropper tube and attach it to a strip of metal (a girder from an Erector set will serve) that is tacked or screwed to the base. The tube spout aims at the turbine wheel blades. Connect the dropper tube to your steam generator. You can make a steam generator from a flask fitted with a *loose* one-hole stopper in which is inserted a short piece of plastic or glass tubing. You might also whittle a one-hole stopper to fit the spout of a tea kettle. Adjust the angle of the tube until the maximum speed of rotation is obtained.

The principle of the steam turbine can also be shown with a small spouted teakettle. Make a turbine from the round top of a tin can as described above. In the center of the tin circle punch a hole with a nail. Mount the turbine wheel either in one of the ways shown in Fig. 25-18 or on the end of a stick with a nail that fits the center hole loosely. You may have to wrap string about the nail on each side of the turbine in order to keep the turbine steady and to prevent it from rubbing on the end of the stick. When the water in the teakettle is boiling vigorously, hold the turbine in the jet of steam escaping from the spout (Fig. 25-19). The smaller the teakettle's spout, the better. The jet from some whistle-type kettles is quite strong; however, you may cork the spout with a stopper that has a small hole through it.

An alternative method of making a turbine wheel is to use a disk of cork or soft wood and insert foil squares along the rim. Their curved shanks act as the turbine vanes.

Toy steam engines make good working demonstrations for science instruction. Most of these are electrically heated and draw about 300 watts, which makes it easy to use them in the classroom. Some pupils may own such models which they can bring to school. Some of these model steam engines drive a small electric generator which lights a small lamp.

Action and reaction

The enormous speed of modern jets is achieved without the use of either propellers or piston engines. The principle of a jet engine was based on Sir Isaac Newton's third law of motion: for every action there is an equal and opposite reaction. Try picking up a heavy boulder and throwing it as far as you can. The weight of the boulder may even force you off balance. This is one of the reasons people are cautioned not to throw things from high places.

Children who roller skate know what happens when they try to throw a ball or other sizable object. As the ball leaves

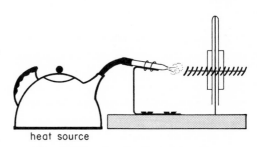

heat source

Fig. 25-19 A teakettle steam turbine.

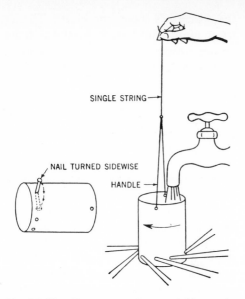

Fig. 25-20 How a rotary lawn sprinkler works. (From C. J. Lynde, *Science Experiments with Home Equipment,* Van Nostrand, 1941.)

both so that they will throw water out in the same angled direction. Now suspend the can by a string attached to the top holes (Fig. 25-20). When water is poured into the can, jets of water come out from the bottom holes in one direction and make the can spin in the other direction. Repeat the experiment, using many angled holes, and note how much faster the can will turn. This experiment should help children understand a rotary lawn sprinkler.

Other examples of action-reaction. A good demonstration of action and reaction can be set up if two sets of curved tracks for wind-up trains are available. Place one circle on the floor or table and set four flatcars on the tracks. Place the second circle of track on a circle of stiff cardboard or pressed wood which, in turn, is supported by the four flatcars. Wind up a locomotive and place it on the upper track. The engine will go one way as the tracks move in the opposite direction by reaction.

The first reaction engine was made almost 2000 years ago in Alexandria by the Greek scientist, Hero. His aeoliphile, as he called it, consisted of a hollow sphere

the hand, they are forced backward. Try throwing a ball while sitting in a swing. Newton's third law of motion is in evidence everywhere. For example,

action	*reaction*
step ashore from skiff or canoe	craft bobs away
frog jumps off lily pad or float in tank	lily pad or float bobs under
rotating lawn sprinkler turned on	nozzle revolves, pushed away by force of water
bullet fired from gun	gun recoils or "kicks" against you

Rotary lawn sprinkler. With a nail punch two holes in a tin can, one on each side of the can near the bottom. Also punch two holes near the top of the can so that the can may be suspended. In each of the bottom holes twist the nail sideways in a direction parallel to the bottom. Twist the nail in the same sideways direction in

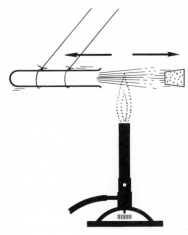

Fig. 25-21 A test tube recoils as its cork pops out. (From A. Joseph et al., *A Sourcebook for the Physical Sciences,* Harcourt, Brace & World, 1961.)

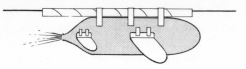

Fig. 25-22 A model jet airplane with a balloon motor. (From A. Joseph et al., *A Sourcebook for the Physical Sciences,* Harcourt, Brace & World, 1961.)

suspended over a fire pot. As steam escaped from two nozzles, the ball revolved in the opposite direction. You can make a similar reaction steam engine with a spice can (see Fig. 25-16).

Heat 1 teaspoonful of water in a small test tube that is lightly suspended by thin wires. Heat slowly and carefully. Observe the tube's movement when the cork pops (Fig. 25-21).

Balance a bottle on two round pencils. Place 2 teaspoons of baking soda into the bottle, add 2 tablespoons of vinegar, and cork loosely. Observe the bottle's movement when the compressed carbon dioxide that forms finally pops the cork.

Children may have watched firemen lean against pressure in a fire hose. Modern plastic hoses are so light that they tend to recoil in your hand as water is turned on. Encourage children to look for examples of action-reaction in nature. For example, the seeds of Eastern jewelweed (touch-me-not) are catapulted into the air if you touch a ripe seed pod. Squids, oc-

topi, sea urchins, and other marine animals move about by squirting water through an orifice in their bodies.

Balloon as motor. The easiest way to illustrate jet and rocket propulsion is with a balloon. To soften the rather stiff synthetic rubber balloons used today, first stretch the balloon in all directions. Inflate; then release suddenly. It will whirl around until all the air has escaped. As air rushes out, the balloon rushes in the opposite direction. Your balloon is really a little jet or rocket engine. The backward push of inside air pushes the balloon forward. The balloon flies about erratically because it has no control surfaces. Oblong balloons therefore work better than round ones.

Fasten the balloon to a lightweight toy auto. Escaping air should jet-propel the toy. Glue paper wings and rudder to a sausage-shaped balloon. Scotch-tape the balloon to a drinking straw, fore and aft (Fig. 25-22). Insert wire through the straw and stretch the wire across the room or other space. Inflate the balloon and watch the air jet move it along the wire.

Make a waxed cardboard (milk carton) or lightweight wood boat and drill or burn a small hole near the stern (Fig. 25-23). Fit a medicine dropper or small plastic tube cut from a plastic drinking straw to

Fig. 25-23 A jet-propelled boat with a balloon motor. (From G. Blough and M. Campbell, *Making and Using Classroom Science Materials in the Elementary School,* Holt, Rinehart and Winston, 1954.)

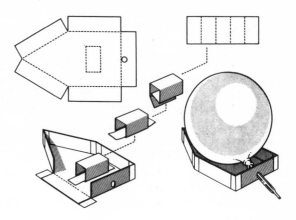

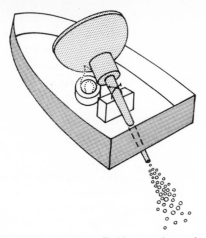

Fig. 25-24 A jet-propelled boat with an oil-can motor.

the back of the boat by running it through the hole in the stern, and slip a balloon over the tube, securing its mouth to the tube with string or a rubber band. Inflate the balloon through the plastic tube. Then place the boat in a large aquarium or a large tray of water and release the air. The boat will move as the air escapes from the balloon, thus producing a jet-propelled boat. If you had a boatload of stones which you threw overboard one by one, the boat would keep moving in the opposite direction. In the case of the balloon-motor boat, millions of air molecules, rather than stones, are being "thrown overboard."

Carbon dioxide cartridge motor. Toy jet-operated cars that can travel 60 mph can be shaped from balsa wood. In the back, carve or drill a hole to receive a carbon dioxide cartridge (sold by drugstores, department stores, mail order houses, and hobby shops). The wheels must be very lightweight and must spin freely. To guide the jet car, place small screw eyes in the top and use long thin wire strung tautly. Race these cars down the school corridor or across the gymnasium floor. To set the carbon dioxide cartridge into action, use a small carbon dioxide cartridge "gun"

(sold by hobby shops) or puncture the lead seal at the mouth of the cartridge with a very sharp nail struck with a hammer. The jet car will scoot down the corridor at very high speed. (*Caution: The end of the jet car's run should be cushioned with pillows or their equivalent. Keep children back.*)

Carbon dioxide model rocket ship. Set up a long thin wire between two posts about 60–100′ apart. Ask a student to fashion a small rocket from balsa wood or use a small plastic toy rocket model. Into the tail securely fix a carbon dioxide cartridge. Suspend the "rocket" from two screw eyes through which the wire guide passes. Release the cartridge in the same manner as for the jet car. The rocket will scoot down the wire at speeds as high as 60 mph. (*Caution: Arrange pillows or their equivalent to cushion the end of the rocket's run.*)

If a pupil has a flying model plane, it can be made to fly for a short time by attaching a carbon dioxide cartridge under the center of balance with cellulose tape. If you wish, the plane can be made to ride a wire like the model rocket.

Oil-can motor. Another action-reaction motor employs a small oil can mounted on a boat at 30° to the horizontal, the spout extending through a hole in the boat's flat bottom (Fig. 25-24). Into the can place an ounce of water and under it place a small can of Sterno as a heat source. After a short time the water will boil, and steam will form. The steam will go out of the can in a jet, causing the boat to move forward.

A way to do this without using heat is to place vinegar and sodium bicarbonate (baking soda) in the can. Bubbles of carbon dioxide gas will form and go out the spout as a jet, causing the boat to move by reaction. Toy plastic boats are sold that operate on this principle. Sodium bicarbonate tablets are better than the powder since the reaction then proceeds at a slower rate.

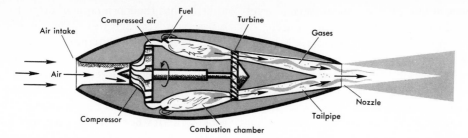

Fig. 25-25 Diagram of a jet engine. (From R. Brinckerhoff et al., *The Physical World,* Harcourt, Brace & World, 1958.)

Labels on diagram: Air intake, Compressed air, Fuel, Turbine, Gases, Air, Compressor, Combustion chamber, Tailpipe, Nozzle

Jet engines

Many schemes for jet propulsion of aircraft had appeared in the years following World War I. The successful development of jet-propelled airplanes came, as a product of World War II, with the first British air-borne jet engine in 1941. Of course, the principle of jet propulsion as applied to a vehicle goes back as far as the rockets devised by the Chinese over 700 years ago.

To help children understand the compression action in a jet engine, inflate a balloon and then release the air against a small pile of oatmeal, puffed rice, or sand. Repeat, this time squeezing the balloon as the air goes out. Let children decide which method blew away more material. One part of a jet engine is a pump which squeezes the air to give it more push.

To help children understand the expansion of gases due to heating a jet engine, fit a balloon over the mouth of a Pyrex baby bottle or other heatproof glass. Set the bottle in a saucepan of hot water and watch the balloon fill. Help the children conclude that the balloon was filled by heated air expanding in the bottle. In a jet engine fierce heat causes sudden and enormous expansion.

Make a rough sketch of a jet engine on the blackboard (Fig. 25-25). Let the children help you label the parts and decide what each part does. Doubtless, one of your "junior space men" or an older

brother would be pleased to make an enlarged drawing for the bulletin board.

Air is sucked into the nose of a jet and under enormous pressure enters a combustion chamber. Kerosene or other fuel is sprayed into the air, and the mixture is ignited. The burning gases expand in all directions and blast their way out the only opening at the rear. The steady burning of air and kerosene sounds very much like a blowtorch, magnified in intensity many times.

To help children understand vapor trails, secure a lamp chimney. Have the chimney cool but not cold. When you allow the vapors from a flame to rise up through the cool chimney, children should observe water vapor forming inside the glass. Hold a cool mirror at an angle above the chimney. Let the children watch for water vapor condensing on the mirror. If the room is very dry, condensation may not occur. At very high altitudes the air is so cold that water vapor from the burning fuel often cools fast enough to freeze into clouds of ice crystals, which can be seen.

Rockets.   The simplest kind of jet engine is a rocket. In some rockets (liquid fuel) the fuel and the oxygen supply are stored separately. When they are combined in the combustion chamber, the resulting gases roar astern at speeds of thousands of miles per hour. Because a rocket does not depend on outside air, it is at present the only practical device developed which could fly in outer space.

People have known about rockets for a long time. The Chinese long ago invented firecrackers filled with gunpowder, and they used gunpowder for firing rockets during a siege in 1232. During the fifteenth century, an Italian architect, Joannes de Fontana, suggested a rocket-driven boat. Two hundred years ago an Indian prince used bamboo rockets with feathers at the end to guide the flight. In 1806, a British colonel, Sir William Congreve, developed rockets with a range of 3000 yards. And it was Congreve's rockets that inspired the familiar line in our national anthem, "the rockets' red glare," written by Francis Scott Key during the 1812 bombardment of Baltimore. The U. S. Army even had a rocket brigade until 1862. But rockets were discontinued in favor of much more accurate cannon. Modern rocketry really began with the inventions and experiments of Robert Goddard, head of the physics department at Clark University in Worcester, Mass. The antitank bazooka used in World War II was a ground-to-ground rocket as were the German rockets which were used to bombard England.

Differences between rocket engines and jet engines. Rocket and jet engines are alike in that their principle of propulsion is based on Newton's third law of motion. Thus, in both cases, expanding gases from the burning fuel travel out from the rear and kick the rocket or jet forward.

There is one basic difference between the rocket engine and the jet engine. The rocket carries not only its own fuel but also its own supply of oxygen. This is necessary for travel into space where there is no air (and therefore no oxygen) to burn the fuel.

Jets carry just the fuel, and use the oxygen from the air to burn the fuel. Since the jet needs a great deal of oxygen quickly, a powerful blower is used to compress the air before it reaches the fuel chamber.

Toy rockets. Toy rockets that work under compressed air and water are now sold and are very popular. These should be operated outdoors to prevent water from being splashed over the classroom. In addition, they do attain great heights.

For the more intrepid, model airplane shops sell small, dry-fuel rocket engines called "Jetex." These engines are attached to small flying model planes. The fuel is ignited by means of a wick. (*Caution: Follow to the letter all precautions and instructions given with this rocket engine.*)

CAPSULE LESSONS

25-1 Bring different types of shears to class—those for cutting paper, metal, etc. Ask the class why the blades and handles are of different lengths. Lead into the study of levers and wedges and their uses.

25-2 Remove the handle of a door and have the pupils try to turn the axle with their hands. Repeat the experiment with a water faucet. Lead into the study of wheel and axles and how they make work easier.

25-3 Set up several pulleys: simple ones which merely change direction, and combinations of fixed and movable pulleys which make work easier as well. Lead into the study of pulleys as machines, and how machines help us.

25-4 Place a heavy boy on a rotating piano stool. Measure the height of the seat from the ground. Have a smaller, lighter boy rotate the seat slowly but steadily, then measure the height again. Lead into the study of the screw, inclined plane, and wedge.

25-5 Have the children make a list of devices that are used to make things go faster. Discuss and study the use of machines to increase speed. You can also do the same with machines that change direction.

25-6 Have one pupil bring his bicycle into class. Rest the bicycle upside down and make a chalk mark on the rear tire. Have the pupil slowly turn the large gear attached to the pedal until it makes one complete turn. Note the number of turns the rear wheel makes while this is going on. Lead into a study of gears and their uses.

25-7 Bring in a compound machine that you can examine carefully, and take it apart if you wish. Make a list of all the simple machines you can find in it. See how they operate as simple machines, and how they combine to form a compound machine. An old typewriter, bicycle, alarm clock, or mechanical toy will serve well.

25-8 Bring in a variety of household tools and appliances. If possible, see that all six simple machines are represented. Observe how these devices function. Lead into the study of machines and mechanical advantage.

25-9 Have a child make a list of household tools or appliances that make work easier at home. Lead into the study of machines and how they operate.

25-10 Have some children visit a machine shop or auto repair shop. Let them make a list of the different kinds of tools and machines they saw. Encourage the class to identify the components of each tool or machine and explain how they operate to make work easier.

25-11 Find pictures of an automobile brake drum. Better still, examine a real brake. Your garage man will be glad to cooperate. Point out how the brake shoe uses friction against the brake drum to stop an auto. Hold a glass tumbler in one hand. Let it represent a brake drum. Place the fingers of your other hand inside the glass to represent the brake shoe. Press the balls of your fingers outward against the glass and try to turn the tumbler at the same time. First press gently, then harder. Point out that the friction of your fingers against the glass makes it harder to turn the glass. Lead into the study of friction.

25-12 Have the children list examples of ways that friction is harmful. Study and try out different methods of reducing friction. Let the children also list ways that friction can be useful.

BIBLIOGRAPHY

Huey, Edward G., *What Makes the Wheels Go Round?,* Harcourt, Brace & World, 1952. Describes how many machines and other work-saving devices operate.

Meyer, Jerome S., *Machines,* World Book, 1958. Clear explanation of the lever, wheel and axle, wedge, and screw.

Schneider, Herman, and Nina Schneider, *Now Try This,* Scott, 1947. Simple, effective explanation of machines.

Sharp, Elizabeth, *Simple Machines and How They Work,* Random House, 1959. Simple explanation of the lever, wheel, inclined plane, wedge, screw, and how they make man's work easier.

Wyler, Rose, and Gerald Ames, *What Makes It Go?,* McGraw-Hill, 1958. Discusses the operation of cars, locomotives, planes, and other types of machines.

Ziner, F., *About Wonderful Wheels,* Melmont, 1959. Primary book on wheels and how man uses them to get work done.

Gravity and space travel

WHAT IS GRAVITY?

Without being aware of it, every pupil in the class knows something about gravity and the effect of this force—as, for example, the weight of each pupil. This weight is the measure of the pull of gravity upon the atoms or molecules that make up his body. The sum of these atoms is called mass. Mass does not change. If you go to the North Pole or to the top of a mountain where gravity is slightly less, the pull on the mass of atoms is less, and you weigh less, but your mass does not change. If you go down into a deep mine, the pull on the same mass is greater, and you weigh more. On the moon a pupil would have the same mass as he has on the earth, but he would weigh one sixth his weight since the pull of gravity on the moon is one sixth that on the earth.

Gravity can be simply defined as the amount of attraction or pull one mass has for another. Only very massive bodies have it in an easily measurable amount. Even though unmeasurable, all bodies possess gravity. Newton's theory holds that all bodies in space attract or pull on each other. The amount of the attraction depends upon the mass of the bodies and the distance between them. At a particular distance the larger the mass, the greater the gravitational attraction. For any two bodies the farther apart they are, the less the amount of gravitational attraction be-

tween them. At twice the original distance the gravitational attraction is one fourth its original value; at three times the distance, it is one ninth, etc.

SHOWING GRAVITY

Gravity pulls all bodies toward the center of the earth. To show this, take a small cardboard geography globe and separate it at the seam. Then glue small magnets to the inside of the globe's surface. The greater the number of magnets you use, the better the experiment will work. Now reassemble the globe, seal the seam with cellophane tape, and place the globe back in its stand. Using tin snips from the round cover of a tin can, cut out a simple outline figure of a man 1″ high. Include a section of metal below the legs of the mannikin, and then bend the section underneath to act as a stand. Now place the figure on the globe near one of the magnets, and it will be held in place by the magnet. Use the model to show that the figure is pulled toward the center when it is both at the North Pole and at the South Pole. Now is the time to ask the class which way is "up." By moving the little man, the pupils should readily see that "up" simply means away from the earth, while "down" always means toward the center of the earth.

If a cardboard geography globe is un-

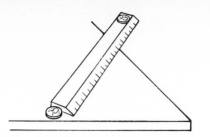

Fig. 26-1 Objects falling from the same height hit the floor at the same time.

available, use a grapefruit and toothpicks. Insert the toothpicks into different points of the grapefruit so that they all stick out straight. Then fasten tiny paper figures to the protruding ends of each toothpick.

Rising and falling objects

When a ball is thrown up into the air, the earth's gravity pulls on the ball as soon as it leaves your hand. Soon the ball slows down, stops, then is pulled back toward the earth. Help the children understand that gravity is always acting on the ball. If the ball had been thrown out horizontally instead of vertically, gravity would immediately begin to pull it down even while it was traveling horizontally. In fact, it would not take any longer time for the ball to fall than if it had been just dropped from your hand at the same level you threw the ball out horizontally.

You can show this quite effectively. Place a 12″ ruler obliquely at one corner of a table top. Let one end of the ruler just project over the edge of the table, and have the other end about 1″ from the edge (Fig. 26-1). Now place a penny on top of the projecting end of the ruler. Place a second penny on the table, between the other end of the ruler and the edge of the table. With the flat part of another ruler strike the projecting end of the first ruler sharply, using a horizontal motion. Draw the second ruler quickly back as soon as you have struck the first ruler. One penny will fall straight to the

floor while the other travels in a long arc. Listen to the sounds of both pennies as they hit the floor. They will both hit at the same time. To get this desired effect, you may have to practice a few times in order to acquire the knack of releasing both coins at the same time.

The sun, the moon, the planets, and the stars all have their own forces of gravity. Each one has a gravitational force different from that of the earth, depending upon the materials that make it up and how tightly packed it is. A wonderful way to show the effect of the moon's gravity on the earth is to study the tides. Also, the sun's gravity holds the planets in their orbits, while the earth's gravity holds the moon in its orbit.

If we want to escape the earth's gravity completely and take off into space, we need a rocket traveling at a speed of about 25,000 mph. This is called the escape velocity.

The fall of two objects

What effect do you think size and weight have on the time it takes two bodies to fall the same distance? Obtain two marbles of different size, a wooden block, and a hammer. Set the block near the edge of the table and place the marbles against the side of the block nearer to the table's edge (Fig. 26-2). Tap the center of the block moderately with a hammer. You must hit the block in the center to get accurate results. Both marbles will hit the

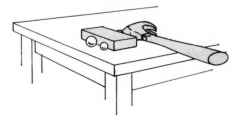

Fig. 26-2 The weight of an object does not affect its rate of fall.

floor at the same time. Help the children understand that when gravity pulls on a body, the pull is the same, ounce for ounce or pound for pound. Every ounce of matter is pulled with an equal force of 1 ounce. Thus, size and weight have nothing to do with the time it takes for objects to fall.

However, the resistance of the air does make a difference. Get a flat piece of aluminum foil and a marble. Hold them out in each hand at arm's length and let them drop. The foil will float down, taking longer to fall. Now fold the foil up very tightly and compactly. Hold the folded foil and the marble at arm's length again and let them fall. This time they will both hit the ground at the same time. Point out that when the foil was dropped the first time, the air resisted the movement of the foil more than it did that of the marble. The second time the air resistance was cut down by reducing the amount of foil surface exposed to the air. You can also use two sheets of typing paper, one rolled into a ball, the other flat.

WEIGHT AND GRAVITY

All the pupils know about weight and the use of pounds and ounces in weighing materials. They will be interested to know that weight is simply the measure of the pull of gravity upon themselves. Ask each child his weight by saying, "How much does gravity pull on you?"

Obtain a small cardboard box, a large rubber band, a ruler, thread, and some marbles. Place the ruler on a table so that about 3″ extends beyond the table. Place a pile of books on the rest of the ruler so that it will not topple over during the experiment. Insert one end of the rubber band into a paper clip and loop the other end of the rubber band over the protruding end of the ruler. Then insert into

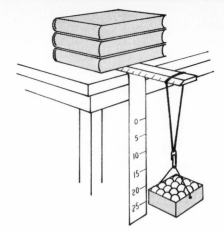

Fig. 26-3 Weight is a measure of the pull of gravity.

the lower end of the paper clip a loop of thread attached to the sides of the cardboard box (Fig. 26-3). Make a pointer by bending one end of the paper clip into a horizontal position.

Now add marbles one by one and notice how the rubber band stretches. The stretch of the rubber band clearly shows the pull of gravity on the marbles. Replace the rubber band with the spring from an old window-shade roller and repeat the experiment. Suspend the spring from a cup hook screwed into the underside of the ruler. If a window-shade roller is unavailable, you can obtain a light porch-door spring from the hardware store.

Obtain a laundry scale or other spring balance. Use it to weigh objects as examples of measuring the pull of gravity. Point out that the laundry scale and other such balances make use of the spring which operates just like the one in the experiment above.

If you like, you may make your own spring balance, using the cardboard box, marbles, paper clip, and spring from the window-shade roller or porch door. Simply cut out a long narrow strip of white cardboard. Slide one end underneath the ruler and let the rest hang down. With the cardboard box empty, mark with a black crayon the point where the pointer touches the card (Fig. 26-3). This is zero. Now add one or more marbles at a time and make a mark at each new position of the pointer. Label each mark to denote how many marbles it took the pointer to reach this mark. You now have a balance with marbles as the unit of weight. Take out all the marbles from the cardboard box. The pointer may not go back to the zero mark if the rubber band has become strained. If this happens, adjust the loop of thread until the pointer does read zero. Now add a stone or any other object to the box and see how many "marbles" it weighs.

Weight in other places

You can intrigue the children by giving them an idea of what they would weigh on the moon, on Mars, and on the sun. For example, the moon's pull of gravity is about one sixth that of the earth, so that a person would weigh only one sixth his weight on the earth. On Mars the pull of gravity is one third that on the earth, so that a person would weigh only one third his weight on earth. But on the sun he would find a force of gravity 26 times as strong as the earth's gravity, so that he would weigh 26 times as much on the sun. Now let the pupils figure out their weights on the other planets.

The pupils may also be astounded to know that they weigh a minute amount less on top of a high mountain than they do at the foot of the mountain. The higher up you go above the center of the earth, the less the force of gravity. At 8000 miles a person's weight is only one fourth as much as at the earth's surface; at 12,000 miles, one ninth as much; and at 16,000 miles, one sixteenth as much. Have the pupils compute their weights at these altitudes.

Increasing one's weight

Some pupils may have heard or read about the violent forces called "g's" when rockets and jet planes are discussed. A "g" is simply a force equal to the earth's gravity. Thus, one "g" on a 30,000-pound airplane equals 30,000 pounds. Each pupil can tell what the "g" force is on himself. The answer is his own weight. If a boy weighs 90 pounds, the one "g" on the boy is 90 pounds, and five "g's" on the boy is five times 90 or 450 pounds.

Increasing speed or changing direction of movement increases the "g" forces during the acceleration or change. A pupil can show this with an inexpensive balsa wood glider. Fasten a weight to the wing with a thread and move the glider in level flight. The wing does not break. Next have the pupil dive the model and then suddenly level the glider. The wing snaps off because the "g's" increased during the dive. Test pilots find out how many "g's" a plane can stand by diving it and then flattening out.

The U. S. Air Force tests the effect of increased "g's" on a man by swinging a man around a circle in a closed cockpit. You can show this by using a ball attached to a rubber band and swinging it in a circle. The faster you swing the ball, the larger the circle because the ball acts as if it is heavier. This is because the ball has more "g's" acting on it.

Finding the center of gravity

Obtain a piece of cardboard and cut out an irregular shape like that shown in the diagram (Fig. 26-4). With a thin nail puncture the cardboard at four different points. Label these points A, B, C, and D with black crayon. Push a small nail or long tack through point A and suspend the cardboard from the bulletin board. Drive the nail only a short way into the bulletin board and make sure that the

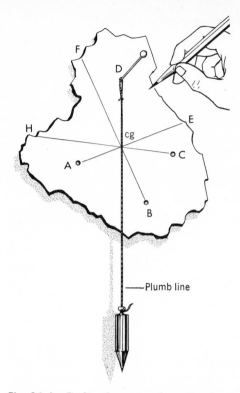

Fig. 26-4 Finding the center of gravity of an irregular shape. (From R. Brinckerhoff et al., *Exploring Physics*, Harcourt, Brace & World, 1959.)

is called the center of gravity. Help them understand that this is the point where all the weight of the cardboard seems to be concentrated, or centered. When we find the center of gravity of an object we have actually located the center of the object's weight.

Cut out a cardboard rectangle and determine its center of gravity in the same way. Make a pinhole through the center. Now turn the cardboard on the other side. Using a ruler and pencil draw two diagonals from the top of one end to the bottom opposite end. Both diagonals should crisscross at the pinhole. The pupils should now realize that for regular-shaped or uniform objects the center of gravity is at the mid-point.

Have one of the children balance a yardstick on his finger. Note that, when the yardstick is balanced, the pupil's finger is on or about the halfway mark, or 18″. Because the yardstick is uniform, the center of gravity is at the mid-point. Now tie a jackknife or any other object to one end of the yardstick. Let the pupil balance the stick again. When the stick is balanced, the pupil's fingers will be much closer to the heavier end. The center of gravity is now located nearer the heavier end.

Take a large soda bottle and stand it on its base. The bottle does not tip very easily because the center of gravity is located nearer the heavier end, below the middle of the bottle. Now stand the bottle upright on its narrow mouth. The bottle will tip over very easily because the center of gravity is located above the middle. This tends to pull the bottle off its standing position. A bottle in this position is usually denoted as top-heavy.

Some of the pupils may point out that the base of the bottle is broad, while the mouth is narrow, and that this seems to make a difference. This is an excellent observation and will provide you with an opportunity to show the relationship be-

cardboard is always able to swing freely back and forth. This is important to the success of the experiment.

Now tie a thread to a small stone and make a loop at the free end of the thread. Pass the loop over the end of the nail and let the stone and thread hang down. With a pencil mark off a point on the cardboard directly underneath the thread, to show the vertical direction of the thread. Label this point E. Repeat the procedure with points B, C, and D and label the new direction points F, G, and H, respectively. Now draw the lines AE, BF, CG, and DH. These lines will all meet at one point. If you now push a pin through this point, you will find that the cardboard will be perfectly balanced in any position you place it.

Point out to the children that this point

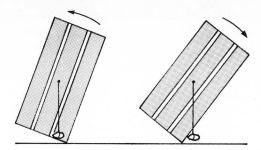

Fig. 26-5 Stability depends on the relationship between the center of gravity and the base of an object.

tween the center of gravity and the base of an object.

From the supermarket obtain a wooden crate with the original cover. Nail the cover back on so that you have a uniformly rectangular object. Find the center of gravity by drawing two diagonals and locating the mid-point. Now place the crate on its narrow end. Drive a nail halfway into the mid-point, and loop a black thread attached to a rock over the head of the nail. Make sure the thread and stone can swing freely. The thread should be long enough so that the rock almost touches the floor (Fig. 26-5). Now tilt the crate at various angles. Point out that, as long as the vertical line of the thread and stone falls inside the base, the crate will not tip over. But once the vertical line falls outside the base, the crate will tip over.

Repeat the experiment, placing the crate on its broad side. You will have to shorten the thread. Note how difficult it is to tip the crate over this time. The crate must be tilted quite some way before it will topple over. Have the pupils measure the distance between the center of gravity and the ground when the crate is on its narrow side and on its broad side.

Balancing objects

The pupils should now readily understand that there are two ways of making an object stable so that it will not tip over.

You can lower its center of gravity or you can broaden its base. Auto designers have done just this. Modern cars have wide bases, and also their weight is concentrated at a low point.

Many toys and stunts make use of the low center of gravity or broad bases to create startling effects. The children would enjoy making some of them.

Obtain an orange and some pipe cleaners. Cut the orange in half. Arrange the pipe cleaners so that they form a little mannikin, then insert the figure into the center of one half of the orange. Whenever the orange is pushed over, it will bob up again.

Obtain a jackknife and a sharpened pencil. Open the large blade so that it is at right angles with the handle. Push the point of the blade into the pencil at a point near the sharpened end. Balance the knife and pencil (Fig. 26-6). When the pencil is balanced, a gentle push on the knife will make both knife and pencil rock back and forth.

Obtain an apple, two similar forks, a thin nail about 3″ long, and a soda bottle

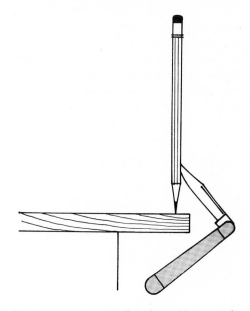

Fig. 26-6 A heavy knife balanced by a pencil.

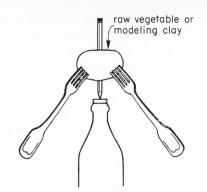

raw vegetable or
modeling clay

Fig. 26-7 Using a low center of gravity to make a sharp point stable. (From *UNESCO Source Book for Science Teachers*, UNESCO, 1956.)

stoppered with a cork. Remove the stem of the apple and in its place push in the nail until all but ½″ is in the apple. Now insert the forks into the apple (Fig. 26-7). Balance the head of the nail on the bottle top. Give the top of the apple a gentle twirl, and the device will spin.

Cut a slice of the apple about 1″ thick. Push the point of a sharpened pencil almost but not quite through the piece of apple. Insert a fork (Fig. 26-8) and balance the setup on the edge of the table. Give the eraser end of the pencil a slight push downward. The pencil will bob up and down.

Obtain two similar forks and a half dollar. Insert the half dollar between the first and second tines of each fork. Then balance the combination on the edge of a water glass (Fig. 26-9).

ON OUR WAY INTO SPACE

The Wright brothers' "contraption" flew 120′ in 12 seconds or about 31 mph. Within 50 years airplane builders achieved propeller-driven planes which flew nearly 600 mph. And that was as far as they could get. With the development of jet engines, speeds increased only to come up to a speed (approximately 760 mph) at which the plane was severely

jolted. This speed is the same as that of sound and is thus called the "sound barrier." At this speed sound waves pile up in front of the plane, thereby increasing resistance. Also the front edges of the plane pile up the air. This huge mass of compressed air would seem to buffet the plane with shock waves so severe that the wings could be torn away. Redesigning aircraft structures finally made possible flight at speeds faster than the speed of sound.

The higher one goes, the fewer the number of molecules. With greater and greater distances between slower and slower molecules, speed of sound also slows. As the chart below shows, sound travels 100 mph slower at 40,000′ than it does at sea level.

sea level	760 mph
10,000′	735 mph
20,000′	710 mph
30,000′	680 mph
40,000′	660 mph

Smashing the sound barrier

Why should it be so hard to make something go faster than sound?

The children have learned (Chapter 15) that the air is made up of tiny particles called molecules. In this chapter are many demonstrations showing how sound waves are moving areas of compression and rarefaction.

A plane engine warming up is surrounded by the sea of sound waves kicked up by its propeller. As the blade cuts into the air, every particle of air in its path is

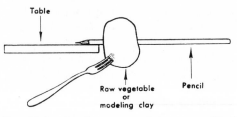

Table

Raw vegetable or modeling clay

Pencil

Fig. 26-8 Another way to balance an object hanging off a table. (From *UNESCO Source Book for Science Teachers*, UNESCO, 1956.)

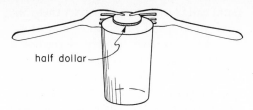

half dollar

Fig. 26-9 A balanced coin. (Redrawn from *UNESCO Source Book for Science Teachers*, UNESCO, 1956.

compressed or bunched, and then rarefied or thinned as it falls behind the plane.

If you hear a plane overhead, the sound waves are pouring off from it in all directions at over 700 mph. What would happen if the plane could go fast enough to catch up to its own sound waves?

As a plane increases its speed, the compression waves in front are crowded closer and closer together. Children who have used hand pumps on their bicycle tires know how hard it is to compress air. In the same way a speeding plane has to push harder and harder as it approaches the speed of sound to compress the air in front of it.

In laboratory wind tunnels, scientists found that ordinary plane models were wrenched apart when air speed approached that of sound. The special kinds of sound waves piled up in front of objects traveling at or above the speed of sound are called *shock waves* (Fig. 26-10). The crack of a whip is an example of such a super-squeezed compression wave.

With the power of jet engines, designers saw the possibility of getting the push needed to drive a plane past the sound barrier into the world of silent and smooth flying beyond.

Flying through space has for centuries been one of man's persistent dreams. Cyrano de Bergerac (1619-55), later the hero of a nineteenth century French play by Edmond Rostand, wrote of a space ship made like a huge box with holes at each

end. Air heated by lens-focused sunlight was to rush out one of the holes and drive the box ahead. Many adults as children read Jules Verne's books as fantasy. Yet *20,000 Leagues Under the Sea* has come to full reality. His space travel novel, *From the Earth to the Moon,* written in 1865, is on the edge of becoming fact.

Many of the principles behind flight in space are of such a nature that they cannot be easily demonstrated in the classroom. In some instances analogies can be drawn; in others your firmest ally will be the children's imagination.

GRAVITY AND SATELLITES

The legend about the famous apple falling on Newton's head is supposed to have started him thinking about the pulling power of the earth—gravity. He won-

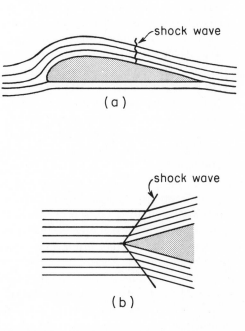

Fig. 26-10 Shock waves: (a) created by a normal airplane wing at subsonic air speed; (b) created by a supersonic airplane wing at supersonic air speed. (Redrawn from E. A. Bonney, *Engineering Supersonic Aerodynamics,* McGraw-Hill, 1950.)

dered why the moon did not fall into the earth. On the other hand, he knew the moon was moving—why didn't it simply fly off into space? From observation he calculated that each second the moon moves two thirds of a mile. During this time it falls toward the earth one twentieth of an inch. These two motions are such that a nearly perfect circle about the earth results. There are two major forces acting upon the moon—its forward momentum and the pull of the earth's gravitation. When the curve of a falling object on the average of its path matches the curvature of the earth, that object perpetually "falls" toward the earth without ever hitting it. This is true of the moon. It is also true of the artificial earth satellites. The pull of the earth and the forward momentum must be correctly balanced.

A thrown ball

When you throw a ball, the line it describes through the air is a curve. However, the curve is much steeper than the curvature of the earth, and thus the ball falls back to the surface. Pretend that the earth is perfectly smooth and that there is no air. If one could throw a baseball hard enough, its curve of falling would exactly correspond to the curvature of the earth, and, like the moon, the ball would fall perpetually.

Now the earth is not smooth and it does have an atmosphere. Yet, in essence, what we have had to do to orbit satellites is to throw them hard enough so that they will escape the earth's atmosphere and gravitational field. A satellite is boosted above the atmosphere by a series of rocket stages. Above the atmosphere there is relatively little friction to slow the satellite down once it is moving at a speed where the curve of its fall toward the earth is such that it does not hit the earth.

Let children throw a ball or any object and observe how it follows a curved path, called trajectory. Then let them observe how speed determines trajectory. An object thrown slowly describes a steeper curve than one thrown fast.

There is a paddle tennis game which uses a rubber ball attached to a long rubber band. Whirl this around your head just fast enough so that the ball and elastic are nearly horizontal. The ball is the moon, and the rubber band represents the earth's gravitational pull on the moon. The force pulling the ball inward (centripetal force) is the gravitational pull. The whirling ball exerts a pull outward (centrifugal force). When you whirl the ball at just the right speed, one force balances the other. Observe what happens if you whirl too slowly. Help children make the analogy between this and the speed required to orbit an artificial satellite. Notice that the band stretches outward (i.e., the length of the orbit increases) when the force put into the whirling is increased. If the length of the band is suddenly shortened, the number of revolutions sharply increases. Point out that the moon circles the earth once in 28 days. Artificial satellites, which are only a few hundred miles out as against the moon's distance of 240,000 miles, revolve about the earth many times a day.

You can make your own whirling device by passing a string through a small rubber ball and then through the center hole of a thread spool. For firmer control you may tie a weight on the end of the string that passes through the spool.

One of your older students especially interested in space might point out that the orbits of the artificial satellites are not circular but are elliptical (oval-shaped). You can explain this in the following way. When a satellite is sent up, the last stage (Fig. 26-11) should shoot exactly in line with the earth's surface at the right speed for that altitude. However, nearly always errors occur. If the speed is too great, the

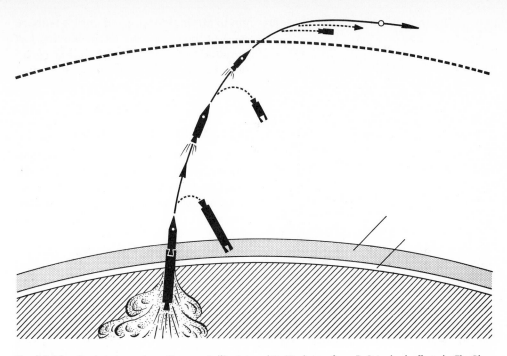

Fig. 26-11 Rocket stages in getting a satellite into orbit. (Redrawn from R. Brinckerhoff et al., *The Physical World,* Harcourt, Brace & World, 1958.)

satellite will swing out further, i.e., the curve of part of its orbit will be a little greater than the curve of the earth. As it curves out, it loses speed, and as it loses speed, the curve approaches that of the earth. Once a satellite is set on a particular orbit, it will keep to that orbit. If the error occurs in the direction in which the last-stage rocket points the satellite, the same kind of oval orbit can result. If the error is too great, the satellite curves out sharply and then curves back to the earth in a sharper curve than the earth's surface. If this curve is sharp enough, the satellite crashes into the earth's atmosphere and burns up from friction. The opposite can occur. If the satellite is shot off with a speed greater than 18,000 mph, the curve of the orbit is so shallow that it never comes back on itself; thus, the satellite swings off into space, never to return. In order to put a satellite into orbit, its curve must never be so steep as to plunge

it into the earth's atmosphere, nor so shallow that it does not come back on itself. In other words, a satellite orbit can either be a circle or an ellipse, but not a parabola.

Launching a satellite

Satellite rockets carry a huge load of fuel to make the speed to orbit the satellite. To make the grade is like climbing an enormous hill which gets easier the longer you climb.

The solution to the problem was piggyback rockets (Fig. 26-11). The bottom stage drops off as it burns out, thereby reducing the over-all weight and permitting increasing speed. The second stage, in turn, burns and drops away, while the third imparts the final speed and direction.

Once the satellite is in an orbit beyond the earth's atmosphere, it requires no further fuel. It merely obeys Newton's law that a body in motion tends to remain in motion.

The atmosphere as a barrier

We live at the bottom of an ocean of air. Just as there are different layers of water at different depths of the oceans, there are different layers of air in the atmosphere. As far back as 1730, Dr. Edmund Halley theorized that the air above earth was divided into layers.

In 1900 a French meteorologist, Léon Teisserenc de Bort, used instrument-carrying balloons to expand Halley's theories. Teisserenc de Bort named the lowest layer the troposphere. In this layer occur major weather phenomena. The depth of the layer differs seasonally and latitudinally, being deeper over the poles than at the equator. Teisserenc de Bort named the second layer the stratosphere because its relatively constant temperatures permitted horizontal layers of wind currents, now called jet streams. Since his time, scientific research has named two other layers: the ionosphere, where the air is electrically charged by the sun; and the exosphere, the outermost layer identified to date, which contains single atoms of nitrogen and oxygen, all circling the earth like microscopic satellites. Nearly all the molecules in the earth's atmosphere are within 23 miles of the ground.

Getting the satellite up through the atmosphere and beyond into orbit is difficult and vital. Any child who has pedaled a bicycle against the wind knows what "air resistance" means. A child who has slid down a rope knows that friction generated heat. In his imagination let him picture tons of air rubbing against a rocket at thousands of miles per hour, and he is on his way to understanding why satellites (and meteors) burn up when they strike the earth's atmosphere at high speeds.

As fast as a rocket rises, it does not begin to attain orbital speed until it is above most of the earth's air. If, in the first few hundred feet, it attained full speed, a good deal of the energy of the rocket's fuel would be wasted pushing against air.

IMPORTANCE OF SATELLITES

All the potential uses of space satellites are not yet known and will, of course, depend upon knowledge yet to be discovered. Some obvious benefits are noted below.

Acquisition of new knowledge

From the kinds of orbits satellites take, we learn the exact shape of the earth. Though it is nearly a perfect sphere, it does have a very slight pear shape. Instruments inside the satellite radio back to earth data on the nature of radiation in space, the number of meteors, temperature, etc., and this data is recorded and studied. At present we are planning to mount a telescope in space as an earth satellite and, for the first time, see the universe without the shimmering, hazy, filter of the atmosphere. Medical and other research needing an environment free of microbes will be possible in space.

Weather forecasting

Until recently man has been in the position of trying to talk about something which he has only seen in pieces—the weather. A satellite can take TV images and photographs of huge areas so that we can see at a glance the weather pattern of the world. These, in turn, may be related to solar flares, sunspots, and other phenomena so that it may some day be possible to predict weather months in advance. Typhoon, hurricane, tornado, and other warnings well in advance will be possible. Savings could run into hundreds of millions of dollars a year.

Communication

Several satellites in orbit whose speed and direction match the speed and direction of the earth's rotation would seem to hang motionless over various spots. These could be used to relay television, radio, and telephone signals to or from any place in the world.

MANNED SPACE TRAVEL

As formidable as are the problems behind the successful launching of a satellite, getting a man into space (and getting him back) is much more difficult. Wherever man goes, he must take a miniature of his world with him.

He must have food, water, pressure, oxygen, and protection against meteors and radiation. He must not be crushed to death by too high speeds of acceleration and deceleration. He must not be frozen or cooked by temperature extremes. He must be able to cope with weightlessness.

Food and water in space

Experiments in condensing food are being performed. Furthermore, when space ships reach a large size, plants such as algae may actually be grown aboard. This possibility has a tremendous economy to it. Not only would the growing plants be food, but, while growing, they would use up carbon dioxide (a human waste product) and produce oxygen, which, in turn, could be breathed by humans. Other wastes could be used to fertilize the plants. Water purification systems are being designed which would enable the same water to be used over and over again.

Taking along pressure

Crossing the 10-mile limit is really man's first step into outer space. Above 10 miles man would blow up because of the difference in pressure between the inside and the outside of the body. In this low-pressure environment, water, and therefore blood, would boil at normal body temperature, 98.6° F.

The space traveler must take pressure with him. He can do this in two ways—either by building an airtight room (or cabin) or by means of a pressurized suit. Both of these have been designed and are being tested.

Oxygen in space

People who drive over high mountain passes sometimes feel the lack of oxygen. In the ascent of Mount Everest, the climbers, Tensing Norkay and Edmund Hillary, each carried oxygen tanks. Help children see the analogy to deep-sea divers and their oxygen tanks. At 18,000′ there is just one half as much oxygen as at sea level. Above 50,000′ there is not enough oxygen to live; you would die in 15 seconds. This is only 10 miles up, or on the lower edge of the stratosphere. Planes flying from 8000 to 40,000′ need to pressurize their interiors or else provide individual oxygen masks. Because of the pressure differential, the plane windows must be very thick and the openings carefully sealed. For this reason anything falling out of a plane at high altitude is pulled out as though by giant suction.

Oxygen compressed in tanks would be carried. As was mentioned earlier, it could also be provided from growing plants. The air would have to be filtered and treated to remove carbon dioxide and water vapor. Because a coasting or orbiting space ship has no weight, fans would be needed to circulate the air; otherwise, a man could suffocate. Review the nature and cause of convection currents to see why such currents would not occur under weightless conditions.

Radiation protection

A space suit or space cabin will also have to protect the space man from cosmic and other radiations. Preliminary satellite signals have already furnished valuable and unexpected information on the kinds and intensities of radiation that would be encountered.

Our atmosphere is, in effect, the earth's space suit, acting as a shielding against cosmic particles, life-destroying ultraviolet and x-rays, etc. In space man must carry his shield. Meteors may also bombard him.

An astronomer calculates that the chances of a rocket with ⅛″ aluminum skin being punctured by a meteorite are 1 in 5000 per day. On a 1000-day trip to Mars this risk becomes 1 in 5. Space men are warned to avoid meteor showers and comet orbits, especially in the region between Mars and Jupiter where thousands of asteroids are located. Rockets may be designed with a "Meteor Bumper" or thin extra outside wall. Perhaps the solution will be similar to that used in puncture-proof tires—a liquid chemical which oozes into any meteor holes in the outer skin.

Acceleration-deceleration

Men traveling inside a space ship must be able to cope also with *enormous changes in speed during takeoff and landing*. Scientists measure the pull of gravity on the earth's surface as 1 "g." Some men can stand the pull of a force many times their ordinary weight. Sometimes test pilots black out under only 2½–5 "g's" unless special provisions are taken. Experiments have shown that a man is much less apt to black out if he is subjected to pressure while lying down. Also the special pressurized suits which prevent blood from leaving the brain and which have been used for years by pilots of high-speed airplanes will be of help. For short periods of time, properly suited and positioned, a man can stand a stress of many gravities.

Space temperatures

There are two sources of heat extremes which will beset space exploration—friction and radiation. Friction from air molecules which can melt metal and burn a meteorite can kill the inhabitants of a ship. However, this problem exists for the most part only at the beginnings and endings of voyages. Even now special materials have been developed to sustain great heat. Also special techniques of moving in and out of the atmosphere are being explored.

Heat from solar radiation, however, will last the entire voyage. Without air to disperse and absorb radiated heat, objects in space will simultaneously boil and freeze. The side to the sun will overheat; the side in shadow will plunge well below freezing.

Let children review the relation of dark and light colors to temperature (Chapters 18 and 20). For example, locate two thermometers which register the same at the beginning of the experiment. Set each in a #10 tin can in a sunny window. The outside of one can should be painted black. Check after 20 minutes. The thermometer in the black can should give a higher reading. Space suits need to reflect the sun's rays on one side and have some heater to keep the dark side warm. Space ships must use a special white reflecting paint or checkerboard design.

Undiluted, unfiltered radiation in space, while a problem, may also be a boon to space travelers. It might be used as a source of energy. Huge mirrors could collect the heat and thereby generate electricity. One theory speculates that the slight but persistent pressure which radiation exerts could be used to drive a space ship. Large sails made of metal foil would be spread out to pull the ship along.

Being airless, space presents another problem, a seeming contradiction. Filled with intense light, it will also be jet black. On earth we are used to light flowing all about us. Shadows are dark but not so black that nothing can be seen in them. Air breaks light up and sends it off in every direction. In space there is only the incredible glare of the sun and impenetrable shadows—no grays, no shadings. The stars will not twinkle but, unblinking, will be sharp and bright in an eternity of black velvet. It is the air that gives us the blue sky and the colors of sunset. It is air that makes it possible to walk about without special shielding against the sun's intensity. In space special glass and lenses will be necessary if man is to survive.

Weightlessness

Let children jump and feel weightlessness at the top of the jump. Children who have been in a quickly descending elevator can describe momentary experiences of near weightlessness. Anyone who has been in a small plane during a nose-over will never forget how unattached objects momentarily floated in air.

This feeling of weightlessness can be very confusing to our posture sense—our sense of balance. However, there is much evidence that most people with training can learn not only to deal with weightlessness but actually also to enjoy being freed from the tyranny of gravity. During long voyages unused muscles, those used on earth to hold us up against the pull of gravity, may become weak and flabby. Consequently, the voyagers may have to exercise frequently so as not to become so weak they cannot stand or walk once they return to earth. Even a few weeks in bed can make it hard to walk about.

"Empty" space?

If a fish in the ocean considered such things, he would probably regard the air above his world as "empty." Space is not empty; it is airless.

Space is flooded with intense radiation —x-rays, radio, infrared, visible, ultra-violet, cosmic. Recent evidence indicates that there is also a very tenuous presence of free hydrogen. Affecting all this in various ways are the forces of the planets and stars. Gravitational and magnetic attractions fluctuate in intensity from place to place. At times the sun eruptively flares up, throwing out streams of hydrogen and helium nuclei and other elements. There is evidence that bands of electrical current, great streams of moving electrons, encircle the earth. In short, space may be described as filled with energy.

Space is not empty. Airless, unpopulated, hot and cold at the same time—it attracts man by its very challenge.

Space and tomorrow

Undoubtedly what has been done so far is only a beginning. So far no impenetrable barrier has been found which would forever bar man from space. Even though radiation is intense and there are giant steps yet to be made before an efficient, economic motor for space is perfected, the host of problems is within man's capacity to solve.

We have purposefully been very general in our review of getting man into space. All science and technology are growing rapidly, but the pace of space knowledge is breath-taking. Today all attempts to reach and probe beyond the atmosphere use the rapid-thrust rocket. Speed is acquired in the first few minutes of flight, and the rest of the rocket's trip is coasted along by momentum. To escape the earth's attraction, a rapid-thrust rocket or group of rockets arranged piggyback must acquire a speed of 25,000 mph in those first few minutes. Yet it may be that the final answer will lie with space ships whose take-off is relatively slow but which maintain a slow but steady acceleration. A space ship can get to the moon or Mars or Venus by going 25,000 mph. But one can also make the trip by the application of low but continued thrust. We have avoided describing particular rockets, particular technological methods. Since these change rapidly, we could not hope to stay up to date. Many of the current space handbooks (often in paperback editions) provide specific and valuable data. New books of this sort are published frequently. See also the bibliography at the end of this chapter.

CAPSULE LESSONS

26-1 Have the children make two lists: one which contains ways in which gravity may help man, and the other which contains ways in which gravity may hinder man. Lead into the study of gravity and its effects.

26-2 Weigh common objects in the classroom, using a laundry spring balance. Tie the objects with a string and suspend them from the balance. Lead into the study of weight and the force of gravity.

26-3 Balance a yardstick on one finger. Lead into a discussion of center of gravity and balance.

BIBLIOGRAPHY

Berghaust, Erik, *Rockets Around the World,* Putnam, 1958. A report on what the major countries of the world are doing in the field of rockets. Many photographs.

Branley, F. M., *Experiments in the Principle of Space Travel,* Crowell, 1955. Well-designed experiments showing the principles of space travel.

Colby, Carroll B., *Our Space Age Jets,* Coward-McCann, 1959. Describes and gives complete statistics on different kinds of jet aircraft. Traces advances in design since 1951.

Crosby, Alexander L., and Nancy Larrick, *Rockets into Space,* Random House, 1959. Story of rockets and how modern rockets work. Includes man's plans to reach the moon and living conditions on the moon.

Daugherty, Charles M., *Wider than the Sky,* Harcourt, Brace & World, 1958. Describes the development of aviation to our present-day work with jets, missiles, and rockets. Also gives current vocational opportunities in aviation.

Del Rey, Lester, *Rockets Through Space,* Holt, Rinehart and Winston, 1960. Good overview of space sciences to date.

Freeman, Mae, *You Will Go to the Moon,* Random House, 1959. Simple but effective treatment of the feeling of an actual trip to the moon.

Gottlieb, W. P., *Jets and Rockets and How They Work,* Doubleday, 1959. Many interesting and instructive experiments on all phases of aeronautics.

Joseph, A., *Rockets into Space,* Science Research Associates, 1960.

Lewellen, John, *You and Space Travel,* Childrens Press, 1958. Describes the principles of flight and their application to space travel.

Parker, Bertha, *Gravity,* Row, Peterson, 1942. Simple, well-defined explanation of gravity.

Podendorf, Illa, *The True Book of Space,* Childrens Press, 1959. Beginning book on satellites, space travel, and rockets.

Flight

See Chapter 9 for experiments showing that air is a form of matter having weight and able to exert pressure even though it cannot be seen.

BIRD FLIGHT

For centuries men watched and envied and sought to imitate the free flight of birds. Flying has been compared to swimming. Children who swim may be able to describe the freedom of three-dimensional movement in water versus two-dimensional locomotion on land. It may help to think of air as a lighter fluid than water. Encourage children to be "air watchers": observe the flight of air-borne seeds, insects, birds, and planes. A bulletin board and a three-dimensional table exhibit might include examples and/or pictures of some of these. Even our largest cities provide opportunities to observe such birds as common rock doves or pigeons. Encourage children to watch how birds use the wing as a lever to raise the whole body. The downbeat lets through as little air as possible; the upbeat lets through as much as possible. Let the children study a bird wing, even a chicken wing, to see how this is so. Let children push their fingers through the wing feathers from the top down and then from below up to see how well the wing cover is adapted for "swimming" in the air. Look at a long wing feather (primary) and note how the lead-

ing or front edge is soft and wide. On the upstroke, air slips easily through this flexible part of the feather. On the downstroke, the surface resists the air. Help children see the relation between anatomy and function in bird bones, i.e., the keel or breastbone permits attachment space and leverage for the big wing muscles (the white meat). Let children discover by observation how bird wings, like plane wings, are tilted slightly at the point of attachment to the body (fuselage).

Changing the line of flight is accomplished by movements of feathers in tail and wing tip. Encourage children to observe how pigeons use tail feathers to "brake" their speed when coming in for a landing.

Children who live near the ocean or desert or any height of land can observe how gulls, buzzards, hawks, and ravens soar with motionless wings on thermals (updrafts of warmer air).

Watch for bird flight where warmed air rises against the face of a cliff or along a mountain range. Glider pilots meet at places where the geography offers such thermals in combination with good take-off and landing topography.

Children who own roller skates or ice skates may have already tried a kind of flying by paddling themselves forward with a piece of cardboard in each hand. On a windy day, they may have used a larger single cardboard as a sail.

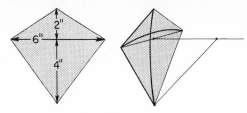

Fig. 27-1 A miniature bow kite.

Children will be amused and entertained by the hero's plaintive "Birds can fly, an' why can't I?" in J. T. Trowbridge's famous story poem, *Darius Green and His Flying Machine.*

KITES

Kites were man's first flying machines. From these, gliders evolved and were ultimately developed into engine-powered aircraft. But before the Wright brothers could invent their first plane (1903), they had to learn to use gliders. And before that, like most boys, they learned to fly kites.

Most children know that you have to run with a kite to get it up in the air unless a wind is blowing against the kite. They also know that a kite will not stay up unless there is wind—the stronger, the better. Let the children show you where to tie a kite string or "bridle" so that the wind can *push up* on the kite surface (plane surface).

Miniature bow kite

Two 6″ heavy broom straws that are to serve as spine and bow of the framework should be notched slightly at the ends (Fig. 27-1). Soak one of the sticks in water for a few minutes so that it will bend easily. Notch the sides of it near each end and bend it into a bow.

Lay the bow across the spine 2″ from the top. Be sure the two sides of the bow are equal. Bind the sticks together with coarse thread. Make a number of turns

with the thread, first through one diagonal of angles and then the other.

Beginning at the top of the spine stick, using nylon or silk thread, string the kite by connecting all the points—from upper tip of spine to tip of bow to lower tip of spine and from there to the other bow tip and back to the upper tip of the spine. From tip to tip of the bow, run a crossing string, and then tighten the string to hold the bow. Wind string around the ends of the sticks to hold the framework string in place and to reinforce the ends of the sticks. Brush glue on the string at the ends of the sticks and at the point where the spine and bow meet.

Lay the framework on tissue or thin paper and cut around it, allowing an extra inch of paper all the way around. Fold this extra inch of paper over the string and glue it. Allow time for drying.

Make a very small hole in the paper at the crossing point of the bow and spine. Run thread through the hole and tie it securely to the crossing string. The bridle string should be the distance from the crossing to the end of the bow plus the distance from the end of the bow to the bottom of the spine. Tie the kite line to the bridle at a distance from the top of the spine that is equal to the distance from the crossing to the end of the bow.

Miniature box kite

With ruler and pencil, draw the lines as shown in Fig. 27-2A on a piece of 6″ × 8¼″ typing paper. Cut out the dark areas and fold on the dotted lines. Fasten the sides of the box together with mending tape, rubber cement, or glue, using the ¼″ overlap as an anchoring strip.

The length of the bridle equals two thirds of the length plus the width of one side—6″—attached as shown in the figure. Tie the line to the bridle at the point which equals the distance of the width of the box.

Miniature triangular kite

A triangular kite is made like the four-sided box kite (Fig. 27-2B). Children can learn much about the motion of kites by flying miniatures in front of a fan or outdoors.

Full-size kites

To make a big kite, follow the same pattern as for the miniature kite. Increase the dimensions proportionately and use strong material; bamboo slits are good. For the box kite first make a form of the slits in the shape of the miniature and then cover with paper. Full-size kites are regular and inexpensive items in variety stores.

Air resistance

Let children run with stiff cardboard, first folded, then open. The folded cardboard, of course, offers more resistance, and thereby makes motion more difficult. Be sure cardboard is not too large to keep children from running safely. Even young children can begin to understand the principle of air resistance in kites by running with a strip of stiff paper at the end of a string. Let children experiment with different lengths of string and sizes, shapes, and weights, of paper. Compare results from walking and running.

The secret of any "plane" surface riding the air is air resistance. Young children can understand this by extending a sheet of notebook paper and pirouetting in place. Note the "kite" effect when you push a horizontal piece of notebook paper against the air. Here you are seeing dynamic "lift" at work. Hold the paper slightly curved so that it doesn't droop; then quickly shove it forward. The leading edge lifts.

If you pull a strip of paper toward you quickly, the drooping end of the paper will come up against the pull of gravity. The reason is the same as for the previous

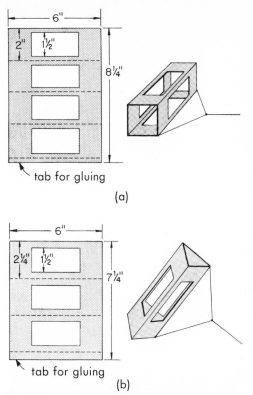

Fig. 27-2 (a) A miniature box kite. Compare with the design of the first planes. (b) A miniature triangular box kite.

experiment. Air molecules are squeezed and crowded so thickly under the *leading* edge of the paper that they push up against the pull of gravity and the pressure of air above.

Like planes, kites are heavier than air and can therefore remain aloft for the same reason—air movement on their surfaces. The kite string and bridle, like the "sheet" and mast of a sailboat, can be adjusted to make an angle of deflection which moves the kite or sailboat. In other words, when a kite is held so that the top part leans into the wind, the air molecules crowded up under the kite will again create a difference in air pressure. As long as there is greater pressure on the lower side (front of kite), the kite will rise in the wind. On a windless day, children may try flying

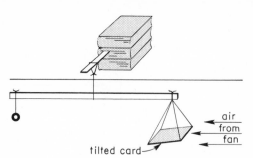

Fig. 27-3 The effect of air pressure on balance.

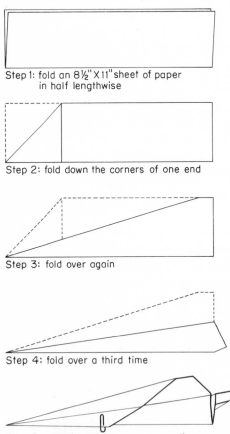

Step 1: fold an 8½"×11" sheet of paper
in half lengthwise

Step 2: fold down the corners of one end

Step 3: fold over again

Step 4: fold over a third time

Step 5: attach one or more paper clips
for stable flight

Fig. 27-4 Making a paper dart glider. Try cutting and bending the rear flaps up, down, or in opposite directions, and observe the effect on flight behavior.

a kite by running with it or towing it behind a bicycle.

Air moving past the kite provides two forces—one pushing up, lifting the kite, and one pushing back, pulling on the kite string. In a strong wind, kites may even carry weather instruments. The fore part of the Wrights' plane was really a huge box kite. When the Niagara Falls suspension bridge was begun, the first line was carried across the gorge by a kite. Tailless kites, like a box kite, are able to fly in a upright position because two sides are bowed back from a center spine stick to form a dihedral angle. Let children observe how the wings of modern planes also form a dihedral angle to the fuselage. Air moving against the two planes of the kite keeps it in position. If wind comes from one side, the kite's motion is self-correcting.

Air movement against a tilted plane surface provides lift. Fasten a card to a ruler. Then with card slightly tilted swing the ruler at arm's length. Watch how air resistance sustains and pushes the tilted card upward.

Repeat, hanging a tilted cardboard at one end of a yardstick or doweling (Fig. 27-3). When the stick is balanced, make the air move against the card by blowing or fanning. Immediately the card rises, and the balance is destroyed.

GLIDERS—PLANES WITHOUT ENGINES

Many children know how to fold a dart from a piece of notebook paper (Fig. 27-4). Slip a paper clip over the fold near the center. This changes the center of gravity in such a way that the dart will provide long, graceful glides.

While the basic principles of aerodynamics explain why a dart flies, the dart does not look like the conventional type of airplane that a child is most likely to know.

You may want to buy for a few cents one or two balsa wood gliders. After showing the children how to hold and care for the glider, have them make their own out of tagboard or, better, manila folders (Fig. 27-5). The positioning of the paper clip weights has a great effect on how well the glider glides. The method of throwing the glider is also very important.

The object of the weights is to shift the glider's center of gravity so that it is approximately on the center line of the wing (Fig 27-5). If you balance the glider by setting the wings on the tips of your forefinger and thumb, you can readily estimate the center of gravity. Another method is to lay the glider on a ruler and nudge it back and forth until the point is reached where it just begins to fall off. Add paper clips until the center shifts under the wing's center line. This does not have to be exact.

After some use you may find it necessary to reinforce the wings. The glider whose shape and dimensions are given in Fig. 27-6 is considerably larger than the

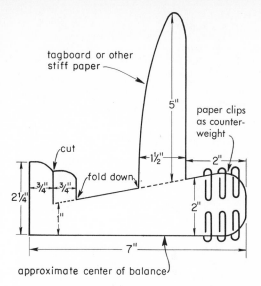

Fig. 27-5 Pattern for a small model glider.

glider described in Fig. 27-5. You may find this size handy as a demonstration model. In general, the bigger the glider, the longer its glide and the slower its shifts in direction.

For the older children a carefully made large glider can be modified to show some

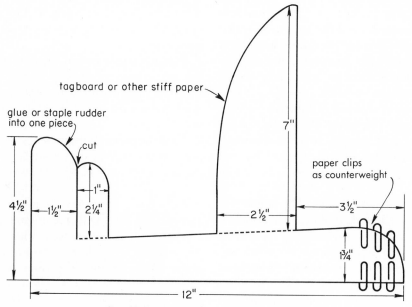

Fig. 27-6 Pattern for a large model glider.

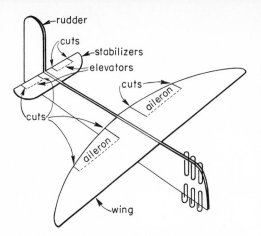

rudder
cuts
stabilizers
elevators
cuts
aileron
cuts
aileron
aileron
wing

Fig. 27-7 A large model glider, showing control surfaces.

of the means by which airplanes are able to turn, to climb, and to descend (Fig. 27-7). Watch the glider's flight when both elevators on the tail stabilizers are bent up, or when one is up and one down, or when one is up and one is level. Bend the ailerons in various positions and note the effects.

Gliders, in general, can be adjusted and manipulated in many ways. Try your own models. For instance, see what happens when the surface of the tail stabilizers is increased. (You will likely need less weight in the nose.) Try narrowing the wing or shortening it. Does the glider now need a sharper, faster "take-off" speed?

A correct method of throwing is very important. The glider should be held at the center of gravity. When released, it should be tilted slightly upward but not tipped to one side or the other. The force of the throw should be gently firm, not with a sharp snap of the wrist. The object is to make the glider float out of your hand.

Man-carrying gliders are sometimes launched by a tow from a car or an airplane or even a windlass. Sometimes gliders are catapulted into flight by giant slingshot-like mechanisms. Gliders can cover astonishing distances and remain

aloft for hours, depending upon pilot skill and thermals, or upward air currents.

PRINCIPLES OF AERODYNAMICS

Lift

Let children work in pairs. Use strips of paper about $2'' \times 10''$ or the size of a wide foot rule. Let them take turns blowing down the length of a paper strip and watching the behavior of the paper. If a child blows *under* the paper, it will rise. Yet if he holds it just under his lower lip, and blows *over* it, it will also rise and flutter in the air stream.

The causative principle is that discovered by Bernoulli, a Swiss physicist and mathematician, about 200 years ago. He observed that, in a flowing fluid, pressure decreases as the speed of the fluid increases. The same principle applies to flowing air.

Let children pull a strip of paper rapidly through the air. The free end rises because of the resistance of the air, but another factor is also operating—namely, the decreased pressure on top of the paper due to the flow of air across it. Two thirds of the lift comes from the reduced air pressure on top.

Fold the paper so that the part beyond the fold curves up slightly. Again notice how the paper is lifted from its original position by a difference in pressure due to an air stream.

Turn the paper back on itself, joining opposite edges to give a curved surface. Blowing across the top will again cause it to lift.

Let a piece of paper extend from the end of a book. Blow over the top. The tail end will rise level with the air stream.

Tape or tack a card to a ruler so that the card curves up like the top of an airplane wing. Balance the ruler across a six-sided pencil so that it very lightly tips down at the end with the card. Direct an air stream parallel to the ruler's length through a soda straw across the curved top of the card (Fig. 27-8). The ruler will rise. Be sure to use the soda straw in directing the air stream. Finding the ruler's point of balance may require some patience. Even without the curved card, an air stream along the balanced ruler will cause it to rise. However, the curved surface produces a more pronounced effect.

Fold down the ends of a card. If you blow straight at it, the card will not blow over. Instead, it will hug the table top because of decreased air pressure on the under surface.

Lay a piece of notebook paper across two books a few inches apart. If you kneel and blow under the paper, it will sink into the space between the two books (Fig. 27-9). Repeat, varying the space between books.

Repeat, placing the paper near the top of a pile of a half dozen books. Make a second pile and cover the two piles with another book. Directing the moving air across the piece of paper again makes it rise.

Bernoulli vs. gravity. Blowing through the hole in a spool, you would expect a 3″ square card placed underneath to fall off. Because of Bernoulli's principle, it does not. A pin or thumbtack through

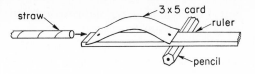

Fig. 27-8 An air stream lifts a ruler. Try blowing through a funnel or large rubber tubing to produce more air flow.

the card holds the card from slipping sideways under pressure of the air stream. Hold the card lightly in place, with your finger on the pinhead, until the space between spool and card is adjusted so that the moving air exerts reduced sideways pressure down on the card. Then remove your fingers, and the card will appear to defy gravity. *Normal* air pressure from below holds up the card as long as you blow. If the spool hole is small, you may need to reduce the size of the card.

Make two paper rolls from 6″ squares, using glue, tape, or a *few* staples. Place near a table edge and blow between them with a straw. If properly adjusted, the papers will roll together instead of apart. To reduce friction, lay rolls on two round pencils. Repeat, using tin cans instead of paper rolls.

The same principle operates if you suspend two balls, apples, or oranges close to-

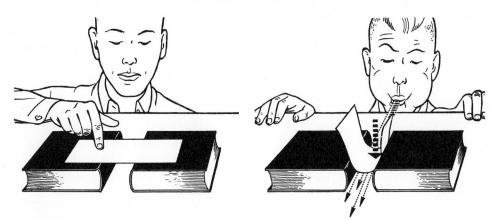

Fig. 27-9 An air stream under a paper causes it to fall. (From R. Brinckerhoff et al., *Exploring Physics*, Harcourt, Brace & World, 1959.)

gether but not touching. Blowing between them forces them together.

Blow between two sheets of paper. The sheets move together as long as you continue blowing. Repeat, suspending the sheets 1–2" apart between pages of a book. Again the sheets draw together.

If a vacuum cleaner hose is attached to the blower end, a ping-pong ball will remain suspended in a straight, upwardly directed air stream. Try to blow a ping-pong ball out of a thistle tube or glass funnel. If you hold your hand over the funnel and invert it, you may remove your hand; the ball will not fall out as long as you blow through the stem. You should be able to pick up the ball from a table by blowing through the stem of the funnel.

Hold two spoons, bowls back to back, under a running faucet. Hold the handle of one spoon between the second and third fingers, and the other between the fourth and fifth fingers of the same hand. As water attains the proper force, the spoons will move together. Repeat, suspending spoons back to back and blowing between them through a straw until they touch with a click.

Bernoulli and ball curves. Throw a ping-pong or tennis ball out of a mailing tube to induce a spin. Watch it curve. The principle is the same as that put to work by a pitcher when he puts a spin on a baseball. The friction of the air against the cover of the ball increases the effective air velocity around one side of the ball and decreases it on the other. Because the pressure is reduced on the side where the velocity is less, the ball curves toward the side of greater effective air flow.

Airfoils

Make a crude airfoil by doubling under a piece of thin copy paper or onion skin. Do not crease the paper at the fold. Hold with one hand on each side of the fold or paste the edges together. If you

blow against the underside of the paper, it will rise. However, if you blow under it, the paper will dip down. If you hold the fold against your lower lip and blow *over* the top, an observer will see the curved sheet rise in apparent defiance of the law of gravity.

Make a loop from a 10" × 1" strip of paper. Put a crease in the loop so that it resembles a plane wing in cross section with flat undersurface and curved top. Slip the loop, curved surface outward, over a pencil and hold just under your lips. Blowing downward on the more curved surface should bring the whole up to a nearly horizontal position.

Let children examine a chicken or pigeon wing. They will see that it is neither flat nor straight, but curved. The front or leading edge is much thicker, especially when the wing is spread, than the trailing edge. Plane wings like those of birds are not flat on the bottom; they are slightly curved, with the top usually having a greater curvature. Even a quarter of an inch change in the curvature can make a significant difference in the way the plane flies.

An airplane wing with an airfoil such as that shown in Fig. 27-10 has an average pressure of 10 pounds per square foot less on top than below.

A commercial transport (propeller plane) may have 18,000 square feet of upper wing surface. At cruising speed such a plane may have a lift of 41,400 pounds, able to lift itself and its crew and cargo with a total weight of 20 tons.

Draw on the board a cross section of an airfoil. Let children measure with string across the top and bottom and compare the two distances. The *partial* vacuum created by the lower pressure on top produces an upward thrust or "lift" on the underside. Ask children if they think a vacuum can "lift" anything. Some will say yes, some no. Let them decide for

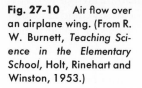

Fig. 27-10 Air flow over an airplane wing. (From R. W. Burnett, *Teaching Science in the Elementary School,* Holt, Rinehart and Winston, 1953.)

path of air above wing—
distance and speed greater
pressure less

Cross-section of airplane wing

path of air under wing—↗
distance and speed less
pressure greater

themselves by using a "plumber's friend" and tools or toys depending upon partial vacuum to be effective.

The knowledge we use today in designing the shape of airplane wings comes from years of continuous study of air flow in wind tunnels. However, we owe much of our knowledge to early students of gliders. For example, they found that air streaming over a flat wing swirled in eddies and reduced the lift. Gliders made with curved wings allowed air to flow smoothly over the top, but eddies swirled underneath. A wing curved on top and much less curved below allowed a smooth flow of air over both surfaces. Modern wings are curved on both surfaces for high-speed flight. Only a very light plane has a flat wing on bottom.

Areas of low pressure. Set a lighted candle behind a 3″ × 5″ card. Have one child blow hard toward the card. Children watching the flame will see it bend toward the card. Air movement created low pressure behind the card.

Place a bottle in front of the candle. Blow hard against the candle and again watch the flame.

Cut a square or oblong window in a quart-size tin can. Set a candle inside so that the flame is close to the window. Blow hard against the side of the can opposite the window and note how the flame is sucked out of the tin can window.

Making and using a wind tunnel. The first necessity for the study of how air moves by airfoils is a steady moving stream of air. An electric fan is not good without modification because its stream of air is a

whirling one. This may be shown by passing smoke from a smoldering dampened newspaper through a running fan; the smoke will be seen to whirl.

A simple demonstration wind tunnel has four basic parts: a fan; a honeycomb to make the stream of air move in a straight line; a means for mounting the model planes, airfoils, and other objects into the air stream; and a source of fog or smoke which will make the moving air visible.

To straighten out the stream of air, some sort of honeycomb arrangement should be placed in front of and close to the electric fan (Fig. 27-11). This will provide a fairly straight stream of air as can be shown by using smoldering newspaper. Possible sources of a honeycomb include the criss-crossed partitions inside an egg carton. Boxes used to ship bottled products often have honeycomb partitioning. Or you can make your own honeycomb from strips of cardboard slotted at regular intervals to fit into and across each other to form a pattern of squares.

Mounting objects in the air stream can

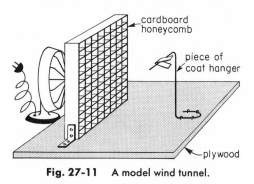

cardboard honeycomb

piece of coat hanger

plywood

Fig. 27-11 A model wind tunnel.

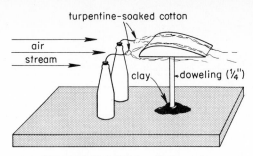

turpentine-soaked cotton

air stream

clay   doweling (¼")

Fig. 27-12 Using a wind tunnel.

be done several ways. For instance, take coat hanger wire and bend in the shape of an upside down L (see Fig. 27-11). One end can be bent so that it can be nailed to a base, or it can be stuck in a cork which is glued or nailed to the base or inserted in a bottle containing counterweighting water or sand. A wood doweling sticking up from a lump of modeling clay will also serve (Fig. 27-12). The model can be wired, tied, or glued to the mounting support.

Mount a complete model on a hanger or doweling. By bending the ailerons, elevators, and rudder in various positions and then passing smoke over the surfaces, you can show how these parts affect the flow of air. A more graphic demonstration can be made by hanging the model (Fig. 27-13). Suspend the model from its point of balance (should be approximately the center of the wing). Below attach the thread to a lightly stretched rubber band. The plane will take certain attitudes in response to different aileron, elevator, and rudder positions.

The source of smoke and fog can be varied. One fog generator can be made by putting dry ice and hot water in a bottle which has a one-hole stopper and glass tube. (Do not stopper the bottle tightly.) The dry ice can be put in a pan with the hot water and set between the object and the honeycomb. In Fig. 27-12, wires mounted in corks in bottles have tufts of cotton on their ends. These tufts are mois-

tened with turpentine and ignited as a smoke source. One can also hold smoldering punk or damp tubes or rolled paper in the air stream.

The wind tunnel is more effective inside an empty aquarium or box. Cut out one side of a box and cover the space with cellophane or glass taped in place. You should leave an end or the top open for the air to escape and enter.

When setting up your wind tunnel, experiment with various positions of the parts, intensities of fan, positions of models, and so forth. Ask a pupil to make an airplane wing out of balsa wood; the wing should be curved on top and flat on the bottom. Mount or hang it in the air stream. Mount and hang objects of other shapes—a ball, a cube, a flat wing, a toy glider (Fig. 27-5).

Four forces—gravity, lift, thrust, drag

Whether it be bird, propeller-driven plane, jet plane, or rocket, four forces act on a body traveling through air.

Gravity pulls down on everything. *Lift* pushes up against the force of gravity. *Thrust,* such as given by a bird's wing beat, a turn of a propeller, the exhaust from a rocket or jet engine, pushes forward. *Drag,*

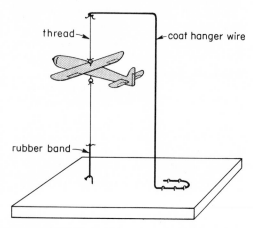

thread   coat hanger wire

rubber band

Fig. 27-13 A hanging airplane model for use with a wind tunnel.

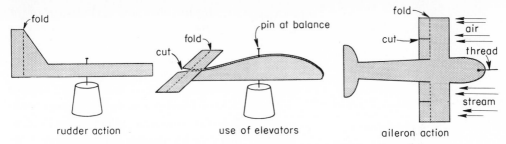

Fig. 27-14   Models for showing the action of the control surfaces of an airplane.

caused by air resistance and air friction, is the force which tries to hold things back.

At constant flying speed, drag is balanced by thrust. At take-off, thrust must be greater than drag. The Wrights finally succeeded in powered sustained flight by adding to their glider a small engine which would keep pulling the whole forward with a force that exceeded the drag.

A collection or exhibit of airplane models should illustrate the decrease in wing spread as power has increased in the newer planes. Reduction of surface reduces resistance to air and, therefore, drag. Doubling the speed quadruples the lift. But double speed requires eight times the power—hence the enormous fuel consumption of newer, faster planes. In the bird, the wings push back against the air, acting like a lever in much the same manner as one uses a paddle in water. While the bird wing pushes back, it also pushes down.

Controlling a plane

As we have said, men for centuries tried to find out how birds flew. The Wright brothers were successful because of their epochal invention of a mechanism which, by one lever motion, could operate the vertical rudders and flex the horizontal elevators. Both changes had to be simultaneous. The addition of a small gas engine to their glider enabled them to fly.

Children will already have learned much about plane controls by making and studying paper darts or gliders. Let them label these with standard part names. An airplane turns when the ailerons are moved. The rudder prevents slipping sideways in the turn. It is a common misconception that a rudder steers an airplane, as the rudder steers a boat.

To find out how a plane climbs or dives, make a tagboard model of the fuselage and elevators. Cut two outlines from pattern. Glue these together, except for stabilizer tail pieces which are folded down (Fig. 27-14). Pin through the balance point of the model into a cork. Place the cork in a bottle and set in your wind tunnel or blow air over the surfaces with a straw. Observe action with elevators up, elevators down. Children may already have learned about stabilizers from the glider models described earlier in this chapter. Rudder action can be shown in a similar manner.

To find out how a plane banks, cut out a tagboard model (Fig. 27-14). Hold in an air stream by attaching a thread to the nose. Action of the ailerons controls banking left or right. The ailerons always move in opposite directions. With the right aileron down, the left aileron is up and the plane banks to the left, as a result of pushing the control stick to the left. If the control stick is pushed to the right, the right aileron is up, and the left is down, the plane now banks to the right. In both cases, the side with the aileron down has the

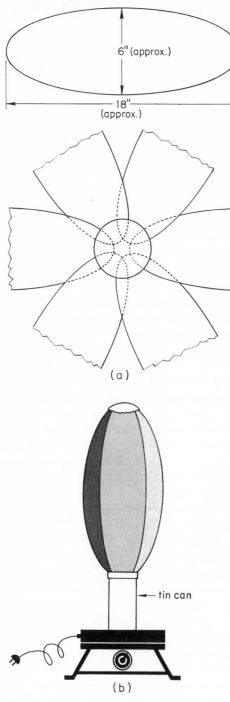

6" (approx.)

18" (approx.)

(a)

tin can

(b)

Fig. 27-15 (a) Pattern for a hot-air balloon; (b) filling a hot-air balloon.

greater lift, thus tilting that wing of the airplane.

LIGHTER-THAN-AIR CRAFT

Man's first trip in the air was made not in a plane but in a balloon. Two Frenchmen, the Montgolfier brothers, deserve the main credit for this adventure. The sons of a papermaker, for years they experimented in making balloons which would rise when paper was burned inside. The principle involved is that warmed air rises because the molecules of air expand with heat. The Montgolfiers built and released a balloon which carried a sheep and two barnyard fowl 1500′ aloft. The balloon floated 2 miles and came down with the passengers unharmed.

Balloons used today, such as a navy dirigible, rise because they are filled with a gas lighter (less dense) than air. The first balloons contained hydrogen, which is a very explosive gas when removed from its quiet partnership with other elements, as in such compounds as water (Chapter 12). The great number of accidents with hydrogen balloons led to the use of helium, an inert gas, which is also lighter than air though less so than hydrogen.

Just as the buoyancy or lifting power of water holds up ships in the ocean, the buoyancy of air holds up planes and balloons in the ocean of air. A hundred cubic feet of helium weighs 2.2 pounds, whereas the same amount of air weighs 8 pounds. Therefore, helium can lift 5.8 pounds per 100 cubic feet. A balloon with a 100,000 cubic foot load of helium can therefore lift 1000 × 5.8 or 5800 pounds.

Some of the children's parents or grandparents may have seen hot-air balloon ascensions at county fairs. The mouth of the bag was placed over a hole in the ground. As kerosene burned at the bottom of the hole, hot gases would rise and fill the bag of the balloon which stood two to three stories high.

Children may enjoy having their own miniature balloon ascension. Cut a central circular piece and six tapered sections of tissue (Fig. 27-15A). Paste edges of the gores together and lap ends over onto the middle circle. Different colors of tissue can be used, and the size of the pieces can be increased as desired. Reinforce and weight down the mouth of the balloon with 1″ masking tape. Fill with hot air rising from a heater or electric plate (Fig. 27-15B). Collect through a stove or cylinder made by cutting the top and bottom off a tin can. Tie 12–15′ of light cotton string to the mouth of the balloon. When the balloon is saturated with hot air, children will feel tension and can then pay out the line to let the ballon rise gradually.

Model dirigible

Tie 3/16″ reeds or canes together at nose and tail to make ribs for a typical blunt-nosed, streamlined dirigible shape. Use balsa wood strips to form hoops and secure them to the reeds with light cord or glue. Since dirigibles are classed as lighter-than-air craft, always use the lightest materials possible.

Cut gores (about six) from tissue paper and paste to ribs. Insert empty balloons, small ones in nose and tail, larger ones in mid-section. These will have to be filled with lighter-than-air gas. Natural or illuminating gas will lift a balloon. However, remember that these gases are explosive. Helium is sometimes available from local commercial firms. If you have "watched your weight" throughout construction and if balloons are fully inflated, the model dirigible should rise. To keep your model on an even keel, secure front and rear with light mooring cords made from thread.

It may be useful to repeat experiments that will reinforce the children's concept of why heated air rises; i.e., it becomes lighter, has fewer molecules per cubic foot, etc. (See Chapter 9.)

PARACHUTES

We have seen how, in the case of kites, even a puff of wind can support weight.

To reinforce the idea, let children stand on a chair and drop a flat piece of paper. It flutters slowly to the floor. Repeat, wadding paper in a ball. Ask children which piece fell more quickly and why. Repeat, letting children drop a flat sheet and a crumpled sheet simultaneously.

Let children make a model parachute with a handkerchief. A large silk one with its four corners tied to a thermos cork as ballast works well. Fold carefully so that the strings do not tangle, throw as high as possible, and watch its descent. Let children jump off a chair, with and without the aid of an open umbrella.

Encourage children to find seeds which travel by parachutes. For example, a seed of dandelion, milkweed, or sycamore is provided with radial fuzz which can carry it far afield and thus spread the plant.

Just as a rubber life belt holds up a man in water, a parachute utilizes the buoyancy and resistance of air to save man's life in the air. A man falling unimpeded would increase his speed 32′ every second. If he were to fall one fourth of a mile, he would be falling 3 miles a minute.

An old story has it that the first time a parachute was used for practical purposes was not to save a man from a falling plane, but to help a man escape from prison. Imprisoned in Budapest during the French Revolution, he used a bed sheet and "floated" to the ground and freedom.

A. J. Garnerin, an early investigator in the nature of air travel, made a parachute

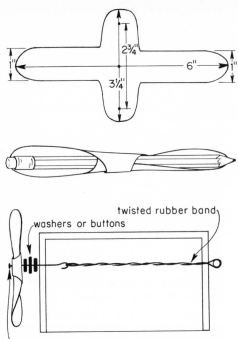

twisted rubber band

washers or buttons

large pin head, hat pin or wire bent into ball

Fig. 27-16 A working-model propeller.

which had a diameter of 24′ and whose shape was convex when open. The passenger rode in a wicker basket fastened to the parachute by cords.

For his exhibition leap (1797), the inventor was carried aloft in a balloon. When he started his drop, the parachute opened, but the basket began to swing violently from side to side. The air trapped in the dome of the chute could not get out and acted like a pivot on which the chute could swing like a pendulum. The hole in the top which Garnerin made in subsequent parachutes is still used today.

PROPELLERS—PINWHEELS AND HELICOPTERS

The plane's propeller is really an airscrew biting its way through the air. A propeller may also be regarded as a windmill threshing the air. Let children exam-ine model plane propellers and various kinds of common screws.

Let children look for seeds with "propeller blades," i.e., maple, ash, elm, linden, etc. Let children stand on a chair and watch the helicopter blade action as they drop such dry seeds.

Some children may enjoy using a box, rubber band, and paper to make a model propeller (Fig. 27-16). Make a paper outline of the pattern shown and trace on cardboard. Roll the cardboard around a pencil until the three holes come together. Push wire through the center to form a shaft. Before mounting on a box, place some buttons or washers over the shaft. Several rubber bands twisted together will serve as the "motor."

A pinwheel can be a very rewarding construction. Use ordinary paper cut in a square, making cuts and folds as shown in Fig. 27-17. Lengths of wire with short pieces of soda straw as bearings can be used to mount pinwheels. They rotate

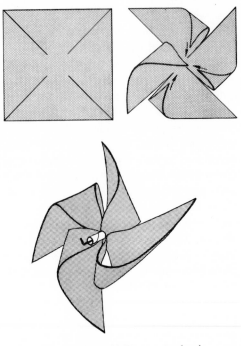

Fig. 27-17 Making a pinwheel.

quite fast even when moved through the air while one is walking.

The propeller's job is not to blow a stream of air over the wings but to push air back so that the airplane is pushed forward, like a rowboat moving away in an opposite direction when an oar is pulled through water. Jets send their exhaust gases backward so that the reaction forces the airplane forward. Study the propeller action, using a fan mounted on roller skates, on a wheeled cart, or on a wood block, box, or desk drawer on rollers (see pp. 427–29). Note action if the fan has different speed settings. Encourage children to decide by observation whether bird wings in flight are flat or curved, and whether propeller blades on models or real planes are flat or curved.

Study the principle of helicopter flight by making paper and/or wood models. Throw a card model (Fig. 27-18) into the air and observe the spin. The upward thrust caused by the spin will not lift the helicopter but will reduce the rate of fall in landing. The soft wood model, when the dowel is spun quickly between the hands, will rise into the air. The rotating propeller blades force the model up by pushing the air down.

Helicopters really have moving wings. Children with toy helicopters or models can show the class how the usual airplane wing and propeller are replaced by a large horizontal rotor. The change in pitch of these rotor blades approximates the flexibility and multidirectional motions of bird wings in flight. The helicopter rises because the rotor blades push down against the air. A rotor wing also develops lift because it is an airfoil.

Another model to show the principle of the helicopter is made with the aid of two spools, a model propeller blade, doweling, string, and a wood block. Note the two finishing nails on top of the spool (Fig. 27-19). These fit into holes in the propeller

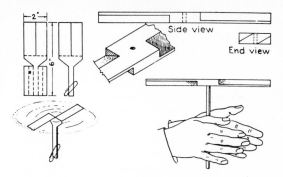

Fig. 27-18 Filing card and soft wood model helicopters. The card model spins in the air like a maple or basswood wing (seed). (From *General Science Handbook, Part II*, New York State Education Department, 1952.)

and keep it from slipping when the string wound around the spool is pulled quickly. The blade should spin rapidly and rise several feet. Similar toys are sometimes found at a variety store or hobby shop.

The helicopter develops thrust by tilting the blades of the main rotor. A small rotor in the rear helps steer the helicopter. It also counteracts the twisting motion produced by the main rotor. The rotating main blades act like wings to produce lift.

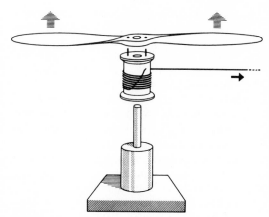

Fig. 27-19 A model helicopter using wood propeller. (From G. Blough and M. Campbell, *Making and Using Classroom Science Materials in the Elementary School*, Holt, Rinehart and Winston, 1954.)

CAPSULE LESSONS

27-1 Encourage children to do research on hurricanes and tornadoes and their effects on buildings. Often the roof is blown off and the shell left standing because the flow of air over the roof creates lift, as on an airplane wing, due to the differential in air pressure inside the house and on the roof at the time of the blow.

27-2 If possible, secure or construct a flannel board. Let children cut out a model airfoil, and then arrows to denote air pressure above and below. *Lift* results from removal or reduction of pressure faster on the top surface than on the underwing. Let children demonstrate this principle.

27-3 Let children use lengths of yarn to compare polar or "great circle" flight distance with that of a transatlantic route to Europe.

27-4 Some challenging arithmetic can result from letting children use commercial airline route maps to figure time and distance covered and check points along various routes. For instance, knowing the flight time and distance for a nonstop flight from Chicago to Los Angeles, at approximately what time should the passengers begin to look for Lake Mead and Boulder Dam? The distance is approximately 1750 miles, the flight time approximately 180 minutes. The air speed is then approximately 585 mph. Using the scale of miles on the map, the children will find that the plane approaches Lake Mead about 2½ hours out from Chicago.

27-5 It may be possible to secure aircraft panel instruments from the nearest airfield repair shop. Let children do research and/or construct simple models to explain the basic principles involved.

27-6 Let children do research on pressurizing planes for high altitude flying. If possible, borrow an oxygen mask from a commercial airline, and let children demonstrate and explain its use. Some children may be able to develop a table showing the progressive reduction in pressure from sea level to commercial flight levels.

27-7 Some children may wish to study the CAA weather reporting procedures and relationships to flight plans. Radar and its use to avoid bad flying weather is another interesting subject for children to investigate.

BIBLIOGRAPHY

Allison, Dorothy K., *Helpful Helicopters,* Melmont, 1954. Primary.

Beeler, N. F., *Experiments with Airplane Instruments,* Crowell, 1953. Middle. Children learn use of plane instruments through problem exercises.

Bendick, Jeanne, *The First Book of Airplanes,* Watts, 1958. Primary. Basic concepts for small children. Well illustrated. Brief history of aeronautics included.

Brinckerhoff, R. F., *Smashing the Sound Barrier,* SRA Modern World of Science Series, 1954. 48 pp. Simple, useful explanations and illustrations. Excellent teacher reference.

Kettelkamp, Larry, *Kites,* Morrow, 1959. Middle. Much information on atmosphere as well as on kite construction.

Knight, Clayton, *Big Book of Real Jet Planes,* Grosset and Dunlap, 1952. Middle. History and construction of planes and pilot suits.

Lent, Henry B., *The Helicopter Book,* Macmillan, 1956. Middle. Accurate information.

National Aviation Education Council (Washington 6, D.C.), *The Arithmetic of Flying,* 1959. 42 pp. Resource unit in air age concepts for grades seven to eight or for gifted pupils in intermediate grades. Needed and challenging.

Neurath, Marie, *New Wonders in Flying,* Lothrop, 1957. Middle. One of the more simple books on modern planes and how they fly.

Poole, Lynn, *Ballooning in the Space Age,* McGraw-Hill, 1958. Upper. Past, present, and future of this form of aerial transport.

Schneider, Leo, and Maurice U. Ames, *Wings in Your Future,* Harcourt, Brace & World, 1955. Middle. Simple experiments, interesting contents about principles of flight; jets, helicopters, gliders, rockets in space exploration.

Tannenbaum, Harold E., and Nathan Stillman, *We Read About Airplanes and How They Fly,* Webster, 1960.

Working with science materials

HANDLING SHEET METAL

The first step in handling sheet metal is to lay out the dimensions required. Do not use a pencil for marking. Instead use a scribing tool of some type such as a sharpened ice pick or awl. Sheet metal up to 18 gauge can be cut with tinner's snips or shears. Duckbill shears are handy for cutting circles and curves. For thicker pieces use a coping saw. Ordinary coping saw blades made for cutting wood will also cut sheet metal. The teeth of the blades should point toward the handle. Work vertically with the handle down. Thicker pieces of metal should be cut with a hacksaw. Always when working with sheet metal be sure to clamp it down tightly. This is particularly important when drilling.

Drilling

Sheet metal is drilled with the same drill points as those used for heavier metal. Always place a piece of wood under the metal to be drilled. A hand drill or electric hand drill is suitable. For steel use high-speed bits. For other metals ordinary carbon steel drill points will do. Before drilling a hole, mark the point by tapping a center punch with a hammer to make a small impression in the metal. This gives the drill point a place to start without skidding away and possibly causing an accident. For drilling into rods, use a vise. To prevent a vise from damaging metal or plastic, cover its jaws with sheet copper. After drilling a hole or cutting, always file the burrs off the metal to prevent cuts.

Fastening

The simplest way of fastening sheet metal together is to use sheet metal or Parker screws. Drill a hole in both pieces that is the diameter of the screw in its grooves. Then simply tighten the screws with a screwdriver. No nuts are required. If desired, screws and nuts can be used. The best to use are brass 6/32 and 8/32 thread. Round head will be the most useful type if the budget is low.

Drilled holes in heavier pieces of metal and plastic can be tapped (threaded) to receive screws. A tap wrench is required, as are an 8/32 and a 6/32 tap. All of these are quite inexpensive. Also ask the dealer in the hardware store to sell you the correct high-speed drill points for preparing the hole before tapping or cutting a thread. One drill is used to prepare a hole for threading. The second is for boring a hole through which a screw will pass without being threaded into place. In tapping, start slowly. Make a half turn and turn back a half turn. Turn again to where you stopped and start another half turn and back off. Do not force the tap or it will snap. Hold the work being tapped in a vise or in a clamp to prevent the work from slipping and breaking the tool or causing an injury.

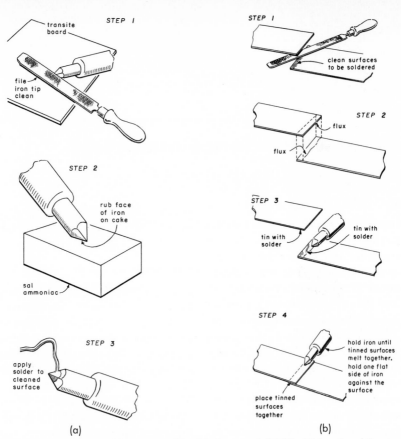

Fig. 28-1 (a) Preparing a soldering iron; (b) soldering metal. (PSSC of Educational Services, Inc.)

Plastics are worked the same way as metals, except that they are always cut with a hacksaw instead of shears.

Soldering

The simplest method for soldering is to use an electric soldering iron. For merely soldering wires, a 75-watt iron is sufficient. The iron in a child's wood-burning set is excellent for small-wire soldering. For soldering sheet metal and heavier pieces, a 150-watt or larger iron should be used. The first step in soldering is to get the iron properly heated. It is possible to use a common soldering iron that is heated in a gas flame. Once it is hot, the instructions are the same as with other irons except for rewarming the iron.

Once the iron is hot, the point is filed

clean. The iron is dipped into powdered sal ammoniac or rubbed on cake sal ammoniac and then rubbed with solder to "tin" the iron (Fig. 28-1). This prevents oxidation of the tip. If an oxide coat is present, heat will not transmit to the work. Next prepare the work by thoroughly cleaning the parts to be soldered by using sandpaper or steel wool. Next apply flux to the work. Soldering flux in paste form prevents oxidation of the metal by the air. It makes soldering easier. For nonferrous metals, use noncorrosive soldering paste. For soldering ferrous metals and coated ferrous metal such as galvanized iron and tin plate, use 15% zinc chloride solution as flux.

Next tin each surface to be soldered. Do this by adding solder to the fluxed surface, holding the point of the soldering iron against the metal until the solder melts onto the metal. Next place the two surfaces to be soldered together and apply the iron. Hold the iron until the metal is heated sufficiently so that molecules of solder from each piece of metal combine. The solder will take hold when the metal is warmed to the melting point of the solder and then cooled.

In soldering copper wires, first see that the wires are clean and completely free of insulation. Some wires are insulated with an almost transparent enamel coating. Make sure that this is removed with steel wool or sandpaper. Splice the wire together; then solder with rosin-core solder. Never use acid-core solder on nonferrous metals. Soldering aluminum is difficult for the amateur. It requires special fluxes and special solders. Also different aluminum alloys require different fluxes and solders. For the amateur it is therefore best to make joints by using screws and nuts or sheet metal screws. Clean the aluminum with sandpaper before fastening an electric wire under a screw head or a nut. This is necessary to remove the aluminum oxide coating.

HANDLING GLASS

Cutting sheet glass

The most important thing required is a sharp glass cutter. Keep the cutting wheel covered with a thin film of thin oil or kerosene while not in use so that its cutting edge will not rust. Next cut out a paper pattern of the size of sheet glass to be cut. Place this on the glass and then place a steel edge or steel rule on the edge to be cut. As shown in Fig. 28-2, move the cutting wheel along the ruler applying considerable pressure. You can tell the wheel is cutting by the cracking sound made by the cutting wheel. Make sure that you

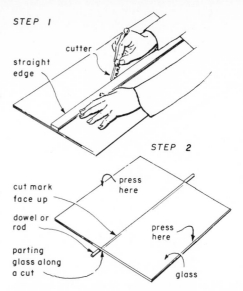

Fig. 28-2 Cutting sheet glass. (PSSC of Educational Services, Inc.)

work on absolutely level surface. Then turn the glass over and place a thin dowel stick or thin metal rod directly under the mark made in the glass by the cutter as shown in Fig. 28-2. Next press against the glass on opposite sides of the cut, and the glass will break evenly along the cutting wheel mark. If only a narrow portion is to be cut, pliers are used to remove the glass after the cut is made. To cut circles of sheet glass, a circular glass cutter is used. Simply set the radius of the circle to be cut and swing the arm. An ordinary glass cutter can also cut circles if a circular object of the desired dimension is used as a guide or a string or wire is used as a radius to swing a circle. Hold the center of the wire or string in the center of the circle, while you move the cutter around to describe the circle. As usual, apply pressure. To remove the circle, make side cuts as shown in Fig. 28-3. If it is necessary to cut a large circular hole in sheet glass, follow the same procedure; then make cuts in the center. The center portions are carefully tapped out. This leaves a hole in the

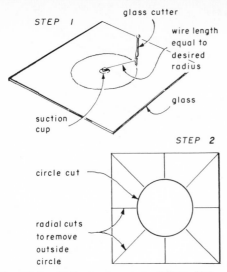

STEP 1

glass cutter

wire length equal to desired radius

glass

suction cup

STEP 2

circle cut

radial cuts to remove outside circle

Fig. 28-3 Cutting a glass circle. (PSSC of Educational Services, Inc.)

center as desired. Cut heavy glass by first marking a line with the glass cutting tool. Then lay a hot coil of wire removed from a cone-shaped electric heater replacement unit (you can buy one in an electrical shop or large hardware store) over the cut line as shown in Fig. 28-4. Work on a sheet of asbestos to prevent shock or fire. This procedure will cut glass almost an inch thick. Your local glass dealer can also cut precise shapes for you.

Large circles or large holes in glass of heavy weight can also be cut if a drill press is available. A hollow sheet metal tube or tin can as shown in Fig. 28-5 is used as the cutter. The glass is firmly clamped to the drill press table. Soft wood separates the jaws of the clamp from the glass and a sheet of wood is placed under the glass. If a tin can is used for wide diameters, the bottom lip is cut away with shears and notches are made in the edge. A ¼″ diameter or large bolt passes through the center of the other end of the can to hold the can in the drill chuck.

Next a mixture of coarse carborundum or emery powder and water is made and applied to the glass. The tube or tin can is now spinning in the chuck. Slowly lower it until it touches the glass. Apply very gentle pressure and keep adding the grinding powder and water mixture. Continue the process until the circle or hole is cut out. A very smooth job results. It may take an hour or more to cut through a thick sheet of glass.

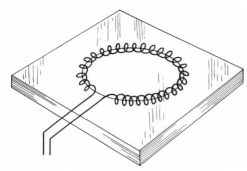

Fig. 28-4 Cutting a circle in thick glass by heating a scratch in the glass. (From A. Joseph et al., *A Sourcebook for the Physical Sciences*, Harcourt, Brace & World, 1961.)

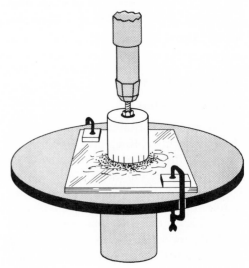

Fig. 28-5 Cutting a circle in thick glass with a drill press. (From A. Joseph et al., *A Sourcebook for the Physical Sciences*, Harcourt, Brace & World, 1961.)

Drilling

In many types of apparatus made of glass, it is extremely convenient to have a side hole for inserting a glass tube or a wire. This means drilling glass. This sounds difficult, but it is very easy. Do not drill very thin glass. Sheet glass is also drilled in the following manner. The first step is to take a sharp triangular file. Snap off about 1″ of the end. The tang or point should have a handle or cork over it for safety. Next mark the point where you wish to drill the hole. The tool will be the end of the file as shown in Fig. 28-6. Notice the way it is held in the hand, only one point of the triangular tip being used for cutting. Note how pressure is applied by the thumb. Once the initial mark is made to locate the point to be drilled, dip the file tip in turpentine. Then work the file point with a circular motion. Continue until the point comes through the glass. Keep dipping in turpentine. The turpentine cools the glass and makes a grinding paste of the glass that is removed. If the cutting action stops, change to another triangular point at the tip. If all three points get dull, snap off a short length of the file to make a new set of points. When the points come through the glass, stop drilling. Now take a thin rattail (round) file. Dip the end in turpentine and use it slowly to enlarge the hole to the size desired. Switch to a large rattail file for larger holes. If wires are to be inserted in the hole, seal with hot sealing wax or glyptal paint. If tubing is to be inserted in the hole, slip rubber tubing over the glass tube that is to be inserted in the hole. Then slip the tube and rubber covering into the drilled hole.

Cutting and bending glass tubing

The first step in cutting glass tubing is to get a sharp triangular file. Next draw it across the glass tubing at right angles in one single stroke as shown in Fig. 28-7.

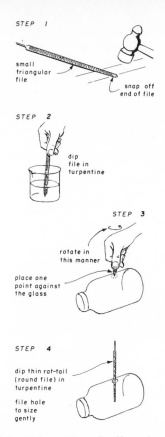

Fig. 28-6 Using a triangular file and turpentine to drill glass. (PSSC of Educational Services, Inc.)

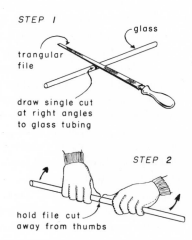

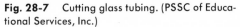

Fig. 28-7 Cutting glass tubing. (PSSC of Educational Services, Inc.)

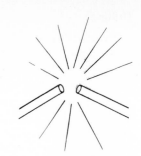

Scratch tube
with wheel

Place scratched
line on wire
Turn on current

Allow drop of
water to fall
on line

Result: A clean
break

(a)

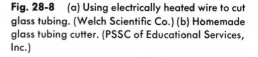

1000-W
heater unit

15-amp
fuse

No. 24 or 22
nichrome

110-V
plug

porcelain-
base
sockets

nut

¼″ bolt

(b)

Fig. 28-8 (a) Using electrically heated wire to cut glass tubing. (Welch Scientific Co.) (b) Homemade glass tubing cutter. (PSSC of Educational Services, Inc.)

Then hold the glass tubing at arm's length away from you. The cut should be facing the ceiling. Place the thumbs on the opposite side of the glass tubing underneath the cut. The thumbs should be touching each other directly underneath the cut. Then press up with the thumbs and the glass will snap evenly. If the glass will not break easily under this slight pressure, draw the file across the cut in the glass tubing a second time, using a little more pressure this time. Some people wear thin leather gloves when doing this, to protect their fingers in case the glass should snap at the wrong point. For large tubing make a cut around the glass. Cover the tubing with cloth and then snap. Large tubing must be cut with a glass tubing cutter as shown in Fig. 28-8. For tubing over 1″ in diameter, use the same technique followed for cutting bottles, as explained in the next part of this chapter.

Once tubing is cut, the ends must be fire-polished. This is done by holding the cut end of the tubing in a gas flame or in the center of an electric heating unit. When the edge of the tube melts slightly, remove and place on a sheet of asbestos to cool. When inserting tubing into a stopper, first wet the tubing or use a bit of Vaseline. Then push in the tube while holding the tubing next to the stopper. Never push from the center or the opposite end, as this can fracture the tube and force it into the palm, causing serious injury.

To bend tubing, hold it over a wing top or fish tail placed on the burner. For simple bends allow the tube to heat while rotating it. Then allow it to bend by gravity to form a right angle. This procedure prevents flattened bends. (See Fig. 28-9.)

U-tubes must be bent by starting with a right-angle bend. With the tubing red hot, place it on an asbestos sheet and

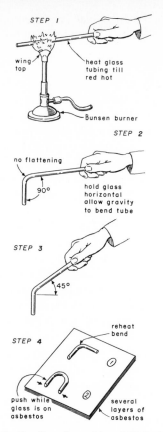

wide end to red heat and then push against an asbestos sheet to form a flange as shown in Fig. 28-10.

All tubing that is bent should be annealed. To anneal, set the burner to a yellow flame by reducing the air supply. Heat the tubing until it is black with soot. Place on asbestos to cool slowly. Later wipe off the soot, and the tubing is ready for use.

LABORATORY EQUIPMENT

Electric test tube heater

An ordinary cone-shaped electric heater replacement unit can serve as an excellent source of heat in place of a Bunsen burner. On a sheet of rigid asbestos sheet such as Transite or on an asbestos house shingle mount a porcelain-base electric socket. Do not nail or screw without making a guide hole. Connect an electric iron or heater cord to the socket and connect the

Fig. 28-9 Bending glass tubing. (PSSC of Educational Services, Inc.)

complete the bend by using forceps or pliers. For larger tubing fill with dry sand and then bend. The sand will prevent the collapse of wide tubing. To flare the ends of the tubing, use a copper triangle with one point in the hot soft glass end. Turn it to widen or flare the end of the tube.

To make a capillary tube, heat thin tubing over a wide wing top and stretch when red hot until the desired small diameter is reached as shown in Fig. 28-10. Allow to cool and then cut. To make pipettes or droppers, heat the center of tubing, then pull until the center thins out slightly. Cut in the center. For a pipette select the tubing length desired and fire-polish the wide end. For medicine droppers cut to the length desired. Heat the

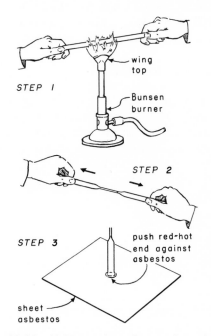

Fig. 28-10 Making medicine droppers from glass tubing. (PSSC of Educational Services, Inc.)

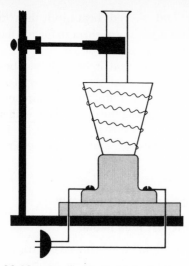

other end of the wire to a heavy-duty, two-prong plug. Into the socket place the heater unit as shown in Fig. 28-11. Wrap about a ½″ layer of asbestos paper or cloth about the heater to prevent possible accidental burns to the hand. To use, hold the test tube in the hollow center section of the cone of the heating unit.

Drainage facilities

If a sink is available for getting rid of liquid refuse, make certain that concentrated chemicals are not poured in. A large earthenware crock makes a good temporary sink which can be emptied regularly. Empty it when it is half full.

Laboratory balance

A very accurate balance can be made by using a knife edge of a razor blade as the pivot (Fig. 28-12). First make a wide wood base about 16″ long. Insert a short length of broomstick into a 1″ hole drilled in the center of the base. Cover the top of the broomstick with a circle cut from copper. File a V-shaped groove in the copper at right angles to the length of the base.

The next step is the beam. Take a piece of wood ¾″ square in cross section and 12″ long. In the center make a knife cut about ⅜″ deep. Insert a double-edge razor blade of the thicker variety into the slot and cement it into place with Duco cement. Next drill a hole at each end of the balance to carry three strings for the balance pans. Cut out two 3″ circles of plastic or aluminum for the pans. Drill three small equally spaced holes around the edges of the plastic or aluminum disks and insert the strings as shown in Fig. 28-12. Place the beam on the stand with the razor blade edge in the V-slot in the copper on top of the broomstick post. Next balance the beam by adding Scotch tape around the end of the beam end that is lightest in weight until the beam is in balance. Cut up pieces of sheet lead in gram weight size by testing them on a school balance or

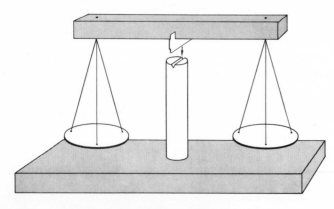

Fig. 28-12 A balance that pivots on a razor blade edge.

on a druggist's balance. Cut others out for 10, 20, 50, and 100 grams. Coins can also be used as weights if they are first weighed on an accurate balance such as a druggist's balance.

Homemade flasks

Large clear electric light bulbs are made of heat-resistant glass and can be used to make Florence flasks. The first step is to cover the burned-out bulb in a heavy cloth bag. Then twist the brass screw base with a pair of pliers until it is loose. Do not force it. A bit of heating with a burner will loosen the cement. Remove the brass base. You will find a long thin sealed tube extending out of the glass neck. Holding it with gloves, place the bulb under water and snip off the end of the pointed seal with a pair of tinner's snips. Next file a line around the neck and cut off the bottom of the neck by using the hot-wire method explained below. Pyrex baby bottles can sometimes be used as flasks.

If possible, fire-polish the cut edge by heating in a flame. Allow the flask to dry and it is ready to use. The 100-watt clear lamps are about 100-cc capacity. The 500-watt will make flasks of ½ liter capacity. Actually the same wattage bulbs come in different size glass envelopes or bulbs. Once a "flask" is made, its capacity can be measured accurately by pouring in water and then removing the water. The water is then measured in a glass graduate. Rough calibrations can be made by using a kitchen measuring bowl or cup.

Liquid-measuring devices

Inexpensive glass or plastic measuring cups can be used in place of graduates. The plastic ones are useful for all chemicals other than concentrated acids. If they are used for concentrated acids, they must be washed out immediately. A simple emergency measuring device is an empty 8-ounce baby bottle. These are graduated in ounces and half ounces. A tall olive jar can be used as a graduate cylinder by making a scale on the side. Add water by the cubic centimeter and make an India ink mark on the scale. Then cover the marks with Scotch tape to protect the scale.

Ring stands and clamps

One quarter inch or thicker threaded rod with two nuts to fit and a wooden base makes a good ring stand. Drill a hole in the wood base. Countersink the bottom of the hole to allow the head of the screw to go flush with the surface and bolt the threaded end to the base. You may want to treat the base with black asphaltum varnish to acid-proof the wood.

Small C-clamps and strong spring-back steel clamps used for holding paper together can serve to hold apparatus to the ring stand. Wooden clothespins of the spring type make good test tube holders for heating thin test tubes.

Cutting bottles and jars

Bottles, jars, jugs, and other cylindrical glass containers found around the kitchen can be converted into useful jars for use in elementary science. You will, of course, need a sharp glass cutter. This cutter must be securely held while you scribe a cut around the circumference of a bottle as in Fig. 28-13. If you have a strong hand, you may rest the glass cutter on some books. You can vary the height of the cut by changing the number of books under the hand holding the cutter. Another way is to set up two boards at right angles as in Fig. 28-13 and fasten the cutter to one end by means of a wood screw. The block against which the base of the jar or bottle you are cutting rests is held in place with a C-clamp or a long nail.

Once you have made the cut you are ready to use a hot electric wire to finish

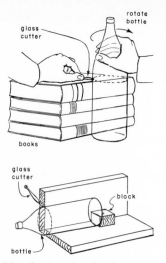

Fig. 28-13 Cutting glass bottles. (PSSC of Educational Services, Inc.)

the job. On a baseboard about 10″ × 12″ × 1″ place two porcelain-base sockets at the left. One carries a 15-ampere fuse. This is the one connected to the 110-volt wire and plug. This wire and plug are of the type sold for electric iron cords. The other socket has a 1000-watt, cone-shaped electric heater unit which you may purchase in a large electrical supply house or from a large hardware store. From a physics teacher in a local high school get several feet of #22 or 24 Nichrome wire. You can buy a small spool of this wire from a scientific supply house. Next, at the end of the board drill ¼″ holes to carry ¼″ bolts that are 6″ long. Fasten the bolts to the board with nuts. Then use additional nuts to fasten a 12″ length of the Nichrome wire between the long bolts. Cover the underside of the board with sheet asbestos to prevent short circuits. Plug the unit into an outlet and you are ready to finish cutting a jar or bottle. Simply place the cut line you have made on the bottle against the red-hot Nichrome wire. Press gently and rotate the bottle or jar against the Nichrome loop. Remove the bottle and let it cool. You will hear the glass crack along

the cut as the glass cools. Throw away the neck of the bottle or jar or keep and use as a funnel. File the sharp edges of the jar you have formed with an ordinary file to get rid of the sharp edge. Your jar is now ready for use.

Workshop table and tools

Any workshop table will do if one part is covered with Transite (hard sheet asbestos) on which you can solder and use other heating devices. You will want a vise to hold wood and a small metal vise. The back of the bench should be fixed to hold tools. You might also want an electric outlet in the bench. The number of each kind of tool depends upon the nature of the program. If for the teacher alone, one of each suffices.

hammer—¾ lb claw
hammer—½ lb ball peen
screwdriver—6″
screwdriver—telescoping set or kit
nail set
center punch
wood mallet
electric soldering iron
soldering paste
rosin-core solder
pliers, gas
pliers, long nose
pliers, electricians
pliers, diagonal (wire cutters)
shears—10″ tinner's
hand drill
drill bits set—⅛″ to ¼″ diam.
bit brace
augur bits set—⅓″ to 1″
C-clamps (assorted sizes)
crescent wrench—open to 1″
Phillips head screwdrivers—set
saw, cross cut
saw, hack with spare blades
saw, coping with spare blades
saw, back 12″
plane, smoothing 10″

carpenters square—trisquare
steel dividers
yardstick
steel rule
file, bastard
file, smoothing
file, mill
file, triangular—¼″ and ½″ section
file, rattail—⅛″ diam., 3/16″ diam.

One important thing is to have a special area for painting so that you do not mess the floor, workbench, or classroom.

GENERAL DIRECTIONS

Pupils

Following are suggestions for safety procedures when you are working with science materials in the classroom.[1]

(1) Pupils are to be under the direct supervision of a teacher at all times and in all places.

(2) Pupils are NOT to carry laboratory equipment or apparatus through the halls during the intervals when classes are passing.

(3) Pupils are NOT to transport dangerous chemicals at any time.

(4) Pupils are NOT to handle materials on the demonstration desk except under the direction of the teacher.

(5) Pupils are NOT to taste chemicals or other materials.

(6) Before permitting pupils to work with sharp tools, the teacher must be assured that pupils are fully competent to use the tools.

(7) At the beginning of each term, pupils should be instructed in general safety precautions.

(8) Pupils should be specifically instructed regarding the dangers and the precautions required, at the beginning of

[1] Excerpts from New York City Schools booklet *For Greater Safety in Science Teaching*, September, 1949.

each period where there is a special hazard.

(9) Pupils should be cautioned about hazardous activities involving the use of chemicals outside the school—e.g. mixing chemicals to "See what happens," setting fire to gasoline cans, breaking open fluorescent tubes.

Teachers

(1) When using volatile, inflammable liquids, such as alcohol, in a demonstration experiment, care must be taken that any flame in the room is at an absolutely safe distance from the liquid.

(2) Never add water to concentrated sulfuric acid. If it is necessary to prepare diluted acid, the concentrated acid should always be added in small quantities to the water, with continuous stirring.

(3) Combustible materials of all types are to be kept in a metal cabinet provided with proper means for closing and locking.

(4) Do NOT demonstrate devices or equipment brought in by pupils before pretesting.

(5) In performing experiments where there is a possibility of spattering, where there is the slightest chance of a serious flash or explosion, or where the teacher deliberately uses mixtures which he intends to explode, the following precautions should be observed:

(a) Keep pupils at a distance not less than 8′ from the demonstration table.

(b) Use a screen of strong, fine wire mesh, wire glass, or, for spattering experiments, ordinary glass as a shield for both pupils and teacher.

(c) Wherever possible, glass vessels wherein explosions may take place should be made shatterproof by cementing several layers of cellophane onto the glass with collodion. This will provide safety without affecting visibility.

(6) On inserting glass tubing into rubber stoppers or tubing, observe the following precautions:

(a) Never attempt to insert tubing having a jagged end. Fire-polish, if possible. Otherwise, bevel the edge with a file, wire gauze, or emery cloth.

(b) Use water, soap solution, glycerin, or Vaseline as lubricant, and force the tube into the hole by a twisting motion.

(c) Always aim the tubing *away* from the palm of the hand that holds the stopper or rubber tubing.

(d) Always hold glass tubing as close as possible to the part where it is entering the rubber stopper.

(e) The use of a cloth wrapped around the hand or the tubing at the point of contact with the hand will help prevent injury if the glass breaks.

(7) In inserting a thistle tube into a rubber stopper, do not grasp the thistle tube by the bowl. Always wet the tube and use a twisting motion when applying pressure.

(8) Keep all bottles labeled at all times. If no other kind of label is available, a piece of adhesive tape will serve the purpose.

(9) Liquids or solids found in unlabeled bottles should be discarded. Do not guess as to the nature of the substance.

(10) Bottles containing acids or organic volatile liquids should never be placed near heating pipes nor allowed to stand in the sun; dangerous gas pressures may be built up.

(11) Never cork a bottle containing dry ice; always plug loosely with cotton.

(12) It is suggested that Bunsen burners be mounted individually on wooden blocks for stability.

(13) Alcohol or other volatile liquids should not be used in a room where there is a flame or where a flame may be used shortly thereafter. Rags or cotton swabs soaked in any of these substances should be carefully disposed of in fireproof receptacles.

(14) Glass wool and steel wool should be handled carefully to avoid getting splinters in the skin.

Safety suggestions in the preparation of oxygen

(1) Care must be taken to avoid exposing potassium chlorate, manganese dioxide, sodium peroxide, or any other oxidizing agents to contamination. Dangerous explosions may result from the presence of organic material in an oxidizing agent.

(2) In the experiment where oxygen is prepared by heating manganese dioxide and potassium chlorate, make certain that the bottles of manganese dioxide and charcoal powder are not placed on the same shelf or near each other in the laboratory. Keeping them in different parts of the room will prevent the possibility of a pupil's mistaking one for the other and thereby possibly causing a serious explosion.

(3) Warn pupils against allowing the carbon from wood splints to fall into the hot potassium chlorate-manganese dioxide mixture. If this should occur, heating must be stopped immediately.

(4) If the sodium peroxide method is used for perparing oxygen, the following precautions should be observed to insure safety:

(a) Avoid contact of skin with moist sodium peroxide.

(b) Make certain that no active sodium peroxide is left in contact with paper or other easily ignitible substance. If paper is used for pouring the chemical into the generator, soak it thoroughly with water before discarding.

(c) It is suggested that an Erlenmeyer or Florence flask be used as a generator instead of a bottle, thus preventing the possibility of cracking the generator due to heat of reaction.

(5) Oxygen may be safely prepared from a 3–5% solution of hydrogen peroxide which is dropped on either powdered manganese dioxide or pelleted activated charcoal. No heat is necessary.

Safety rules for handling electrical devices

(1) Pupils should be taught never to grasp any electrical device which has just been used. Most electrical devices are hot after use, and serious burns may result if the degree of heat is not ascertained before the device is grasped.

(2) Pupils should be instructed never to short-circuit dry cells or storage batteries. High temperatures developed in the connecting wires can cause serious burns.

(3) Sharp edges on mirrors, prisms, or glass plates should be reported by pupils to the teacher in charge. Raw glass plates should be bound with adhesive or Scotch tape. Waxing edges of plates with melted paraffin is highly effective.

(4) Students should be cautioned about the danger of shock from the secondary of an induction coil.

(5) In removing an electrical plug from its socket, pull the plug, not the electric cord.

(6) In inserting an electrical plug, hold plug so that any flashbacks due to a short circuit will not burn the palm of the hand. This also applies to holding a soldering iron.

(7) Electrical extensions used in the classroom for projection machines, etc., should be inspected regularly for defects in insulation or connections.

(8) If the current is constantly used near any metal object, the object should be permanently protected with an insulating cover to avoid possible contact. General care should be observed to see that live wires do not contact grounded metallic objects.

(9) Care should be observed in teacher and pupil handling of a storage battery. It is a source of danger, in spite of its low voltage, because of the acid it contains and because of the very high current which may be drawn from it on a short circuit.

(10) All types of induction coils should be clearly marked for the low-voltage and high-voltage connections in order to prevent the possibility of shocks.

(11) In the handling of radio equipment by teachers and pupils, the following precautions should be observed:

(a) Make certain that the current is off before putting hands into the radio.

(b) In handling the so-called transformerless type of radio (a.c.-d.c.), where the tubes are series-connected and the set works directly from the line, take caution to prevent any grounded metallic object from coming in contact with the metallic chassis.

(c) In using a standard transformer radio, be cautious about the handling of B voltages. The high-voltage secondary is in the order of 600 volts a.c., and the rectified B voltage about 300 volts d.c. Severe burns and shock can result from contact.

(12) Care should be taken to prevent pupil injuries due to sharp edges on mirrors, prisms, and glass plates. Such apparatus should be inspected before being handed to pupils, and sharp edges should be removed by grinding them with emery cloth or carborundum stone or by painting them with quick-drying enamel. Pupils should be instructed to report at once

any sharp-edged apparatus handed to them.

(13) (a) The practice of removing thermometers and glass tubing from rubber stoppers as soon as possible after use will prevent the possibility of the glass' "freezing" to the rubber.

(b) To remove thermometer or glass tubing that has been frozen into a rubber stopper, the following method has proved safe and efficacious. Use a wet cork-borer, just large enough to slip over the tube, and slowly work the cork-borer through the stopper, thus boring the frozen tube out of the stopper.

(c) As an alternate method to the above, it is suggested that the rubber stopper surrounding a frozen thermometer be slit open with a razor. The stopper can then be repaired with rubber glue, or can be used as a split stopper.

Safety suggestions
for biological experiments

(1) Great care should be exercised by pupils in securing epithelial cells from the inside of the cheek for study under the microscope. Only a clean wood tongue depressor or the *blunt* edge of a flat toothpick should be used. Pointed instruments or any part of a scalpel should never be used for this purpose.

(2) Handling laboratory animals. Rats, mice, guinea pigs, and other laboratory animals should be handled gently by students in order not to unduly excite the animals into biting. Thick rubber gloves should be available and used whenever necessary, that is, when there is danger of being bitten (by excited animals, injured animals, new additions to cage, pregnant or feeding females, etc.). Students and visitors in the laboratory should be cautioned not to insert fingers in wire mesh of a cage. Appropriate signs such as "Keep Hands Off" should be displayed about a cage. Only specially trained members of the laboratory squad should be permitted to handle laboratory animals. Poisonous snakes should not be kept in the laboratory.

(3) Use of formaldehyde. Specimens preserved in formaldehyde should be thoroughly washed in running water for 24 hours before being handled by students. In taking specimens out of formaldehyde, wear rubber gloves or use tongs or forceps, depending on the size of the specimen. Adequate ventilation should be provided in any room where formaldehyde is used.

(4) Use of carbon tetrachloride. Adequate ventilation should be provided in any room where carbon tetrachloride is used. Some schools have legal restrictions against the use of carbon tetrachloride.

(5) Precautions for field trips:

(a) Pupils should be instructed about identification of poison ivy, poison sumac, and local poisonous snakes.

(b) First-aid kits should be taken on all field trips.

(c) Students should be instructed about the proper clothing for a field trip in order to avoid illnesses due to undue exposure.

(6) In handling flowers and bread mold, care should be taken that pollen or spores are not excessively distributed through the classroom. Some students may be allergic to pollen or spores.

(7) Only sterile needles or lancets should be used by the teacher for pricking his finger to draw blood. Blood should be drawn from the dorsal side of the finger in back of the cuticle. Rub the finger with alcohol before pricking it; then cover with bandage.

(8) Operation of pressure cooker for sterilizing bacteria media:

(a) Before operating the pressure cooker, familiarize yourself thoroughly with the proper directions for operation.

(b) Examine the safety valve before use and make sure it is in working order.

(c) Don't allow the pressure to go above 20 pounds.

(d) Stop heating before removing the cover. Pressure should be down to normal before removing cover.

(e) Be sure to open the stopcock before releasing the clamps.

(9) Teachers should take special care when allowing pupils to handle any of the following:

(a) Denatured alcohol and wood alcohol.

(b) Apparatus left hot by use, i.e., stereopticon, micro-projector, etc., that could cause burns. Allow hot projectors to cool before replacing in cases.

(c) Carpentry tools.

(d) Electrical apparatus and equipment.

Storing inflammable liquids

Inflammable liquid is any liquid that will generate inflammable vapors at a temperature below 100° F.

crude petroleum	tin can
benzene, benzole, or naphtha of any kind	tin can
coal tar	tin can
coal tar oils (heavy)	tin can
wood creosote	g.s.b.[2]
varnishes, lacquers, etc.	tin can
acetone	g.s.b.
alcohol, ethyl	tin can
alcohol, denatured	tin can
alcohol, methyl	tin can
aldehyde, ethyl	g.s.b.
amyl acetate	g.s.b.
amyl alcohol	g.s.b.

[2] g.s.b. means glass-stoppered bottle, or one with a plastic screw cap.

kerosene	tin can or g.s.b.
turpentine	tin can
toluol	tin can
xylol	tin can
essential oils	g.s.b.
glycerin	g.s.b.

Storing combustible substances

Combustible substances are compounds or mixtures that emit inflammable vapors at a temperature of 100–300° F.

phosphorus, white	under water in glass bottle surrounded by sand
phosphorus, red	g.s.b.
sulfur	tin can
metallic magnesium (strip and powder)	g.s.b.
camphor	g.s.b.
rosin	g.s.b.
pitch (coal tar)	tin can
tar, refined (wood)	tin can
naphthalene	g.s.b.
shellac	g.s.b. or tin can
resins, balsams, and other varnish gums	tin can
pulverized charcoal	tin can
lampblack	tin can
cotton, absorbent	paper box
cotton batting	paper box
lycopodium	g.s.b.
zinc dust	g.s.b.

Storing dangerously corrosive chemicals

hydrochloric acid	g.s.b., 6 lb each bottle
sulfuric acid	g.s.b., 9 lb each bottle
phenol (carbolic acid)	g.s.b.
sodium hydroxide	g.s.b.

Storing peroxides and other oxidizing agents

hydrogen peroxide, U.S.P. 3%	g.s.b.
sodium peroxide	tin box
potassium peroxide	g.s.b.
potassium chlorate	g.s.b. or tin can
strontium nitrate	g.s.b.
cobalt nitrate	g.s.b.
iron nitrate (ferric)	g.s.b.
silver nitrate	g.s.b.

Storing substances made dangerous by contact with water

quicklime	tin can
sulfuric acid	g.s.b.

APPENDIX:

TEACHERS' REFERENCES

Adapting the classroom

to science teaching

Do you teach in an average classroom? A room with a bank of windows along one side, with radiators up to the window sills? One already crowded with desks and chairs and overflowing when these are occupied by children? Very likely the nearest running water is in the janitor's mop closet down the hall, and electricity comes into the room only through overhead lights suspended from a long wire. You have no special scientific equipment and no place to put it if you did. Even if you had the equipment, when would there be time in your overloaded day to plan for and teach any science? Moreover, you probably took as few science courses as possible in high school and college and never distinguished yourself in these.

Even so, what could you do with what you have of time, space, equipment, and energy? Have you considered the science possibilities of standard schoolroom equipment? Take a look around your room. The pencil sharpener is an ingenious machine combining the principles of a wheel (gears) and axle, a lever (handle), and an inclined plane (blades), among others. A door handle and latch combine the wheel and axle and the wedge. Most hardware fittings are held in place by screws (inclined planes) and bolts. A hinge is an example of the wheel and axle principle. Window fasteners supply other combinations of simple machines. Window pulleys operate because of the wheel. Sometimes window casings all too effectively illustrate friction! Let children rub soap or wax in the grooves or on the pulley ropes and speculate on the reasons for improvement in operation.

One day a student teacher was well into a carefully planned lesson when the "blind man" and the custodian arrived, as usual without advance notice, to repair the Venetian blinds. The teacher was urged not to compete for the children's attention, and the custodian and the repairman became teachers for a few minutes, illustrating some simple scientific principles to everyone's interest and satisfaction.

INDOOR WINDOW SILLS

As every teacher knows, window sills are magnetic for the restless youngster who has sat still as long as he could. If you use window sills for growing plants, you might put these plants to work to illustrate such basic principles as the water cycle of evaporation and condensation. Plants can help correct the superheated air of most schoolrooms in winter. On a cold morning, a terrarium on a north or east window sill should supply a beautiful illustration of condensation.

An aquarium exhibits its inhabitants to best advantage near a window. A wax crayon mark at the water line shows the rate of evaporation from the aquarium. Your high scorers in arithmetic might be challenged to calculate the amount of evaporation from containers of different surface areas. A superabundance of algal growth in their aquarium led a first grade into some real adventures in planning ways of solving this difficulty. The metamorphosis of a frog, toad, or salamander from its egg in a gallon glass jar is always exciting to watch, but care must be taken to protect the egg from direct sunlight.

The effect of light on samples such as colored cloth, paper, and plastics placed on the window sill can be a challenge to critical thinking. The dust that blows in from the playground to lodge upon the window sill might be observed on white paper with a magnifying glass for color, density, etc., and for its relation to wind direction and weather. In one new school such investigations led to a school planting project involving the whole community. You might also try using the new plastic seed germination trays that are widely available.

An upper grade teacher in eastern Washington adapted a shadow box to the middle window of his classroom. It made an ideal display center for new and interesting objects. To the window sill below he attached a U-shaped cleat with a button fastener. This just fitted the base of an inexpensive microscope and held it safely and securely near the maximum light. The shadow box held many intriguing objects for examination, e.g., a flake of mica, a bit of feather, a fish scale, and some alum crystals.

You may wish to teach your children how to use museum or nature trail techniques in labeling the classroom collections. The simplest label can be a piece of notebook or chart paper folded in three parts so that it forms an isosceles triangle, one side making a base and the other two bearing legends or questions. Because of the psychological value of viewer involvement, you may wish to try tags fastened to objects, as, for example, the water spigot. Its tag might read, "How many other examples can you find of the wheel and axle in our room?" A "peephole" sign is always intriguing to children. Usually good examples set the children to imitating and often improving on the originals.

OUTDOOR WINDOW SILLS

One of the most neglected but useful parts of a school's architecture is the outdoor window sill. This is the closest point to the out-of-doors that can be reached directly from the traditional classroom. Here insects can be raised in special containers with no danger of their being let loose in the classroom. Plants that grow better outside will thrive. This is the place where the seasons and the weather change, and therefore the ideal spot for the class weather station.

Homemade and dime store thermometers, apple box weather vanes, dime store humidity indicators, and barometers from evaporated milk cans make up a working weather station. (See Chapter 7.)

The children can measure the amount of sunshine, the amount of rain, and the amount of snow on the outdoor sill. The class farm can thrive in cheese boxes on the outdoor sill. With proper provision the children can build a feeding station and birdhouses that will attract birds year after year. The particular lesson at hand can utilize the outdoor window sill whenever continuous out-of-doors conditions are required.

WINDOWS

Unless you teach in an ultramodern air-conditioned classroom, your windows serve to let in fresh air as well as light. No doubt you have window monitors to check the wall thermometer and adjust the ventilation accordingly. You will undoubtedly find it useful to plan a class lesson on how to read a thermometer. Initiate a general discussion of the room thermometer and its range and position for optimum room temperature. Like any lesson, the discussion will tell you what the children do and do not know. Give each child a sheet of graph paper and ask him to draw a thermometer illustrating desirable room temperature and another illustrating outdoor temperature at lesson time, at freezing point, etc. Children love to manipulate a large zipper thermometer (pp. 97–98). Painting the zipper red with nail polish gives it additional interest. Often there is narrow wall space between door casings that can be used for mounting thermometers and yardsticks. If possible, introduce centigrade thermometers and meter sticks along with the ordinary measures. No lengthy explanations are necessary—only long-term exposure, so that the unfamiliar becomes familiar and eventually useful. Try also simple wet- and dry-bulb thermometer mountings (p. 103) to let children discover that "closeness" in the room is due more to water vapor than to high temperature.

Windows serve also as the initial approach to understanding convection currents, the great cyclic movements in the atmosphere which create weather. The health books tell us to open windows at both top and bottom. More often than not this advice is ignored, either because the windows stick or because the window monitors are unaware of the underlying principles. When the room gets too warm, the children open windows at the bottom. Cool air comes in, but none of the warm air near the ceiling can escape. There is no real interchange of air, and so the room remains warm and stuffy.

Ask the children how they think the room should be ventilated. The obvious answer—open the windows—needs probing to find exactly how and why. In case some know that windows should be opened at both top and bottom, ask them whether they can think of a way to prove their point. Some may suggest using strips of Kleenex. If these are Scotch-taped to the radiator or to the edge of a transom, children will begin to observe and learn about air currents within the room. A bit of clothesline or thick cord set on fire and then extinguished gives off smoke which traces the air currents at window tops and bottoms. The convection currents for casement windows are not so clear-cut but nonetheless can be observed to some degree.

When outdoor air heated by the sun rises, cool air rushes in to take its place just as it does in a properly ventilated classroom. On the West Coast, large air masses over the desert eastward are warmed and rise to the point where cool air flows in from the ocean as it does nearly every afternoon of a sunny day. The same principle holds in varying degree in other parts of the country and can be related to the daily weather report map on TV and in the newspaper.

Further evidence of microclimates within the room may be secured by keeping temperature records from thermometers placed near the ceiling and near the floor. If the custodian's ladder is not easily available for the high reading, some enterprising youngsters may undertake construction of a periscope (p. 251).

A window's other function of admitting light may be utilized to teach some fundamental concepts about light and the earth's seasonal gyrations with respect to the sun.

If possible, secure a photographic light meter, and let the children record the intensity in different parts of the room. Take readings at the beginning of the school day, at noon, and at the close of the school day. Repeat in 2 weeks or a month and correlate to the change in the length of daylight as revealed in the daily paper. If the children have been plotting the progress of shadows on the floor over a period of time, they are in a better position to correlate variations of light intensity within the room to the earth's progress in its annual orbit around the sun.

Light streaming through the chinks and apertures in Venetian blinds usually reproduces rounded images of the sun at some places on the floor. Although the chinks are angular, the spots of light are rounded because the light source is round. Let the children construct a pin-hole camera (p. 245) to help them discover why this is so.

WALLS AND CEILING

You can begin a study of the earth's crust right in your own classroom and extend and enrich it with trips down the hall and out around the school building. Many classrooms have walls and ceilings of plaster with wood trim and moldings. Let the children investigate the source of plaster and, if possible, secure small samples from the custodian or a local plasterer or building supply. The soft white plaster of Paris is made by heating gypsum until it loses most of its water content. When water is added to plaster of Paris, it sets in about half an hour to a solid mass of gypsum. Let the children set a slab of plaster by mixing and smoothing a shallow section in a shoebox lined with foil or in a half-gallon milk carton cut longitudinally. The heat generated when water is mixed with plaster is the same as the heat used when water is driven out of gypsum in the manufacture of plaster. Restoring the water content permits recrystallization to take place.

An old-type slate blackboard illustrates another earth material useful because of its flat planes and fracture lines. Slate was formed from layers of shale subjected to enormous heat and pressure deep underground. This change in rocks, as in insects and frogs, is called *meta-*

morphosis. Slate is a metamorphic rock. The handsome marble slabs seen in older school lavatories were metamorphosed by the same forces from deep layers of limestone. Wet a piece of shale; it has the same "earthy" smell as wet slate.

Even newer schools often use tiling in their hallways and other areas of heavy use. Why? Let the children experiment with removing marks from a piece of tile and from other kinds of building materials. Encourage them to find out how tile is made, where it comes from, and why the factory is located where it is. Children who have clay work fired in a local kiln can contribute some useful knowledge about the effect of high heat on earth materials such as clay. Let the children discuss and suggest experiments to show why clay and not other kinds of soils is used in making tile. You may relate such studies to new ceramics and missile nose cones.

Another kind of earth material processed by heating for use in your classroom is window glass. Glass is made by heating sand with limestone and washing soda until the mass melts and flows like liquid. The same thing happens inside a volcano, and the volcanic glass that sometimes results is called *obsidian*. This shiny black material was prized by Indians and traded all over the West because of its adaptability to spear and arrow points. The same conchoidal fractures which make artificial glass cuts so severe were prized by these primitive hunters.

Woodwork, even synthetic, can be useful for developing awareness and understanding of the world around us. What kinds of wood are used in your classroom? Where did they come from? How does the grain or pattern compare with that of a tree cut in cross section? Perhaps a local carpenter or lumberyard owner can help the children understand how the way the tree is laid on the saw can produce interesting and different designs.

New synthetic or plastic materials used in constructing classrooms all have interesting stories and many science implications and concepts available for children to discover at their own level. (See Chapter 20.)

Now what about design in construction? A modern classroom chair or desk is designed for the greatest strength with the lightest weight from a minimum of materials. Examine the furniture you have. How is it braced? Is the basic design of the arch incorporated into the chair you use? How has the designer saved weight and material? If the furniture is part metal and part wood or plastic, which part is metal and why?

How many metallic elements are found in your room? Copper in electric wires or water pipes, iron in furniture or hardware, aluminum, lead, tin? An exhibit of the elements to be found in or near the schoolroom will surprise you by its extent. (See Chapter 12.)

VERTICAL SPACE

Have you jump ropes or some other relatively light equipment which could be hung up, say, in the cloakroom? If so, secure a fair-sized "plumber's friend." Wet the edge of the rubber disk and apply to the wall surface just at shoulder height for the children. This will be the place to keep jump ropes and will also provide the children with an object lesson in a partial vacuum and in the lateral pressure of air. Too often the traditional experiments leave children with the idea that air presses only down or up, never sideways.

Do your children bring in such magazines as *Life, National Geographic,* and *Popular Science* or other general periodicals with interesting articles and pictures about science? These are actually textbooks in modern science. Suspend the magazines over the bars of an inexpensive wooden towel rack, the kind that can be extended high or folded down as needed.

BULLETIN BOARDS

A conscientious student teacher recently planned a second grade display entitled "Why the Sun Is Important to Us." If you were a second grader, would you consider the sun important enough to be worth a second look? She finally settled on a less academic title. It may not have impressed the supervisor, but the children were curious about it. Modern advertising furnishes a clue when it understates or otherwise arouses curiosity and interest.

Once the teacher has set a standard, upper

grade children can often carry on the labor and planning and executing of new bulletin board displays. Indeed, it is labor to think out and collect the material for a good display and change it often enough to keep it from becoming "wallpaper." Wherever space permits, some teachers use more than one kind of bulletin board. One may summarize the results of some particular study, so that the group can gloat over its accomplishments. Another may be the children's own board to be arranged as *they* wish. Herman Schneider found one of these, delightfully named the "Glumble Board." A classroom teacher thus describes such a board, as well as a third type:[1]

To the children it is not a clutter; rather it is filled with vastly interesting items that are not propounded by the school. Perhaps there is something psychological about this; perhaps that's what keeps the interest high. At any rate, the standards are theirs, both in methods and materials.

The little fellow who can't bring himself to stand before the group to "show and tell" will draw a picture and pin it on this board, probably when nobody is watching him. Some youngsters cut from magazines and newspapers pictures and articles about special interests that are never mentioned in class—subjects that may be a far cry from the curriculum outlined for the grade. Yet a little imagination and ingenuity can pull these unlikes into interesting relationships. For example, a sixth grade I knew was studying Greece, but Peter had disoriented himself from the group for days. His contributions to the clutter board had been several star maps and an article about a planetarium. A book containing star myths by the ancients was the tie that once more bound him to the group. (This sort of thing happens when one takes time to look at the children's board and to note who offered the materials on display.)

Neatness of the clutter board will vary according to age and ability. Middle graders have a strong sense of design as well as fair play. They will not allow monopolies. Sometimes children will choose a class member they look up to for fair play and quiet leadership. They are occasionally quicker than the teacher to see in someone an aptitude for

neat lettering and effective arrangements. Or it may be the teacher who will choose a child for this type of ability not yet recognized by his classmates who may excel him in other things. Primary children need a helping hand—when they ask for it. A committee or manager may have to be chosen to keep things under control and see that old items are removed and reclaimed by their owners. I find this works better when instigated as a result of difficulties. If too many restrictions are set up in the beginning and it becomes a chore, the clutter board will be short-lived and unproductive. Duration of display, spacing, mounting, and labeling offer opportunities for problem solving and group work. The children are brought together by sharing interests, and often are stimulated to discover and develop new ones.

Type three is my own board, and I am as jealous of it as the children are of theirs. Here I can do what I wish, from some "terribly clever" review of an old and troublesome lesson, to ideas for modern art or stimulus for a new science project. I can be formal or informal; I can arrange it myself or assign it to a class committee who will work under my direction. I prefer to have my board at or near the front of the room, where the wandering eye comes to rest most often; for I like to think, at least, that this silent teaching has several effects; that it gives a sense of orderliness of color and arrangement (I sometimes go so far as to measure distances) and that it stimulates thinking. I can use every trick of the trade from peep shows to 3-D to create interest. A shoe box with a window cut in it may harbor anything from a small living creature to an important notice I want everybody to read. Small shelves can be built of oak tag or construction paper to hold "real" objects, or they can be wired or pinned on. Questions and captions can be devised to lead to experiments, to observations, or to the use of books available close by. Often a series lesson can be taught with nothing more than good pictures and captions: papermaking from the forest to the mill, with a follow-up study of paper products. (I have found follow-up lessons useful and rewarding, for they tell me who has done the work in this particular field, and how much understanding has been gained.) This bulletin board has offered a satisfying way to deal with questions that arose from small groups and which could not be handled adequately in class

[1] Patricia Adams, *Schoolroom Science Center,* Cornell Rural School Leaflet, Teacher's Number, Vol. 49, No. 1, Fall, 1955, pp. 28–30.

time. Maple syrup from tree to pancakes, milk from cow to dinner table, a letter from mailbox to mailbox—social studies, science, arithmetic, spelling—all find a place on my board and appeal to some in the group. To try to reach everybody every time is to court despair. Certain things everyone must do, such as march in a fire drill and learn the multiplication tables; but bulletin boards to be fun must have strong interest appeal. If they look like fun and lead to individual activities, most of the children will be interested most of the time. The bulletin board is often the answer for "What shall I do when I have nothing to do?"

Good ideas on my board often carry over to the clutter board. Through the year choice of materials, labels, use of colors for mounting, and effectiveness in arrangement improve. Indeed I have found more than once that some of the best ideas for display do not emanate from my board. I have found, above all, that "easy does it" in preparing a board. If it is as important as I think to have a fresh, new display often, then I cannot be a perfectionist in all things. It is important for me to be neat and accurate because my work must be a model in writing, lettering, spelling, and all the skill subjects I teach. I want to develop good taste insofar as I understand good taste. But I cannot and do not reletter an entire poem if one letter blurs, or send for a new ream of paper if one corner of the last sheet is torn. Neither do I ink over carefully penciled letters; I start with ink or crayon or whatever medium I have chosen. I find a kit handy, so that tools and materials can be kept in order, apart from the general classroom supplies. Mine was a cardboard box that contained a long-bladed scissors, a box of crayons, an alcohol pen, a ruler, some cut-out letters, thumb tacks, Scotch tape, and a small, firm brush I especially prefer for lettering. The kind of stapler that opens up flat cuts mounting time to almost nothing.

Teaching may be a "position," but it is also a mighty hard job. It is only natural to try to find ways to minimize effort with optimum results. I have found using bulletin boards one of those ways. If they were hard to set up and tedious to do, I know I wouldn't do them. But they aren't. They save hours of talking, and add hours of teaching. And because my ingenuity has been tapped again and again, teaching has become more nearly the creative experience it was meant to be.

A 3-D bulletin board

To achieve a 3-dimensional effect, try a pegboard display of toys or other *realia* in science. If pegboard is not within the school supply or teacher's budget, heavy cardboard can be perforated with an ice pick to do almost as well. Wire or tie objects in place.

A ROCK HOUND'S TRAIL

A young rock collector displayed his specimens most effectively on a map folded over bricks laid up in a series of steps. The rocks were placed near the map locales from which they came. One fourth grade teacher tied rock specimens to a vertical map with colored yarn. The children learned the geography as well as the geology of their state.

DISPLAYS AND EXHIBITS

A display may be anything from a few sea shells on a table to an elaborate exhibit in a glass case. The important thing is not the medium but the display. Generally it should be the child's work and appropriate to the current science unit. However, a wise teacher often makes room for irrelevant material because of its status value for the child who brought it. A real dust and space saver for exhibiting such offerings is a vertical display case such as an old bookcase. Have the children paint the shelves different colors in light shades (use rubber-base paints, for they dry in a short time and are fireproof, odorless, and washable—the paint brushes can be washed out in warm water), one shelf for shells, one for bird nests, one for rocks, one for reference books on science, etc. Fasten cellophane sheets at the top to form windows that will protect the shelves from dust and still permit handling of the exhibits. Outline the objects in place on the shelves so that the children will know where to replace them and so that they will notice whether anything is missing. Appoint a boy-girl team of your rapid learners as junior curators of your "Science Corner." In the beginning, work with them to establish high standards of arrangement and labeling of materials. The writing of labels can be a valid and valuable group practice in language. Strive to encourage observation and accuracy by asking for labels that tell where and when the object was found and that, if possible, give a tentative classification pending conclusive identification. Use a section of a marked highway map to pinpoint the place of origin and add interest to the exhibit.

Nearby set a piece of Cellotex or Bristol board in an old picture frame repainted in bright colors. This will make a neat frame of reference for science news and notices.

Most children are collectors. A teacher's problem is not to get them to bring in materials for a science exhibit, but to help them select and organize their treasures. In East and West Coast schools, for example, the usual autumn flood of sea shells from summer beachcombing can be overwhelming and useless from an educational viewpoint. Permit only perfect specimens or one of a kind in your exhibit. Use cardboard egg cartons to exhibit up to 12 small shells. The box cover is a good place for the labels. Or spread sand on one of your exhibit shelves. Fence up the "leading" edge of the shelf to prevent sand leakage and consequent custodial mutterings! The artists in your class might paint a diorama background of summer sky. Someone might bring in a toy shovel and bucket to adorn your "beach." Your labels for the shells on your beach shelf might be toothpick flags stuck in the sand.

Beware lest all your exhibits illustrate biological science only. For example, have one youngster collect electric light bulbs which illustrate the history of lighting. Many school systems have school service museums. State departments of education or conservation may have loan exhibits. Use such material to stimulate children to make their own exhibits, rather than to serve as your science exhibit per se. One teacher goes to the county museum every two weeks to borrow a stuffed bird or animal, an unusual shell or rock. This he exhibits with a slotted question box entitled "What is it?" to stimulate research and discussion that often are the most valuable by-products of the device. At the end of the week the class examines the children's written answers and learns what the object really is.

Living displays such as fish and turtles may need window space for health as well as visi-bility. In any case, the owner and a responsible alternate should be appointed to give such exhibits the best of care. And it is much better to change exhibits too frequently than too seldom. The same old dusty rocks in the "Science Corner" and half-dead plants in the window belie the living quality of interest which science should have for children. The spate of insects in glass jars which often follows the sea shells in children's fall collections can very quickly become worthless. The insects can teach the children only as long as the children are interested in them, or a week or two at most; then the insects should travel home or outdoors in plastic rather than glass containers. For simple, practical suggestions on the care of insects in your classroom, see Chapter 3.

THE SCIENCE DISCOVERY TABLE

Many classrooms today have a large work table with multiple uses. When there is a need to use it for science, a plastic cover preserves the finish. Orange crates at the corners may provide storage space for simple science equipment. A slightly remodeled cafeteria cart may afford storage space below and work or demonstration space on top, all on four wheels. Here again linoleum or a similar protection for the top will prove of value. Small items, for instance, electric plugs, switches, doorbells, etc., tend to disappear unless they are fastened to stiff, heavy cardboard which can be stored vertically until occasion for their use arises.

WATER AND HEAT

Now you have a place for science exhibits and science experiments, but you are probably hampered by a lack of running water. A gallon tin or a bucket of measured capacity will carry water from the mop closet sink and also do duty for investigations in volume arithmetic. Rubber tubing from the drugstore will provide running water at the same time that it illustrates air pressure at work in siphoning.

Still your classroom has no gas outlets like those in your high school or college science laboratory. A can of Sterno or even a cluster of candles provides considerable heat, if not light.

Even better is an electric hot plate to plug into the nearest wall outlet. Perhaps you teach in an old building with the nearest current outlet an overhead chandelier. Someday after school when the custodian is working in the room and can keep a watchful eye on proceedings, let some sixth grade or junior high school boys make a plug connection for you. This is a matter of good interschool relations as well as one of practical value to you in your science work. You can use the double wire from the ceiling fixture or the two-pronged wall outlet for electric current to illustrate electric circuits—an input wire and an output wire.

If there is no cooking gas in the school, you may buy one of the small portable gas burners that have their own supply of gas. However, any unfamiliar equipment, such as a Bunsen burner, may distract and confuse young children from the real purpose of your experiments. You can circumvent this difficulty by casually introducing such equipment some days ahead of the time you propose to use it. Let the children examine it and ask questions.

HOUSEKEEPING AND STORAGE

Science may introduce new materials and activities into the classroom which may place additional burdens on our friend the custodian. In many schools he works on a very tight schedule, so many minutes per room, with generally antediluvian cleaning equipment. Enlist the children's ideas and responsibility in thinking of ways to keep science materials well organized and "shipshape."

Some teachers store materials for related areas of investigation in shoeboxes—one for magnets, one for flight, one for insects, etc. One scientific supply house markets a mobile science lab table. It is about the size and shape of a cafeteria cart. The inner cupboards are filled with plastic hydrator boxes, each holding a different kind of equipment.

If you have the luxury of a sink in the room, requisition, if possible, a rack of dowel rods countersunk at about a 45° angle. Hung above the sink, such a rack permits the drying and storage of glassware as soon as it has been washed clean.

Some schools have central storage closets. Such a closet is described as follows:[2]

Many new science materials were being ordered for our school, and we needed a place to put them. We wanted to display them so that teachers could readily see what was available. We wanted a check-out system that would be easy and not too time-consuming. We needed an orderly arrangement so that materials could be replaced with a minimum of upkeep for the persons in charge. The following plan had worked in other schools, and so we decided to try it.

Just off the office is a supply room. The ditto machine is kept there, and many teachers use the room. Above the machine are shelves which hold the science books. They are arranged to correspond to the sections of the science guide in the district, as follows:

Living Things—Plants
Living Things—Animals
Conservation
The Earth
Beyond the Earth
Our Atmosphere—Weather and Climate
Matter and Energy
General Books on Science

As the teacher takes a book, she signs the card and drops it in a file box, replacing the card and book when she is through with it. The file box lists all the books arranged alphabetically by topic.

Next to the ditto machine are many shelves which hold the science materials. Different types of materials are placed together. Materials for measuring will be on one shelf. Another shelf has all the electrical materials. Another has tools, etc.

Each object is marked with nail polish. If misplaced, it is easy to know where it belongs. On the front of the shelf there is a label for each object. It can be replaced in the right spot. At the side of each label is a hook with a string tag. This is also labeled. When the teacher takes a piece of equipment, she also removes the string tag with the name on it. This she hangs on a board by her name. When the equipment is returned, it and its tag are replaced on the proper shelf. If someone needs a piece of

[2] Marjorie Pursell, Oak Grove School, La Canada, California.

equipment that is not on the shelf, it is easy to check the board to see who has it.

Partial list of science materials:

Electric hot plate	Magnifying glasses
Teakettle	Microscope
Sauce pans	Plastic container—
Cake pans	to hold water
Cookie sheet	Corks
Pie tins	Sponges—real
Batteries—many	Pipe cleaners
Wire	Balloons
Sockets—many	Rubber bands
Switches—many	Tools
Light bulbs—many	Hammer
Thermometer—F,	Saw
C, candy	Screwdrivers
Scales—spring,	Tin snips
balance	Square
Tape measure	Paring knife
Measuring cups—	Marbles
various sizes	Toys to show
Measuring spoons—	Wheels
various sizes	Gears
Compass	Springs
Magnets—horseshoe,	Egg beater
bar—several	Scrap materials
Lamp chimneys	Spools
Flasks	Mailing tubes
Beakers	Wire
Rubber stoppers—	Candles
with and without	Vinegar
holes	Soda
Glass tubes	Limewater
Soda straws	Food coloring
Bunsen burner—	Salt
alcohol	Sugar
Prisms	

In other schools one teacher and one class are designated the science distribution center for the school. The duties involved are often challenging to the children who learn and finish other work readily.

One school which was so fortunate as to have an elementary science specialist[3] had a room to which children could come for individual activities. The following description was contributed by a nonteaching observer:

The children sit at tables in the lab. The teacher has earlier listed on the blackboard the activities from certain cards (1–11) in her card file, leaving space for names under each entry. First she asks the children whether they wish to add any other activities to the list. Sometimes they do, and sometimes they do not. Then she asks who wishes to do what. Some activities, of course, are limited to a certain number of children. As each child indicates his choice, she writes his name under the particular heading on the board. Then she assigns tables for work. Before the work begins, the teacher invites questions concerning anything that the children do not understand. When their questions have been answered, the children go to work. They all know where the supplies are kept, and they obtain them before working and put them away afterward.

1. *Telephone* demonstrates vibration. Two tin cans are attached by a string through their bottoms. The string, stretched tight, carries the sound. One child talks into one of the cans, while the other child holds the other can to his ear. This experiment is most effectively carried out in a big room.

2. *Candles* are used in the oxygen experiment. The children light the candles and stand them in jar tops (some melted paraffin is allowed to drip into the tops to hold the candles steady). Then different-size jars are inverted over the candles to see how long they will burn. Small jars of sand are kept handy to put out matches.

3. *Crystals* are made on cotton string in Petri dishes. Ferrous sulfate or a similar salt is dissolved in hot water and stirred. The dishes are covered with Scotch tape. Some are allowed to stand longer than others to illustrate crystal formation.

4. *Ball and fire* experiment is the favorite with elementary children. It requires a pan of cold water, a large bath thermometer immersed in the water, a Bunsen burner, and a rod of metal on a wooden handle. The metal is heated and then put into the water. The water temperature rises.

5. *Electricity* is used to make doorbells ring. Several medium-size batteries, wires, and bells are needed. Six children may participate in this rather noisy experiment.

6. *Air and water pressure* are demonstrated with a bottle of colored water fitted with a two-hole stopper. A hose is attached to one hole of the stopper. When a child blows into the hose, water comes out the other hole.

[3] Anna Greve, Elementary Science Supervisor, Bronxville Public Schools, Bronxville, N.Y.

This experiment is rather messy and very popular.

7. *Builder magnets* are pieces of magnetized metal that can be put together to make things. They are available in all sizes and shapes.

8. *Fishing with magnets* catches cutouts of fish with paper clips or bits of metal attached. The fish are dropped into a large jar. Children fish with magnets on the ends of strings.

9. *Magnetic bulletin board* holds papers by means of magnetized clips or bars.

10. *Sound* experiment involves the use of tuning forks in simple demonstrations so that the children can see, feel, and hear sound vibrations.

11. *Light* experiment uses blueprint paper. The children take the paper outside or to the window and make prints of leaves, magnetic fields, etc.

Conservation through science

and social studies

Do you teach social studies? Do the objectives of your social studies curriculum include a study of the child's physical and cultural environment? To accomplish this objective, do you not directly or indirectly draw upon the findings and applications of science which have made an enormous difference in the standard of living? If you could think of conservation as a bridge between science and social studies, you might use conservation activities as a way of streamlining your program by integrating science and social studies. Of course, not all aspects of these subjects can or should be integrated, but it will make for time saving to integrate whenever feasible. The symbiotic relationship of science and conservation is illustrated by the dual table of contents for a recent book, *Teaching Science Through Conservation,* by Paul F. Brandwein and Martha E. Munzer, McGraw-Hill, 1960. The first lists the contents according to interrelationships: e.g.,

Part 2—Conservation as a Study of Interrelationships Between Living Things and Their Environment
Part 3—Conservation as a Study of Interrelationships Between Matter and Energy
Part 4—Conservation as a Study of Future Resources

The second lists the contents according to subject areas: e.g.,

Biology, General Science, and Conservation
Chemistry, General Science, and Conservation
Physics, General Science, and Conservation

In the opinion of one nationally known writer:[1]

Certainly conservation education presents an excellent vehicle for science in general education. It must depend to a considerable extent on both the natural and the physical sciences, and must be concerned with the improvement of the habits of human beings who use or abuse the environment in which they live. It demands an understanding of the world about us and of worthy membership in the society of which we are a part. We can teach the principles and facts of science without doing much to modify human behavior. In the social sciences we can modify human behavior without the necessity of much knowledge of science. We cannot, however, have a sound conservation program without involving these two.

THREE CATEGORIES OF RESOURCES

In order to use conservation teaching as a vehicle for science, we need to consider conservation in a somewhat different light from that in which the *majority* of books and curricula treat the subject. Most people think and write about conservation as it applies to *renewable* resources, such as soil, water, animal life, and plant life. This approach is understandable if we remember that sixty years ago Theodore Roosevelt and Gifford Pinchot applied the term *conservation* to the movement which fortunately

[1] E. Laurence Palmer, *As I Have Known the Cornell Nature Program,* Cornell Rural School Leaflet, Vol. 46, No. 1, Fall, 1952, p. 27.

led to the establishment of our National Forests, National Parks, wildlife refuges, and the like. We can build soil, however slowly; we can re-cycle water; we can preserve our wildlife and keep our forests green. But every day we use and discard tin cans (metals) that contained food. Every day we eat food that contains minerals from the soil. For example, 30 bushels of potatoes take from the soil about 6 pounds of nitrogen, 2.7 pounds of phosphorus, and 9 pounds of potash; about 120 pounds of a 5-10-5 fertilizer must be added to replace this loss of mineral elements. Every day we depend on *fossil fuels* such as oil and coal for heat, light, and/or transportation. Metals, minerals, and fossil fuels we term *nonrenewable* resources because we do not yet know how to create them. For example, we do not know how to create copper; we know only how to prospect for it, mine it, and process it. If you have the children list only a few of the things everyone uses daily, they will quickly see how heavily a modern industrialized society depends upon nonrenewable resources. See "How We Can Save Our Minerals" in *The Big City Book of Conservation* by Catherine Urell and others, Follett, 1956. If the children look about them and name those things improved by science and those not improved by science, they will immediately see the connection between science and social studies.

The third group of resources within our environment consists of the people, the human resources, the community helpers we study in primary grades, the farmer who knows how to grow food from the soil, the carpenter who knows how to build homes, the factory worker who builds stoves and automobiles, the scientist who discovers alternatives for copper, the city and county planners who see to it that there is space for schools and parks when they issue building permits, say, for housing tracts. The list is endless and enlightening in terms of a modern view of conservation education. See "Man-Developed Resources," Part II, in *Things to Do in Science and Conservation* by Byron Ashbaugh and Muriel Beuschlein, Interstate, 1960.

You may now be thinking that conservation includes everything; it is an umbrella-type idea with no solid content or confines. If we go back to the true derivation of *conservation*, we will find that Webster says it comes from the Latin prefix *con*, meaning "together" or "with," joined to the Latin verb *servare*, meaning "to guard, take care of, preserve." Interpreted strictly, the term implies an ethic, an attitude of responsible citizenship which most teachers attempt to teach daily, as, for example, the care and *wise use* (not just saving) of personal and school property, of time, and of space within the classroom or on the playground. In order to develop the conservation attitude or ethic, we need to arrange for very practical activities to help children understand all three categories of resources.

Since the majority of children attend elementary schools in areas the census bureau classifies as "metropolitan," we are especially concerned to point out ways of "Using the Natural Environment of the City as a Curriculum Resource."[2]

AROUND THE SCHOOL

Foundation Stone of the School Building
Natural Stone in Building
The School Yard
Drain Pipes
Sidewalks
Between the Sidewalk and the Curb
Gutters
Curbstones
Street Covers
Street Trees
Hedges
Lawns

IN THE NEIGHBORHOOD

Flood Areas
Hills
Plains
Vacant Lots
Rocks
Excavations
Soil Exposed by Road Cuts
Nature Trail
Coal Yards
Lumber Yards
Mason Supply Yards
Garden Nurseries
Monument Works
Railroads

[2] *Operation New York: Using the Natural Environment of the City as a Curriculum Resource,* Board of Education of the City of New York, Bureau of Curriculum Research, 1960, p. 3.

LAND AS SPACE

Among the conservation education possibilities nearest you—ones you doubtless utilize daily without thinking of them as conservation—is conservation of space, almost always a critical problem in the average classroom. You exhibit and store materials vertically whenever possible. You work with the children to develop traffic flow patterns, even with the aid of masking-tape arrows on the floor. You use window sills for display and growing space. In short, you utilize every inch of the room from floor to ceiling for every teaching potential you can think of. Is this not in miniature a kind of area planning for multiple use? Have you tried planning and replanning the area with the children, using a simple floor plan, say, on large graph paper? You may wish to check the building blueprint in the principal's office for architectural symbols to denote windows, doors, electric outlets, heat, water pipes, and the like. Extend the same activity, after checking with the principal, to the school grounds; make a master plan of the area. If a city park is within walking distance, attempt the same survey there of *what is* and what could be. If it is not convenient for the entire class to participate in this activity, perhaps a local Girl and/or Boy Scout Troop could undertake the project and report back. Make a rough count of parks and other recreation areas in the community. Make a survey of vacant lots in the community. Compare your survey with maps prepared at the municipal or town hall for tax rolls. One group was encouraged to report its findings to the local Board of Supervisors. The officials became so interested in the intelligent efforts of the young citizens that they took out "conservation easements" on certain parcels for recreational development. We must not become so accustomed to thinking of land only in terms of its agricultural use that we forget it has ever-intensified value as space for homes, shops, and service stations.

Models

Mapping and consideration of wise use for the schoolroom, school grounds, or community areas might lead into model building (perhaps of a community with all wires underground). Primary grade social studies units often produce a map or mural or model of the local community. Some grades use a sandbox base; others, a cardboard box diorama. The medium and method are immaterial as long as the children are led to observe and consider possibilities for "Tomorrow's World." See "Space" in *Things to Do in Science and Conservation.*

A fifth grade elementary science text has a final unit entitled "We Live and Work Together." There are sections on planning for animals which encompass pictures and stories related to wildlife management and conservation. The last two pages touch on city planning in a section called "People Are Planners."

LAND AS SOIL

Use of land for growing things can also be a meaningful study whether we teach in urban or rural schools. One writer reports as follows:[3]

As chance would have it, a visit of mine to a school in a small Eastern city found a teacher giving a lesson on soil conservation. The students in his class seemed to know the major principles involved in the wise use and intelligent development of soil, and, indeed, the lesson seemed to be good evidence that these students had made the tools of soil conservation part of their stock in meeting life's problems. After lunch, we went out on the sloping lawns, and there a few feet away from the classroom were several gullies; there was a good deposit of soil in the cement gutters of the street; there was every evidence, in short, that soil conservation was a part of the classwork but was not operative in the lives of the students.

Signs of erosion around the roots of a playground tree, soil from the lawn washed out along the sidewalk, and sediment in the gutter of a city street all are evidence of the continuous weathering and change in our environment. All are miniature examples of the large-scale shifting of earth materials and can help children understand why people settled along fertile valleys for crops and trade. Let the chil-

[3] Paul F. Brandwein, *Conservation in Urban Schools,* excerpt from collected papers, Purdue Conference, Resource Conservation Education, Sept. 16, 1952, pp. 54–57.

dren sprout seeds in small samples of soil collected from gutters, sidewalks, etc. Compare with seed germination from subsoil from a nearby excavation or road cut.

Natural areas for schools

Some schools are so fortunate as to have property not entirely covered with buildings or blacktop. One school developed a nature trail and a miniature park area as follows:[4]

One school district has recently initiated a project designed to provide outdoor science and conservation activities for the entire school population of 250 boys and girls in kindergarten through eighth grade. The project is a *nature trail* on school district property. . . .

The district superintendent felt that good use could and should be made of this terrain. He called in to discuss possible projects the eighth grade teacher, a local naturalist (who resides in Carmel), and the science consultant from the Office of the County Superintendent of Schools. . . .

The naturalist and the science consultant surveyed the area and after much exploration finally decided on a route to follow. Wooden stakes were then placed approximately twenty feet apart so student construction workers could see the line to follow. The path took a more or less winding pattern so as to come in close contact with the greatest number of interesting things.

The eighth grade students then borrowed shovels and during recesses and lunch hours proceeded to "dig" their way along the trail. Large logs, brush, and poison oak were removed by the custodian. At steep spots the students terraced the inclines with steps and, to avoid washouts, blocked the face of the steps with wood. Many parents were surprised to find that the students considered this work experience as fun.

The County Office had on file a number of written sources dealing with nature trails. One in particular, "How to Build a Nature Trail," published by the National Audubon Society, proved to be the guiding light. This bulletin pointed out ways to get the most out of a nature trail, pictured examples of trail markers, and offered other helpful hints.

[4] Edwin Leach, "K-8 Children Build a Nature Trail for School Use," *California Journal of Elementary Education*, Vol. 29, No. 2, Nov., 1960, pp. 92 ff.

The naturalist took over here and with his expert knowledge of local flora and fauna temporarily labeled many of the amazing and hard-to-recognize plants. Educationally, it was felt that many things should be left unmarked and allowed to stir the imagination and curiosity of those who were to eventually use the trail. Students should have opportunities to make discoveries of their own.

From then on it was up to the students to finish the job. The pupils divided the plants and birds to be investigated equally among themselves. With all available resources, including library books, encyclopedias, and particularly the actual specimens, they sought out information concerning the plants and birds for which they were responsible. For plants, they listed such things as leaf patterns and whether such were deciduous or evergreen. In some cases the students found narratives concerning uses made of the plants by the Indians or pioneers. For birds, such data as habitat and behavior were recorded. Songs were also noted.

It was agreed that the information that was to appear on 8-inch by 10-inch redwood plaques should include the common name, scientific name, pertinent statements about the specimen, and, if possible, one or two provocative questions that would require the reader to think, to look, to touch (except poison oak), to smell (except poison oak), in order to answer the questions. It was felt that the written material on the plaques would be informative, but that the questions would probably do more to stimulate the thinking processes. . . .

The plaques are now in place and the trail is open. One of the first groups to take to the hundred-and-fifty-yard lower trail was the kindergarten class. They cannot read the signs but enjoy hearing their teacher describe what the signs say. Many of the questions are not too difficult to answer even for five-year-olds. When the teacher takes her class for their frequent walks to see the seasonal changes or the first flowers of spring, they can now share a real trail built by the "big kids down the corridor."

The teachers are finding the trail a good in-service training device. New teachers, in particular, who are not familiar with the area's natural features can use the labeled information to develop background information. The teacher need not feel insecure because he does not know enough about nature to teach it. The trail is his instructional aid.

The interest of the community in the project has been satisfying. The local Garden Club, for example, is augmenting the trail by donating trees and shrubs native to the County.

The trail is not totally complete yet; perhaps it never will be. Maintenance will always be necessary; there will be occasional revisions and changes of information on the plaques; and an upper trail route will be completed in 1960, bringing the total trail length to approximately five hundred yards. Mammals, reptiles, amphibians, geology, and other subjects will be given equal attention. In the meantime, we can expect the students to gain a deeper appreciation of the type of community in which they live. The science curriculum throughout the entire school should be enriched, and it is hoped that this introduction to the local natural resources will result in the development of more conservation-minded citizens for the future. We would like to expect at least this, and perhaps more.

Louis Agassiz, the great 19th century Swiss-born American naturalist, once said, "Study nature—not books." Reading material is more numerous and accessible than it was then, so we would like to alter Louis Agassiz' words just a little to read, "Study nature—*then* books." We now have a statement that comes very near to describing the intent of the Washington Union Elementary School Nature Trail.

Land-use maps

Recently we visited a classroom and noted a charming water color in shades of green that changed the perspective from a meadow foreground to intermediate slopes and on to the top of a hill capped with trees. The teacher saw it as an art lesson. We saw it as an example of land classification, the lower lands for crops and the upper lands for restricted grazing.

Reading the landscape

Some of you were introduced as children to R. L. Stevenson's *Child's Garden of Verses*. If you remember "The Land of Counterpane," the poem about the sick child playing with toy soldiers, you may come to the idea that the world in microcosm lies around you. You can see land forms in miniature in most school yards and home yards, just as you see mountains and cities in miniature from a plane window.[5] You have to train your eyes to this new method of "primary" reading, of reading objects rather than their symbols. Even a slight effort to develop this kind of perception pays dividends in revealing a whole array of teaching aids and resources at your back door and under your feet. The Cornell Rural School Leaflets provide a wealth of suggestions for you even if you have little or no background in science. A recently published book[6] will illuminate you while it charms you. Its chapter entitled "Readin, Ritin, and Recess, or Tree Rings in a Country Schoolyard" may be of especial interest.

HUMAN RESOURCES

In all conservation activities, the key is the human resource, the person or persons, both producers and consumers, without whom a resource is not a resource. For example, taconite lay untouched in the cull heaps of the Mesabi iron mines until metallurgists found a method whereby it could be treated to produce a useful iron ore. The engineers and businessmen who made use of this scientific knowledge were human resources. The plastic goods that fill our stores we likewise owe to the genius of our chemists and engineers. These are illustrations of what might be termed our "new and to-be-discovered resources; those depending on the brains and skills of specially trained people for discovery and development."

A recent publication for the Camp Fire Girls contains 21 specific suggestions for the wise use of human resources. Some are reprinted here by permission.[7]

What do people do?

Purpose: To show that people are resources because they can give service; that people rely on each other for service.

Site: Your home.

Procedure: Think of one thing that you do on an ordinary day. Write it down on a

[5] "The Interpretation of Air Photographs," in P. E. James and C. F. Jones, eds., *American Geography,* Syracuse Univ. Press, 1954.

[6] May Theilgaard Watts, *Reading the Landscape,* Macmillan, 1957.

[7] *Conservation,* Camp Fire Girls, 1959, pp. 64–66.

piece of paper. Opposite it write down all the occupations of the people that made it possible for you to do whatever activity you choose. Even if you are just sitting in a chair reading, your list would be very long. For example: (1) Who made the house the chair is in? (2) Who got the materials the house is made of? (3) Who made the chair? (4) Who sold the family the chair? (5) How did the chair get from the factory to the store and then to your house? (6) Who built the truck or car to transport the chair? (7) Who took care of the money that the chair cost? (8) Who printed what you are reading? (9) Who made the letters and ink that were used to print it? (10) Who wrote it? . . . and on and on. Everyone is important because everyone has a job to do. If even the smallest jobs weren't done, you might not have the pencil and paper to start this activity.

Your town needs natural resources

Purpose: To investigate one phase of your town's dependence on natural resources.

Site: Shipping docks. (This could also be adapted for railroad yards or trucking depots.)

Procedure: Visit the loading and unloading docks on river, lake, and ocean. Take pictures of the kinds of raw materials and finished products that are being imported and exported. Use photographs to illustrate exhibit on the importance of raw materials to your city's or town's economy or to show how people in one area depend on the resources of another area.

Places to play

Purpose: To see if the people in your community all have a chance to be healthy and happy through good outdoor recreation.

Site: Your community.

Procedure: Think of your family or the family next door. Is there a park where you can walk with your grandparents or sit in a pretty place and chat? Is there a place where Mom and Dad can play golf or tennis or whatever they like to do? Do you have a tree to climb, a place to wade or see water, a vacant lot for a game of Red Rover? Make a list of the things you and your family enjoy and opposite each thing indicate the number of blocks you must travel to do them.

Are there schools in your town that are not as pretty as yours? Do the children in any of the schools not have a place to play? They probably like to do the same things you do. Make a list and try to find out how many

blocks *they* must go to do what they like to do. Do you think their parents would let them go very far? Where do the children play who live downtown in a big city? Would you like to play in these places? If not, why not? What kinds of places do children in the country have to play in? Do you think they have enough people to play with? Do you ever get to meet any of the people who live in the country?

A better yard

Purpose: To get the wisest and fullest benefits from your yard.

Site: Your yard.

Procedure: Plan your yard space for greater beauty, enjoyment, and use. Draw a map of the yard and put in improvements such as new planting, transplantings to provide a larger space for games, etc., and to insure attractive views from house windows. Choose shrubs and other plants that will beautify the yard as well as attract beneficial insects and birds by their flowers, fruits, or the kind of cover they provide. Look for ways of camouflaging garbage cans and increasing privacy. You may wish to put in a screen planting and start a compost heap behind it. Look for areas of poor drainage or erosion that might be improved by simple fills or breaking up of compacted surface soil. You may wish to have a nearby agricultural experiment station or university analyze your soil and make suggestions for improving its texture and nutrient content.

The picture story for children, *The Big City Book of Conservation,* tells with text and photos about many relatives and friends of the children whose daily work is "Protecting Our City."

Conservation at home

Training in the conservation ethic or attitude of responsible citizenship begins at home with the child's first teachers, his parents. For valuable suggestions, with text and pictures for reading aloud, see "Conservation Begins at Home" in *The Big City Book of Conservation.* Two other sources for parents whose children may be human resources in science rather than social science are Marianne Besser, *Growing Up with Science,* McGraw-Hill, 1960, and Albertina Weinlander, *Your Child in a Scientific World,* Doubleday, 1959.

Conservation at school

A primary grade curriculum bulletin for a large city school system lists the following suggestions for practicing the wise use of resources:[8]

CLOTHING

Use name labels to insure return.
Polish to preserve leather.
Wear rubbers to protect shoes from rain.
Put on aprons to protect clothing when painting or cooking.

TOYS

Handle toys carefully.
Play properly with toys.
Store toys in suitable places.
Repair toys as needed.

TOOLS, EQUIPMENT, AND FURNITURE

Handle tools and school equipment correctly.
Cut appropriate materials with scissors blades.
Place protective covering over some work areas.
Use slides and climbing bars carefully.
Care for tools immediately after use.
Move furniture properly.

PAPER

Use one paper towel completely.
Think before writing or drawing.
Utilize mistakes in drawing to add something interesting to a picture.
Cross out a writing mistake with one line and continue.
Save the unused part of a paper for later use.

FOOD

Take less foods not cared for.
Balance foods eaten at a meal.
Use left-over foods in combinations.
Give suitable left-over foods to animals.

WATER

Drink properly from drinking fountains without wasting water.
Wash a glass someone has used, before using it again.
Drink water from a reliable source; avoid drinking water from springs or streams.
Swim in water that is not polluted; swim in safe areas.
Observe rainfall and water run-off; see the effects of floods and man's efforts to control water.

[8] *Some Suggestions for Practicing the Wise Use of Resources on the Primary School Level,* Curriculum Bulletin 300, Cincinnati Public Schools, Cincinnati, O., 1957.

TIME

Plan work and use of time carefully.
Gather necessary materials in as few trips to source as possible.
Work at a reasonable rate.
Facilitate cleaning-up by storing tools and materials so they are easily accessible. Preplanning for this is necessary. Such storage also speeds up work preparations.

ENERGY

Prevent muscle strain by using furniture of correct size.
Play hard in gym and play areas.
Plan loads so that two trips might save drain on energy.
Lift load by bending knees; learn to recognize one's limit of load.
Prevent eye-strain by working in good light.

SOIL

Observe soil erosion.
Collect water from a puddle after a rain, and let it stand to settle; observe the sediment.
Observe soil in the air in a dust storm.
Test soils for plant foods by growing plants and adding or deleting foods.
Observe the action of earthworms in soil.
Observe air in the soil by adding water that has been in the room to the soil in a glass and note results.
Grow plants in different kinds of soil; sand, clay, humus, and the like.
Visit areas or find pictures showing contour plowing and strip farming.

ANIMALS

Learn how farmers provide homes and other protection for animals.
Provide food for wildlife in bad weather.
Review health and safety rules to protect human life.
Learn about care of birds through observation during mating and nesting periods; visit a bird sanctuary; find out places where birds rest during migration.
Visit local fish hatcheries; learn about fishing laws and licenses.
Learn to balance an aquarium; find out difference between kinds of fish (characteristics of some tropical fish).
Write to find out what the national government is doing to protect natural resources.
Collect pictures of national parks and tell of visits to these places.
Try to find out if any local agencies deal with conservation of natural resources.

PLANTS

Learn to identify some wildflowers of the area; find out which can be picked in abundance.

Learn how to gather flowers.

Obtain permission to plant trees or shrubs in eroded areas of the school grounds.

A social studies curriculum for the third grade suggests observing and reporting on some good conservation practices, such as:[9]

1. The construction of retaining walls, storm sewers, drainage ditches.
2. The protection of wildlife in Aquatic Park.
3. The care of trees, shrubs, and flowers in the parks.
4. The care of trees along the streets.
5. The use of benches at bus and train stops.
6. The use of paper towels in public rest rooms.

It has been the opinion of many outstanding educators that the study of conservation practices was more appropriate to upper elementary grades than to primary grades. They have considered conservation concepts too advanced for primary pupils, even though they have recognized that many of the experiences designed for young children help to prepare them for a better understanding of conservation. Our comment follows:[10]

This might be so, if one thinks of conservation as a group of facts or information—for instance, about soil erosion. Except in rare instances, however, metropolitan children do not frequently see examples of the need for the conservation of trees, soil, or wildlife.

A baby starts to learn about life from his environment, an environment which is set up primarily to conserve him. One of the first and most difficult lessons he learns is due regard for the objects in this environment—what is touchable and what is not.

The preschool child must learn some simple responsibilities and consideration for things in his home environment. The primary teacher attempts to continue and ex-

tend this education in responsibility for one's environment. In school, the child must learn to take care of what belongs to the group as well as what belongs to him or his family. The teacher shows children the reasons for and advantages of such habits as hanging up coats, bringing in play equipment, putting away smocks after painting, and so forth. At every opportunity the teacher tries to take time to explain or even to demonstrate why we write on paper or the chalkboard instead of on tables or walls, or why we spread newspapers before doing any painting.

If a chair becomes loose because we have tipped back in it too much, our friend the custodian comes and tells us exactly how he might fix it, how much time it will take, and how much it will cost in labor or materials. (We have, of course, consulted with him beforehand as to how this might be explained within the comprehension of our group of children.) In other words, we are trying to help our children learn to appreciate and take care of the resources in their environment. We want them to learn an attitude, a way of behaving, which will, as they grow older, identify them as conservation-minded citizens.

BEGIN WHERE THEY ARE

For example, in construction, children can learn to use only the wood necessary for the ship or truck they want to build. They can learn to use leftover pieces when possible, or to cut wood from the end rather than from the middle of a board. They learn how to use tools and to take care of them. They learn to use the right tool for the job to avoid damage or destruction of tools. Perhaps we may visit a friendly hardware merchant who will tell us about the prices of some of our tools, where they come from, and how many people are involved in the making of, say, a hammer.

Even through art, children can learn to be conservationists. For example, they can learn to mix paints so as to avoid wasting both time and paint. They can try to think of ways of keeping leftover paint from becoming dry and useless. They learn how much paint to use at each stroke, in order to make better pictures and have more paint. They learn how to hold their brushes, how to clean and store them. At the same time they learn wise, not wasteful, use of painting paper.

We teachers take time, day after day, at playtime to illustrate and explain the proper

---

[9] *Social Studies—Grades 1 Through 4,* Berkeley Unified School District, Berkeley, Calif., Sept., 1954, p. 28.

[10] K. M. Houck and E. Hone, "Conservation," *Grade Teacher,* Nov., 1957, pp. 26, 104. Reprinted from *Grade Teacher* magazine by permission of the publishers.

use of blocks, building boards, jungle gym, sand equipment, and mechanical toys. We encourage reporting of small breakages before they get to be big ones. We consult, as a group, with the custodian about problems of repair. We consider that careless breakage really deprives everybody. We think about all the people who have worked hard to build and bring in our play yard equipment. Thus, conservation involves social studies as well as science.

Whether children bring lunch to school or whether there is a school lunchroom, there is need and opportunity for teaching conservation of our food resources. Older primary children, as part of their social studies, may decide to have a grocery store in the room. In addition to the arithmetic learnings and the social experiences in a project such as this, children can also learn something of the people and processes involved in getting our food to us. Further, they may also secure some conception of the farmers' problems in raising our food if it is possible to grow radishes or other quick-germinating vegetables on the school grounds. (Lacking a school garden or a strip of ground under the schoolroom window, try growing seeds in flowerpots or wooden boxes on the window sill.)

Education in the conservation of energy is implied in much of what has been said. For the same reasons that we try to teach children to use, not waste, water, we also teach children to turn off lights when not in use. Whether our power is steam generated or hydroelectric, we believe primary children are not too young to gain some appreciation of the fact that many people work to see that we have electricity, that the coal which may be used to generate it comes from far away, or that many people worked hard to build a dam to hold back the water which makes electricity for us. Assuming we have the imagination to motivate them, every child can do something about conserving an increasingly scarce community resource such as water.

SAVE HUMAN ENERGY

Children who learn to put away their own things where they can find them quickly are learning to save time for more important, enjoyable activities. A kindergarten group on the first day of school had a wonderful time playing with blocks of various sizes and shapes. These had been shelved together in groups. When it came time to clean up, the teacher wisely let the children struggle for a while stacking the blocks any old way. Eventually they saw a need for shelving according to the original grouping by size and shape.

In addition to education in responsibility for personal and school property, children need to learn the care and wise use of community property. For example, we may "adopt" a tree on our street, watch it through the seasons, and report any damage or sign of disease to the municipal Park Commission or its equivalent. Perhaps one of our friends on the Commission can give us an object lesson in the results of mutilating or carving on trees. He may perform—or we can—some bark-girdling on expendable branches of trees or shrubs near school. We can watch for results. The ensuing discussion may lead to the question of carving initials on park or bus benches as well as on trees. We gain more with young children by stressing practical rather than ethical reasons for regarding such practices as questionable.

The interdependence of living things with their environment is a basic assumption of the social studies. For examples and illustrations at the children's level, see "Conservation Helps Everybody," pp. 83–91, in *The Big City Book of Conservation.*

ECOLOGY

Give and take, one of the first lessons in social relations, is true also in the natural world. The whole delicately balanced system of living things rests on the foundation of the green plant world. Let the children try to think of one living thing that does not ultimately depend on green plants—only green plants make their own food. Animals that do not live on green plants live on animals that do. We call these life interdependencies based on food *food chains* (see p. 50). There is also a give and take between green plants and the nongreen plants, which include bacteria, yeasts, and all the fungi. These nongreen plants are, fortunately, agents of decay. In other words, they constantly hasten the breakdown of plant and animal matter on which they grow into simpler chemicals which green plants can use to make food. If it were not for decay, scientists estimate that all the CO_2 in our atmosphere would be used up within a generation (about 30–40 years). Much of the soil nitrogen and other essential chemicals would also disappear. One scientist estimates that an acre of farmland could support three 30-pound woodchucks. The same amount of land could carry 240 pounds of bacteria and an equal amount of fungi and animal protozoans.

One of the ways we build background and feeling-tone and kindle the spark for research in social studies is to read aloud excerpts from source material, for example, the Lewis and Clark Journals, the William Manley account of the Death Valley expedition of 49'ers, and the like. The life stories of some more recent but nonetheless colorful figures in Western history are well summarized in an upper grade supplemental reader, *Everybody's Riches,* by Grace M. Brown and Guy H. Browning, Century Schoolbook Press, 1959. This book presents biographies of Gifford Pinchot, the forester, Clarence King, the geologist, John Wesley Powell, the land surveyor, and John Muir, the mountaineer, narrated especially for children. The teacher's edition contains much supplementary science information, text activities, answers and objectives, addition questions, and activities. There are also many suggestions by reading experts, intended to enrich the basic reading program.

OUTDOOR SCIENCE AND CONSERVATION EDUCATION

The conservation movement began with people who loved the out-of-doors and wanted to preserve it. Those schools that have a school camping program are natural heirs to this motivation and sense of trusteeship. However, many schools do not have such programs, and only about 12% of the children ever go to camp. Whether or not you teach in a school system with a camp program or in a grade that goes to camp (in most schools at present, only sixth graders go), you can do much at any grade level by taking a hard look at your immediate environment. Kindergarten teachers often take the children in their classes on walking trips around the school. This practice may be repeated at every grade level. One group adopted a tree on the school ground and watched it through the school year; another group made a location map to identify trees on the school ground. For other useful suggestions, see any of the references listed below:

American Association for Health, Physical Education, and Recreation, *Outdoor Education for American Youth,* National Education Association of the United States, 1957. 150 pp.

California Association for Outdoor Education, *Teaching Conservation and Natural Science in the Outdoors,* Conservation Education Section, State of California, Dept. of Natural Resources, Jan., 1958. 47 pp.

California Journal of Elementary Education, State of California, Dept. of Education, Nov., 1957. 128 pp.

California Journal of Elementary Education, State of California, Dept. of Education, Nov., 1960. 128 pp.

Conservation, Camp Fire Girls, 1959. 72 pp.

Conservation of the Camp Site, American Camping Association, Bradford Woods, Martinsville, Ind., 1960. 36 pp.

Guide to Teaching Conservation and Resource-Use in Michigan, State of Michigan, Dept. of Public Instruction, 1960. 186 pp.

Johnston, Verna, *Natural Areas for Schools,* Conservation Education Section, State of California, Dept. of Natural Resources, 1959. 32 pp.

Leadership Guide in Conservation Education, State of Michigan, Dept. of Public Instruction and Dept. of Conservation, Bulletin No. 421, 1959. 55 pp.

Operation New York: Using the Natural Environment of the City as a Curriculum Resource, Board of Education of the City of New York, Bureau of Curriculum Research, 1960. 117 pp.

Outdoor Education: A Handbook for Teachers, Stanislaus County Schools, Calif., Spring, 1959. 104 pp.

Teaching Conservation in Indiana Schools, State of Indiana, Dept. of Public Instruction, Bulletin No. 232, Title III, N.D.E.A., No. 2, 1959. 50 pp.

Weaver, Richard L., ed., *Manual for Outdoor Laboratories: The Development and Use of Schoolgrounds as Outdoor Laboratories for Teaching Science and Conservation,* Interstate, 1959. 81 pp.

Summer science

Using the summertime is a way of stretching the year. On a warm spring day review the year's work in science as a basis for recalling things the children wish they had done. Such discussions can result in a timetable of summer activities, as follows:

Making collections
Trying experiments
Taking pictures
Keeping records
Making models
Visiting museums, planetaria, or other places of interest
Reading and talking to people about science
Keeping a scrapbook or file of newspaper and magazine articles about science
Keeping and studying living things
Logging radio and TV science programs
Recording weather, shadows, startime, etc.

A few specific examples with chapter references for details may illustrate the value of planned summer science experiences.

Water—indoors and out (see also Chapter 11). *Listen* to water filling a container in the sink, running in a hose or through a sprinkler head, running in a stream and falling on the beach. *Feel* water. Take its temperature at different times of the day. How cold does the cold water run in your tap? Does the temperature vary? *Look* at water—tapering as it runs from the spigot; swirling and whirlpooling down the drain; flowing around rocks in a stream; making eddies and waterfalls ("I come from haunts of coot and hern," Tennyson, *The Brook's Song*.); making a rainbow in a cloud, a waterfall, or a lawn sprinkler; forming dew on plants. Does dew form as a film or only in drops? What air temperature produces dew? What do you suspect in addition to air temperature is also a cause for dew? What is the most efficient way to water a lawn or garden? Can you think of experiments to prove your point? (See Chapter 7.)

Insects. The cicada's trill signals the height of midsummer and of seasonal insect population. Collect individual insects or groups of insects alive and observe in glass jar zoos. For specifics, see Chapter 3.

Reading tracks. Cultivate sensitivity to tracks of all kinds—insect and invertebrate tracks at the beach, bird and mammal tracks in mud flats, along streams and ponds, or in soft dust. Make wax or plaster of Paris castings where possible. (See Chapter 2.)

Sky watching. Lie on your back and watch the summer sky. What's in the sky? Sun, moon, and stars, of course, but how about birds and planes and insects and even flying seeds? Think of a way to collect and look at air dust under magnification. Make a culture of air dust to see what bacteria and other spores it may carry. (See Chapter 9.) The night sky in summer is especially beautiful and inviting to those who have been housed all winter within the shield of city lighting. Like the ancient Eygptian astrologers, scientists watch one star night after night. Does it appear to move with relation to a fixed line of sight?

A telescope opens a new world, especially when trained on the nearer planets. But a fine background in astronomy and general interest can be derived with no more than a pair of binoculars. Binoculars with a wide field of vision rather than a high magnification are recommended. (See Chapter 10.)

The world of Lilliput. An inexpensive Japanese or American microscope can open a whole world of interest to children—newsprint, salt crystals, sunburned skin, fish scales, leaves, etc., under low power; plant and animal cells, life in dust, and life in a drop of water under higher magnification.

Summer weather. One of the nicest things about summer is the weather. Planning outings is easier if we can predict the weather, and there are values in the attempt. Sixth graders who attend a mountain school camp predict the weather and plan the next day's activities accordingly. Their equipment consists of a thermometer, barometer, wet and dry bulb indicator (relative humidity), and a wind vane. Most of the time the children's predictions are essentially correct.

Science sensing. Summertime is rich with unforgettable sensory experiences—sights, sounds, smells, tastes, textures. We can intensify and deepen these experiences for children if we help them see patterns and diversity within such experiences. For instance,[11] we might

[11] Harry Milgrom, "Science and the Senses," *Elementary School Science Bulletin,* No. 19, Sept., 1955, pp. 1–2.

dust particles dancing in sunlight, the sun stealing below the horizon, the match flame that always points up, the play of colors in a soap bubble, ripples on the surface of water, the construction of a spider web, a halo around the moon, a cold water pipe "sweating" on a hot day, the shimmering air over a radiator, the curve of a pitched ball, a reflection in a mirror. How do we explain these things?

ASK THEM TO COMPARE—THE SLOW

MOTIONS OF:

the leaves of a plant turning toward the sun, the tidewaters rising or falling, water evaporating from a glass, the hour hand of a clock.

WITH—THE HIGH SPEED OF:

the flash of a firefly or lightning, a jet plane streaking across the sky, a picture sent by television, voice by radio. How do we measure time? What is time?

ASK THEM TO FEEL:

the force of wind-driven rain against the face, the crunch of sand or snow underfoot, the spine-tingling screech of chalk drawn across a blackboard, the heat pouring out of a sun-scorched brick after sunset, the earth-shaking rumble of a blast of thunder. With what do we feel?

CALL THEIR ATTENTION TO THE ODOR OF:

new-mown hay, air after a lightning storm, ocean spray, fresh leather, a swamp, a rose, gasoline fumes, smoke, broiling steak, wintergreen, earth. What brings these odors to the nose?

ASK THE CHILDREN TO TOUCH AND LEARN THE

TEXTURES OF:

sandpaper, cellophane, felt, wool, rabbit fur, hamster fur, flower petals, water, mercury, aluminum, beech bark, shagbark hickory, oil, soap, leather, bone, silk, glass, waxed paper. What produces these varied feelings?

ASK THEM TO LISTEN TO:

purr of a pussycat, sound of an idling engine, roar of a subway train, sound of a jet plane, ocean waves, hiss of escaping air, screech of brakes, wailing of a siren, clang of a bell, gurgling brook, lapping of water, rustling of

leaves, howling of winds, sounds of frogs, birds, insects, animals, people, instruments. What makes these sounds? What makes them different?

AND TO THE SILENCE OF:

the moon journeying across the sky, lake waters on a calm misty morning, a hawk circling high in the sky, a flower bud unfolding, snow falling, electricity moving in a wire, a sailboat skimming over distant waters. What is silence?

POINT OUT TO THE CHILDREN THE COLOR

MARVEL OF:

a red sunset, a harvest moon, a rainbow, the purple mountains' majesty, a dancing flame, a blue sky, autumn leaves, the sparkle of gems, an oil slick on water, butterflies, beetles, birds, reptiles. What is color?

ASK THEM TO THINK ABOUT THE FASCINATING

SHAPES OF:

leaves, snowflakes, eggs, starfish, snail shells, clouds, lightning, star groups, icicles, suspension cables, airplane wings, birds, fish, drops of water, frost. What causes the formation of these shapes?

GIVE THEM OPPORTUNITIES TO SOAR ON THE

WINGS OF FANTASY:

What would happen if trees, gravity, insects, flowers, humans, and so on, disappeared; if air stopped moving; if water stopped flowing? If I were a seed, dust particle, piece of paper, drop of water, leaf, meteor fragment, comet fragment, sound, radio wave, microbe, light ray, where would I wander?

My journey into the world of: invisible microbes, invisible atoms and molecules, outer space, the earth's interior, the ocean bottom, the mountain peak.

Summer collector's harvest. Encourage the children to make significant collections. Show them how to organize, select, and arrange their materials for study and display. Collection is an individual matter but can be utilized to enrich the understanding of the group and in some cases enhance the status of the young collector. The following chart is reproduced by permission of the L. W. Singer Co. (*Singer Science News,* Vol. XII, No. 9, May, 1959, pp. 2–3).

Summertime science collections

what to collect	where to go	what to look for	equipment needed
Rocks	Around home, road cuts, excavations, quarries, hills, mountains	Rocks with interesting colors, streaks, shapes; rocks containing clear and colored crystals; rocks with fossils	Hammer (geologist's or carpenter's), chisel, newspapers, cloth bag, notebook and pencil, compass, guidebook such as *Rocks and Minerals* by Zim and Shafer, Simon and Schuster, 1957
Insects	Around home, fields, gardens, beaches, woods, around ponds, almost everywhere	Butterflies, ants, moths, beetles, flies, wasps, bees, crickets, grasshoppers, water bugs, many others	Long-handled cloth net, flashlight, small glass bottles with covers, envelopes, pencil and paper, tweezers, magnifying glass, a glass bottle partly filled with 80–90% ethyl alcohol (killing jar), large sieve, cigar boxes, guidebook such as *Insects* by Zim and Cotta, Simon and Schuster, 1951
Feathers	Fields, gardens, woods, near pools of water, places where birds dust themselves, city parks, near bird nests, almost everywhere	Bird feathers of various colors, sizes, and shapes	Magnifying glass, envelopes, gummed tape, colored construction papers, guidebook such as *Birds* by Zim and Gabrielson, Simon and Schuster, 1949
Leaves	Streets, woods, parks, almost everywhere	Leaves of various colors, sizes, and shapes	Flat board, books, newspapers, gummed tape, colored construction papers, guidebook such as *Trees* by Zim and Martin, Simon and Schuster, 1953
Animals (other than insects) in and near a pond	Near a small pond	Tadpoles, salamanders, snakes, turtles, crayfish, minnows, fairy shrimp, snails, toads, frogs, lizards, slugs, newts	Kitchen sieve or butterfly net, old sneakers for wading, glass jars with covers, guidebook such as *Reptiles and Amphibians* by Zim and Smith, Simon and Schuster, 1958

how to collect	*care of the collection*
Use hammer and chisel to collect samples about the size of walnuts. Be careful of flying chips. Do not collect too many specimens. Be selective. Wrap each rock in newspaper. Before wrapping, assign a number to the sample. Use a numbered piece of adhesive tape to do this. In a notebook, write this number down and after it, write the date, place collected, and kind of rock, if known. Place samples in cloth bag	Place specimens in compartmentalized trays. Use egg cartons or plastic trays. Number samples. Make 3 × 5 index cards to correspond with the numbers. On each card show the number of the rock, date, place collected, kind of rock, and name of collector
With large net for pursuing butterflies and other airborne insects, and with sieve for scooping insects from shallow pond water, and with flashlight and glass jars for collecting insects at night, gather as wide a variety of insects as possible. Place most insects into killing jar (see guidebook for directions for killing moths and butterflies). Remove with tweezers and store in envelopes until ready to mount. During collections, observe movements and feeding habits of live insects	Use cigar boxes to house insect collections. Place a pin through the body of an insect. Stick the pin into cardboard placed on the bottom of the box. Arrange the pins in an orderly fashion. Make small cards which give information about the sample. With the pin, pierce the cards and mount them with the insect. Mount butterflies and moths on cotton in cigar boxes. Cover these mounts with cellophane or glass to make permanent mounts
No special method is needed to collect feathers. Pick them up wherever they may be seen. Store the samples in envelopes to help protect them before mounting	Mount feathers on colored construction paper. Use gummed tape to hold feathers in place. Label each sample. Use the guidebook to help identify the feathers
No special method is needed to collect leaves. Collect leaves from the ground. Try to find leaves that have not been partly eaten by insects or damaged in any way	Place leaves on a thick layer of newspapers. Place the newspapers on a board. Cover the leaves with another layer of papers and then place about three heavy books on top of the papers. When the leaves are thoroughly dried, remove them from the paper press and with gummed tape attach them to sheets of colored paper. Record the names of the leaves and any other interesting information on the papers
Over and under logs and rocks near the pond's edge find salamanders, turtles, snakes, etc. In shallow water find tadpoles, minnows, fairy shrimp, crayfish, etc. Use hands or sieve or net to collect these animals. Wear sneakers in the water to prevent cuts from rocks and debris. Place animals such as minnows, crayfish, and fairy shrimp in water in glass jars; place other animals in glass jars without water	Animals collected from the water in the pond need to be placed in an aquarium, and animals collected near the pond's edge need to be placed in a terrarium. From the library, obtain a book which gives instructions on how to make and maintain aquariums and terrariums. When the animals have been studied, they should be returned to their natural homes

BIBLIOGRAPHY

Ashbaugh, B. L., and M. Beuschlein, *Things to Do in Science and Conservation,* Interstate, 1960. Simple and practical suggestions for activities to illustrate broad aspects of conservation, viz., space, air, the sun, soil, water, minerals, plants, and animals; also man-developed resources such as electricity, synthetics, nuclear energy. Leading questions, basic concepts, and bibliographies for each subtopic.

Bathurst, Effie, and Wilhelmina Hill, *Conservation Experiences for Children,* Bulletin No. 16, 1957, U. S. Dept. of Health, Education and Welfare, Government Printing Office. 192 pp. Useful compilation of case-study examples of conservation mainly as applied to renewable resources. Useful chapter on water and mineral conservation and on conservation in camps and clubs.

Besser, Marianne, *Growing Up with Science,* McGraw-Hill, 1960.

Blough, Glenn, *Lookout for the Forest,* Whittlesey, 1955. Middle. The work of "forest farmers" and forest rangers in renewing and guarding our forest resources.

Brown, Grace M., and Guy H. Browning, *Everybody's Riches,* Century Schoolbook Press, 1959.

Conserving Our Natural Resources, Girl Scouts of the U. S. A. Simple and intriguing ideas for conserving fire, wildlife (small), wild plants, forests, water, soil. Selected references.

Gates, Richard, *The True Book of Conservation,* Childrens Press, 1959. The format is primary, but the traditional concept of renewable resource conservation is probably too abstract to hold the attention of young children or their teachers.

Handbook for Teaching Conservation and Resource-Use, Interstate, 1955. Fruits of a three-year project by the National Association of Biology.

Munzer, Martha M., and Paul F. Brandwein, *Teaching Science Through Conservation,* McGraw-Hill, 1960. Teachers' compendium of selected practical laboratory and field studies for secondary school or advanced elementary school. Special features include broad, modern view of conservation, dual table of contents, chapter on air pollution, annotated bibliography of supplementary instructional materials.

Operation New York: Using the Natural Environment of the City as a Curriculum Resource, Board of Education of the City of New York, Bureau of Curriculum Research, 1960. Group report of action research to develop concrete ways of studying and understanding an urban environment. Creative and challenging. Applicable to science or social studies.

Palmer, E. L., *Conservation, A Handbook for Teachers,* Cornell Rural School Leaflet, Vol. 45, No. 1, Sept., 1951. 64 pp. Basic principles, background, and demonstrations for understanding forest and wildlife, soil and water, water; the two latter are particularly interesting and valuable.

Peter, Katherine, and Robert Wadham, *California Wonderworld,* Century, 1957. Middle. Picture story book of western wildlife interrelationships. Colored illustrations fair. Vocabulary analysis list.

Smith, F. C., *The First Book of Conservation,* Franklin Watts, 1954. Middle. Ecological interrelationships, the history of and need for the conservation movement, modern conservation workers and their methods, the role of the individual, glossary of terms. Good drawings.

Urell, Catherine, et al., *The Big City Book of Conservation,* Follett, 1956. Middle. Unusual and challenging illustrations of conservation for urban children. Excellent photographs, word list, and five pages of useful notes to the teacher.

Watts, May T., *Reading the Landscape,* Macmillan, 1957. A distinguished ecologist and botanist reads for us a host of clues to such varied environments as a prairie sod plowing, a lakeshore dune, a quaking bog, tree rings in a rural schoolyard, a forest in the Great Smokies, and timberline trees in the Rockies. Delightfully instructive.

Reference tables

Weights and measures

Common or English system

Linear measure
1 foot (ft) = 12 inches (in)
1 yard (yd) = 3 feet
1 rod (rd), pole, or perch = 5½ yards
1 furlong (fur) = 40 rods
1 statute mile (mi) = 8 furlongs
1 league = 3 miles
1 fathom (f) = 6 feet

Square measure
1 square foot (sq ft) = 144 square inches (sq in)
1 square yard (sq yd) = 9 square feet
1 square rod (sq rd) = 30¼ square yards
1 acre (A) = 160 square rods
1 square mile (sq mi) = 640 acres
1 section (sec) = 1 mile square
1 township (tp) = 36 sections

Cubic measure
1 cubic foot (cu ft) = 1728 cubic inches (cu in)
1 cubic yard (cu yd) = 27 cubic feet

Liquid measure (U.S.)
1 pint (pt) = 28.875 cubic inches = 4 gills (gi)
1 quart (qt) = 2 pints
1 gallon (gal) = 4 quarts
1 barrel (bbl) = 31½ gallons

Dry measure (U.S.)
1 quart (qt) = 67.20 cubic inches = 2 pints
1 peck (pk) = 8 quarts
1 bushel (bu) = 4 pecks

Liquid and dry measure (British)
1 pint = 34.677 cubic inches = 4 gills
1 quart (qt) = 2 pints (pt)
1 gallon (gal) = 4 quarts
1 peck (pk) = 2 gallons
1 bushel (bu) = 4 pecks
1 quarter (qr) = 8 bushels

Apothecaries' fluid measure
1 fluid dram (fl dr or ʒ) = 0.2256 cubic inch = 60 minims (min or m)
1 fluid ounce (fl oz or ʒ) = 8 fluid drams
1 pint (pt or o) = 16 fluid ounces
1 quart (qt) = 2 pints
1 gallon (gal) = 4 quarts

Avoirdupois weight
1 dram (dr) = 27 11/32 grains[1] (gr)
1 ounce (oz) = 16 drams
1 pound (lb) = 16 ounces
1 stone (st) = 14 pounds
1 hundredweight (cwt) = 100 pounds[2]
1 ton[3] (t) = 20 hundredweights

Troy weight
1 carat (car) = 3.086 grains[1] (gr)
1 pennyweight (dwt) = 24 grains
1 ounce (oz t) = 20 pennyweights
1 pound (lb t) = 12 ounces troy

Apothecaries' weight
1 scruple (s ap or ℈) = 20 grains[1] (gr)
1 dram (dr ap or ʒ) = 3 scruples
1 ounce (oz ap or ʒ) = 8 drams
1 pound (lb ap or ℔) = 12 ounces

Metric system

Linear measure
1 centimeter (cm) = 10 millimeters (mm)
1 decimeter (dm) = 10 centimeters
1 meter (m) = 10 decimeters
1 dekameter (dkm) = 10 meters
1 hectometer (hm) = 10 dekameters
1 kilometer (km) = 10 hectometers

Square measure
1 square centimeter (cm²) = 100 square millimeters (mm²)
1 square decimeter (dm²) = 100 square centimeters
1 square meter (m²) = 100 square decimeters
1 are (a) = 100 square meters
1 hectare (ha) = 100 ares
1 square kilometer (km²) = 100 hectares

Cubic measure
1 cubic centimeter[4] (cm³) = 1000 cubic millimeters (mm³)
1 cubic decimeter (dm³) = 1000 cubic centimeters
1 cubic meter (m³) = 1 stere (st) = 1000 cubic decimeters

---

[1] The "grain," 0.0648 grams, is the same in avoirdupois, troy, and apothecaries' weights.
[2] British 112 pounds.
[3] Short ton (s t) = 2000 pounds; long ton (l t) = 2240 pounds.
[4] 1 milliliter = 1.000027 cubic centimeters. For all practical purposes, they are equivalent.

Liquid measure
1 centiliter (cl) = 10 milliliters (ml)
1 deciliter (dl) = 10 centiliters
1 liter (l) = 10 deciliters
1 dekaliter (dkl) = 10 liters
1 hectoliter (hl) = 10 dekaliters
1 kiloliter (kl) = 10 hectoliters

Weight
1 centigram (cg) = 10 milligrams (mg)
1 decigram (dg) = 10 centigrams
1 gram (g) = 10 decigrams
1 dekagram (dkg) = 10 grams
1 hectogram (hg) = 10 dekagrams
1 kilogram (kg) = 10 hectograms
1 metric ton (t) = 1000 kilograms

Equivalents in common or English and metric systems

1 inch = 2.54 centimeters
1 mile = 1.6093 kilometers
1 quart (U.S.) = 0.9464 liter
1 quart (British) = 1.1351 liters
1 pound = 453.59 grams

Miscellaneous

1 dozen (doz) = 12
1 gross (gro) = 12 dozen
1 great gross (gt gro) = 12 gross
1 quire = 24 sheets of paper
1 ream = 20 quires
1 cord foot (cd ft) = 16 cubic feet (cu ft) of wood
1 cord (cd) = 8 cord feet

Table A-2
Specific gravities of some common materials[1]

(grams per cc at 20° C)		(grams per cc at 20° C)	
Acetone	0.79	Limestone	2.7
Agate	2.5–2.6	Magnesium	1.74
Alcohol (95%)	0.81	Marble	2.7
Aluminum	2.7	Mercury	13.6
Brass	8.5	Milk	1.03
Butter	0.86	Mortar	1.44–1.6
Brick (common)	1.79	Nickel	8.8
Carbon tetrachloride	1.6	Opal	2.1–2.3
Celluloid	1.4	Osmium	22.5
Cement	2.8	Paraffin	0.82–0.94
Clay	1.92–2.4	Plaster of Paris	1.18–1.28
Coal (anthracite)	1.5	Platinum	21.4
Coal (bituminous)	1.3	Polystyrene	1.06
Concrete	1.92–2.24	Porcelain	2.38
Copper	8.9	Quartz	2.6
Cork	0.22–0.26	Rock salt	2.1–2.2
Diamond	3.1–3.5	Rubber (gum)	0.92
Earth (loose)	1.15–1.28	Sand	1.44–1.76
Earth (packed)	1.44–1.76	Sea water	1.03
Gasoline	0.68	Silver	10.5
German silver	8.4	Slate	2.72–2.88
Glass (common)	2.5	Steel	7.8
Gold	19.3	Sulfur (roll)	2.0
Granite	2.7	Tile	1.76–1.92
Graphite	2.2	Tin	7.3
Gravel	1.6–1.92	Tungsten	18.8
Gypsum	2.32	Wood	
Human body (normal)	1.07	balsa	0.16
Human body (when lungs		red oak	0.67
are filled)	1.00	rock elm	0.76
Ice	0.92	southern pine	0.56
Iron	7.9	white pine	0.4
Lead	11.3	Zinc	7.1

[1] Specific gravity is the ratio of the weight of any volume of a substance to the weight of an equal volume of water, taken as 1; that is, it is the ratio of the density of a substance to the density of water. Values vary for substances not having a constant composition.

Table A-3
Temperature conversion table

°C	°F	°C	°F	°C	°F	°C	°F	°C	°F
−20	−4	17	63	38	100	59	138	80	176
−15	+5	18	64	39	102	60	140	81	178
−10	14	19	66	40	104	61	142	82	180
−5	23	20	68	41	106	62	144	83	181
0	32	21	70	42	108	63	145	84	183
1	34	22	72	43	109	64	147	85	185
2	36	23	73	44	111	65	149	86	187
3	37	24	75	45	113	66	151	87	189
4	39	25	77	46	115	67	153	88	190
5	41	26	79	47	117	68	154	89	192
6	43	27	81	48	118	69	156	90	194
7	45	28	82	49	120	70	158	91	196
8	46	29	84	50	122	71	160	92	198
9	48	30	86	51	124	72	162	93	199
10	50	31	88	52	126	73	163	94	201
11	52	32	90	53	127	74	165	95	203
12	54	33	91	54	129	75	167	96	205
13	55	34	93	55	131	76	169	97	207
14	57	35	95	56	133	77	171	98	208
15	59	36	97	57	135	78	172	99	210
16	61	37	99	58	136	79	174	100	212

Bibliography:

books for a science library

Some of these publications are recommended for the teacher's library; others are suggested as a starting point in building a school science library for the use of both students and teachers. The listing of books and pamphlets for teachers and students contains recommended textbooks and textbook series in addition to many sources of supplemental reading. The teacher will be especially interested in the section entitled "Criteria for Evaluating Science Textbooks," and in the section on scope and sequence charts. See also the bibliographies at the ends of the chapters.

STANDARD REFERENCES

Encyclopedias

Britannica Junior (15 volumes), Encyclopaedia Britannica, Chicago, latest edition.

Collier's Encyclopedia (20 volumes), Crowell Collier, New York, latest edition.

Compton's Pictured Encyclopedia (15 volumes), F. E. Compton, Chicago, latest edition.

Our Wonderful World Encyclopedia, Spencer Press, Champaign, Ill., 1957.

World Book Encyclopedia (19 volumes), Field Enterprises, Chicago, latest edition.

Yearbooks

Rethinking Science Education, Univ. of Chicago Press, 1960. 59th yearbook of the National Society for the Study of Education, Part I, ed. by J. Darrell Barnard. National authorities discuss the role of science; the creativity and personality of the scientist; status of science

education in elementary and secondary schools and colleges; science programs; curriculum development; supervision; facilities and materials; training and professional growth of science teachers; and research.

Science Education in American Schools, Univ. of Chicago Press, 1947. 46th yearbook of the NSSE, Part I. A milestone in laying down basic objectives and goals. Compendium of articles by authorities.

Science for Today's Children, No. 33, National Elementary Principals, September, 1953. Articles by authorities on theory and application in most aspects of elementary science teaching.

U.S. Dept. of Agriculture, *Insects: Yearbook of Agriculture: 1952,* U.S. Govt. Printing Office, Washington 25, D.C., 1952.

———, *Trees: Yearbook of Agriculture: 1949,* U.S. Govt. Printing Office, Washington 25, D.C., 1949.

The World Almanac and Book of Facts, New York World-Telegram, latest edition.

PERIODICALS AND JOURNALS

The American Biology Teacher, National Association of Biology Teachers, Interstate Press, 19 N. Jackson St., Danville, Ill. $6.00 (8 issues) per year.

American Journal of Physics, American Institute of Physics, 335 E. 45th St., New York 17, N.Y. Monthly; $7.50 per year.

Audubon Magazine, National Audubon Society, 1130 Fifth Ave., New York 28, N.Y. Bimonthly; $5.00 per year.

Biology and General Science Digest, W. M. Welch

Manufacturing Co., 1515 Sedgwick St., Chicago 10, Ill. Free.

Elementary School Science Bulletin, National Science Teachers Association, 1201 Sixteenth St., N.W., Washington 6, D.C. $1.00 (8 issues) per year.

Fauna, Fauna, 34th and Girard Ave., Philadelphia, Pa.

The Grade Teacher, Educational Pub. Co., Darien, Conn. $5.00 (10 issues) per year.

Journal of Chemical Education, American Chemical Society, 1155 Sixteenth St., N.W., Washington 6, D.C. Monthly; $4.00 per year.

The Junior Astronomer, Benjamin Adelman, 4211 Colie Dr., Silver Spring, Md.

Junior Natural History, American Museum of Natural History, Central Park West at 79th St., New York 24, N.Y. $1.50 (10 issues) per year.

Metropolitan Detroit Science Review, Metropolitan Science Club, 4830 Grady St., Detroit 7, Mich. Quarterly.

Natural History, American Museum of Natural History, Central Park West at 79th St., New York 24, N.Y. Monthly, October–May; bimonthly, June–September; $5.00 per year.

Nature Magazine, American Nature Association, 1214 Sixteenth St., N.W., Washington 6, D.C. Monthly, October–May; bimonthly, June–September; $5.00 per year.

Outdoors Illustrated, National Audubon Society, 1130 Fifth Ave., New York 28, N.Y.

Physics and Chemistry Digest, W. M. Welch Manufacturing Co., 1515 Sedgwick St., Chicago 10, Ill. Free.

Physics Today, American Institute of Physics, 335 E. 45th St., New York 17, N.Y. Monthly; $4.00 per year.

Popular Mechanics, Popular Mechanics Co., 250 W. 55th St., New York 19, N.Y. Monthly; $3.50 per year.

Popular Science, Popular Science Publishing Co., 355 Lexington Ave., New York 17, N.Y. Monthly; $3.40 per year.

School Science and Mathematics, Central Association of Science and Mathematics Teachers, 450 Ahnaip St., Menasha, Wisc. Monthly October–June; $4.50 per year.

Science, American Association for the Advancement of Science, 1515 Massachusetts Ave., N.W., Washington 5, D.C. Weekly; $8.50 per year.

Science Digest, Science Digest, Inc., 250 W. 55th St., New York 19, N.Y. Monthly; $3.50 per year.

Science Education, National Association for Research in Science Teaching, University of Tampa, Tampa, Fla. $5.00 (5 issues) per year.

Science News Letter, Science Service, 1719 N St., N.W., Washington 6, D.C. Weekly; $5.50 per year.

The Science Teacher, National Science Teachers Association, 1201 Sixteenth St., N.W., Washington 6, D.C. Monthly; $3.00 per year.

Science World, Scholastic Magazines, Inc, 33 W. 42nd St., New York 36, N.Y. $1.50 (15–16 issues) per year.

Scientific American, Scientific American, Inc., 415 Madison Ave., New York 17, N.Y. Monthly; $6.00 per year.

The Scientific Monthly, American Association for the Advancement of Science, 1515 Massachusetts Ave., N.W., Washington 5, D.C.

Sky and Telescope, Sky Publishing Corp., Harvard College Observatory, 60 Garden St., Cambridge 38, Mass. Monthly; $5.00 per year.

Skylights, National Aviation Education Council, 1205 Connecticut Ave., N.W., Washington 6, D.C.

The UNESCO Courier, UNESCO Publications Center, 801 Third Ave., New York 22, N.Y. Monthly; $3.00 per year.

Weatherwise, American Meteorological Society, 3 Joy St., Boston 8, Mass. Bimonthly; $4.00 per year.

BOOKS AND PAMPHLETS FOR TEACHERS

Abell, Fred H., *The How Book of Grade School Science,* Stansi Scientific Co., 1957. Booklet to accompany Stansi science kit; describes 144 experiences with heat, light, sound, electricity, astronomy, health, and other phenomena.

Arey, Charles K., *Science Experiences for Elementary Schools: Practical Suggestions for Teaching Series,* No. 4, Bur. of Publications, Teachers College, Columbia Univ., New York, N.Y., n.d. 98 pp. Upper. Experiences with plants, atmosphere, earth and seasons, magnetism and electricity, heat, light, and sound.

Ashley, Tracy H., et al., *An Administrator's Guide*

to the *Elementary School Science Program,* Association of Public School Systems, 525 W. 120th St., New York 27, N.Y. 30 pp.

Baker, Emily V., *Children's Questions and Their Implications for Planning the Curriculum,* Bur. of Publications, Teachers College, Columbia Univ., New York, N.Y., 1945. 172 pp. More than 9000 unstructured questions from 1500 children throughout the country—grouped and analyzed. Approximately 30 pp. on science.

Barnard, J. Darrell, *Teaching High-School Science: What Research Says to the Teacher Series,* No. 10, Dept. Classroom Teachers, NEA, 1956. 32 pp., 25¢. Why, what, and how of teaching science; materials, facilities, and evaluation; training of science teachers.

Blackwood, Paul, *Experimenting in Elemenetary Science,* Education Brief No. 12, rev. ed., U.S. Dept. of Health, Education and Welfare, 1957. 7 pp., free. How to develop scientific methods in the elementary grades.

Blough, Glenn O., *It's Time for Better Elementary School Science,* NSTA, 1958. 48 pp. Of special interest to administrators and supervisors. Theory for science curriculum construction.

———, and Paul Blackwood, *Teaching Elementary Science: Suggestions for Classroom Teachers,* Bulletin No. 4, 1948, U.S. Dept. of Health, Education and Welfare, 1953 reprint. 40 pp., 20¢. Definitions and basic assumptions, ways of learning, developing a unit, science resources at home and school.

———, and Marjorie Campbell, *Making and Using Classroom Science Materials in the Elementary Schools,* Holt, Rinehart and Winston, 1954. Clear, well-illustrated suggestions for constructing demonstration materials for various areas of science. Extensive bibliography for each area; sources of materials.

———, et al., *Elementary School Science and How to Teach It,* rev. ed., Holt, Rinehart and Winston, 1958. 608 pp. Five introductory chapters and 24 two-part chapters developing ocntent and method for various areas of science.

Brandwein, P. F., et al., *Teaching High School Science* series, Harcourt, Brace & World. Our favorites among high school text references for elementary teachers. Challenging, completely up to date, beautifully organized and illustrated. Especially strong in new developments and in enrichment activities.

Burnett, R. W., *Teaching Science in the Elementary School,* Holt, Rinehart and Winston, 1953. 541 pp. Child developmental approach in introductory chapters. Especially good on atomic and other forms of energy.

California Association for Supervision and Curriculum Development, *Leadership for Science in the Elementary Schools,* 1960. 88 pp. A handbook for teachers, administrators, consultants, and supervisors. Practical suggestions for the science program, science experiences, developing attitudes and problem-solving abilities, materials and equipment, and continuous professional growth. Examples of forward-looking leadership practices. Excellent photographs.

California State Dept. of Education, *California Journal of Elementary Education,* Vol. 21, No. 2, November, 1952. 63 pp. Special issue on science for every child and every teacher; characteristics of a good program; equipment and materials.

———, *Looking Ahead in Science,* 1960. 88 pp. Report of the Production Seminar and Conferences on the Improvement of Science Education in the Elementary School. Purposes, appropriate experiences and content, equipment and materials, scheduling, evaluation, pre- and in-service education.

Camp Fire Girls, Inc., *Frontiers—Fun with Science for Camp Fire Girls,* 1953. 119 pp. Creative, challenging, and well-illustrated activities. Sections on sound, light, magnets, electricity, chemistry, air, weather, and aviation. Final section on "Things to Make and Do" of particular value.

Children's Books for $1.25 or Less, Association of Childhood Education International, Washington 5, D.C. 38 pp.

Children's Books for Nature Study, 2nd in series, *Kansas School Naturalist,* Vol. 3, No. 2, Kansas State Teachers College, Emporia, Kans., December, 1956. 16 pp. Useful categories, suggested grade level groupings, and perceptive annotations. Includes titles of trade book series, magazines, and publishers' addresses. Extensive list of other biographies.

Clark, Ilene C., *Science for Primary Children,* Chico State College, Laboratory School, Chico, Calif. 64 pp. Reference book for teachers and parents. Elements and forces in nature; seasonal activities; records and music books.

Comstock, Anna, *Handbook of Nature Study,* rev. ed., Comstock (Cornell Univ. Press), 1953. Written for inexperienced teachers by a wise and compassionate teacher and mother. The most useful reference for identifying most of the natural objects children bring to school.

Conservation and Nature Activities, comp. by *Canadian Nature Magazine,* 1951, Audubon Society of Canada, Toronto, Can. Resource materials, nature teaching, seasonal activities, bibliography.

Cornell Rural School Leaflet, *Science Books for Children,* Teachers' Number, Vol. 51, No. 1, N.Y. State College of Agriculture, Cornell Univ., Ithaca, N.Y., Fall, 1957. 64 pp., 20¢. About 400 books personally examined in this list of titles published since the 1949 Elementary Science Library number of the leaflet.

Craig, G. S., *Certain Techniques Used in Developing a Course of Study in Science for Horace Mann Elementary School, N.Y.,* Teachers College, Columbia Univ., New York, N.Y., 1927. 73 pp. Dissertation was a turning point in the development of elementary science from nature study toward its present scope.

———, *Science in Childhood Education: Practical Suggestions for Teaching Series,* No. 8, Bur. of Publications, Teachers College, Columbia Univ., New York, N.Y., 1944. 86 pp. Science in the lives of children, attitudes and methods of work, curriculum, community resources.

———, *Science in the Elementary Schools: What Research Says to the Teacher Series,* No. 12, Dept. of Classroom Teachers, NEA, 1957. 33 pp. The role of elementary science, behavior patterns, content, universal patterns, conservation, community problems, developmental point of view, modern science, teaching and learning science, types of activities, evaluation.

———, *Science for the Elementary-School Teacher,* 2nd ed., Ginn, 1958. 894 pp. Encyclopedic classic. Especially strong on earth and universe.

Curriculum Research Report, *A Selected Bibliography in Elementary Science,* Board of Education of the City of New York, Curriculum Center, 130 W. 55th St., New York, N. Y., 1955. 15¢.

Deason, Hilary J., *Science Booklist for Children,* American Association for Advancement of Science, and NSF, Washington, D.C., 1960. 138 pp. Guide to recreational and collateral reading in the sciences (including mathematics) through the eighth grade. Also acquisition guide for elementary school and public librarians.

———, *The Traveling Elementary School Science Library,* American Association for Advancement of Science, and NSTA, Washington, D.C. 25¢. The Traveling Library, initiated in 1955, consists of 160 titles representing the major areas of science. Classified as primary, intermediate, or advanced. Also listed by subject index. Recommended for acquisition as basic collection by schools, public libraries, and parents. Comprehensive list published in 1960.

DeVries, Leonard, *The Book of Experiments,* trans. by Eric G. Breeze, John Murray Publishers, London, Eng., 1959. Delightful descriptions and diagrams of experiments with air, force, sound, heat, water, electricity, light, chemistry, and other phenomena. Good for the gifted pupil. (Distributed by Macmillan.)

Dunfee, Maxine, and Julian Greenlee, *Elementary School Science: Research, Theory and Practice,* Association for Supervisory and Curriculum Development of the NEA, 1957. 67 pp., $1.00. Practical suggestions for teaching and evaluating elementary science in relation to research evidence.

Education for the Age of Science, Statement by the President's Science Advisory Committee, the White House, Supt. of Documents, May 24, 1959. 36 pp., 20¢. The place of science and technology, the major tasks, national goals. Consideration of opportunities for the gifted student.

Elementary School Science. Sample-page booklet from *Compton's Pictured Encyclopedia.* Covers insects, astronomy, heat, light, atoms, air, and other topics, and includes color plates.

Fitzpatrick, F. L., ed., *Policies for Science Education,* Teachers College, Columbia Univ., New York, N.Y., 1960. Science Manpower Project monographs; national authorities contribute chapters on improvement of programs in elementary, junior, and senior high schools, teacher education, existing programs.

Forler, Gladys, and Dorothy Forler, *Day by Day with Science,* Whitman, Racine, Wisc., 1954. 64 pp. Inexpensive, work-type edition.

Freeman, Kenneth, et al., *Helping Children Understand Science,* Holt, Rinehart and Winston, 1954. 314 pp. Planning and organizing science instruction, community resources, equipment, and audio-visual aids.

Gans, R., and C. Stendler, *Teaching Young Children in Nursery School, Kindergarten and Primary Grades,* Harcourt, Brace & World, 1952. See especially Chap. 10, "The Child as a Scientist," pp. 236–60.

Greenlee, Julian, *Better Teaching Through Elementary Science,* Brown, 1954. 204 pp. A science supervisor and first-grade teacher learn with the children about workable techniques in elementary science. An anecdotal presentation of objectives and procedures. Easy reading.

———, *Teaching Science to Children,* Brown, 1951, 1956. 185 pp. Prepared as source book for primary teachers. Anecdotal treatment of children investigating various areas of science.

Growing Up with Science Books, American Library Association, Chicago, Ill. Issued annually in September.

Harris, Thistle Y., *The Teaching of Nature Study,* Australian Council for Educational Research, Melbourne, Aus., 1954. 100 pp. Basic philosophy, objectives, activities, programing, and testing. Designed for teachers who feel inadequate in this area.

Headley, J., and N. E. Headley, *Education in the Kindergarten,* American Book, 1955. See pp. 320–57. Suggested activities and observations on air, wind, clouds, dew.

Heffernan, H., and V. E. Todd, *The Kindergarten Teacher,* Heath, 1960. Excellent chapter on science.

Hochman, V., and M. Greenwald, *Science Experiences in Early Childhood Education,* Bank Street Publishers, New York, N.Y., 1953. 24 pp., 50¢. Sensory experiences, cooking experiences, mechanical processes, weather, science in the social studies program.

Hubler, Clark, *Working with Children in Science,* Houghton Mifflin, 1957. 425 pp. Very strong in physical science. Well illustrated.

Hyde, M. O., and F. W. Keene, *Hobby Fun Book for Grade School Boys and Girls,* Seashore Press, Pelham, N.Y., 1952. 218 pp. Selected creative or to-do hobbies and crafts. Good line drawings.

Improving Science Programs in Illinois Schools, Univ. of Illinois, Urbana, Ill., 1958. 87 pp. Analysis and recommendations of a joint committee on improvement of science teaching. Considers teacher recruitment and preparation.

International Conference on Public Education, *Introduction to Natural Science in Primary Schools,* UNESCO, New York, N.Y. $1.40.

Johnson, June, *838 Ways to Amuse a Child,* Harper, 1960. Crafts, hobbies, nature lore, travel ideas for the child from 6 to 12.

Jordan, E. L., *Hammond's Guide to Nature Activities,* Macmillan, 1958. 64 pp. Collecting rocks, minerals, and shells; terraria and aquaria; plant and bird hobbies; collecting insects; nature photography; fishing and hunting. Excellent illustrations.

Laboratories in the Classroom: New Horizons in Science Education, Science Materials Center, New York, N.Y., 1960. 96 pp. Contributions from outstanding educators and creative classroom teachers on basic aims, new curricula, and new plans and procedures.

Mallinson, G. G., and J. V. Buck, *A Bibliography of Reference Books for Elementary Science,* NSTA, Washington, D.C., 1958. 35 pp., 50¢. Books for teachers and children.

Meister, Morris, and P. F. Brandwein, *Your Future in Science,* Science Research Associates, 1958. 56 pp. What successful scientists have in common; preparation and career opportunities.

Merritt, Eleanor, *Instructional Materials Bulletin: Sources of Elementary School Science,* Bibliography No. 2, Curriculum Laboratory, Iowa State Teachers College, Cedar Falls, Ia., June 1959. 18 pp. Curriculum guides, pamphlet series, miscellaneous bulletins and pamphlets, elementary science texts, publishers, professional books, standard references, resource units, sources of free and inexpensive materials, audio-visual materials. No annotations but a great many useful reference data.

The Nature and Science List, New American Library.

Navarra, J. G., and Joseph Zafforoni, *Science Today for the Elementary-School Teacher,* Row, Peterson, 1960. 470 pp. Developmental approach to evaluation, and current content and method in nine major areas—air, weather, and aviation; space, time, and the earth; matter, energy, and life.

Nelson, Esther K., *A Bibliography of Science Books for Elementary School Children,* Bulletin, California State Dept. of Education, Vol. 28, No. 5, September, 1959. 115 pp. Sections on living things, the earth, universe, physical and chemical phenomena, people and events in the sciences; multiple topics; general grade level groupings; annotations.

Nelson, L. W., and G. C. Lorbeer, *Science Activities for Elementary Children,* rev. ed., Brown, 1959. 178 pp. Two hundred and forty-nine activities on typical areas of science organized into general and specific area problems and grade levels; information on materials, procedures, and results.

New York State Education Dept., *General Science Handbook, Part I,* Bur. of Curriculum Development, Div. of Secondary Education, 1951. 197 pp. Deals with living things, health, electric circuits, gravity and friction, fire, light, seasons, rocks, flowers, seeds. First of series of three paperbound pamphlets describing experiments, demonstrations, and other activities for a three-year general science curriculum. Excellent line drawings.

Obourn, E. S., and C. H. Boeck, "Sixth Annual Review of Research in Science Teaching," *Journal National Association for Research in Science Teaching,* Vol. 44, No. 5, December, 1960, pp. 374–99. Bibliographies. Research abstracts appear in the four annual issues.

———, and C. L. Koelsche, *Analysis of Research in the Teaching of Science,* July 1956–July 1957, Bulletin No. 2, 1960, U.S. Dept. of Health, Education and Welfare. Continues annual series begun in 1950. Assembles, summarizes, and interprets research in science education at elementary and secondary levels with regard to curricula, learning, teacher education, and measurement and evaluation of achievement.

Includes studies on the college level concerning status, texts, syllabi, science personnel.

Parker, Bertha M., *Science Experiences in Elementary School,* Row, Peterson, 1952. Mainly physical science. Directions for simple experiments and construction of apparatus and toys illustrating various principles. Designed primarily for the middle grades.

Partridge, J. A., *Natural Science Through the Seasons,* Macmillan, Toronto, Can., 1955. One hundred teaching units arranged by months. Well illustrated.

Read, J. G., and P. A. Nelson, "A View of Science Education—Review and Forecast," *Boston University Journal of Education,* Vol. 141, No. 2, December, 1958. Philosophy, elementary and secondary school science, research findings on current status and trends, bibliography.

Research Studies in Education, Phi Delta Kappa, Inc., Bloomington, Ind. Annual review with subject and author index and bibliography on research methods.

Richardson, John S., *Resource Literature for Science Teachers,* College of Education, Ohio State Univ., Columbus, O., 1957. 65 pp. Extensive references.

Sauer, Pauline L., *Nature Study Equipment, How to Make and Use It,* rev. ed., Bur. of Extension Service, Iowa State Teachers College, Cedar Falls, Ia., 1955. 25¢.

Schwartz, Julius, and Herman Schneider, *Growing Up with Science Books,* Library Journal, 62 W. 45th St., New York, N.Y., 1958. 32 pp., 4¢. Age groupings: 3–5, 5–9, 9–12, 12–15; developmental characteristics.

Science, Bulletin 2b, Elementary School, Govt. of the Province of Alberta, Dept. of Education, Edmonton, Alta., 1957. 130 pp. Objectives, development of the program, sample unit—the zoo, scope and sequence for grades 1–6. Reference list. Well illustrated.

Science Contributes to the Arts (arts in childhood), Series VII, No. 2, Fisk Univ., Nashville, Tenn., 1952. 19 pp. Science centers, children's museums, young artists and scientists at work, National Audubon Society.

"Science Education," *The Nation's Schools,* February, 1960, pp. 65–118. Special issue including three surveys; 36 illustrations by editorial staff and science educators.

"Science Learnings; Using What We Know

About Children," *Childhood Education,* Vol. 26, No. 7, ACEI, Washington, D.C., March, 1950. Articles by authorities.

Science and Mathematics—Countdown for Elementary Schools, Frontiers of Science Foundation of Oklahoma, April, 1960. 71 pp. Symposium held at Oklahoma City, Okla., Dec. 5, 1959. Authorities consider education differences between science and technology; school mathematics; administration problems. An anthropological view of science, mathematics, and curriculum change.

Science for Our Children, N.Y. State Association of Elementary School Principals, Watertown, N.Y., January, 1949. 95 pp., $1.00. Information on background of science education in the state, present status, helpful supervisory practices, characteristics of effective program. Outlines college programs in teacher preparation.

Science in the Primary School, John Murray Publishers, London, Eng., 1959. 46 pp. Published for the Association of Teachers in Colleges and Depts. of Education. Such sections as principles of teaching, science exploration with young children, the role of the teacher, equipment and books.

Science Teaching in the Primary School, Educational Abstracts, Vol. 7, No. 7, UNESCO, New York, N.Y., September, 1955. 25 pp. Status of elementary science teaching based on available literature and data from correspondents; short bibliography; abstracts; sample texts and materials.

Science II for Intermediate and Upper Grades, Educational Pub. Co., Darien, Conn., 1956. 32 pp. Useful articles by science teachers.

Shapp, Martha, *Planning and Organizing Science Programs for Elementary Schools,* Grolier Society, 1959. 72 pp. Keyed to *Book of Knowledge.* Covers weather, earth, living things, magnetism and electricity, atmosphere, astronomy, transportation, communication.

Sheckles, Mary, *Building Children's Science Concepts: Experiences with Rocks, Soil, Air, and Water,* Teachers College, Columbia Univ., New York, N.Y., 1958. 138 pp. Pamphlet.

Shuttlesworth, Dorothy E., *Exploring Nature with Your Child,* Hawthorn, 1952. Well illustrated.

Simonton, William H., *British Science Examinations,* J. Weston Walch, Portland, Me., 1959.

30 pp. Selections from questions used from 1951–1958 by various British colleges for entrance and subsequent screening at several levels. Of possible interest for teacher pre-service preparation in science.

Straight, G. M., comp., *Science Experiments,* Hart, New York, 1957. 64 pp. Simple, inexpensive. Clear illustrations.

Suggested Science Books for the Pupil and Teacher, Grades K-9, College of Education, State University of Iowa, Iowa City, Ia., n.d. 32 pp. Books consulted and used in the elementary science education program at the university. Emphasis on activities and the physical sciences. Estimated grade levels checked against Bowker's *Books in Print* (1959). Teacher references on methods, activities, biology and general science, free and inexpensive materials, booklists, texts, and publishers.

Tannenbaum, H. E., and N. Stillman, *Science Education for Elementary School Teachers,* Allyn and Bacon, 1960. 339 pp. Presents goals, science materials, and relevant aspects of child development. Section on working with gifted pupils. Excellent chapter on evaluation. Many classroom examples.

Underhill, Orra E., *The Origins and Development of Elementary School Science,* Scott, Foresman, 1941. Synthesis of trends. Basic references.

UNESCO Source Book for Science Teaching, UNESCO, New York, N.Y., 1959. Originally designed as "suggestions for science teachers in devastated countries," this volume has been revised, expanded, and reprinted in many editions. International references and sources of science materials. Useful tables.

Vessel, M. F., and H. Wong, *How to Stimulate Your Science Programs: A Guide to Simple Science Activities,* Fearon, 1957. 32 pp. Ideas for construction, planting, keeping pets, health, safety, and conservation.

———, *Science Books 1958,* Fearon, 1959. 14 pp., 75¢. Guideposts to selection. Why teachers should read science books. References on living things, earth, universe, matter and energy, scientists at work. Sample bulletin board and table displays. Professional science references. Useful annotations.

Watson, F., P. F. Brandwein, S. Rosen, et al., eds., *Critical Years Ahead in Science Teaching,* Harvard Univ., Cambridge, Mass., July 15–August 12, 1953. 48 pp. Report of Conference on Nationwide Problems of Science Teaching in Secondary Schools. Considers nature of problem, teacher supply and demand, preparation, and science teaching as work and career.

Weinlander, Albertina A., *Your Child in a Scientific World*, Doubleday, 1959. What science is all about; the child in the space age from birth to 6, from 6 to 10; science interests and children's problems; the forces of nature; community resources; home experiments; the child with special interests; sources of science materials.

Wells, Harrington, *Elementary Science Education in American Public Schools*, McGraw-Hill, 1951. 333 pp. Guide to study of methods of instruction for first eight grades. Discusses theory and practice and resource aids. Emphasis on biological science. Extensive appendix.

Wells, H. G., et al., *The Science of Life*, Doubleday, 1934. 1514 pp. The living body, groups of living things, evolution, ecology, health and disease, behavioral science, human biology. Comprehensive and creative. Worth searching for in secondhand bookshops.

"Your School's Science Program," *School Management*, May, 1959, pp. 42 ff. General and specific considerations of curriculum and staff problems, viz., K-12 articulation, multitrack groupings, interdisciplinary approach, special programs.

Zim, Herbert S., *Science for Teachers and Children*, Association of Childhood Education International, 1953. 55 pp. Problems of science teaching in primary grades.

BOOKS AND PAMPHLETS FOR TEACHERS AND STUDENTS

Andrews, Roy Chapman, *All About Whales*, Random House, 1954.

Atkin, J. M., and R. W. Burnett, *Elementary School Science Activities* series, Holt, Rinehart and Winston. Pamphlets to date on air, winds, weather, working with plants, working with animals.

Baker, Arthur O., et al., *Junior Scientist* series, Rand McNally, 1955. A reading about science-type text. Weak in physical sciences. Little explanation on functions or mechanisms.

Barlowe, Sy, *About Insects*, Maxton, 1953.

Beauchamp, Wilbur L., et al., *Basic Studies in Science* series, Scott, Foresman, 1957. Science presented in traditional pattern, with emphasis on biology in early grades and on physical science in later grades. Teacher's manual provides "cut and dried" method. Little new material. (1–6)

Bond, A. D., G. L. Bond, et al., *Developmental Science* series, Lyons and Carnahan, 1959. Science in a story form. (1–6)

Cormack, M. B., *The First Book of Stones*, Franklin Watts, 1950.

———, *The First Book of Trees*, Franklin Watts, 1951.

Cornell Science Leaflets, N. Y. State College of Agriculture, Cornell Univ., Ithaca, N. Y. A veritable gold mine on every aspect of science. Annual subscription, $1.00 for four issues. For example, 1958–59 pamphlets were: *Earth and Beyond* (Teacher's Number), *Ancient Sea Life* (Pupil's Number), *Chemicals in Action* (Pupil's Number), *Birds* (Pupil's Number). Some back issues still available.

Craig, Gerald S., et al., *Science Today and Tomorrow* series, Ginn, 1956. Emphasis on explaining everyday phenomena. Strong physical science sections. Teacher's manual complete. Includes background material with suggested activities. (1–8)

Dickinson, Alice, *The First Book of Plants*, Franklin Watts, 1953.

Dowling, Thomas I., et al., *Understanding Science* series, Holt, Rinehart and Winston, 1957. Social studies approach. Strong in health and descriptive biology. Less emphasis on the physical sciences and explanation of phenomena. Many suggested activities. Teacher's manual offers very little background material. (1–6)

Dreany, Joseph, *Book About Horses*, Maxton, n.d.

———, *Book About Mankind Through the Ages*, Maxton, 1955.

———, *Book About Rivers*, Maxton, 1955.

Feidel, Alexander, *Book About Wild Birds*, Maxton, n.d.

Frasier, George W., et al., *Science* series, Singer, 1959. Replete with activities. Emphasis on biological science and health, with up-to-date data. Good teacher's manual. (1–6)

Freeman, Ira M., *All About the Atom*, Random House, 1955.

———, *All About Electricity*, Random House, 1957.

————, *All About the Wonders of Chemistry*, Random House, 1954.

Friskey, Margaret, *The True Book of Air Around Us*, Childrens Press, 1953.

————, *The True Book of Birds We Know*, Childrens Press, 1954.

Frost, Bruno, *Book About Jungle Animals*, Maxton, 1954.

Haynes, Olive V., *The True Book of Health*, Childrens Press, 1954.

Harmer, Mabel, *The True Book of the Circus*, Childrens Press, 1955.

Henderson, Luis M., *Book About Birds*, Maxton, 1950.

————, *Book About Dogs*, Maxton, 1950.

Kay, Dorothea, *Book About Fishes*, Maxton, 1953.

Lane, Ferdinand C., *All About the Insect World*, Random House, 1954.

————, *All About the Sea*, Random House, 1953.

Lemmon, Robert S., *All About the Birds*, Random House, 1955.

Lewellen, John, *The True Book of Farm Animals*, Childrens Press, 1954.

————, *The True Book of Moon, Sun and Stars*, Childrens Press, 1954.

Medler, James V., *Book About Mountains and Volcanoes*, Maxton, 1954.

Meister, Morris, et al., *Wonderworld of Science* series, Scribner's, 1955. Despite an unattractive format, this series contains many activities and basic explanations. Weak in biology. Emphasizes astronomy, physics, and geology. (1–8)

Miner, Irene, *The True Book of Plants We Know*, Childrens Press, 1953.

Parker, Bertha M., et al., *Basic Science Education* series, Row, Peterson, 1959. Inexpensive pamphlets. Over 80 titles on many aspects of science. Simple text and color pictures attract children. Excellent supplemental references. (Middle; some titles at primary level)

Podendorf, Illa, *The True Book of Animal Babies*, Childrens Press, 1955.

————, *The True Book of Insects*, Childrens Press, 1954.

————, *The True Book of Pets*, Childrens Press, 1954.

————, *The True Book of Science Experiments*, Childrens Press, 1954.

————, *The True Book of Seasons*, Childrens Press, 1955.

————, *The True Book of Sounds We Hear*, Childrens Press, 1955.

————, *The True Book of Trees*, Childrens Press, 1954.

————, *The True Book of Weeds and Wildflowers*, Childrens Press, 1955.

Pough, Frederick H., *All About Volcanoes and Earthquakes*, Random House, 1953.

Pratt, Fletcher, *All About Rockets and Jets*, Random House, 1955.

Purcell, John Wallace, *The True Book of African Animals*, Childrens Press, 1954.

Schneider, Herman, and Nina Schneider, *Heath Elementary Science* series, rev. ed., Heath, 1961. Encyclopedia-type content with many suggested demonstrations. Teacher's manual is arranged page by page and might lead to cut and dried teaching if followed too closely. Good reference. (1–6)

Sinnickson, Tom, *Book About Planes*, Maxton, 1951.

Smith, Victor C., and Barbara Henderson, *Science for Modern Living* series, Lippincott, 1956. "Talking about science" type with up-to-date information needed. Of value in the reading program. (1–6)

Stone, G. K., and L. W. Stephenson, *Science You Can Use*, Prentice-Hall, 1959. Emphasis on biological science and nature study. Handsome illustrations. Junior and senior high school basic text.

————, *Book About Bees and Wasps*, Maxton, 1955.

Swenson, Valerie, *Book About Reptiles and Amphibians*, Maxton, 1955.

————, *Book About Trees*, Maxton, 1955.

Tannenbaum, H. E., and Nathan Stillman, *Webster Junior Science* series, Webster. Titles to date on television, fire, electricity, lightning and thunder, airplanes, seeds, animals, earth and space, photography, microbes, sounds, rockets.

Thorn, S. A., and C. D. Duncan, *Science and Conservation* series, Beckley-Cardy, 1956. Traditional "telling about science" text. (1–6)

Thurber, Walter A., *Exploring Science* series, Allyn and Bacon, 1955. Strong on activities. Problem-solving approach. Requires references and doesn't cover everything but explains what is covered. (1–6)

Tibbets, A. B., *The First Book of Bees,* Franklin Watts, 1952.

Watson, Jane W., *The World of Science,* Golden Press, 1958. 265 pp. Exciting peep over the shoulders of scientists in the fields of geology, astronomy, mathematics, physics, chemistry, biology, and engineering. Unusual color photographs and diagrams. Unusual end papers provide diagrammatic explanation of orders of magnitude and the electromagnetic spectrum.

White, Anne Terry, *All About Our Changing Rocks,* Random House, 1955.

———, *All About the Stars,* Random House, 1954.

Wilde, Irma, *Book About Flowers,* Maxton, n. d.

Williamson, Margaret, *The First Book of Birds,* Franklin Watts, 1951.

———, *The First Book of Mammals,* Franklin Watts, 1957.

Zim, H. S., and I. N. Gabrielson, *Birds,* Golden Press, 1949.

———, and Alexander C. Martin, *Flowers,* Golden Press, 1950.

———, *Insects,* Golden Press, 1951.

———, and Hobart M. Smith, *Reptiles and Amphibians,* Golden Press, 1953.

———, and Alexander C. Martin, *Trees,* Golden Press, 1952.

CRITERIA FOR EVALUATING SCIENCE TEXTBOOKS[1]

I. UP-TO-DATENESS

A. Is the material current? Does it include those items in the world of science about which we read in the daily papers?

B. Are there background developments to help children understand some of the new discoveries, inventions, and evolutions in up-to-the-minute science? For example, is there a discussion of *molecules,* and does this treatment support an understanding of *atoms* and *atomic energy* and *atomic power?*

II. PHYSICAL MAKE-UP

A. Does the text have immediate interest appeal to boys and girls?

[1] Helen Heffernan, Chief, Bureau of Elementary Education, State of California, Department of Education. Books are rated excellent, average, or poor on each point.

B. Are the illustrations functional, i.e., do they contribute to increased or easy understanding of content? Do captions as questions help tie the illustrations to the content of the text?

C. Are sentence length, size of type, and space between lines conducive to easy reading?

III. AUTHORSHIP

A. Do the authors have an experienced background both in science and in elementary education?

B. Are the authors acquainted by experience with the problems of the classroom teacher who must teach science but who is not a science teacher?

C. Have the authors written and the publisher published a professional book to serve as guidance and training in the teaching of science?

IV. AIDS TO INSTRUCTION

A. Is there a teacher's edition for the text?

B. Is the teacher's edition a valuable aid to the classroom teacher of science who is not a trained science teacher?

C. Does the text contain a glossary, table of contents, index?

D. Is the text so organized that units are sufficiently independent to allow for a degree of "incidental" teaching, thereby making it possible to "fit" the text to the interest factors of the learners?

V. CONTENT AND METHOD

A. Is provision made for fostering scientific attitudes and for developing critical thinking through content and concept formation?

1. *Quantity* of opportunities—the clue is the number of *how, why,* and *what* questions *in content* or allied with concept formations which imply critical thinking on the part of the learner.

2. *Quality* of the material designed to foster scientific attitudes and to develop abilities to do critical thinking.

a. Extent to which open-mindedness, careful observation, weighing evidence, seeing relationships, generalizing, and making applications are developed in content and in concept formation.

b. Variety and kinds of opportunities for development.

c. Manner in which content is presented to develop such attitudes. Clues: (1) "The Wise Use of Our Natural Resources," (2) "This Is Another Way to Find Out," (3) "Do Another Experiment to Find Out," (4) "There Is More to Be Found Out," (5) "Scientists Have Wondered About This for a Long Time."

B. Is provision made for improving skill in problem solving?

1. Quantity.
   a. Number of questions or problems which suggest further investigation (through reading, experimenting, etc.).
   b. Number of science experiences (an experiment is a type of science experience) which meet the above criteria.
   c. Listing of experiments and experiences included in the content which help answer a question or solve a problem.

2. Quality.
   a. Extent to which questions imply a problem situation requiring the reader to make further investigation as: "How do you know?" "What fact of science will you try to use?" "How can this be explained?"
   b. Extent to which experiments and other kinds of science experiences *within the develpment of the unit* use questions to guide the learner into making more careful observations, gathering data, and drawing conclusions.
   c. Inclusion in the content of such suggestions as: "Try and see." "Try the same experiment with different materials." "See if you get the same results." "Do another experiment."

3. The approach to experimentation, discovery, and problem solving must always include a summary or an outline of *what we already know* about the problem so that new science experiments become extensions of facts and concepts already known or acquired.

4. Each experiment must be preceded by a complete understanding of what is to be found out.

5. Pupils must be expected to generalize the results of experiments.

C. Does the text encourage the learner to go beyond the ideas in the text?

1. The quantity of such suggestions must be such as to keep the learner working to capacity.

2. The quality of such suggestions is equally as important as the quantity of them.
   a. There must be a variety of suggestions.
   b. Suggestions must be problem-centered and extend main learning of the unit.
   c. Suggestions must help the pupil to learn about the application of science to the areas within the social studies, such as home, transportation, work, communication, etc.
   d. Suggestions must stimulate the child to be creative in his own methods of finding out.

D. Are opportunities provided for children to manipulate, investigate, explore, experiment, and discover for themselves?

1. There must be a sufficient quantity of opportunities.

2. The quality of opportunities must:
   a. Make children aware of the problem for investigation, exploration, or discovery.
   b. Provide ample opportunity for drawing conclusions following investigations, explorations, experimentations, etc.

E. Is the relationship of science to its applications in the field of the social studies obvious and close-knit to include many illustrations of:

1. How science is applied to home, schools, community, community helpers and services, clothing, food, shelter?

2. How science has influenced history with inventions, etc.?

3. Tie-up with geography as land forms, etc.?

4. Applications with various cultural groups and relations to the cultures—transportation, communication, etc.?

VI. PROVISIONS FOR AND TYPE OF EXPERIMENTS
A. Are the experiments *child-centered*, not teacher-dominated?
   1. Experiments must be easy to set up and control.
   2. Experiments must require only simple and easy-to-get materials.
B. Are the experiments preceded by a complete understanding of what is to be found out?
C. Is provision made for guiding the learner in generalizing observations and results?

J. B. Lippincott Company, 333 West Lake St., Chicago 6, Ill.

The Macmillan Company, 60 Fifth Ave., New York 11, N.Y.

Rand McNally and Company, 8255 Central Park Ave., Skokie, Ill.

Scott, Foresman and Company, 433 East Erie St., Chicago 11, Ill.

Charles Scribner's Sons, 597 Fifth Ave., New York 17, N.Y.

L. W. Singer Company, 249 West Erie Blvd., Syracuse 2, N.Y.

PUBLISHERS' SCOPE AND SEQUENCE CHARTS

Allyn and Bacon, Inc., 150 Tremont St., Boston 11, Mass.

Ginn and Company, Statler Office Building, Boston 17, Mass.

D. C. Heath and Company, 285 Columbus Ave., Boston 16, Mass.

Holt, Rinehart and Winston, 383 Madison Ave., New York 17, N.Y.

Scope and sequence charts on conservation

Indiana Department of Conservation. Scope and sequence chart for teaching conservation in Indiana schools, grades 1–12. May 1959. Printed.

Ohio Department of Education. Chart for the development of basic conservation concepts in the elementary grades. 1958. Printed.

Films and filmstrips

Inasmuch as films and filmstrips are in production constantly, no listing can be complete, and price quotations may vary. Teachers are therefore advised to obtain catalogs from distributors and to consult local film libraries.

The film or filmstrip may be shown in its entirety, or a particular part of it may be used. The teacher may stop the film from time to time to permit questions and discussion or even rerun a section for closer examination.

DIRECTORY OF DISTRIBUTORS

AEC   U.S. Atomic Energy Commission, Pictorial Public Information Service, Washington 25, D.C.

Academy   Academy Films, 800 N. Seward St., Hollywood 38, Calif.

AlmanacFlms   Almanac Films, Inc., 516 Fifth Ave., New York 36, N.Y.

AmerPetrolInst   American Petroleum Institute, 50 W. 50th St., New York 20, N.Y.

AmerSocMetals   American Society for Metals, Metals Park, Novelty, O.

Assn   Association Films, Inc., 347 Madison Ave., New York 17, N.Y. Branch offices in Ridgefield, N.J., La Grange, Ill., San Francisco, Calif., Dallas, Tex.

Atlantis   Atlantis Productions, Inc., 7967 Sunset Blvd., Hollywood 46, Calif.

Audubon   National Audubon Society, Photo & Film Dept., 1130 Fifth Ave., New York 28, N.Y.

AV-ED   AV-ED Films, 7934 Santa Monica Blvd., Hollywood 46, Calif.

AVSchServ   Audio-Visual School Service, 114 E. 31st St., New York 16, N.Y.

Avis   Avis Films, P.O. Box 643, Burbank, Calif.

Bailey   Bailey Films, Inc., 6509 De Longpre Ave., Hollywood 28, Calif.

Barr   Arthur Barr Productions, 1265 Bresee Ave., Pasadena, Calif.

BellTel   Bell Telephone System. Apply to regional offices.

Brandon   Brandon Films, Inc., 200 W. 57th St., New York 19, N.Y.

BurCommResearch   Bureau of Communication Research, Inc., 13 E. 37th St., New York 16, N.Y.

BurMines   U.S. Bureau of Mines, Graphic Services Section, 4800 Forbes St., Pittsburgh 13, Pa.

Burns   G. C. Burns Productions, 17160 Tulsa St., Granada Hills, Calif.

BurSportFish   Bureau of Sport Fisheries & Wildlife, Wildlife Service. Offices in Albuquerque, N.M., Atlanta, Ga., Boston, Mass., Minneapolis, Minn., Portland, Ore.

CanNFB   National Film Board of Canada, 680 Fifth Ave., Suite 819, New York 19, N.Y.

Capital   Capital Film Service, 224 Abbott Rd., East Lansing, Mich.

Carousel   Carousel Films, Inc., 1501 Broadway, New York 36, N.Y.

Churchill   Churchill-Wexler Film Productions, 801 N. Seward St., Los Angeles 38, Calif.

Contem   Contemporary Films, Inc., 267 W. 25th St., New York 1, N.Y.

Coronet   Coronet Instructional Films, 65 E. South Water St., Chicago 1, Ill.

Curriculum   Curriculum Materials Corp., 1319 Vine St., Philadelphia 7, Pa. Offices in Jackson, Miss., Raleigh, N.C., Tujunga, Calif.

DeKalbAgr   De Kalb Agriculture Association, Inc., Education Dept., De Kalb, Ill.

DeRoche   Louis de Rochemont Associates, Film Library, 267 W. 25th St., New York 1, N.Y.

Disney   Walt Disney Productions, Educational Film Dept., 2400 W. Alameda Ave., Burbank, Calif.

DoAllCo   DoAll Co., 254 N. Laurel Ave., Des Plaines, Ill.

DouglasAir   Douglas Aircraft Co., Inc., Advertising Film Services, 3000 Ocean Park Blvd., Santa Monica, Calif.

Dowling   Pat Dowling Pictures, 1056 S. Robertson Blvd., Los Angeles 35, Calif.

EBF   Encyclopaedia Britannica Films, Inc., 1150 Wilmette Ave., Wilmette, Ill. Branch offices in Atlanta, Ga., Dallas, Tex., Hollywood, Calif., Minneapolis, Minn., New York, N.Y., Portland, Ore.

EducTest   Educational Testing Service, 20 Nassau St., Princeton, N.J. Branch office in Los Angeles, Calif.

EyeGate   Eye Gate House, Inc., 146-01 Archer Ave., Jamaica 35, N.Y.

FieldTrip   Field Trip Films, Pittsburg, Calif.

FilmAssoc   Film Associates of California, 11014 Santa Monica Blvd., Los Angeles 25, Calif.

Filmscope   Filmscope, Inc., Box 397, Sierra Madre, Calif.

Ford   Ford Motor Co., Motion Picture Dept., The American Rd., Dearborn, Mich. Libraries in Oakland, Calif., and New York, N.Y.

FosterFlms   Foster Films, 6 Kneeland Ave., Binghamton, N.Y.

Gateway   Gateway Productions, Inc., 1859 Powell St., San Francisco 11, Calif.

GenPicProd   General Pictures Productions, Inc., 621 Sixth Ave., Des Moines 9, Ia.

Grover   Grover-Jennings Productions, Inc., P.O. Box 303, Monterey, Calif.

Hilf   Earl L. Hilfiker, 284 Somerhire Dr., Rochester 17, N.Y.

IllNatHist   Illinois Natural History Survey, 189 Natural Resources Bldg., Urbana, Ill.

IndU   Indiana University, Audio-Visual Center, Bloomington, Ind.

InstrFlms   Instructional Films, Inc. *See* Encyclopaedia Britannica Films.

IowaU   State University of Iowa, Bureau of Audio-Visual Instruction, East Hall, Iowa City, Ia.

JamHandy   Jam Handy Organization, 2821 E. Grand Blvd., Detroit 11, Mich. Branch offices in Chicago, Ill., Dayton, O., Hollywood, Calif., New York, N.Y.

JohnsonHunt   Johnson Hunt Productions Film Center, La Canada, Calif.

KaiserSteel   Kaiser Steel Corp., Public Relations Dept., Box 217, Fontana, Calif.

KnowledgeBldrs   Knowledge Builders, 625 Madison Ave., New York 22, N.Y.

McGraw-Hill   McGraw-Hill Book Co., Text-Film Dept., 330 W. 42nd St., New York 36, N.Y.

MarineStudios   Marine Studios, Saint Augustine, Fla.

Middleham   Ken Middleham Productions, P.O. Box 1065, Riverside, Calif.

MinnFdn   Minnesota Foundation, 305 Wilder Bldg., St. Paul 2, Minn.

MinnU   University of Minnesota, Audio-Visual Education Service, Westbrook Hall, Minneapolis 14, Minn.

ModernTP   Modern Talking Picture Service, 3 E. 54th St., New York 22, N.Y. Film libraries in most major cities.

Moody   Moody Institute of Science, 11428 Santa Monica Blvd., Los Angeles 25, Calif.

NET   NET Film Service, Indiana University, Audio-Visual Center, Bloomington, Ind.

NYTimes   New York Times, Office of Educational Activities, 229 W. 43rd St., New York 36, N.Y.

Petite   Petite Film Co., 6101 Fremont Ave., Seattle 3, Wash.

Rothschild   Rothschild Film Corp., 1012 E. 17th St., Brooklyn 30, N.Y.

Science   Science Slides Co., 22 Oak Dr., New Hyde Park, Long Island, N.Y.

Shell   Shell Oil Co., Public Relations Dept., 50 W. 50th St., New York 20, N.Y.

SoilConsService   Soil Conservation Service, U.S. Dept. of Agriculture, Washington 25, D.C. Distributed by state offices.

Stanbow   Stanbow Productions, Inc., Valhalla, N.Y.

Sterling   Sterling Educational Films, 6 E. 39th St., New York 16, N.Y.

SterlMovUSA   Sterling Movies U.S.A., 100 W. Monroe St., Chicago 3, Ill.

SVE   Society for Visual Education, Inc., 1345 Diversey Parkway, Chicago 14, Ill.

Tanin Seymour Richard Tanin Films, 6060 Sunset Blvd., Hollywood 28, Calif.

TFC Teaching Film Custodians, Inc., 25 W. 43rd St., New York 36, N.Y. Films may be used for classroom purposes only.

UW United World Films, Inc., 1445 Park Ave., New York 29, N.Y. Branches in Atlanta, Ga., Chicago, Ill., Dallas, Tex., Los Angeles, Calif., Portland, Ore.

YA Young America Films, Inc., c/o McGraw-Hill Book Co., Text-Film Dept., 330 W. 42nd St., New York 36, N.Y.

VirginiaEd Virginia Dept. of Education, Film Production Service, State Office Bldg., Richmond, Va.

VirginiaPoly Virginia Polytechnic Institute, Film Library, Sandy Hall, Blacksburg, Va.

SELECTED LISTING OF FILMS AND FILMSTRIPS

All the films listed here are sound unless otherwise indicated by "si" (silent) or "si/cap" (silent-captions). Prices are for purchase unless otherwise noted. When both purchase price and rental price are given, the purchase price appears first. For films listed as free, the school pays postal charges only. When films are available in both black and white and color, the first price refers to black and white, and the second to color. The following abbreviations are used throughout:

p = primary	fs	= filmstrip
el = elementary	si	= silent
jh = junior high	cap	= captions
f = film	b&w	= black and white
	c	= color

The classroom—a place for daily discovery

Addition Is Easy (p) (f, b&w, c), Coronet, $50.00, $100.00.

Adventure in Science: The Size of Things (jh) (f, b&w, c), FilmAssoc, $60.00 (apply for rental), $110.00.

Arithmetic for Beginners (p) (f, b&w), Bailey, $90.00, $4.50 rental.

Arithmetic Series (p-el) (6 fs, si/cap, c), McGraw-Hill, $32.50 set, $6.00 each.

Arithmetic Without Pencil and Paper (el) (5 f, b&w), IowaU, $50.00 each, $2.50 rental each.

Better to See You (eyes; p) (fs, si/cap, c), EBF, $1.66.

Borrowing in Subtraction (el-jh) (f, b&w), TFC, lease.

Decimal Fractions (el-jh) (f, b&w, c), Johnson-Hunt, $45.00, $90.00.

Decimals Are Easy (el-jh) (f, b&w, c), Coronet, $50.00, $100.00.

Division Is Easy (p-el-jh) (f, b&w, c), Coronet, $50.00, $100.00.

Division of Fractions (jh) (f, b&w), Knowledge-Bldrs, $40.00, $2.00 rental.

Elementary Biology (jh) (fs, si/cap, b&w), Science, $3.50.

Finding Out About Your Body (p) (fs, si/cap, c), SVE, $4.50.

Friction (p) (f, b&w), Gateway, $49.50, $4.50 rental.

Friction (el-jh) (f, b&w), YA, $45.00.

Fundamentals of the Nervous System (jh) (f, b&w, c), EBF, $90.00, $120.00.

Gateway to the Mind (jh) (f, b&w), BellTel, free loan.

Harnessing Solar Energy (jh) (fs, si/cap, c), McGraw-Hill, $6.00.

How Hormones Control the Body (jh) (fs, si/cap, c), McGraw-Hill, $6.00.

How Life Began (el-jh) (fs, si, c), Curriculum, $3.95.

How Long Is a Rod? (measurement; el-jh) (fs, si, c), Ford, free.

How to Add Fractions (el-jh) (f, b&w, c), Johnson-Hunt, $45.00, $90.00.

How to Change Fractions (el-jh) (f, b&w, c), JohnsonHunt, $45.00, $90.00.

How to Divide Fractions (el-jh) (f, b&w, c), JohnsonHunt, $45.00, $90.00.

How to Find the Answer (mathematics; jh) (f, b&w, c), Coronet, $50.00, $100.00.

How to Multiply Fractions (el-jh) (f, b&w, c), JohnsonHunt, $45.00, $90.00.

How to Subtract Fractions (el-jh) (f, b&w, c), JohnsonHunt, $45.00, $90.00.

Introduction to Fractions (el-jh) (f, b&w, c), JohnsonHunt, $45.00, $90.00.

Introduction to Physics (jh) (f, b&w, c), Coronet, $50.00, $100.00.

Language of Mathematics (el-jh) (f, b&w, c), Coronet, $50.00, $100.00.

Laws of Motion (jh) (f, c), EBF, $100.00, $4.00 rental.

Let's Count (p-el) (f, b&w, c), Coronet, $50.00, $100.00.

Lever and the Pulley (jh) (f, b&w), GenPicProd, $17.25.

Life of the Molds (jh) (f, c), SterlMovUSA, free loan.

Man of Long Ago (el-jh) (fs, si, c), Curriculum, $3.95.

Mathematician and the River (relates problem of flood control on the Mississippi; jh) (f, c), EducTest, $210.00.

Meaning of Long Division (el-jh) (f, b&w), EBF, $50.00, $2.50 rental.

Meaning of Percentage (el-jh) (f, b&w), YA, $45.00.

Meaning of Pi (el-jh) (f, b&w, c), Coronet, $50.00, $100.00.

Measuring Areas: Squares, Rectangles (el-jh) (f, b&w, c), Coronet, $60.00, $110.00.

Measuring Simple Areas (el) (f, b&w), KnowledgeBldrs, $40.00, $2.00 rental.

Mechanics of Liquids (jh) (f, b&w, c), Coronet, $50.00, $100.00.

Meet the Human Family (p) (fs, si/cap, c), EBF, $1.66.

Multiplication Is Easy (p-el) (f, b&w, c), Coronet, $50.00, $100.00.

Multiplying Fractions (el-jh) (f, b&w), KnowledgeBldrs, $40.00, $2.00 rental.

Musical Notes (jh) (f, b&w), UW, $50.00.

Nature's Techniques (jh) (f, b&w), AlmanacFlms, $45.00.

Origin of Mathematics (jh) (f, b&w), Brandon, $50.00, $2.50 rental.

Our World of Science (p-el) (f, b&w, c), EBF, $60.00, $120.00.

Parts of Nine (p-el-jh) (f, b&w), YA, $45.00.

Parts of Things (fractions; p-el) (f, b&w), YA, $45.00.

Percent in Everyday Life (el-jh) (f, b&w), Coronet, $50.00.

Percentage (el-jh) (f, b&w, c), JohnsonHunt, $45.00, $90.00.

Seeds of Destruction (conservation; el) (f, b&w), SoilConsService, free loan.

Seeing the Use of Numbers (p) (10 fs, si/cap, c), EyeGate, $25.00 set, $4.00 each.

Simple Fractions (el-jh) (f, b&w), KnowledgeBldrs, $40.00, $2.00 rental.

Smell of Things (p) (fs, si/cap, c), EBF, $1.66.

Story of Dr. Carver (jh) (f, b&w), TFC, lease.

Subtraction Is Easy (p-el-jh) (f, b&w, c), Coronet, $50.00, $100.00.

Teen Numbers (p-el) (f, b&w), YA, $45.00.

Units of Measurement (p) (5 fs, si/cap, c), McGraw-Hill, $5.00 each.

We Discover Fractions (el-jh) (f, b&w, c), Coronet, $50.00, $100.00.

What Are Decimals? (el) (f, c), InstrFlms, $45.00, $2.50 rental.

What Are Fractions? (el-jh) (f, b&w), InstrFlms, $45.00, $2.50 rental.

What Is Four? (p-el) (f, b&w), YA, $55.00.

You Are Alive (p) (fs, si/cap, c), EBF, $1.66.

You Have an Idea (p) (f, si/cap, b&w), EBF, $1.66.

Animals in the classroom zoo

Adventure with Andy (p) (f, b&w, c), McGraw-Hill, $60.00, $125.00.

Animal Fare (p-el) (f, b&w), NET, $3.00 rental.

Animal Town of the Prairie (el-jh) (f, b&w, c), EBF, $60.00, $120.00.

Animals of Long Ago (el-jh) (fs, si, c), Curriculum, $3.95.

Animals of the Polar Regions (el-jh) (fs, si, b&w), UW, $3.50.

Animals Protect Themselves (p-el) (f, b&w, c), Coronet, $60.00, $110.00.

Badger's Bad Day (p-el) (f, c), Grover, $115.00.

Cells and Tissues (el-jh) (fs, si, c), UW, $5.00.

Desert Life Community (el-jh) (fs, si, c), Curriculum, $3.95.

Discovery at Brookfield Zoo (el-jh) (13 f, b&w), NET, $4.75 rental each.

Engineer in a Fur Coat (p-el-jh) (f, c), Hilf, $100.00.

Finding Out How Animals Live (p) (fs, si/cap, c), SVE, $4.50.

Forest Babies (p) (f, c), Grover, $115.00.

Four Seasons (el-jh) (f, c), CanNFB, $157.50.

Four Seasons (p-el) (f, b&w), NET, $3.00 rental.

How Animals Live (p-el) (fs, si/cap, c), EyeGate, $4.00.

How Nature Protects Animals (el-jh) (f, b&w, c), EBF, $60.00, $120.00.

Joey and the Ranger (p-el) (f, c), Tanin, $150.00.

Looking for Animals (p) (fs, si, c), Curriculum, $3.95.

Meet the Animal Family (p) (fs, si/cap, c), EBF, $1.66.

Prehistoric Animals (el-jh) (fs, si/cap, c), Mc-Graw-Hill, $6.00.

Robin Redbreast (p-el) (f, b&w, c), EBF, $60.00, $120.00.

Roll Call of the Animals (jh) (fs, si/cap, c), Mc-Graw-Hill, $6.00.

Spearheads in the Sky (p-el-jh) (f, c), Capital, $85.00, $3.50 rental.

Swamp (wildlife conservation; p-el-jh) (f, c), MinnU, $95.00.

Whooping Crane (el-jh) (fs, si/cap, c), Stanbow, $5.00.

Insects and related animals

Balance in Nature (el-jh) (f, c), Filmscope, $170.00.

Battle of the Bugs (el-jh) (f, c), Middleham, $110.00.

Butterflies and Moths (el-jh) (fs, si, c), UW, $5.00.

Grass-Blade Jungle (el-jh) (f, c), Bailey, $120.00.

The Honeybee (p-el-jh) (f, b&w, c), AV-ED, $75.00, $150.00.

Insect Collecting (el-jh) (f, c), Dowling, $135.00.

Insects (p-el) (f, b&w), NET, $3.00 rental.

Insect World (el-jh) (f, b&w, c), Rothschild, $50.00, $100.00.

Life Story of a Butterfly (p-el-jh) (fs, si/cap, c), Moody, $6.00.

Voice of the Insect (el-jh) (f, b&w), Carousel, $135.00.

Wonder of Grasshoppers (el-jh) (f, b&w, c), Moody, $55.00, $105.00.

Life in the water

Between the Tides (jh) (f, c), Contem, $175.00, $7.50 rental.

Full Fathom Five (el-jh) (f, b&w, c), Sterling, $45.00, $110.00.

How to Make an Aquarium (p) (fs, si/cap, c), Mc-Graw-Hill, $5.00.

Sea Lamprey (jh) (f, b&w), BurSportFish, free loan.

Survival in the Sea (jh) (12 f), NET.

Underwater Adventure (el-jh) (f), MarineStudios, free loan.

Underwater Reflections (el-jh) (f, c), DoAllCo, free loan.

Vertebrates (Dogfish) (el-jh) (fs, si, b&w), UW, $3.50.

We Explore the Stream (p) (f, b&w, c), Coronet, $60.00, $110.00.

Wonder of Reproduction (el-jh) (f, b&w, c), Moody, $55.00, $105.00.

Invisible worlds

Antibiotics—Disease Fighting Champions (jh) (fs, si/cap, c), McGraw-Hill, $6.00.

Big Little Things (p-el) (f, si, b&w), FosterFlms, $25.00.

Microorganisms That Cause Disease (jh) (f, b&w, c), Coronet, $60.00, $110.00.

Our Body Fights Disease (el-jh) (fs, si, c), Mc-Graw-Hill, $6.00.

Salk Vaccine (jh) (fs, si/cap, c), McGraw-Hill, $6.00.

What Are Microbes? (p) (fs, si/cap, c), McGraw-Hill, $5.00.

Plants in the classroom garden

Acres of Science (corn plant; jh) (f, c), DeKalb-Agr, free loan.

Alpine Wildflowers (jh) (f, c), Petite, $100.00.

Audubon Camp of California (jh) (f, c), Audubon, $1.00 rental.

Audubon Camp of Maine (el-jh) (f, si, c), Audubon, $1.00 rental.

Audubon Camp of Texas (jh) (f, si, c), Audubon, $1.00 rental.

Audubon Nature Center—Greenwich, Connecticut (el-jh) (f, si, c), Audubon, $1.00 rental.

Autumn Is an Adventure (p) (f, b&w, c), Coronet, $50.00, $100.00.

Classification of Plants (el-jh) (fs, si, c), UW, $5.00.

Finding Out About Seeds, Bulbs, and Slips (p) (fs, si/cap, c), SVE, $4.50.

Flowerless Plants (el-jh) (fs, si, c), UW, $5.00.

Flowers and Inflorescences (el-jh) (fs, si, c), UW, $5.00.

Growth of Seeds (el-jh) (f, b&w, c), EBF, $60.00, $120.00.

How Does a Garden Grow? (p-el-jh) (fs, si/cap, c), Moody, $6.00.

How to Collect and Preserve Plants (jh) (f, c), Ill-NatHist, free loan.

Leaves (el-jh) (fs, si, c), UW, $5.00.

Let's Learn About Seeds (p) (fs, si/cap, c), Mc-Graw-Hill, $5.00.

Life of a Tree (p-el) (f, b&w), NET, $3.00 rental.

Meet the Plant Family (p) (fs, si/cap, c), EBF, $1.66.

Miniature Plants of the Desert (el-jh) (fs, si/cap, c), Moody, $6.00.

Parts of a Flowering Plant (el-jh) (fs, si, c), Curriculum, $3.95.

Plants (p-el) (fs, si/cap, c), EyeGate, $4.00.

Plants and Seeds (p-el) (fs, si/cap, c), EyeGate, $4.00.

Springtime of Life (jh) (f, b&w), Knowledge-Bldrs, $50.00.

This Vital Earth (jh) (f), SoilConsServ, free loan.

Useful Plants (el-jh) (fs, si, c), UW, $5.00.

Weather

All Kinds of Weather (el) (fs, si/cap, c), EyeGate, $4.00.

Finding Out About the Clouds (p) (fs, si/cap, c), SVE, $4.50.

Visit to a Weather Station (el) (fs, si/cap, c), EyeGate, $4.00.

Weather Changes (p-el) (fs, si/cap, c), EyeGate, $4.00.

Weather Maps and Weather Forecasting (el) (fs, si/cap, c), EyeGate, $4.00.

What Is Weather? (p) (fs, si/cap, c), EBF, $1.66.

Wonders of Snow (el) (fs, si/cap, c), Moody, $6.00.

The earth's surface

Asbestos—A Matter of Time (jh) (f, c), BurMines, free loan.

Barrel Number One (oil; jh) (f, b&w), AmerPetrolInst, free loan.

Birth of an Oil Field (el-jh) (f, c), Shell, free loan.

Crude Oil Distillation (jh) (f, b&w), Shell, free loan.

Dismal Swamp (el-jh) (f, c), VirginiaEd, $105.00.

Earth and Sky (el-jh) (5 fs, si, c), Curriculum, $3.95 each.

Earth and the Sun (p-el) (fs, si/cap, c), EyeGate, $4.00.

Earth and the Sun's Rays (jh) (f, b&w), UW, $35.00.

Earth in Motion (jh) (f, b&w), EBF, $50.00, $2.50 rental.

Earth Is Always Changing (p-el) (fs, si/cap, c), EyeGate, $4.00.

Evolution of the Oil Industry (jh) (f, c), BurMines, free loan.

How Metals Behave (jh) (f, c), AmerSocMetals, free loan.

How We Know the Earth's Shape (el-jh) (f, b&w, c), FilmAssoc, $60.00, $110.00.

Journey into Time (jh) (f, b&w, c), Sterling, $75.00, $160.00.

Minerals (p-el) (f, b&w, c), Gateway, $55.00, $110.00.

Our Planet Earth (p) (fs, si/cap, c), EBF, $1.66.

Planet Earth (el-jh) (f, b&w, c), AV-ED, $50.00, $100.00.

Primeval Forests (el-jh) (fs, si, c), Curriculum, $3.95.

Project "Mohole" (jh) (f, c), EducTest, $210.00.

Prospecting for Petroleum (el-jh) (f, c), Shell, free loan.

Putting Sulfur to Work (jh) (fs, si/cap, c), McGraw-Hill, $6.00.

Rocks and Gems (el-jh) (f, b&w, c), AV-ED, $50.00, $100.00.

Rocks for Beginners (el) (f, c), JohnsonHunt, $165.00.

Secrets of a Volcano (el-jh) (f, b&w), Carousel, $135.00.

Story of Fossils (jh) (fs, si/cap, c), McGraw-Hill, $6.00.

Surface of the Earth (jh) (f, b&w, c), AV-ED, $50.00, $100.00.

Volcano (el-jh) (f, b&w), Sterling, $90.00.

What Is the Earth Made Of? (p) (fs, si/cap, c), McGraw-Hill, $5.00.

What's Inside the Earth? (el-jh) (f, b&w, c), FilmAssoc, $70.00, $135.00.

Wonder of Crystals (el-jh) (fs, si/cap, c), Moody, $6.00.

Work of Internal Forces (el-jh) (fs, si/cap, c), SVE, $6.00.

Work of Snow and Ice (el-jh) (fs, si/cap, c), SVE, $6.00.

World in a Marsh (jh) (f, c), McGraw-Hill, $250.00.

The air

Air (p) (f, b&w), Gateway, $49.50, $4.50 rental.

Air All Around Us (el-jh) (f, b&w), YA, $45.00.

Air Pollution, Everyone's Problem (jh) (f, c), KaiserSteel, free loan.

Oxidation (Lavoisier's experiments; jh) (fs, si/cap, c), McGraw-Hill $6.00.

Wind at Work (el) (f, c), Dowling, $110.00.

Work of Wind (el-jh) (fs, si/cap, c), SVE, $6.00.

The stars and seasons

Ages of Time (jh) (f, c), Assn, free loan.

Building a Telescope (el-jh) (f, b&w), FieldTrip, $55.00.

Clocks and Time (p-el) (f, b&w), NET, $3.00 rental.

Day and Night (jh) (f, b&w), UW, $45.00.

Eclipse (jh) (f, b&w), AlmanacFlms, $45.00.

Finding Out About Day and Night (p) (fs, si/cap, c), SVE, $4.50.

How We Know the Earth Moves (el-jh) (f, b&w, c), FilmAssoc, $60.00, $110.00.

The Infinite Universe (jh) (f, b&w), Almanac-Flms, $45.00.

Latitude and Longitude (jh) (f, b&w, c), UW, $45.00, $90.00.

Man and the Moon (el-jh) (fs, si/cap, c), EBF, $6.00.

Man Becomes an Astronomer (el-jh) (fs, si/cap, c), EBF, $6.00.

The Moon (jh) (f, b&w), EBF, $50.00, $2.50 rental.

Mystery of Time (jh) (f, c), Moody, $340.00.

Our Earth Is Part of the Solar System (el) (fs, si/cap, c), EyeGate, $4.00.

The Realm of the Galaxies (jh) (f, c), EducTest, $210.00.

Seasons (p) (4 fs, si, c) Curriculum, $3.95 each.

The Seasons (el-jh) (f, b&w), TFC, lease.

The Seasons (jh) (f, b&w), UW, $50.00.

Seasons and Weather (p) (6 fs, si/cap, c), McGraw-Hill, $32.50 set, $6.00 each.

Seasons Come and Go (p) (fs, si/cap, c), EBF, $1.66.

Seasons of the Year (p-el) (f, b&w, c), Coronet, $50.00, $100.00.

Solar Family (jh) (f, b&w), EBF, $50.00, $2.50 rental.

Solar System (el-jh) (f, b&w, c), Coronet, $50.00, $100.00.

Stars and Star Systems (jh) (f, b&w, c), EBF, $90.00, $180.00.

Sun, Earth and Moon (jh) (f, b&w), Almanac-Flms, $45.00, $2.00 rental.

The Sun's Family (el-jh) (f, b&w), YA, $45.00.

This Is the Moon (el) (f, b&w), YA, $45.00.

What Are the Stars? (el-jh) (fs, si/cap, c), McGraw-Hill, $6.00.

What Causes the Seasons? (el) (f, b&w), YA, $45.00.

What Day Is It? (p) (fs, si/cap, c), EBF, $1.66.

What Makes Day and Night? (el-jh) (f, b&w), YA, $45.00.

When Night Comes (p) (fs, si/cap, c), EBF, $1.66.

You and the Universe (p) (fs, si/cap, c), EBF, $1.66.

Water

Adventuring in Conservation (el-jh) (f, b&w, c), IndU, $75.00, $150.00, $5.50 rental.

Conserving Our Soil and Water (jh) (fs, si/cap, c), McGraw-Hill, $6.00.

Forests (p-el) (f, b&w, c), Gateway, $55.00, $110.00.

Our Part in Conservation (el) (f, b&w, c), McGraw-Hill, $65.00, $125.00.

The Story of Water (history of America through its waterways; p-el) (f, b&w), NET, $3.00 rental.

Water and Soil (p-el) (fs, si/cap, c), EyeGate, $4.00.

Water of Life (electrolysis of water; el-jh) (f, c), Moody, $6.00 rental.

Wealth in the Ocean (el-jh) (fs, si/cap, c), Moody, $6.00.

What Makes Things Float? (el-jh) (f, b&w), YA, $45.00.

Wonder of Water (el-jh) (f, b&w, c), Moody, $55.00, $105.00.

Work of Ground Water (el-jh) (fs, si/cap, c), SVE, $6.00.

Work of Running Water (el-jh) (fs, si/cap, c), SVE, $6.00.

Work of the Sea (el-jh) (fs, si/cap, c), SVE, $6.00.

Chemistry for children

Apothecary Shop (p-el) (f, b&w), NET, $3.00 rental.

Solids, Liquids and Gases (el-jh) (f, b&w), YA, $45.00.

What Are Elements and Compounds? (jh) (fs, si/cap, c), McGraw-Hill, $6.00.

Food and nutrition

About the Human Body (el-jh) (f, b&w, c), Churchill, $90.00, $6.50 rental; $165.00, $8.00 rental.

Foods (el-jh) (fs, si, b&w), Science, $3.50.

Fruits (el-jh) (fs, si, c), UW, $5.00.

Living Things Need Food (el) (fs, si/cap, c), EyeGate, $4.00.

Mouth—Digestion and Respiration (jh) (fs, si, c), AVSchServ, free.

Taste of Things (p) (fs, si/cap, c), EBF, $1.66.

Touch, Taste and Vision (el-jh) (fs, si, c), UW, $5.00.

You—The Living Machine (el-jh) (f, c), Disney, $100.00.

Breathing

Heart, Lungs, and Circulation (el-jh) (f, b&w, c), Coronet, $60.00, $110.00.

Sound

Better to Hear You (p) (fs, si/cap, c), EBF, $1.66.

Exploring Sound (el-jh) (fs, si, c), McGraw-Hill, $6.00.

Fundamentals of Acoustics (jh) (f, b&w), EBF, $50.00, $2.50 rental.

How We See and Hear (el) (fs, si/cap, c), Moody, $6.00.

Nature of Sound (el-jh) (f, b&w, c), Coronet, $50.00, $100.00.

Smell and Hearing (el-jh) (fs, si, c), UW, $5.00.

Sound (p) (f, b&w), Gateway, $49.50, $4.50 rental.

What Is Sound? (el-jh) (f, b&w), YA, $45.00.

Light and color

Light and Color (el-jh) (fs, si/cap, c), McGraw-Hill, $6.00.

Light and Heat (p) (f, b&w), Gateway, $49.50, $4.50 rental.

Light and Shadow (el-jh) (f, b&w), YA, $45.00.

Nature of Color (el-jh) (f, c), Coronet, $80.00.

Nature of Light (jh) (f, b&w, c), Coronet, $50.00, $100.00.

Fire

Chemistry of Fire (jh) (f, b&w), BurCommResearch, free loan.

Fire on the Land (p-el-jh) (f, c), MinnFdn, $115.50.

Forest Fire (p-el) (f, b&w), NET, $3.00 rental.

Heat

Combustion and Combustion Products (jh) (f, b&w), NET, $4.75 rental.

Learning About Heat (el-jh) (f, b&w), EBF, $54.00.

Clothing

Clothes We Wear (p-el) (f, b&w), Churchill, $50.00.

Costumes of Our Country (p-el) (f, b&w), NET, $3.00 rental.

Your Clothing (el-jh) (f, b&w), YA, $57.50.

Housing

The Carpenter (p-el) (f, b&w), NET, $3.00 rental.

Magnets and Magnetism

Magnets (p) (6 fs, si/cap, c), JamHandy, $31.50 set, $5.75 each.

Working with Magnets (p-el) (fs, si/cap, c), EyeGate, $4.00.

Electricity

Electricity: How to Make a Circuit (p-el) (f, b&w, c), EBF, $60.00, $120.00.

4-H Electric Congress and Conservation Camp (p-el-jh) (f, b&w), VirginiaPoly, free loan.

How Batteries Work (jh) (fs, si/cap, c), McGraw-Hill, $6.00.

How Electricity Is Produced (el) (f, c), Dowling, $110.00.

Nature of Energy (el-jh) (f, b&w, c), Coronet, $50.00, $100.00.

Using Atomic Energy for Electric Power (jh) (fs, si/cap, c), McGraw-Hill, $6.00.

Communications

Living in the 20th Century (el-jh) (fs, si/cap, c), EyeGate, $4.00.

Messages Travel and Are Recorded (el) (fs, si/cap, c), EyeGate, $4.00.

Atoms and radioactivity

Atomic Energy (jh) (fs, si/cap, b&w), Science, $3.50.

Atoms and Molecules (el-jh) (fs, si/cap, c), McGraw-Hill, $6.00.

Atom and Biological Science (jh) (f, b&w), AEC, free loan.

The Eternal Cycle (jh) (f, b&w), AEC, free loan.

Fallout Atom (jh) (f, b&w), Carousel, $135.00, $15.00 rental.

Living with the Atom (jh) (f, c), Moody, $200.00.

Man Discovers the Atom (el-jh) (fs, si/cap, c), EBF, $6.00.

Matter and Energy (jh) (f, b&w, c), Coronet, $50.00, $100.00.

Our Friend the Atom (el-jh) (fs, si/cap, c), EBF, $6.00.

Science Opens New Doors (el-jh) (fs, si/cap, b&w), NYTimes, $2.50.

Waves of the Future (radio and radar waves; jh) (f, b&w), Carousel, $135.00.

Simple machines and engines

Energy (el-jh) (f, b&w), Gateway, $49.50, $4.50 rental.

Energy (el-jh) (fs, si/cap, c), AmerPetrolInst, free.

Internal Combustion Engine (jh) (fs, si, c), UW, $5.00.

Introduction to Jet Engines (jh) (f, b&w, c), Mc-Graw-Hill, $90.00, $175.00.

Machines (p) (f, b&w), Gateway, $49.50, $4.50 rental.

Machines Do Work (el-jh) (f, b&w), YA, $45.00.

Machines Help Us Travel (el) (fs, si/cap, c), Eye-Gate, $4.00.

New Roadways (jh) (f, b&w), TFC, lease.

Physics and Fire Engines (el) (f, c), Avis, $110.00.

Simple Machines (el) (fs, si/cap, c), EyeGate, $4.00.

Simple Machines Make Work Easier (jh) (fs, si/-cap, c), McGraw-Hill, $6.00.

Gravity and space travel

Down to Earth (jh) (f, c), ModernTP, free loan.

Earth Satellite, A Man-made Moon (jh) (fs, si/cap, c), McGraw-Hill, $6.00.

Exploring Space (rockets; jh) (f, b&w, c), De-Roche, $100.00, $175.00.

Exploring Space (photographed in Hayden Planetarium; jh) (f, b&w), TFC, lease.

Eyes in Outer Space (weather satellites; jh) (f, c), Disney, $250.00.

Flight Around the Moon (el-jh) (fs, si/cap, c), EBF, $6.00.

Flight into Space (el-jh) (fs, si/cap, c), EBF, $6.00.

Flight to Mars (el-jh) (fs, si/cap, c), EBF, $6.00.

Force and Motion (jh) (f, b&w, c), Coronet, $50.00, $100.00.

Force of Gravity (el) (f, b&w), YA, $45.00.

Gravity (jh) (f, b&w, c), Coronet, $50.00, $100.00.

How Vast Is Space? (jh) (f, c), Atlantis, $200.00, $10.00 rental.

Isaac Newton (jh) (f, b&w, c), Coronet, $75.00, $137.50.

Man in Space (el-jh) (fs, si/cap, c), EBF, $6.00.

Reaching for the Moon (el-jh) (f, b&w), Carousel, $135.00.

Space and Space Travel (el-jh) (4 fs, si/cap, c), SVE, $21.60 set, $6.00 each.

Flight

Airplanes: Principles of Flight (el-jh) (f, b&w, c), Coronet, $60.00, $110.00.

Big Reach (U.S. Air Force lunar probes; el-jh) (f, b&w, c), DouglasAir, free loan.

Jet Age Flight (jh) (fs, si/cap, c), SVE, $1.00.

Jet Propulsion and Gas Turbines (jh) (fs, si, c), UW, $5.00.

Man in Flight (adapted from Disney film of same title; aviation in the twentieth century; el-jh) (fs, si/cap, c), EBF, $6.00.

Man Learns to Fly (adapted from Disney film *Man in Flight;* history of flight prior to the airplane; el-jh) (fs, si/cap, c), EBF, $6.00.

Science of Flight (el) (f, c), Burns, $110.00.

Working with science materials

Finding Out How Things Change (p) (fs, si/cap, c), SVE, $4.50.

Science and Superstition (el-jh) (f, b&w, c), Coronet, $50.00, $100.00.

Directory of manufacturers,

distributors, and supply houses

Several companies provide general supplies and equipment for all areas of science. Such supplies include apparatus, instruments, ironware, glassware, rubber and plastic materials, chemicals, models, live and preserved specimens, and charts. Other companies provide specialized supplies and equipment. All of them will send catalogs on request. Many companies and institutions will also make available useful free or inexpensive booklets, charts, films, filmstrips, etc. The teacher should discourage individual students from sending for these items, however, to avoid straining the companies' public relations policies.

DIRECTORY

Allied Radio Corp., 833 N. Jefferson Blvd., Chicago 7, Ill. Radio equipment, meters, etc.

America Basic Science Club, 501 E. Crockett, San Antonio 6, Tex. Kits and manuals on projects in physics.

Baker Science Packets, 650 Concord Dr., Holland, Mich. Card file of 153 indexed science experiments.

Cambosco Scientific Co., 37 Antwerp St., Brighton 35, Mass. General.

Carolina Biological Supply Co., Elon College, N.C. Biological apparatus, supplies, living and preserved specimens. Models, charts.

Castolite Co., Woodstock, Ill. Plastics for imbedding and molding.

Central Scientific Co., 1700 Irving Park Rd., Chicago 13, Ill.; 79 Amherst St., Cambridge 42, Mass.; 6446 Telegraph Rd., Los Angeles

22, Calif. Hobby kits for electronics, medicine, geology, optics, weather. General.

John Cunningham, 23280 Mobile St., Canoga Park, Calif. Monthly packets containing equipment, specimens, chemicals.

Denoyer-Geppert Co., 5235–39 Ravenswood Ave., Chicago 40, Ill. Biological models, charts on biology and astronomy.

Difco Laboratories, Inc., Detroit 1, Mich. Culture media and reagents.

Eastman Kodak Co., Rochester, N.Y. Photographic supplies, equipment, and literature.

Edmund Scientific Corp., Barrington, N.J. "America's greatest optical marketplace."

Ronald Eyrich, 1091 N. 48th St., Milwaukee 8, Wisc. Alnico permanent magnets.

Fischer Scientific Co., 717 Forbes St., Pittsburgh 19, Pa.; 635 Greenwich St., New York 14, N.Y. Molecular models, general.

General Biological Supply House, 8200 S. Hoyne Ave., Chicago 20, Ill. Biological apparatus, supplies, living and preserved specimens, models, charts.

A. C. Gilbert Co., New Haven, Conn. Gilbert toys, including microscope sets, tool cabinets, model telephone and electric construction sets, chemical labs.

C. S. Hammond Co., Maplewood, N.J. Space and weather kits, color maps.

Heath Co., Benton Harbor, Mich. "Build-it-yourself" electronic instrument kits.

"Industrial America," Inc., Merchandise Mart Plaza, Chicago 54, Ill. Educational hobby kits on physiology, light, meteorology, mineralogy, electronics.

Los Angeles Biological Laboratories, 2977 W. 14th St., Los Angeles, Calif. Biological apparatus, supplies, living and preserved specimens, models, charts.

Macalaster-Bicknell Co., 253 Norfolk St., Cambridge 39, Mass. General.

Models of Industry, Inc., 2100 Fifth St., Berkeley, Calif. Three handbooks and 200 essential pieces of equipment for 80 activities beginning in primary grades. In three parts, complete for use in three separate classrooms.

Mountcastle Map Co., 1437 E. 12th St., Cleveland, O. Markable maps and charts.

National Audubon Society, 1130 Fifth Ave., New York 28, N.Y. Inexpensive nature charts and bulletins.

Nature Games, 8339 W. Dry Creek Rd., Healdsburg, Calif. Card games using colorful, authentic pictures of scientific names.

A. J. Nystrom and Co., 3333 Elston Ave., Chicago 18, Ill. Biological models; charts on health, biological sciences, general science, atmosphere, and weather.

Product Design Co., 2769 Middlefield Rd., Redwood City, Calif. Kits for teaching electricity, chemistry, physics, conservation. Working models for student experiments.

Revell Co., Venice, Calif. Models of atomic power plants, nuclear submarines, space stations.

Ross Allen's Reptile Institute, Silver Springs, Fla.

Harry Ross, 70 W. Broadway, New York 7, N.Y. Microscopes and telescopes; science and laboratory apparatus.

E. H. Sargent and Co., 155 E. Superior St., Chicago, Ill. General.

Science Associates, P.O. Box 216, Princeton, N.J. Special instruments and teaching aids for meteorology, astronomy, optics, and earth sciences.

Science Electronics, Inc., P.O. Box 237, Huntington, N.Y. "Breadboard"-type kits for teaching radio, electricity, electronics.

Science Kit, Box 69, Tonowanda, N.Y. Standard laboratory equipment, teacher's manual, astronomy manual and star chart.

Science Materials Center, Div. of Library of Science, 59 Fourth Ave., New York 3, N.Y. Equipment, teaching aids, portable labs, supplementary books and records.

Standard Oil of Calif., Public Relations, 225 Bush St., San Francisco 20, Calif. Catalog of free teaching materials and services.

Stansi Scientific Co., 1231 N. Honore St., Chicago 22, Ill. Teaching kits in electricity and electronics. Science kits for elementary school. General.

Taylor Instrument Co., Rochester, N.Y. Weather and temperature instruments.

Things of Science, Science Service, 1719 N St., N.W., Washington 6, D.C. Monthly kits on various subjects.

Tracerlab, Inc., 130 High St., Boston 10, Mass. Radioactivity apparatus.

Training Aid Studio, 2121 S. Josephine, Denver 10, Colo. Felt-O-Graph classroom aids: geology, coal and oil mining, airplane and rocket parts, biological cells.

Ward's Natural Science Establishment, Inc., P.O. Box 24, Beechwood Sta., Rochester 9, N.Y. Teaching aids, charts, equipment, geology specimens, and other materials for biological, natural, and earth sciences.

W. M. Welch Manufacturing Co., 1515 N. Sedgwick St., Chicago 10, Ill. General.

Weston Electrical Instrument Corp., 614 Frelinghuysen Ave., Newark, N.J. Electrical instruments.

Wilkens-Anderson Co., 4525 W. Division St., Chicago 51, Ill. Semimicro apparatus and equipment for chemistry.

REFERENCE AIDS

Many compilations of free and inexpensive materials have been published to meet the constant search of teachers for classroom aids. For those teachers who will want to go beyond the directory, we have added a short bibliography of publications.

Beuschlein, Muriel, *Free and Inexpensive Materials for Teaching Conservation and Resource-Use,* National Association of Biology Teachers, P.O. Box 2073, Ann Arbor, Mich., 1954. 50 pp.

———, and J. Sanders, "Free and Inexpensive Teaching Materials for Science Education," *Chicago Schools Journal,* Vol. 34, Nos. 5, 6, 1953. Available as reprint.

Cardoza, P., *A Wonderful World for Children,* Bantam, 1956. $1.50.

Choosing Free Materials for Use in the Schools, National Education Association, Washington, D.C., 1955. 24 pp., 50¢. Issued by the American Association of School Administrators. Standard for choosing the most valuable free materials and for eliminating materials that contain obvious advertising or biased information.

Conservation Teaching Aids, Michigan Dept. of Conservation, Education Division, Ann Arbor, Mich., 1951.

Educators' Progress Service Annual, Educators' Progress Service, Randolph, Wisc. Yearly revision. Guide to free curriculum materials.

Fowlkes, John G., et al., *Elementary Teachers' Guide to Free Curriculum Materials,* Educators' Progress Service, Randolph, Wisc. 348 pp., $6.50.

Free and Inexpensive Instruction Aids, Bruce Miller Publishers, Box 369, Riverside, Calif.

Free and Inexpensive Learning Materials, George Peabody College for Teachers, Nashville 5, Tenn., 1960. $1.50.

General Motors Aids to Educators, General Motors Corp., Willow Run, Mich., 1956.

Health Materials and Resources for Oregon Teachers, State Dept. of Education, Salem, Ore., 1955.

Hobby Publications, Superintendent of Documents, U.S. Govt. Printing Office, Washington 25, D.C.

Holland, C., *Free and Inexpensive Teaching Aids for High Schools,* National Association of Secondary School Principals, NEA, 1201 Sixteenth St., N.W., Washington 6, D.C., 1949. $1.00.

Hough, John B., ed., *Something for Nothing for Your Classroom,* Curriculum Laboratory, Div. of Secondary Education, Temple Univ., Philadelphia 22, Pa., 1957. $1.00.

Phillips, Brose, *Index to Free Teaching Aids,* Free Teaching Aids Co., Harrisburg, Ill.

Salisbury, Gordon, and Robert Sheridan, *Catalog of Free Teaching Aids,* P.O. Box 943, Riverside, Calif. $1.50.

Science Service Aids to Youth, Science Service, 1719 N St., N.W., Washington 6, D.C.

Sources of Free and Inexpensive Educational Materials, Field Enterprises, Merchandise Mart Plaza, Chicago 54, Ill., 1958. $5.00.

Sources of Free and Inexpensive Materials in Health Education, Curriculum Laboratory, Teachers College, Temple Univ., Philadelphia 22, Pa., 1954. 25¢.

Sources of Free and Inexpensive Pictures for the Classroom, Bruce Miller Publishers, Box 369, Riverside, Calif., 1956. 50¢.

Sources of Free and Low-Cost Materials, Civil Aeronautics Administration, U.S. Dept. of Commerce, Washington 25, D.C.

Sponsors Handbook, Science Service, 1719 N St., N.W., Washington 6, D.C., 1957. 25¢.

Teaching Aids, Westinghouse Electrical Corp., School Service, 306 4th Ave., Pittsburgh 30, Pa.

Thousands of Science Projects, Science Service, 1719 N St., N.W., Washington 6, D.C., 1957. 25¢.

Using Free Materials in the Classroom, Association of Supervision and Curriculum Development, NEA, 1201 Sixteenth St., N.W., Washington 6, D.C., 1953. 75¢.

Vertical File Index, H. W. Wilson Co., New York, N.Y. Monthly publication devoted to listings of inexpensive materials (not intended to be a complete listing of all pamphlet material).

Weisinger, M., *1001 Valuable Things Free,* Bantam, 1957.

Williams, C., *Sources of Teaching Materials,* Bureau of Educational Research, Ohio State Univ., Columbus, O., 1955.

Wittich, W. A., and G. L. Hanson, *Educators' Guide to Free Tapes, Scripts and Transcriptions,* Educators' Progress Service, Randolph, Wisc.

Worksheets for Use in Constructing Science Equipment, Los Angeles County Superintendent of Schools, January, 1955. 40 pp. Illustrated worksheets with lists of materials and construction directions.

Index

Numbers in italics indicate pages bearing illustrations. No separate listing is given for related text on the same page.

Exosphere, 444
Extinguisher, fire, 278–79
Eyeglasses, 262
Eyelid, 259
Eyes, blind spot in, 260
   compound, of grasshopper, 37
   defects of, *261*, 262
   likened to camera, 259–60
   working of, 258–62

Fabrics. *See* Clothing; Fibers
Fahrenheit scale, 290, 291
Fan, electric, 141–42, 143
Farmaster Automatic Temperature Control, 13
Farsightedness (hypermetropia), *261,* 262
Fats, 211
   tests for, 217
Fault, in rock layer, 113, *114*
Feathers, collecting, 504–05
Feldspar, 115, 117
Ferns, 67
Fibers, 314–20
   animal, 315
   kinds of, 314–16
   plant, 314–15
   properties of, 318–20
   resistance of, 318–19
   strength of, 319–20
   synthetic, 315–16
   tests for, 316–18
   water absorption by, 320
   See also Clothing
Field, magnetic, 340–42
Field magnet, 379, 380
Field trip, 49, 57
   precautions for, 478
Fiesta Ware, 407
Films and filmstrips, 524–32
Filtration, water, 186
Fire, 270–83
   air necessary for, 272–73
   building, 273–74
   films and filmstrips on, 531
   fuels for, 270–71, 280
   kindling temperature for, 271–72
   products of, 279–80
   putting out, 276–79
   See also Combustion; Flame
Fire hazards, 281–83
Firefly, 35
Fireproofing, 283
   of house, 335
First-class lever, 411–12, 420
Fish, 48, 50, 56, 59
   in classroom aquarium, 8–10, 48
   as food, 59
   gills of, 48, 56, 222, 223
Fixed pulley, 414
Fixtures, for house, 329
Flame, candle, 274
   colors of, 275, 280–81
   regions of, 275, *276*
   See also Combustion; Fire

Flashlight, 367–68, 369
Flask, Florence, 473
Flight, 449–64
   films and filmstrips on, 532
Floor, of house, 329
Florence flask, 473
Flowers, 93
Fluorescein, 254
Fly, black, *54*
   caddis, 9, 41, *54,* 57
   damsel, 9, *39*
   fruit, 35–36
   house, 37
   May, 39, *40, 54,* 57
Foam fire extinguisher, 279
Fontana, Joannes de, 432
Fontinalis, 54
Food(s), 210–20, 498
   acid reaction of, 202
   Basic Seven, 210, 219
   calories in, 214–15
   digestion of, 211–13
   films and filmstrips on, 530–31
   oxidation of, 213–14
   tests for, 216–20
Food chain, 50–51, *52*
Foot-pound, 409
Force, and machines, 410, 417–19
Formaldehyde, safe handling of, 478
Fossil roach, 34
Foucault, J. B. L., 154
Foundation, of house, 327–28
Franklin, Benjamin, 363
Freezing point, of mercury, 295
   of water, 184, 290, 291
Frequency, of sound waves, 239
Friction, 421–23
Frog, 11, 50, *51*
   breathing of, 222
   bull, 10
   eggs of, 10
   in terrarium, 84
Fruit fly, 35–36
Fruit stain, removal of, 323
Fuels, 270–71, 280, 431, 432, 493
Fulcrum of lever, 411
Funnel, "Berlese," 23–24
Fur, in experiments with electricity, 357, 358, 359, 360, 361
Furniture, care of, 498
Fuse, *382,* 383
Fusion, atomic energy from, 403

"g" force, 437, 446
Galaxies, 170–71
Galileo, 151, 178, 179
Galls, insect, on plants, 36
Galvanometer, compass, 294, 371–72
   needle, 372–73
   razor-blade, 372
Gamma rays, 406, 407
Garden Club of America, 92
Garden, eggshell, 93

Nylon, 315
in experiments with electricity, 357, 358, 359, 360, 361
moisture absorbed by, 320
strength of, 320
tests for, 317, 318
Nymph, damsel fly, 9
dragonfly, 9, 57
grasshopper, 37
May fly, 57
stonefly, *54*

Oak, as flooring material, 329
Oats, 79, 80
Obelisk, Egyptian, 179
Obsidian, 114, 115, 485
Ocean, life in, 58–59
Oil, fibers tested with, 318
removal of stain, 323–24
Onion skin, microscopic examination of, 65
Opacity, 246
Optic nerve, 259, 260
Orb-weaver spider, 44
Orbits of planets, 166–67
Orion, 170, 176
Orlon, 315
moisture absorbed by, 320
strength of, 320
tests for, 317, 318
Outdoor window sill, as teaching aid, 483
Overshot wheel, *192,* 193
Ovipositor, of cricket, 35
of grasshopper, 37
Oxalic acid, rust removed by, 324
Oxidation, 198
of food, 213–14
Oxygen, in air, 147, 228, 230, 273
in Mars's atmosphere, 168
and oxidation, 198
in respiration, 227
safety rules for preparation of, 476–77
for space travel, 445
in water, 197, 198
Ozalid print, 208, 341

Paint, house, as emulsion, 200–01
Paint stain, removal of, 324
Palomar Observatory, 178
Papain, 219
Paper, conserved at school, 498
Parachute, 461–62
Paradichlorobenzene, 23
Parakeet, 12
Parallax, 158, *159,* 160
Parallel circuit, 369, 370–71
Paramecium, *72,* 73
Parker screw, 465
Parquet floor, 329
Parrot, 12, 13
Parsnip, 219
Pendulum, Foucault's, 154
Pendulum clock, 179
Penicillium, 70

Penumbra, defined, 160
Peperomia plant, microscopic examination of, 65
Pepsin, 213, 219
Perch, for classroom aquarium, 8
Periscope, 251–52
Peroxide. *See* Hydrogen peroxide
Perseid meteorite shower, 170
Perseus, 175, 177
Petiole, 91
Petri dish, 37
Petroleum, storage of, 479
Phenol, storage of, 479
Phenophthalein solution, 185, 197
Philodendron, 75, 86
Phonograph megaphone, *238*
Phosphor, of radium watch, 408
Phosphorus, in food, 220
storage of, 479
Phosphorus pentoxide, 273
Photoelectric cell, 385, 386
Photography, 208
Photosynthesis, 47, 51, 55, 56, 75
Pickerel frog, *51*
Pine, as flooring material, 329
Pine cones, rainbow, 280
Pinhole camera, 245
Pinwheel, 132, 462–63
Piston, of steam engine, 426
Pitch, of sound waves, 239
Pitchblende, 407
Pitcher plant, 55
Planarian, *54*
Planetarium, umbrella, 174
Planets of solar system, 166–69
Plankton, 58
Plant zones, *50,* 51–52
Plants, 75–94, 499
in autumn, 90–91
breathing of, 223
carbon dioxide absorbed by, 230
and erosion, 121, 122–23
fibers from, 314–15
films and filmstrips on, 528–29
and humidity of room, 75, 76
as living things, 84–90
nicotine spray for, 201
nongreen, 67–70
safe handling of, 478
soil for, 79–80, 81
starch stored by, 219
sunlight for, 75, 76
and temperature, 75, 76
vitamins made by, 211
water sought by, 86, 87
watering, 77–78
on window sill, 76, 78–81
See also names of specific plants
Plaster, as building material, 328
Plasterboard, 328
Plastics, in classroom, teacher's use of, 485
cutting of, 466
Platelets, *71*
Pleiades, 175, 176

Plunger, sink, 139, 485
Pluto, 166, 167, 168
Plywood, as building material, 328
Polaris (North Star), 152, 171, 173, 174, 175, 176, 177, 180, 181
Poles, of earth, 346–47
    magnetic, 339–40, *343*
Pollux, 157
Polyethylene, 360
Pond life, study of, 49–50, 51, 52–53, *54,* 504
Pondweed, 50, 55
Pontoon, for raising ship, 189
Popular Science, 485
Positive charge, 358, 359, 360, 361, 362, 363
Potassium, 199
Potassium chlorate, storage of, 480
Potassium chloride, 281
Potassium peroxide, storage of, 480
Potter wasp, 29
Praying mantis, 38–39
    cage for, 20
Pressure cooker, 298
    safe handling of, 478–79
Primary color, 266–67
Prime meridian, 181
Prism, sunlight passed through, 262–63
Profiles, soil, 125–26
Propane gas, 289
Propeller, 462, 463
Protein, 211
    tests for, 216–17
Protons, 357, 358, 401, 402
    numbers of, by elements (table), 404–05
Protozoans, 52, *53,* 71, *72,* 73
Protractor, 180, 181
Psittacosis, 12
Psychrometer, 105
Ptolemaic system, 150, *151*
Ptolemy, 150
Ptyalin, 219
Pulley, 413–15, 420
Pumice, 114
Pump, heat, 312
Pupa, ant, 26
    fruit fly, 36
Pushbutton switch, 366
Pussy willow, 93
Pyrex glass, 304

Quartz, 115, 117
Quartzite, 114
Queen ant, 26, 27
Quicklime, storage of, 480

Rabbit, 14–15
Radiant heating, for home, 311–12, 332, 333
Radiation, heat conveyed by, 307–09
    protection from, in space travel, 445–46
Radio, 397, 398–99
    safe handling of, 477
Radio telescope, 178
Radioactivity, 406–08
    films and filmstrips on, 531–32

Radioautograph, 406–07
Radish, 79, 80
Radium, 406, 407, 408
Rag-doll seed tester, 94
Rain, 301
Rain gauge, 106
Rainbow, 264–65
Rat, white, 15–16
Rattlesnake, 12
Rayon, 315
    moisture absorbed by, 320
    strength of, 320
    tests for, 316–17, 318
Reaction, chemical, 203–07
Receiver, telephone, 396, 397
Red blood cells, 70, *71*
Red cabbage, 92
Red phosphorus, 273
Reference aids, 534–35
Reflecting telescope, 178, *179*
Reflection of light, 247–54
    angle of, 248, 249, *250*
    in mirror, 250
Refracting telescope, 178
Refraction of light, 254–55, *256*
Regulus, 157
Relaxing jar, 22
Renewable resources, 492–93
Reptiles, 50
    as classroom pets, 11–12
Resistance, in mechanics, 411
Resources, human, 493, 496–500
    natural, 492–93
Respiratory system, 227–28, 229, 230
Retina, 259, 260, 261, 262
Rex Begonia, leaf cuttings of, 93
Ring stand, 473
Rock, collecting, 116–17, 487, 504–05
    igneous, 113, 114–15
    impermeable, 118
    metamorphic, 114, 116, 485
    mineral distinguished from, 117
    permeable, 118
    radioactive ores in, testing for, 408
    sedimentary, 113, 115–16
    structure of, 111, 113
Rock wool, 330
Rocket engine, 431–32
Rocket ship, carbon dioxide model, 430
Rocket to the Moon (filmstrip), 164
Roof of house, 329, 332
Root, 81, 86–88
    downward growth of, 85
    hairs on, 86
    microscopic examination of, 66
Rosin, storage of, 479
Rostand, Edmond, 441
Rubber tile, 327
Rudder, airplane, 458, 459
Rust stain, removal of, 324

Safety procedures in classroom, 475–80
    in biological experiments, 478–79

for electrical devices, 477–78
in oxygen preparation, 476–77
Sagittaria, for classroom aquarium, 8
Salamander, 50
eggs of, 10, 11
Saliva, 211, 212, 213, 219
Salt. *See* Sodium chloride
Salt-water tank, 9–10
Sandstone, 114, 115, 116
Saran, 315
in experiment with electricity, 360–61
strength of, 320
Satellite, communications relayed by, 445
and gravity, 441–45
knowledge acquired through, 444
launching, 443–44
weather forecasting by, 444
Saturated solution, 185
Saturn, 166, 167, 168
Saw, coping, 465
Schneider, Herman, 486
Science Corner, classroom, 2, 487
Science discovery table, classroom, 488
Science library, books for, 512–23
Screw, 416–17, 420
sheet metal, 465
Sea, life in, 58–59
Sea shell, 58
Sears Roebuck Company, 398
Seasons, 155–57
films and filmstrips on, 530
Seaweed, gelatin produced from, 59
Second-class lever, 412, 420
Sedimentary rock, 113, 115–16
Seed(s), air needed by, 223
beds for, 78–79
inside of, 94
planting, 80–81, 94
power of germinating, 123
in season, 91–92
sprouting, *77,* 94
Seed germination tray, 483
Seed tester, rag-doll, 94
Selenium, 385
Series circuit, 368–69, 370
Shadow, casting of, 152, 267–68
Shadow box, 483
Shale, 114, 116
Shears, duckbill, 465
Sheathing of house, 328, 329
Sheet erosion, 119–20
Sheet glass, cutting, 467–68
Sheet metal, handling, 465–67
Shellac, storage of, 479
Shells, sea, 58
Shingles of house, 328
Shock wave, *441*
Short circuit, 382, 383
Sidereal time, 179
Silicones, for waterproofing, 335
Silk, 315
in experiments with electricity, 358, 359, 361
moisture absorbed by, 320

strength of, 320
tests for, 316, 317, 318
Silkworm, 7–8
eggs of, 21
Sill, window. *See* Window sill
Silver, cleaning of, 205
Silver nitrate, 267
storage of, 480
Silverfish, 34
Siphon, 145
Siphon tube, 46, *47,* 145–46
Skin diving, 59
Slate, 114, 116, 484, 485
as roofing material, 329
Smog, 230
Smoke box, 245–46, 247
Snail, 41, 50, 84
eggs of, 57
"Snailery," 84
Snake, 11–12, 50
box for, 11, *12*
in terrarium, 84
Snow, 301
Soap, making, 200
Social studies, conservation taught by, 492, 499
Socket, electricity passing through, 365
Soda-acid fire extinguisher, 278–79
Sodium, 196, 199
Sodium chloride, 196–97
in sea water, 59
Sodium hydroxide, 197
fibers tested with, 317
storage of, 479
Sodium peroxide, storage of, 480
Sodium sulfate, 197
Sodium thiosulfate, 324
Soil, for plants, 79–80, 81
study of, 124–26, 494–95, 498
water in, 124, 146–47
Soil Conservation Agent, United States, 126
Solar day, 179
Solar heating, 312
Solar system, 150–70
motion of, 157
origin of, 160
planets of, 166–69
Soldering, 466–67
Solids, 199 *ff.*
expanded by heat, 285–87
melting points of, 295–96
molecular motion in, 296
sound transmitted by, 236
volatile, 201–02
Solution, saturated, 185
Solvents, 201
fibers tested with, 318
Sonometer, 239
Sound, 232–41, 491
films and filmstrips on, 531
vibrating objects as cause of, 232–33
Sound barrier, smashing of, 440–41
Sound wave, 233–41
absorption of, 238–39

Temperature conversion table, 511
Tenent hairs, of grasshopper, 37
Tent, 326
Termites, 27–28
Terrarium, bog (marsh), 55, 81, 82
   desert, 81–82
   glass-box, 81, 83–84
   for insects, 20
   moist woodland, 11, 81, 83, 84
   pickle-jar, 81, 82
Test tube heater, electric, 471–72
Thermometer, 97–98, *99,* 290–94, 295, 483
   air, 291–92
   centigrade scale on, 291
   clinical, 293
   electrical, 294
   Fahrenheit scale on, 290, 291
   gas, 291–92
   maximum-minimum, 293–94
   mercury, 290, 293, 295
   metal, 292–93
   safe handling of, 478
   water, 291
   zipper, 97–98, 483
   See also Temperature
Thermos bottle, 308
Thermostat, homemade, 289–90
Third-class lever, 412–13, 420
Thorium, 406, 407
Thrust, in aerodynamics, 458, 459
Thyroid gland, and iodine, 220
Tidepool, classroom, 9–10
Tile, as building material, 327, 329, 485
Time, conserved at school, 498
   and longitude, 181
   sidereal, 179
Toad, 11, 50, *51*
   eggs of, 10
   horned, 12, 82
   in terrarium, 84
Toast, chemical change illustrated by, 206
Tools, care of, 498
   for laboratory, 474–75
Topsoil, 119, 125, 126
Toys, care of, 498
Trachea, 228
Transite, 474
Translucence, 246
Transmitter, telephone, 395, 396
Transparency, 246
Transplant, watering, 87
Trap-door spider, 43
Tree cricket, 35, 38
Tree study, 89, 90–91, 92
Triangular kite, miniature, 451
Tritium, 401, 402
Tropical fish, for classroom aquarium, 8
Troposphere, 444
Troy weight, 508
Tuber, sprouting, *77*
Tubing, glass, cutting and bending, 469–71
Tuning fork, 233, 234, 237, 238, 491
Turbine, 193–94, 426–27

Turpentine, storage of, 479
Turtle, 11, 50

Ulothrix, 73
Umbra, defined, 160
Umbrella planetarium, 174
Undershot wheel, *192,* 193
United States Soil Conservation Agent, 126
Uranium, 406, 407, 408
   atomic model of, 403
Uranus, 166, 167
Utricularia, 41, *53*

Vacuum, defined, 134, 138
Vacuum bottle, 308–09
Vacuum cleaner, 142
Vallisneria, for classroom aquarium, 8, 66
Valve action, of steam engine, 425–26
Vaucheria, 73
Vega, 157
Ventilation, of classroom, 484
   of home, 230–31, 333–35
Venus, 166, 167, 168, 447
Vermiculite, 76, 88
Verne, Jules, 441
Vibration, sound caused by, 232–33
   sympathetic, 237–38
   See also Sound wave
Vinegar, bone structure eroded by, 202
Vinyl, 327
Violet, African, 75
Vitamins, 211, 219, 259
Vocal cords, 241
"Voices of the Night," 10
Volcano, 113
Voltaic cell, 373–74
Volvox, 73
Vorticella, *53, 72,* 73

Walking stick beetle, 38
   cage for, 20, *21*
Walls, of classroom, teacher's use of, 484–85
   of house, 328, 329
Wasp, 28, 29
Water, absorbed by fibers, 320
   air in, 146
   and air pressure, effect of, 135–38
   for animals in classroom, 5
   for aquarium in classroom, 9
   boiling point of, 184, 290, 291, 295, 297
   buoyancy of, 188
   capillary attraction in, 187–88
   classroom supply of, 488
   as combustion product, 206–07, 279
   conserved at school, 498
   convection currents in, 305
   density of, 185
   as dissolver, 185–86
   distillation of, 186, 301–02
   electric current conducted by, 384
   electrolysis of, 197
   elements in, 197–98